AN INTRODUCTION
TO MODERN MATHEMATICS

AN INTRODUCTION
TO Modern
Mathematics

NATHAN J. FINE

DEPARTMENT OF MATHEMATICS
THE PENNSYLVANIA STATE UNIVERSITY

RAND McNALLY & COMPANY
Chicago

RAND McNALLY MATHEMATICS SERIES

William J. LeVeque, Advisory Editor

To Ruth, Naomi, Emily, and Dorothy

PREFACE

THE TERM "modern mathematics," which is commonly taken to refer to topics such as logic, set theory, Boolean algebra, axiomatics, linear algebra, and probability, is actually a misnomer. All of these have been in existence for all least fifty years—some much longer. It is only in the past decade or two, however, that teachers of mathematics in the colleges have thought it desirable or even possible to present these topics at the lower undergraduate levels. Through the efforts of various curriculum development groups, the "new" mathematics has begun to filter down to the secondary and even the elementary schools, and a generation of "new" students is rising. My own experience as a teacher and as a consultant and writer with the School Mathematics Study Group has convinced me that the new concepts—especially those dealing with the structure of mathematical systems—are of considerable value, not only to the superior student but especially to the average or weaker one.

This is a self-contained introductory test in college-level modern mathematics, for social science and liberal arts students. It is also suitable for advanced high-school students and prospective teachers. The background required is minimal. Two or three years of high-school mathematics should be sufficient, when combined with reasonable diligence and sincerity of purpose. For terminal students, the text is designed to give an insight into the nature of mathematics, plus an acquaintance with some of the major achievements in the field. For those who wish to go on, it should provide a firm basis for continued study. Hopefully, it might induce some in the first category to switch to the second.

The original version of this book was prepared with the generous assistance of a Ford Foundation grant for curriculum development to the

Wharton School of the University of Pennsylvania, and with the kind cooperation of the Mathematics Department and the College of Liberal Arts. The selection of topics was designed to satisfy the cultural needs of students in commerce, industry, economics, the social sciences, and liberal arts, as well as to provide a basis for further study in quantitative methods (for example, statistics and operations research). The material was issued in preliminary form to about 900 students and used in a two-semester three-hour-per-week program. It was also used in several other schools. Since then it has gone through intensive revision based on those teaching experiences and on comments from a number of people who have read it carefully. For all these I am most grateful.

In one respect my goals have been modest. This book is not intended for a "power" course, and the manipulative aspects of mathematics have not been emphasized. For example, only polynomials and the exponential and logarithmic functions are given detailed treatment in the calculus. The intricate counting of permutations and combinations commonly associated with probability is completely absent. The treatment of logic and set theory is intuitive and restricted to those concepts needed—and used—throughout the book.

In another respect I have been ambitious for the student. I have not talked down to him. Instead I have attempted with all the means at my disposal to motivate him so that his desires as a student may approximate his true needs. The determination of these needs must of course be made within the limits of his capabilities, but we should avoid the error of underestimating him. There are some teachers, I fear, who take the easy path of "giving the student what he wants." This amounts to an abdication of responsibility. I believe that the student should be treated as an intelligent human being in search of intellectual maturity. If he makes an honest effort, he should have no great difficulty in understanding a substantial portion of the material presented here.

In writing this book I have kept constantly before me the following question: What lasting information and attitudes would I want students to have five, ten, twenty years from now? Many of them will have important positions as teachers, scholars, lawmakers, statesmen, leaders of industry and commerce. They will need to deal with sophisticated problems in a sophisticated world. Just as it would be criminal to let them think that science is just a necessary adjunct to gadgetry or that history is a mere collection of dates, so also would it be criminal to talk down to them and leave them with the naïve impression that mathematics is nothing more than a collection of formulas and routine manipulations. I would be happy, on the other hand, if they achieve some comprehension of the conceptual nature of mathematics and the realization that it is an abstract science which is man-created, having its roots in the world around us, but distinct from that world. These goals of understanding can be achieved not by talking about mathematics but by doing it. The student is guided through some detailed developments of important mathematical subjects, with numerous opportunities to flex his intellectual muscles. The exercises and illustrative examples have been chosen with care to emphasize and clarify important points. Wherever appropriate applications are available, they have been included.

The work of a textbook writer must necessarily be more complete than that of a teacher planning a course. I have attempted to make the book flexible enough so that the course planner may suit his needs by omission of proofs, sections, or whole chapters. But this is not a collection of disjointed topics, each in its own little capsule. Logic and set theory are introduced in order to be used, and they are used throughout. The discussion of axiom systems is central, and I should be sad to see it omitted. These first three chapters, together with the one on the real number system, make up the heart of the text. A brief description of the chapter contents, with suggestions of options and possible course organization, follows.

The basic tool in the study of mathematics is logic. Chapter 1 is a frankly intuitive and informal treatment of the subject, although there are intimations of the possibility of formal treatment. The purpose here is to introduce symbols and concepts that will be of constant use throughout the book. The same comments apply to Chapter 2, except for the brief reference section on orderings.

Section 3–1 states the central theme of the book, that man creates his own conceptual frameworks for mathematical experience, and the rest of Chapter 3 illustrates and amplifies this theme. The choice of Boolean algebra was dictated by its simplicity and wealth of application. Sections 3–1, 3–2, 3–5, and 3–6 are essential. Either 3–3 or 3–4 or both may be omitted without loss of continuity. The teacher may wish to carry the development of Boolean algebra only through 3–5, omitting 3–7, or he may wish to accept most of the theorems of 3–5 as axioms and proceed directly to the less obvious and more significant results of 3–7, where the elegant representation theorem for finite Boolean algebras is proved. The optional Exercises 3–10 are intended to give the student a glimpse of group theory.

In Chapter 4, the axioms for an ordered field are standard. Having assumed these properties, we find it interesting and instructive that the natural numbers can be singled out and proved to satisfy the induction principle. This integrated treatment of mathematical induction and the real numbers is preferable to the customary separation of the two topics.

(At this level, of course, the development of the reals from the Peano axioms is not appropriate.) Special attention is given to the least-upper-bound axiom, which is used heavily in Chapters 7 and 8. It is also used in the explanation of decimal representation, a topic that sorely needs clarification to most students.

Chapter 5, on linear algebra, may be omitted, or a light treatment may be given by omitting Section 5–5, or Sections 5–3 and 5–5. The concept of linear mapping plays an important role here.

Chapter 6 is quite brief and contains only the essentials of analytic geometry, barely more than is necessary for Chapters 7 and 8.

In Chapter 7, the introduction of finitely additive measures lays the groundwork for area, integration, and probability. The Darboux or "squeezing-process" definition of the integral has intuitive appeal to the student and illustrates admirably the power of the least-upper-bound axiom. Sections 7–5, 7–6, and 7–7 may be omitted if the teacher wishes to treat only the polynomial calculus.

In Chapter 8, limits are introduced after a carefully selected set of examples, and null sequences are used generously to avoid epsilontic proofs wherever possible. Similarly, although the classical definition of continuity is given, it is replaced by the equivalent, but perhaps more intuitive, sequential definition.

Special note should be taken of the proof that a function continuous on a closed interval is integrable. The treatment given here is a pedagogical innovation of some merit, I believe. First, the intuitive "breakout" theorem (i.e., the intermediate value theorem) is proved. Then a simple, almost algorithmic proof of integrability is given, using the breakout theorem and the result that a monotone bounded sequence converges. As easy and natural consequences, we get boundedness, uniform continuity, and the attainment of the maximum.

The derivative is introduced by means of null functions and linear approximation; then the classical definition is shown to be equivalent. Each is useful and worthwhile, but the first is especially good for proving the chain rule. The introduction of the identity function j should be noted as a painless step in the direction of greater clarity.

Chapter 9, on probability, is optional. The groundwork has already been laid in Chapter 7. Basic concepts are stressed, rather than complicated combinatorics. Counting ingeniously may be fun, but it has nothing essentially to do with probability. Experience shows that the nonmathematician who uses probability and statistics needs most a grounding in the fundamentals and a recognition of underlying assumptions.

I have attempted to balance the selection of exercises both as to field of application and difficulty. Starred exercises are, as usual, more challenging. Complete solutions are available in the Teacher's Manual. There are some passages enclosed in open brackets ($[\![\ ]\!]$). These are parenthetical and of greater depth. I would hope that the student is asked to read them even if he is not held responsible for them.

A great deal of thought has gone into the proofs presented here. When there is a choice between terse elegance and pedagogical clarity, the latter usually wins out. I have not included every last detail of every proof in fanatical pursuit of rigor, but I have never felt it necessary or desirable to compromise the correctness of a proof. As for omitted proofs, they are few in number and usually of the kind that the student can supply himself. It seems to me that there are far too many "beyond the scope"'s sprinkled through most texts and that there is room for real investigation by teachers and authors to eliminate them.

Naturally, the teacher has considerable latitude in the time and emphasis to be assigned to exposition, proofs, and exercises, and will employ this latitude in the light of his own goals. To aid in this planning, the following table gives rough but realistic estimates of the number of class hours required for exposition and discussion of text material. All the indicated options are independent, except that Sections 7–5, 7–6, and 7–7 should go or stay together. Section 2–5 is strictly for reference and is not included in the estimate for Chapter 2. I would be grateful to hear from users who find revisions in these estimates necessary.

CHAPTER	EXPOSITION TIME (HOURS)
1	5
2	5
3: 3–3, 3–4, 3–7 optional	5, 6, 7, or 8
4	7
5 optional; omit 5–5; omit 5–3 and 5–5	0, 5, 6, or 7
6	4
7: 7–5, 7–6, 7–7 optional	5 or 8
8	9
9 optional	0 or 5

The minimum choice throughout, corresponding to exposition time of 40 hours, would fit very comfortably into a conventional 90-hour two-semester course, allowing a detailed treatment of the text or a slower pace if desired. The first four chapters would be quite suitable for a terminal one-semester course. The maximum of 58 hours would allow one hour of problem discussion and testing for each two hours of exposition time in a two-semester course. This rather tight schedule is advised only if the class is above average or if additional laboratory time with competent assistants is available. If it is desired to take all nine chapters in two semesters, a possible time allotment is: Chapters 1–5, minimal, for the first semester; Chapters 6–9, maximal, for the second. Another possibility is: Chapters 1–4, maximal, for the first; Chapters 5–9, minimal, for the second. There are obviously many intermediate choices available.

I am grateful to many people for their encouragement, assistance, and helpful comments during the development of this book. I am particularly indebted to David Harrison, who, but for the siren call of his own outstanding research, might have been a co-author; to Henry Hiz, who read and commented carefully on the first chapter, and who constantly encouraged me; to R. Duncan Luce, who used the first version with his psychology students, gave it a thorough and detailed reading, and suggested the inclusion of the section on orderings; to David Rosen, who used a second version with a group of Swarthmore high-school students, and sent me a list of very useful comments; to Malcolm Wyatt, who read and criticized the book line by line, prepared most of the figures and solutions to problems, wielded a mighty paste-brush in the physical preparation of the manuscript, and created the imaginative illustration of the P-plane and C-plane in Chapter 3; to Paul Axt, who read the penultimate version and whose sharp and cogent arguments helped to shape the ultimate; and to Paul Rosenbloom, who miraculously found the time to read and criticize the final version. It is a pleasure also to acknowledge the very patient and competent assistance of Barbara Zeiders and Nancy Orban, both of Science Bookcrafters. Finally, I wish to thank editor W. Philip Gerould and the staff of Rand McNally & Company, whose encouragement and support I have deeply appreciated.

N.J.F.

CONTENTS

AN INTRODUCTION
TO MODERN MATHEMATICS

Chapter 1

LOGIC

1–1. PURPOSE

OUR PURPOSE IN STUDYING LOGIC is twofold. First, we wish to increase our ability to communicate ideas, both to others and to ourselves. Second, we wish to study some of the simple processes by which we pass correctly from one set of statements to another.

To accomplish our first objective, we shall study the language of logic and the symbols and abbreviations used in this language. There is a very small and simple vocabulary and grammar, mainly abbreviating ordinary language and clarifying its terms. Many fields rely heavily on the techniques of logic, but few use its symbolism to any great extent. Mathematics is one subject that does both.

As for our second objective, we observe that to reach full comprehension of any subject, the student must have the facts available and must be able to organize these facts into a reasonable pattern. The body of facts will vary from one discipline to another, and we are not concerned here with the methods of acquiring them. We are interested in the patterns, the structures, the interrelationships for these facts which are common to all disciplines. Just as a pile of bricks, stone, wood, and steel does not constitute a building, so the pile of facts that we accumulate does not constitute a systematic study of a subject. We need to construct an underlying plan or theory. Logic provides us with techniques for doing just that. Given a few well-chosen terms and statements, we can invent and develop the most subtle theories by means of the few simple logical tools presented here.

Our point of view—strongly held but subject to debate, of course—is that we do indeed invent our patterns of knowledge. A famous mathematician has said of mathematics that God made the positive integers, man everything else. Without entering into a debate, we merely point out the importance of theories and their construction. Inevitably, this leads

1

us to the study of logic. We shall not dive too deeply into this pool, but some wading will be necessary.

It should be clear to the reader that we shall not attempt to discuss the psychology of reasoning. Ours is a far easier task, to single out a few of the commonly accepted forms of reasoning in order to formalize and standardize them. Once this is done, the most simple-minded machine can be taught to perform the routine logical operations perfectly, leaving our minds free for more creative efforts. In the same way, we learn the routine arithmetic operations early in life, to save us time and effort later on. In fact, one extra practical dividend of our investment in this study will be an understanding of the logical principles by which modern high-speed computers and automatic systems operate.

Will the study of logic help us to think more clearly? We make no such claim. We don't learn to play tennis merely by reading about it; we have to go out on the court and practice the strokes. Activity is an essential part of the learning process. But by observation and precept we can acquire correct form more rapidly. Perhaps, after studying logic, we may avoid the more common pitfalls in reasoning—provided that we are willing to apply consciously the principles learned. This willingness is not always present; some excellent mathematicians and logicians can be most prejudiced and illogical outside their own fields. In some rare instances logic may provide the analysis of a complex problem, just as a good accounting system may analyze the fiscal affairs of a large corporation. But there is much more to creative thinking in mathematics and elsewhere than the routine application of logical symbolism. Many great mathematicians, past and present, have done their work without the benefit of formal logic.

One further remark is in order here. If we write down the symbols and working rules of logic, then deliberately forget the meaning of the symbols but retain the rules, we arrive at an abstract algebraic system which can be, and is, studied in its own right. One small part of this system goes by the name *Boolean algebra*, which has applications in the theory of computers and switching circuits. Thus we arrive at a curious state of affairs. Logic, which is the working mechanism of all of mathematics, itself becomes an object of study within mathematics, like ordinary algebra.

1–2. SYMBOLS

Perhaps the most forbidding aspect of mathematics, to some people, is its use of symbols. Faced with an array of x's, y's, and z's, they simply give up in despair and assert, almost with pride, that they have a "mental block." Without making light of the difficulty, we believe that the problem is surmountable by any reasonably intelligent person, and that no special mental equipment or talent is required. It is the aim of this section to explain our use of symbols in mathematics.

We have been using symbols almost all our lives. All language is symbolic. The greatest advance that an infant makes in communication is the realization that certain utterances are not merely sounds but serve the purpose of referring to things. They are symbols. Mathematical language uses a very limited set of symbols. Some examples are the upper- and lower-case letters of the English and Greek alphabets, "$=$," "$+$," "$\cdot$," "$\wedge$," "$\vee$," "$\rightarrow$," "$\sim$," "$\leftrightarrow$," and so on. Occasionally we invent new symbols.

The important fact to remember is that symbols are merely linguistic tools that derive their utility from the agreements or conventions made about them *by us*. There is nothing sacred or foreordained about our assignment of a meaning to a symbol. We have complete freedom, subject only to the responsibility for making ourselves understood. For example, we could use the symbol "$\wedge$" for the number 1, "$\vee$" for the number 2, "$=$" for the operation of addition, and "$+$" for the relation of equality. Then the ordinary statment "$1 + 1 = 2$" would be written as "$\wedge = \wedge + \vee$."

It should be clear from the example just given why we would not ordinarily make these assignments. In some cases our agreements about symbols are so standard and universal that they need not be mentioned explicitly at the beginning of every discussion. *When they are not mentioned, it is assumed that the standard assignments of meaning are in force.* On occasion, however, we do allow ourselves the liberty of using a standard symbol with a nonstandard meaning, but then we give fair warning.

One standard symbol deserves special mention. We shall always use "$=$" in the following sense. If "a" denotes an object, concrete or conceptual, and if "b" also denotes an object, then "$a = b$" (read "a equals b") means that the object denoted by "a" is identical with the one denoted by "b."

EXAMPLE 1–1.   The symbols "$2 + 5$" and "7" are different, but they refer to the same mathematical object. It is therefore proper to connect them by "$=$." Thus $2 + 5 = 7$.

EXAMPLE 1–2.   A student writes

$$2x = 10 = x = 5.$$

The first and third "$=$" conform to our usage; the second does not. Correct would be

$$2x = 10.$$

$$\therefore x = 5.$$

EXAMPLE 1–3.   The ratio of the circumference of a circle to its diameter is approximately $\frac{22}{7}$. Some people write

$$\pi = \frac{22}{7}.$$

They don't really mean that "π" and "$\frac{22}{7}$" denote the same number. We would prefer

$$\pi \doteq \frac{22}{7}$$

or, equivalently,

$$\pi = \frac{22}{7} \text{ approx.}$$

It follows from our agreement about "$=$" that
(1) For every a, $a = a$.
(2) If $a = b$, then $b = a$.
(3) If $a = b$ and $b = c$, then $a = c$. ("Things equal to the same thing are equal to each other.")

Often, instead of "$a = b$ and $b = c$ and $c = d$," we write a chain of equalities:

$$a = b = c = d.$$

By (1), (2), and (3) we can deduce that any two symbols in such a chain refer to the same object; they can be connected by "$=$."

EXAMPLE 1–4. $(49)(51) = (50 - 1)(50 + 1) = 50^2 - 1^2 = 2,499.$ Therefore, $(49)(51) = 2,499.$ [Try $(38)(42)$ without paper.]

[*Note:* There are some logicians and mathematicians who use "$=$" in a somewhat wider sense than ours. That is their privilege; their only obligation is to be explicit.]

A *constant* is a symbol that names something. Standard symbols, such as "$=$," "1," and "π," are called *universal constants*. They retain their meanings from one discourse to another. An *arbitrary constant* refers to the same object throughout a particular discussion, but may be used differently in other discussions. For example, if we had to refer frequently to the number $\sqrt{7} + \sqrt{3}$ during the course of a certain problem, we might use "a" as a temporary name for $\sqrt{7} + \sqrt{3}$. In legal documents, "the party of the first part" is an arbitrary constant.

It is not necessary that the object referred to by a constant be fully known to us. Thus, we may swear out a warrant to arrest "John Doe." Or we might say "Let n be the sum of the digits of all the whole numbers from 1 to 1,000 inclusive." Or, if we are told that Ann is a girl whose age (in years) when doubled yields 20, we might begin to solve the problem of finding her age by saying "Let n = Ann's age in years." But we must be sure that there is one and only one object to which the assigned constant refers. Thus, if we are asked to find a number the double of which is 20, it is incorrect to say "Let n = the number . . . ," for we are thereby assuming that (1) there is such a number and (2) there is not more than one such number. It so happens in this case that both (1) and (2) are true, but we do not know that at the beginning of the problem. If the problem is, "Find a number which when divided by a third of itself yields 7 as an answer," then (1) is violated but (2) is true. If the problem is, "Find a number whose square is 4," then (1) is true but (2) is false.

The previous paragraph illustrates our need for symbols of a different sort. Constants are permitted to refer only to uniquely existing objects. A *variable* is a symbol with which we associate a class (collection) of objects. This class is called the *domain* of the variable. Common nouns, such as "a chair," or pronouns, such as "he" and "it," are examples of variables. Proper nouns, such as "The Taj Mahal," are constants. "That chair" (pointing) is a constant. The dotted line on which we are so often asked to sign serves as a variable. The class of persons whose names could be signed is the domain of this variable. The name that we do sign is a constant.

In mathematics, letters of the English or Greek alphabets are usually variables, unless there is prior agreement or understanding that they serve as constants. Thus, in "x is a whole number," the "x" is a variable, but in "π is a whole number" we would ordinarily regard "π" as the universal constant "3.14159 . . . ," because of prior usage. The second statement is false, of course.

It is usually advisable but not absolutely necessary to specify the domain of a variable. When this is not done, the domain is taken to be the widest class of objects for which the assertions involving the variable make sense. The assertations need not be *true* of the objects in the domain, just *meaningful*. Thus, in the problem of finding a number the double of which is 20, we let "x" be a variable whose domain is the class of all numbers. The statement "$2x = 20$" which we then write down is really a demand upon us to find the subclass of that domain consisting of those numbers which make the statement true. This means that when we substitute the name of a number for "x," the statement becomes true. Thus, 5 does not belong to the subclass but 10 does. This subclass is called the *truth set* of the statement. Properly speaking, we should write "$2x = 20$?" to emphasize that we are raising the question, "What is the truth set of this statement?"

If asked to fill the blanks in

_____ is red and _____ is round,

we might wonder whether it is intended that both blanks be filled by the same or different answers. In mathematics the use of variables avoids this ambiguity. Thus, in

x is red and x is round,

the "blanks" must be filled by the same answer. In

x is red and y is round,

the "blanks" may be filled by the same or different answers.

We have just seen that a variable acts as a place holder for the name of an object in its domain, just as the blank in a multiple-choice question is a place holder for the numerals (or letters) attached to the possible answers. There are other common ways of using variables, however.

Consider the statement "$5 + x = x + 5$," in which "x" is a variable whose domain is the class of all real numbers. If we substitute 7 for x, we get a true statement. If we substitute 9 for x, we get a true statement. Thus, 7 and 9 both belong to the truth set. In fact, the truth set coincides with the domain. To express this fact, we introduce the symbol "$\forall$," read "for all" or "for every," and we write

$$(\forall x) (5 + x = x + 5).$$

(Parentheses are used liberally to avoid possible confusion.) The entire statement is read as "For all x, $5 + x = x + 5$" or "For every x, $5 + x = x + 5$." Another notation is

$$5 + x \equiv x + 5,$$

where "$\equiv$" is often read "is identically equal to," and the entire statement is called an *identity*. Finally, there are many who write simply

$$5 + x = x + 5$$

and expect the reader to gather from the context that the assertion is being made for every x. Usually there are key words to indicate this usage, but not always.

"$\forall$" is called the *universal quantifier*. It tells how many (quant-) of the elements of the domain of the variable, namely, *all* of them, are asserted to have a certain property. There is another quantifier, the *existential*, which is often used. A statement with the existential quantifier asserts that *at least one* object in the domain of the variable has a certain property. This quantifier is written "$\exists$" and is read "there exists a ... such that" or "for some...." For example,

$$(\exists x)\,(x^2 = 4)$$

is read "For some x, $x^2 = 4$," or "There exists an x such that $x^2 = 4$." It happens that in this case there are two numbers which satisfy the condition.

The universal and existential quantifiers are the ones most commonly used, but they are by no means the only ones possible. For example, the symbol "$\exists!$" is used to denote "there is exactly one."

The power of a universal statement in mathematics lies in the fact that it means exactly what it says—that for *all* x, something or other is true, *with no exceptions*. The usage is precise, in contrast to the rather loose interpretation of "all" in ordinary language as indicating a vague generality or an overwhelming statistical predominance. Witness the following conversation:

> "All brilliant students are antisocial."
> "What about John Smith?"

(With satisfaction):

> "That's the exception that proves the rule!"

At one time, when "proves" meant "tests" (as in "proving ground"), this was a correct translation of the Latin "Exceptio probat regulam." Actually, the logical and common-sense interpretation of the saying is that the truth of a universal statement stands or falls by the simple question, "Is there an exception?" It is unfortunate—and amazing—that otherwise-reasonable people should so pervert the meaning that they think an exception strengthens the rule.

Given a true universal statement involving the variable "x," we may replace "x" throughout by an expression, involving other variables (or even "x" itself), provided that the expression has values which are all within the domain of "x." The resulting statement is then also universally true. For example, in

(1) $$(\forall x)\,(x^2 \geq 0)$$

("$\geq$" is read "is greater than or equal to"), the domain of "x" is the class of all real numbers. Let "y" be another variable with the same domain. Then "$x - y$" takes its values in the same domain, so the statement "$(x - y)^2 \geq 0$," obtained by replacing "x" by "$x - y$," is true for all x and for all y. Thus we get

(2) $(\forall x)(\forall y)\,(x - y)^2 \geq 0.$

We have just stated that Eq. (2) follows from Eq. (1), and this assertion may be obvious to some students. Nevertheless, because this type of substitution is frequently puzzling to students, we shall carry out a step-by-step proof of its validity. Our procedure will be typical of many proofs of universal statements. First, let "a" and "b" be symbols referring to *arbitrary* real numbers. Thus "a" and "b" are constants, not variables. Now the difference of two real numbers is again a real number, so "$a - b$" refers to an object in the domain of "x" in Eq. (1). Therefore,

(3) $(a - b)^2 \geq 0$

is true, being a special case of Eq. (1). Now a and b were *arbitrary*, and no special properties were used to derive Eq. (3). Therefore Eq. (3) is true *no matter what real numbers a and b are.* This is precisely the meaning of the universal statement (2).

The term "arbitrary," as used above, occurs so often in mathematics that it is worth our while to make its meaning quite clear. You are asked to "Pick a number—any number." You need not tell me what number you choose. I undertake to make my argument work no matter what your choice. If, after seeing my argument, you think that some other choice could ruin it, you are at liberty to change your mind. In effect, I am universally quantifying my argument over all possible choices. Naturally, we do not carry through all our proofs in such great detail, but it is worthwhile to do it once. We now offer an abbreviated proof as it might appear in many a text.

"Let x and y be arbitrary real numbers. Then $x - y$ is a real number. By Eq. (1), $(x - y)^2 \geq 0$. Since x and y were arbitrary, Eq. (2) is proved." This procedure is quite general. Whatever can be proved of a fixed but arbitrary object in the domain of a variable is universally true in that domain.

The order of application of several quantifiers may make quite a difference. Consider, for example, the two assertions

$(\forall x)(\exists y)\,(x \text{ likes } y),$
$(\exists y)(\forall x)\,(x \text{ likes } y).$

The first says (roughly) that there are no misanthropes: Everyone (say x) like someone (say y); y may very well depend on x. The second says that there is someone (say y) who is universally liked. To see that there is a difference, let the common domain of "x" and "y" consist of John, Joe, and Jim, and suppose that John likes Joe, Joe likes Jim, and Jim likes John, but John dislikes Jim, Jim dislikes Joe, and Joe dislikes John. Then the first assertion is true but the second is false.

Among the punctuation marks that we use in mathematics, one kind has a special use. We apply quotation marks to a symbol to form a name for the symbol. Thus

(4)   "x" is a variable whose domain is the class of real numbers,

(5) x is a real number,

are perfectly good statements. We do not wish to be pedantic about this distinction, however, and we recognize that it is fairly common usage to write

x is a real variable

instead of statement (4). In fact, we shall adopt this usage, and write, for example,

Let p and q be propositional variables,

or

Let n be an integer-valued variable,

and so on. But it is important to stress the difference between a name and that which is named, between a symbol and that which is symbolized. (Among some primitive people, to possess knowledge of a man's secret name is to have great power over him.)

EXAMPLE 1–5. Of the following statements,

(1) H_2O = water,
(2)   "H_2O" = "water,"
(3) H_2O = "water,"

the first is correct because the same chemical compound is named on both sides. The second is incorrect, because it asserts that the names are the same. The third is incorrect also, because it asserts that a chemical compound and a name are the same.

Commas need no special comments. Parentheses are used in mathematical language to indicate that what they enclose is to be treated as a single object. Thus

$$2 \cdot (5 + 7)$$

represents the result of multiplying $5 + 7$ by 2, whereas

$$(2 \cdot 5) + 7$$

represents the result of adding 7 to $2 \cdot 5$. When several operations (different or the same) are involved in this way, it is customary to adopt certain conventions about priority of application, to avoid the excessive use of parentheses. Thus, we agree that

$$2 \cdot 5 + 7 = (2 \cdot 5) + 7,$$
$$10 - 3 - 2 = (10 - 3) - 2,$$
$$a + 2xy^2 = a + (2 \cdot (x \cdot (y^2))),$$

and so on. We assume that the ordinary conventions about algebraic symbols have been learned. As we introduce new operations we shall state our conventions about them. For example, when there is no danger of ambiguity, we shall omit parentheses in quantified statements such as

$$(\forall x)\, (5 + x = x + 5)$$

and write

$$(\forall x)\, 5 + x = x + 5,$$

or even

$$\forall x\; 5 + x = x + 5.$$

Some authors write the quantified variable as a subscript:

$$\forall_x\, 5 + x = x + 5,$$
$$\exists_x\, 5 + x = x + 5.$$

Occasionally, when the domain of a variable is to be restricted, an indication is given as follows:

$$\forall_x \text{ real}, x^2 \geq 0,$$
$$\forall_{x \geq 1}\, 3 + x \geq 4,$$
$$\exists_{x < 0}\, x^2 = 4.$$

We could go on with detailed discussion of other symbols and conventions, but the most common ones have been treated and we shall stop here. It must be remembered that the language of mathematics has developed historically, just as all natural languages do, that it has also sprouted idioms and usages, and that these are tolerable so long as they do not lead to ambiguity. The primary purpose is *communication*.

EXERCISES 1–1

1. Are the following true or false?
   (a) If $a = b$, then $b = a$.
   (b) If $a = b$ and $b = c$, then $a = c$.
   (c) If $a + b = bc$ and $b = d$, then $a + b = dc$.
   (d) "$1 + 2$" = "$2 + 1$."

2. Find, in print, two examples of "$=$" in which our convention is violated.

3. Can "x" sometimes be a constant, sometimes a variable? Discuss.

4. Express in ordinary language:
   (a) $(\exists x)$ (The captain is sober at time x).
   (b) $(\forall y)$ (y loves Saturday night).
   (c) $(\forall n)$ ($n^2 - n$ is even).
   (d) $(\forall m)$ ($m^3 - m$ is divisble by 3).
   (e) $(\exists x)$ $(0 \cdot x \neq 1)$. ("$\neq$" means "is not equal to.")

5. Do the following have the same meaning?
   (a) $(\forall x)$ (If x is a ball, then x is round).
   (b) $(\forall y)$ (If y is a ball, then y is round).

6. Express in ordinary language:
   (a) $(\forall x)(\exists y)$ $x + y = 0$.
   (b) $(\exists y)(\forall x)$ $x + y = 0$.

7. Using "$N(x)$" to denote "the number of hairs on the head of x," express in ordinary language:

$$(\exists y)(\exists x) (x \neq y \text{ and } N(x) = N(y)).$$

8. Using "$S(x)$" for "x is a sucker" and "$B(x,t)$" for "x is born at time t," express in ordinary language:

$$(\forall t)(\exists x) [S(x) \text{ and } B(x,t)].$$

9. Express in symbolic form:
   (a) The product of three successive whole numbers is always divisible by 3.
   (b) Some numbers are greater than their own squares.
   (c) The square of no number is negative.

10. Using "xFt" to denote "you can fool x at time t," express in symbolic form:
    (a) You can fool some of the people all of the time.
    (b) You can fool all of the people some of the time.

11. Using "$\geq$" and "$<$" ("is less than"), express in symbolic form:
   (a) There is a greatest number.
   (b) There is no greatest number.

12. Using "xMy" to denote "x is married to y," express in symbolic form:
   (a) Polygamy exists.
   (b) Polygamy does not exist.
   (c) Polygamy is compulsory for all married people.

$$[(\forall x)(\forall y) \text{ If } xMy, \text{ then } (\exists z) \, xMz \text{ and } z \neq y.]$$

13. What is the truth set of "$x^2 = 5$" if the domain of "x" is
   (a) the class of real numbers?
   (b) the class of positive real numbers?
   (c) the class of integers (whole numbers)?

14. Are the following true or false? (In each case, state appropriate domains first.)
   (a) $(\forall x)(\exists y) \, y^2 = x.$
   (b) $(\forall x)(\forall y)(\forall z) \, (x - y) - z = x - (y - z).$
   (c) $(\forall x)(\forall y)(\forall z) \, (x + y) + z = x + (y + z).$

15. Compare:
   (a) $(\forall x)(\forall y) \, x$ likes y.
   (b) $(\forall y)(\forall x) \, x$ likes y.

16. Compare:
   (a) $(\exists x)(\exists y) \, x$ likes y.
   (b) $(\exists y)(\exists x) \, x$ likes y.

17. Write down special cases of the universal statement

$$(\forall x) \, (10 + x)(10 - x) = 100 - x^2.$$

18. Write down special cases of the universal statement

All geniuses are mad.

Is the universal statement true?

19. Write down special cases of the universal statement

$$(\forall n) \, n^2 - n + 41 \text{ is a prime.}$$

Is the universal statement true?

20. Write down a single universal statement of which the following are all special cases:

$$1 = \frac{(1)(1 + 1)}{2},$$

$$1 + 2 = \frac{(2)(2 + 1)}{2},$$

$$1 + 2 + 3 = \frac{(3)(3 + 1)}{2}.$$

21. Write down a single universal statement of which the following are all special cases:

$$1 = 1^2,$$
$$1 + 3 = 2^2,$$
$$1 + 3 + 5 = 3^2.$$

22. Write down a single universal statement of which the following are all special cases:

$$\sqrt{2 \cdot 3} \leq \frac{2 + 3}{2},$$

$$\sqrt{2\pi} \leq \frac{2 + \pi}{2},$$

$$\sqrt{\sqrt{3} \cdot \sqrt{7}} \leq \frac{\sqrt{3} + \sqrt{7}}{2}.$$

23. In this example our "number system" will consist of Joe, Jim, and John. Our operation " + " will be defined by Table 1-1. From the entry in the second row and third column, Jim + John = Joe. Complete the following:

(a) Jim + Joe =
(b) (Jim + Jim) + Jim =
(c) John + (Joe + Jim) =

Are the following true?

(d) $(\forall x) (x + \text{Joe} = x)$.
(e) $(\forall x)(\forall y) (x + y = y + x)$.
(f) $(\forall x)(x + (x + x) = \text{Joe})$.

Does the " + " here have anything to do with ordinary addition?

TABLE 1-1

+	Joe	Jim	John
Joe	Joe	Jim	John
Jim	Jim	John	Joe
John	John	Joe	Jim

1–3. PROPOSITIONS

The term *proposition* has various meanings in ordinary speech. To us, it will mean a statement which is either true or false but not both. We need not become involved in philosophical questions about truth, relative truth, absolute truth, and so on. It suffices that we can select a large class of statements and assign to some a *truth value* T and to all others a truth value F. (T and F are intended to mean truth and falsity.) This assignment of truth values is not arbitrary, for it is subject to certain reasonable rules, as we shall see. It is not necessary that we know whether a particular statement is true or false in order that it be classified as a proposition. For example, "The Dow–Jones Industrial Average rose on June 23, 1961" is a perfectly good proposition, even though few of us know whether its truth value is T or F. But "Hail to thee, blithe spirit" is not a proposition, because it is neither true nor false. Similarly, "This statement is false" is not a proposition, for if it is true it is also false, and if it is false it is also true.

We do not classify "x is red," where "x" is a variable, as a proposition. But if we quantify over x or "freeze" it by substitution, we do get a proposition. For example,

$$(\forall x)\ x \text{ is red,}$$
$$(\exists x)\ x \text{ is red,}$$
$$\text{This ball is red,}$$

are all propositions. Expressions like "x is red" will be discussed more fully later on.

Determine whether each of the following is a proposition:

1. Go down, Moses.
2. 5 is less than 3.
3. Where are the snows of yesteryear?
4. _____ is less than 3.
5. x is less than 3. ("x" is a constant referring to a real number.)
6. x is less than 3. (x is a real variable.)
7. He is 20 years old.
8. $(\forall x)\ x < 3$.
9. $(\exists x)\ x < 3$.
10. A plague on both your houses!
11. $(\forall a)(\forall b)(\exists x)(\exists y)\ ax + by = 1$.

12. $(\forall x)\ x < y$. (Your answer depends on how you regard "y" here.)
13. The gross national product will be less than 1 trillion dollars in 1980.

When certain propositions have truth values assigned to them, other related propositions have determined truth values. These related ones are constructed by means of five basic logical connectives, which are given in Table 1–2. These connectives are expressed in various ways in ordinary language. We shall now explain and illustrate each one.

The first, *negation*, is the simplest one. If p stands for a proposition, then $\sim p$ stands for the complete denial of p. Another term for the negation of p is the contradictory of p. It may be expressed by "it is false that p" or "it is not the case that p" or "p is false," or otherwise. Thus, if p stands for "This ball is black," then $\sim p$ may be expressed by "This ball is not black." Observe that "This ball is white" is not a correct negation. This illustrates the principle that of a proposition and its negation, exactly one must be true and exactly one false. A common fallacy in argumentation is illustrated by "You say that it is false that all men are honest. Therefore you must think that all men are dishonest." Incidentally, it is fairly common usage in English to negate "All men are honest" by "All men are not honest," although the unambiguous "Not all men are honest" is far preferable.

EXERCISES 1–3

Negate the following propositions in good English:
1. John is young.
2. John is not young.
3. John is young and wealthy.
4. John is neither young nor wealthy.
5. All professors are absent-minded.
6. Some professors are absent-minded.
7. No professors are absent-minded.
8. Some professors are not absent-minded.
9. Whenever it rains, it pours.

TABLE 1–2

Symbol	Meaning	Name of operation
$\sim$	not	negation
$\wedge$	and	conjunction
$\vee$	or	alternation (disjunction)
$\rightarrow$	if...then	implication (conditional)
$\leftrightarrow$	if and only if	equivalence (biconditional)

TABLE 1-3

p	$\sim p$
T	F
F	T

To express in compact form the relationship between the truth values of a proposition and its negation, we write down the *truth table* for $\sim p$, which exhibits all the acceptable combinations of truth values (Table 1-3).

Given two propositions p, q, their *conjunction* $p \wedge q$ (read "p and q") is the joint assertion of both. It is true when both are true, and false otherwise. Examples: "The sun is shining and rain is falling," "He is young and (he is) wealthy," "I like him but I hate his wife," "Life is real, life is earnest." The corresponding truth table is given in Table 1-4.

Note that in this case we need four rows in the table, because there are four possible combinations of truth values for the variables p and q. If we had a propositional formula P containing three variables p, q, r, the corresponding truth table would require eight rows. In general, if P contains n variables, the truth table would contain 2^n rows. There is no special significance to the order of appearance in these rows of the different combinations of truth values. Thus, we could write the table for $p \wedge q$ as shown in Table 1-5.

Just because it makes no difference, there is no harm in agreeing to a standard order of presentation, namely, the first one given above. For three variables, the pattern would be as given in Table 1-6.

The general pattern should be clear from these examples. This standardization makes it easy to compare truth tables for different propositional formulas. The student should compare in this way the tables for $p \wedge q$ and

TABLE 1-4

p	q	$p \wedge q$
T	T	T
T	F	F
F	T	F
F	F	F

TABLE 1-5

p	q	$p \wedge q$
T	F	F
F	T	F
F	F	F
T	T	T

$q \wedge p$. We shall return to this point later, but it is worthwhile to keep our eyes open for other cases in which truth tables are identical.

Our next connective, "or," is used ambiguously in English. The *exclusive* "or" indicates that one of two alternatives holds, but not both. Example: "Your money or your life." The *inclusive* "or," sometimes written "and/or" indicates that at least one of the alternatives holds, possibly both. Example: "If either your or your wife is at least 65 years old, you may be entitled to a larger medical expense deduction." *We shall agree to use the inclusive* "or." Thus the *alternation* $p \vee q$ has the truth table shown in Table 1-7. (The word "disjunction" is often used in place of "alternation.") There is no question here which interpretation is correct. We merely choose one meaning and agree to abide by it to avoid the sin of ambiguity. If we really wish to express the exclusive "or," "p or q but not both," we can write $(p \vee q) \wedge \sim (p \wedge q)$.

TABLE 1-6

p	q	r
T	T	T
T	T	F
T	F	T
T	F	F
F	T	T
F	T	F
F	F	T
F	F	F

TABLE 1–7

p	q	$p \vee q$
T	T	T
T	F	T
F	T	T
F	F	F

Students are sometimes disturbed by an assertion $p \vee q$ when p is obviously true and q is obviously false. Thus, it may seem strange to say "5 is less than or equal to 7" (written "$5 \leq 7$") when clearly "$5 < 7$" is true and "$5 = 7$" is false. Nevertheless, the alternation is true, even though it is not the strongest true statement that could be made.

The connective "if... then" (*implication* or *conditional*) appears in ordinary usage in various forms. Thus we may find "p implies q," "if p then q," "p is sufficient for q," "q is necessary for p," "q follows from p," "p only if q," "p entails q." Notice that we do not include "p, hence q" or "since p, q," which are best translated, perhaps, by $(p \wedge (p \rightarrow q)) \wedge q$. This is different from $p \rightarrow q$, as we shall see. In "$p \rightarrow q$," p is the *antecedent* and q the *consequent* of the conditional. Ordinarily there is the connotation of a causal relationship between p and q, but this interpretation is too difficult to make precise here. Therefore we give it the following slightly artificial but very useful meaning. The proposition "$p \rightarrow q$" is taken to be true in all cases but one, namely, when p is true and q is false. Thus, the truth table is as shown in Table 1–8.

If you object that it doesn't quite capture the sense of "implies" or "if... then...," we agree with you. The principal difficulty is that it may connect

TABLE 1–8

p	q	$p \rightarrow q$
T	T	T
T	F	F
F	T	T
F	F	T

unrelated propositions. You may very well take the position that "$2 = 1$ implies I am the Pope" is neither true nor false but simply meaningless. If so, then "$p \rightarrow q$" fails to be a proposition at all for certain pairs of propositions p and q. The difficulties involved in this position are enormous. If the application of "$\rightarrow$" is restricted to certain related pairs of propositions, we must state unambiguously which pairs, and that is quite a task. For example, should we prohibit a useful sentence like "If you're right then I'm a monkey's uncle?" We prefer not to undertake this difficult task.

Well, then, let us agree that we want "$p \rightarrow q$" to yield a proposition for every pair p, q. What should its truth table be? Clearly p true and q true should yield $p \rightarrow q$ true, and equally clearly p true and q false should yield $p \rightarrow q$ false. Suppose now we refuse to consider as true any conditional in which the antecedent is false. Then we must enter F's in the last two places, the truth table becomes identical with the one for $p \wedge q$, and we might as well not introduce "$\rightarrow$" at all. Suppose we make the third entry F and the fourth T. Then the propositions "p implies q" and "q implies p" would always have the same truth values. For example, "If Susie is a cat, then Susie is an animal" would be true or false according as "If Susie is an animal, then Susie is a cat" is true or false. The remaining alternative is to make the third entry T and the fourth F. But then the truth table becomes identical with the one for q. Thus we see that our choice of values for "$p \rightarrow q$" is the least unacceptable of our alternatives. Indeed it works extremely well in mathematical reasoning.

To get used to our definition, the student may regard "$p \rightarrow q$" as a conditional promise which is false if violated and true otherwise. For example, "If you paint my house then I will pay you $300." Under what circumstances is such a promise violated? Precisely when you do paint my house (p true) and I do not pay you $300 ($q$ is false). Notice that it is not a two-sided promise—you do not promise to paint if I pay you. This is the reason for the last two entries: If p is not fulfilled (p is false), then my promise of q has not been tested, so it certainly cannot be regarded as violated. The case p true, q true is a clear fulfillment, and the case p true, q false is a clear violation. Thus we are led to the truth table given as Table 1-8.

The proposition "$p \leftrightarrow q$" may be read "p if and only if q," "p is equivalent to q," "p implies q and q implies p," "p is necessary and sufficient for q." An abbreviation which is rapidly gaining acceptance is "p iff q." The truth table is as shown in Table 1-9.

The *converse* of an implication "$p \rightarrow q$" is the implication "$q \rightarrow p$." It is a common error to confuse the two, or to assert that one follows from

TABLE 1–9

p	q	$p \leftrightarrow q$
T	T	T
T	F	F
F	T	F
F	F	T

the other. When both are true, then "$p \leftrightarrow q$" is true. Conversely, when "$p \leftrightarrow q$" is true, so are "$p \rightarrow q$" and "$q \rightarrow p$."

We are now ready to compute truth tables for complex combinations of propositions. To avoid excessive use of parentheses in the writing of formulas, we introduce conventions about the range of application, or *scope*, of the five basic connectives, just as we introduced conventions about the operations in ordinary algebra. Thus, "$\sim$" has the smallest scope possible, so that "$\sim p \vee q$" means "$(\sim p) \vee q$," not "$\sim(p \vee q)$." Next come "$\wedge$" and "$\vee$," which have equal scope. Thus "$p \wedge q \vee r$" is never used; instead we specify our meaning as "$p \wedge (q \vee r)$" or "$(p \wedge q) \vee r$." Next comes "$\rightarrow$." Thus, "$p \wedge q \rightarrow r$" means "$(p \wedge q) \rightarrow r$," not "$p \wedge (q \rightarrow r)$." Last of all comes "$\leftrightarrow$." Thus "$p \rightarrow q \leftrightarrow r$" means "$(p \rightarrow q) \leftrightarrow r$," not "$p \rightarrow (q \leftrightarrow r)$." If dropping parentheses does not lead to ambiguity, taking into account the above conventions, we may do so.

EXAMPLE 1–6. $p \wedge \sim q \rightarrow r \vee s$ means $[p \wedge (\sim q)] \rightarrow (r \vee s)$.

EXAMPLE 1–7. $p \wedge (p \rightarrow q) \leftrightarrow p \wedge q$ means $[p \wedge (p \rightarrow q)] \leftrightarrow (p \wedge q)$.

$p \rightarrow q \leftrightarrow \sim q \rightarrow \sim p$ means $(p \rightarrow q) \leftrightarrow [(\sim q) \rightarrow (\sim p)]$.

EXAMPLE 1–9. $\sim p \leftrightarrow q \rightarrow r \wedge \sim s$ means $(\sim p) \leftrightarrow [q \rightarrow (r \wedge (\sim s))]$.

The computation of truth tables is a routine matter. After writing down all the possibilities for the propositional variables p, q, r we assign the truth values occurring in each row and successively reduce, using the truth tables for our five basic connectives. Thus, suppose that we have p true, q false in Example 1–7:

$$p \wedge (p \rightarrow q) \leftrightarrow p \wedge q,$$
$$T \wedge (T \rightarrow F) \leftrightarrow T \wedge F,$$
$$T \wedge F \leftrightarrow F,$$
$$F \leftrightarrow F.$$
$$T$$

TABLE 1-10

I	II	III $(I \to II)$	IV $(I \wedge III)$	V $(I \wedge II)$	VI $(IV \leftrightarrow V)$
p	q	$p \to q$	$p \wedge (p \to q)$	$p \wedge q$	$p \wedge (p \to q) \leftrightarrow p \wedge q$
T	T	T	T	T	T
T	F	F	F	F	T
F	T	T	F	F	T
F	F	T	F	F	T

It sometimes is convenient to introduce intermediate columns in the computation and then to calculate the values running down these columns. Thus, in the same example, we might have the results given in Table 1-10.

We have been speaking rather loosely about propositional formulas, such as "$p \to (q \wedge r)$" or "$(\sim q) \to (p \vee r)$." Nothing we have said so far prevents us from writing down nonsensical formulas like "$pq \wedge \wedge \sim \to$." Now, having introduced the five logical connectives and given some examples of "decent" formulas, we are in a position to be more precise. The meaningful formulas are called *propositional functions*. They are defined by the following rules:

(1) Every propositional variable p, q, r, ... is a propositional function.

(2) If P and Q are propositional functions, then $(\sim P)$, $(P \wedge Q)$, $(P \vee Q)$, $(P \to Q)$, $(P \leftrightarrow Q)$ are also propositional functions.

(3) Only by virtue of (1) and (2), applied a finite number of times, is a formula a propositional function.

The conventions about parentheses and scope will be admitted in the application of these rules.

EXAMPLE 1-10.   Show that $p \to (q \wedge r)$ is a propositional function.

Solution: By (1), q and r are propositional functions. By (2), so is $(q \wedge r)$. By (1), p is a propositional function. Again, by (2), so is $(p \to (q \wedge r))$. Dropping the parentheses in accordance with our conventions, we see that $p \to q \wedge r$ is also a propositional function.

Actually, it is possible to give an algorithm or prescription for determining whether any given formula is a propositional function or not. This is neither necessary nor worthwhile for us here. The interested student might amuse himself, though, by proving that "$p \rightarrow q \sim \wedge$" is not a propositional function.

Every propositional function has associated with it a truth table. It is quite possible for different propositional functions to have the same truth table, and it is important to know when this happens. The branch of logic that deals with such problems is called the *propositional calculus*.

As we have stated, one of our objectives in studying logic is to establish methods for passing correctly from one set of statements to another. The calculus of propositions can help us to find these correct modes of reasoning or patterns of proof. A few examples will show us the utility of truth tables for this purpose.

EXAMPLE 1–11.   Let us examine the truth table for the conditional. Suppose that P and Q are any propositions and that we know by any means at all that P and $P \rightarrow Q$ both are true. From the truth table given in Table 1–11 we see that the first two lines are the only ones in which P is true and that, of these, the first line is the only one in which $P \rightarrow Q$ is true. In the first line Q is true. We may therefore infer that Q is true. Our pattern of proof is

$$P$$
$$P \rightarrow Q$$
$$\therefore \quad Q.$$

This *rule of inference* bears the imposing name "modus ponens" or "the rule of detachment." It is certainly no surprise to the student, but it is worth his attention as one of the most common modes of correct reasoning.

EXAMPLE 1–12.   Suppose that P is false and $P \rightarrow Q$ is true. Can we correctly infer anything about Q? The two premises correspond to the last two lines of Table 1–11. In the third line Q is true and in the fourth it is false. We

TABLE 1–11

P	Q	$P \rightarrow Q$
T	T	T
T	F	F
F	T	T
F	F	T

TABLE 1–12

P	Q	$\sim P \to Q$
T	T	T
T	F	T
F	T	T
F	F	F

can say nothing about the truth of Q. The following is an *incorrect* inference:

EXAMPLE 1–13. Consider the truth table for $\sim P \to Q$ (Table 1–12). Suppose we know that the falsity of P implies the truth of Q and that Q is false. Our premises are then $\sim P \to Q$ and $\sim Q$. There is exactly one line of the table in which both premises are true—the second. In that line P is true. Our pattern of proof is therefore

$$\sim P \to Q$$
$$\sim Q$$
$$\therefore\ P.$$

This is called an *indirect proof* or a *reductio ad absurdum*. It occurs frequently in mathematics, particularly when one is trying to show the non-existence of a certain kind of object. If we let P stand for "no such object exists," then we may begin by assuming $\sim P$, that is, the existence of such an object. We then develop the various consequences $Q_1, Q_2, \ldots$ of our assumption in the hope that some Q turns out to be false. If so, then both premises above are true and so, therefore, is the desired conclusion P. It is as though we put the suspect $\sim P$ on the witness stand in the hope that he will perjure himself. Sometimes the search for a false consequence is long and involved, and sometimes it never succeeds. The discovery of non-Euclidean geometry was the result of an attempted *reductio*.

EXAMPLE 1–14. There is fallacious pattern that some people try to use by analogy with indirect proof. They wish to prove P, so they assume it true, derive a true conclusion Q, and then infer, *incorrectly*, that P is true.

The scheme is

The inference is incorrect because a true conclusion is implied by any antecedent, whether true or false. The student may check this from the truth table for $P \to Q$.

To summarize, a mode of reasoning is correct if the conclusion is true under all circumstances in which the premises are true.

EXERCISES 1-4

1. Let

    "p" stand for "interest rates rise,"
    "q" stand for "stock prices fall,"
    "r" stand for "bond prices rise,"
    "s" stand for "commodity prices fall."

Assume for the purpose of these exercises that "rise" and "fall" precisely negate each other. Express in symbolic form:

    (a) Bond prices rise if interest rates fall.
    (b) If stock prices and commodity prices fall, interest rates rise.
    (c) Either interest rates or bond prices rise.
    (d) If stock prices or bond prices fall, commodity prices rise iff (if and only if) interest rates rise.
    (e) Bond prices fall when stock prices rise, and conversely.
    (f) It never happens that stock, bond, and commodity prices all rise.
    (g) Stock prices rise iff bond prices fall.
    (h) Stock prices fall iff bond prices rise.
    (i) If bond prices fall, interest rates rise.

Interpreting each of the formulas obtained above as a propositional function, write down the corresponding truth tables.

2. Show by means of truth tables that the following are correct modes of reasoning:

(a) $\sim Q$
    $\dfrac{P \to Q.}{\therefore \sim P}$

(b) $P \vee Q$
    $\dfrac{\sim P}{\therefore Q.}$

(c) $\dfrac{P \to Q}{\therefore \ \sim Q \to \sim P.}$

(d) P
$P \to Q$
$Q \to R$
$\therefore \ R.$

(e) $P \to Q$
$Q \to R$
$\therefore \ P \to R.$

3. Construct three more correct modes of reasoning.
4. Write down the truth tables for the following propositional functions:
   (a) $p \lor q \leftrightarrow q \lor p.$
   (a′) $p \land q \leftrightarrow q \land p.$
   (b) $p \land (q \lor r) \leftrightarrow (p \land q) \lor (p \land r).$
   (b′) $p \lor (q \land r) \leftrightarrow (p \lor q) \land (p \lor r).$
   (c) $p \lor (q \land \sim q) \leftrightarrow p.$
   (c′) $p \land (q \lor \sim q) \leftrightarrow p.$
   (d) $p \lor \sim p.$
   (d′) $\sim (p \land \sim p).$
   (e) $p \to q \leftrightarrow \sim p \lor q.$
   (f) $(p \leftrightarrow q) \leftrightarrow (p \land q) \lor (\sim p \land \sim q).$

5. Write down the truth tables for the following propositional functions:
   (a) $\sim p \land \sim q.$
   (n) $[(p \to q) \land \sim p] \to \sim q.$
   (b) $\sim (p \land \sim q).$
   (o) $p \to q \leftrightarrow \sim q \to \sim p.$
   (c) $\sim \sim p \land \sim \sim q.$
   (p) $(p \to q) \lor (q \to p).$
   (d) $p \land p.$
   (q) $p \lor \sim p \leftrightarrow q \lor \sim q.$
   (e) $(p \land q) \land r.$
   (r) $p \land \sim p \leftrightarrow q \land \sim q.$
   (f) $p \land (q \land r).$
   (s) $(p \to q) \land (q \to p) \leftrightarrow (p \leftrightarrow q).$
   (g) $(p \lor q) \lor r \leftrightarrow p \lor (q \lor r).$
   (t) $(p \to q) \to (\sim p \to \sim q).$
   (h) $(p \lor q) \land r \leftrightarrow p \lor (q \land r).$
   (u) $\sim (p \to q) \to p.$
   (i) $\sim (p \lor q) \leftrightarrow \sim p \land \sim q.$
   (v) $\sim (p \to q) \to \sim q.$
   (j) $\sim (p \land q) \leftrightarrow \sim p \lor \sim q.$
   (w) $(\sim p \to p) \to p.$
   (k) $(p \to q) \land q \to p.$
   (x) $p \to (\sim p \to q).$
   (l) $p \land (p \to q) \to q.$
   (y) $(p \to q) \to ((q \to r) \to (p \to q)).$
   (m) $(p \to q) \to (q \to p).$
   (z) $((p \to q) \to r) \to (q \to r).$

1–4.   TAUTOLOGIES

When we examine any particular compound proposition, we are able to say, at least theoretically, whether it is true or false, by investigating the truth of its component parts. Thus, "Diamonds are hard or crows are black" is true because one at least of the component propositions happens

TABLE 1–13

p	$p \vee \sim p$
T	T
F	T

to be factually true. "Diamonds are hard or it is false that diamonds are hard" is also true. Somehow, though, we recognize an essential difference in these two examples. No knowledge of diamonds is necessary to determine the truth of the second one. It is true because of its form, not its substance. To see this, consider the propositional function "$p \vee \sim p$," of which our proposition is an instance. Its truth table is given as Table 1–13. Such a propositional function, for which the truth value is always T, is called a *tautology*. All the parts of Problem 4 of Exercises 1–4 are tautologies.

Tautologies are important to us because they represent, in symbolic form, correct modes of reasoning. Suppose, for example, someone says to us "The sun is shining, and whenever the sun shines my wife is cheerful, so my wife must be cheerful." To test the logic of this argument, we write down the corresponding propositional function:

$$p \wedge (p \to q) \to q.$$

We find that this takes the value T no matter what propositions replace "p" and "q." Thus the reasoning is correct. But suppose the statement had been "My wife is cheerful and whenever the sun shines my wife is cheerful, so the sun must be shining." The corresponding propositional function is

$$q \wedge (p \to q) \to p.$$

It has the truth table given as Table 1–14. This is not a tautology, and the

TABLE 1–14

p	q	$q \wedge (p \to q) \to p$
T	T	T
T	F	T
F	T	F
F	F	T

reasoning is incorrect. To pinpoint the error, we need only consider the possibility that the sun is not shining but the wife is cheerful, corresponding to the third line of the table. Of course, it may be factually true that the sun is shining, but that would only make the statement accidentally true, not logically true.

In general, to each inference

$$P$$
$$Q$$
$$\vdots$$
$$\therefore R$$

there corresponds a propositional function

$$P \wedge Q \wedge \cdots \rightarrow R.$$

An examination of the meaning of correct inference and of tautology will show that the inference is correct exactly when the propositional function is a tautology.

Tautologies may seem trivial because they appear to convey no real information. But we have just seen that the modes of reasoning incorporated in the propositional calculus can be reduced to tautologies. A great deal of mathematical reasoning is tautological, but much of it is far from trivial.

To express the fact that a propositional function A is a tautology, we write $\models A$. Thus

$$\models p \wedge q \rightarrow p \vee q.$$

If A and B are propositional functions with the same truth table (for all truth values of all variables appearing in either), we say that A and B are *tautologically equivalent* and we write $A \equiv B$. This means the same as $\models A \leftrightarrow B$. In many ways the relation "$\equiv$" behaves like "$=$." For example, it is *reflexive:* $A \equiv A$; *symmetric:* if $A \equiv B$, then $B \equiv A$; *transitive:* if $A \equiv B$ and $B \equiv C$, then $A \equiv C$. Furthermore, if $A \equiv B$, and if D represents any propositional function, then

$$\sim A \equiv \sim B,$$
$$A \vee D \equiv B \vee D,$$
$$A \wedge D \equiv B \wedge D,$$
$$A \rightarrow D \equiv B \rightarrow D,$$
$$D \rightarrow A \equiv D \rightarrow B,$$
$$(A \leftrightarrow D) \equiv (B \leftrightarrow D).$$

Thus, we may replace any or all occurrences of A by B in any compound formula in which A appears, and the resultant formula will be tautologically equivalent to the original. This we call the *rule of replacement*. In particular, the resultant is a tautology iff the original is one. The replacement need not be complete. For example, let

$$A = p \to q,$$
$$B = \sim p \vee q.$$

Then $A \equiv B$. If

$$P = (p \to q) \to q \wedge (p \to q) = A \to q \wedge A,$$
$$Q = (\sim p \vee q) \to q \wedge (p \to q) = B \to q \wedge A,$$
$$R = (p \to q) \to q \wedge (\sim p \vee q) = A \to q \wedge B,$$
$$S = (\sim p \vee q) \to q \wedge (\sim p \vee q) = B \to q \wedge B,$$

then $P \equiv Q \equiv R \equiv S$. (This chain of tautological equivalences is shorthand for $P \equiv Q$ and $Q \equiv R$ and $R \equiv S$. We use a similar shorthand for other relations, like "$=$," "$<$," "$\leq$.")

Let us take careful note of the distinction between $A \leftrightarrow B$, $A \equiv B$, and $A = B$. The first is merely another propositional function, like $A \vee B$. The second is an assertion *about* the propositional function $A \leftrightarrow B$, namely, that its truth table has all its (final) entries T, and the third is an assertion about A and B, namely, that they are *identical* as strings of symbols. For example,

$$p \wedge q = p \wedge q,$$
$$p \wedge q \equiv q \wedge p,$$

but not

$$p \wedge q = q \wedge p.$$

Some authors do not make our distinction between "$=$" and "$\equiv$." They are not necessarily wrong; see our discussion of the use of "$=$" in Section 1–2.

There is a second rule which is useful in working with tautologies. If P is a tautology involving a propositional variable p, and if A is any propositional function, we may replace all occurrences of p *throughout* P by A, and the resultant Q will also be a tautology. Referring to "replacement in all occurrences" as "substitution," we call this the *rule of substitution*. For example, let

$$P = (p \to p \vee q),$$
$$A = (p \to q).$$

Then the resultant is

$$Q = ((p \to q) \to (p \to q) \vee q).$$

The replacement of p by A in P must be *complete*. If in P above we made the replacement in the first occurrence of p only, we would get

$$R = ((p \to q) \to p \vee q),$$

which is not a tautology.

There is a strong similarity here to the replacements and substitutions that we find in ordinary algebra. Corresponding to the rule of replacement, we see that

$$(x - 1)(x + 1) = 3x$$

and

$$(x - 1)(x + 1) = 3((x + 2) - 2)$$

have the same truth sets. In particular, if one were an identity, the other would be one. Corresponding to the rule of substitution, we see that since

$$(x - 1)(x + 1) = x^2 - 1$$

is an identity, so is

$$((x + y) - 1)((x + y) + 1) = (x + y)^2 - 1.$$

A third useful remark is that any of the correct modes of reasoning can be applied to obtain tautologies from other tautologies. For example, applying the *rule of detachment*, we see that if P and $P \to Q$ are tautologies, so is Q. This can be justified easily by appealing to the truth tables.

We summarize our three rules for deriving tautologies:

Rule 1. Replacement.

Rule 2. Substitution.

Rule 3. Applications of correct inference.

In our treatment, the ultimate test for tautology of a propositional function lies in its truth table. The three rules above are then merely short cuts that enable us to derive or infer tautology without going through the labor of writing down all possible truth values for the variables and calculating the corresponding truth values for the given formula. They enable us to talk *about* the tables instead of calculating blindly *within* them. We have not proved the rules, nor shall we do so. The reader may satisfy himself about them by an appeal to the truth tables.

EXERCISES 1–5

1. Prove $\models p \wedge \sim q \leftrightarrow p \wedge \sim q$ by means of
   (a) Truth tables.
   (b) "Common sense."
   (c) The given tautology $p \leftrightarrow p$ and one of the rules.
2. Which of the parts of Problem 5 of Exercises 1–4 are tautologies?
3. In each of the following, is the reasoning correct?
   (a) You said you'd spank me if I spilled my milk. I didn't, so you shouldn't spank me.
   (b) If Socrates is immortal or harmless, then we cannot sentence him to death. But Socrates is a man, and all men are mortal. Also Socrates is a gadfly, and no gadfly is harmless. Therefore, we can sentence him to death.
   (c) Every positive number has a multiple greater than 1. The number a is either positive or zero and it has no multiple greater than 1. Therefore the number a is zero.
4. Prove, in any way, that the following auxiliary rules are correct:
   (a) Given $\models P$, $\models Q$, we may infer $\models P \wedge Q$.
   (b) Given $\models P$, $\models \sim P \vee Q$, we may infer $\models Q$.
   (c) Given $\models P$, $\models \sim (P \wedge Q)$, we may infer $\models \sim Q$.
   (d) Given $\models \sim P$, $\models P \vee Q$, we may infer $\models Q$.
   (e) Given $\models P$, $\models Q \rightarrow \sim P$, we may infer $\models \sim Q$.
5. Discuss the difference between $\sim \models P$ and $\models \sim P$.
6. Given $P \wedge Q \equiv P \vee Q$. Prove $P \equiv Q$. [*Hint:* Make a table headed by P, Q, $P \wedge Q$, $P \vee Q$.]
*7. Define the new connective "$|$" by $(p|q) = \sim(p \wedge q)$ and write out its truth table. Prove:
   (a) $\sim p \equiv (p|p)$.
   (b) $p \vee q \equiv ((p|p)|(q|q))$.
   (c) $p \wedge q \equiv ((p|q)|(p|q))$.
   (d) $p \rightarrow q \equiv (p|(q|q))$.
   (e) $p \leftrightarrow q \equiv A$, where A is some propositional function (construct it) in which the only connective used is "$|$."
*8. Can the connective "$*$," defined by Table 1–15, be used to express the five basic connectives?
9. Let $p, q, r, \ldots$ be variables with domain consisting of the two numbers 0 and 1. Write down the tables for the following functions:

      (a) $1 - p$.   (b) pq.   (c) $p + q - pq$.
      (d) $1 - p + pq$.   (e) $1 - p - q + 2pq$.

TABLE 1-15

p	q	$p * q$
T	T	F
T	F	F
F	T	F
F	F	T

For example, the table for pq is as given in Table 1-16. Write a short paragraph discussing your results.

10. Using the conditions and notation of Problem 9, prove that the following are identities:

(a) $p(1 - p) = 0$.

(b) $p + (1 - p) - p(1 - p) = 1$.

(c) $1 - p - q + 2pq = pq + (1 - p)(1 - q) - pq(1 - p)(1 - q)$.

(d) $1 - pq = (1 - p) + (1 - q) - (1 - p)(1 - q)$.

Construct three other identities of this kind.

11. Given $P \wedge Q \equiv Q$, $Q \wedge R \equiv R$, prove $P \wedge R \equiv R$.

12. Given the propositional variable p only, how many different propositional functions can be formed? How many different truth tables? Answer the same questions for two variables p, q.

1-5.   PREDICATES

We have already met and used statements involving variables, such as "$x < 7$" and "x is married to y." Such a statement is called an *open statement*, a *predicate formula*, or simply a *predicate*. When a predicate is preceded by a quantifier with respect to a variable, that variable is said to be

TABLE 1-16

p	q	pq
1	1	1
1	0	0
0	1	0
0	0	0

bound. An unbound variable is called *free*. For example, in "(∃x) (x is married to y)," "x" is bound and "y" is free. The number of different free variables that actually appear is called the number of places in the predicate. Thus "x < 7" is a one-place predicate, "x < y" is a two-place predicate, "(∀y) (x < y ∨ x = y)" is a one-place predicate, and "(∀y)(∃x) (x is married to y ∧ x loves y)" is a zero-place predicate, or simply a proposition.

Just as we found it necessary to use propositional variables and functions like "p," "q," "p ∧ q" in the propositional calculus, so we shall need to introduce predicate variables and functions like "P(x)," "Q(y)," "P(x) ∧ Q(y)" in the predicate calculus. This is done to achieve a proper degree of generality. For example, it should be apparent that the negation of "(∀x) (x is red)" is equivalent to "(∃x) ∼ (x is red)," that the negation of "(∀x) (x + 2 = 7x)" is equivalent to "(∃x) ∼ (x + 2 = 7x)," and so on. Instead of the vague phrase "and so on," we can be precise by using a predicate variable, say "P," and asserting that the negation of "(∀x) P(x)" is equivalent to "(∃x) ∼ P(x)," no matter what predicate is substituted for "P." This general statement is similar to the assertion that the negation of "p ∧ q" is always equivalent to "∼p ∨ ∼q," no matter what propositions are substituted for "p" and "q." This assertion was symbolized by

$$\models \sim (p \wedge q) \leftrightarrow \sim p \vee \sim q$$

or

$$\sim (p \wedge q) \equiv \sim p \vee \sim q.$$

We have used "⊨" and "≡" in the propositional calculus to indicate tautology and tautological equivalence. Now we extend the application of these symbols. If we have a formula **F** involving free predicate variables $P, Q, R, \ldots$ and free individual variables $x, y, z, \ldots$, we shall write "⊨ **F**" to indicate that **F** is true for all values of $P, Q, R, \ldots$ and $x, y, z, \ldots$. In this case we shall say that **F** is *valid*. If "**F** ↔ **G**" is valid, we have a *valid equivalence*, and write "**F** ≡ **G**." The example of valid equivalence given above is

$$\models \sim (\forall x)\ P(x) \leftrightarrow (\exists x) \sim P(x)$$

or

$$\sim (\forall x)\ P(x) \equiv (\exists x) \sim P(x).$$

The formal study of the concepts introduced above is contained in the intricate and highly technical *predicate calculus*. We cannot hope even to introduce the subject adequately here, let alone develop it. Our very limited goals will be to give a few examples of logical truths involving predicates and to warn the student of a few common pitfalls. The treatment will be entirely intuitive and there will be no attempt at proofs.

In the following set of exercises, the student should try to convince himself of the reasonableness of the assertions of validity by means of examples.

EXERCISES 1–6

1. (a) $\sim(\forall x)\,P(x) \equiv (\exists x) \sim P(x)$. E.g., "It is false that every number is even" is equivalent to "There exists a number that is not even."

    (b) $\sim(\exists x)\,P(x) \equiv (\forall x) \sim P(x)$. E.g., "It is false that there is an animal that has five legs" is equivalent to "Every animal fails to have five legs."

2. (a) $(\forall x)\,(P(x) \wedge Q(x)) \equiv (\forall x)\,P(x) \wedge (\forall x)\,Q(x)$. E.g., "Every man is both wise and wealthy" is equivalent to "Every man is wise and every man is wealthy."

    (b) $\models (\exists x)\,(P(x) \wedge Q(x)) \rightarrow (\exists x)\,P(x) \wedge (\exists x)\,Q(x)$. E.g., "There is a man who is both wise and wealthy" implies "There is a man who is wise and there is a man who is wealthy."

    (c) From $(\exists x)\,P(x) \wedge (\exists x)\,Q(x)$ we *cannot* infer that $(\exists x)\,(P(x) \wedge Q(x))$. We leave it to the student to find several examples in which the first statement is true and the second false.

    (d) $(\exists x)\,(P(x) \vee Q(x)) \equiv (\exists x)\,P(x) \vee (\exists x)\,Q(x)$. E.g., "There is a man who is either wise or wealthy" is equivalent to "There is a wise man or there is a wealthy man."

    (e) $\models (\forall x)\,P(x) \vee (\forall x)\,Q(x) \rightarrow (\forall x)\,(P(x) \vee Q(x))$. E.g., "All men are wealthy or all men are wise" implies "All men are either wealthy or wise."

    (f) From $(\forall x)\,(P(x) \vee Q(x))$ we cannot infer that $(\forall x)\,P(x) \vee (\forall x)\,Q(x)$. We leave it to the student to find several examples.

3. (a) $(P(x) \rightarrow Q(x)) \equiv (\sim P(x) \vee Q(x))$. E.g., "If x is a man then x is mortal" is equivalent to "Either x is not a man or x is mortal."

    (b) $(P(x) \rightarrow Q(x)) \equiv (\sim Q(x) \rightarrow \sim P(x))$. E.g., "If x is a man then x is mortal" is equivalent to "If x is immortal then x is not a man."

4. (a) $\models [(\forall x)\,(P(x) \leftrightarrow Q(x)) \rightarrow ((\forall x)\,P(x) \leftrightarrow (\forall x)\,Q(x))]$. E.g., "If for all men being wise were equivalent to being wealthy, then universal wisdom of men would be equivalent to universal wealthiness of men."

    (b) Give an example to show that the single arrow in Problem 4(a) cannot be reversed.

5. (a) $(\forall x)(\forall y)\,P(x,y) \equiv (\forall y)\,(\forall x)\,P(x,y)$. E.g., let "$P(x,y)$" stand for "$x$ likes y."

    (b) $(\exists x)(\exists y)\,P(x,y) \equiv (\exists y)(\exists x)\,P(x,y)$. Let the student give an example or two.

(c) $\models (\forall x)(\forall y)\, P(x,y) \rightarrow (\forall x)\, P(x,x)$. E.g., "If every x likes every y, then every x likes himself." (The variables are assumed to have the same domain.) Can the arrow be reversed?

(d) $\models (\exists x)(\forall y)\, P(x,y) \rightarrow (\forall y)(\exists x) P(x,y)$. E.g., "If there is an x who likes every y, then every y has some x that likes him." Can the arrow be reversed?

6. (a) $\sim(\forall x)(\forall y)\, P(x,y) \equiv (\exists x) \sim (\forall y)\, P(x,y) \equiv (\exists x)(\exists y) \sim P(x,y)$. E.g., let "$P(x,y)$" stand for "$x$ is married to y."

(b) $\sim(\forall x)(\exists y)\, P(x,y) \equiv (\exists x) \sim (\exists y)\, P(x,y) \equiv (\exists x)(\forall y) \sim P(x, y)$. E.g., "It is false that every x has some y that he likes" is equivalent to "There is an x that likes no y."

(c) $\sim(\exists x)(\exists y)\, P(x,y) \equiv (\forall x) \sim (\exists y)\, P(x,y) \equiv (\forall x)(\forall y) \sim P(x,y)$. Let the student give an example or two.

(d) "It is false that there is some x that likes every y" is equivalent to "Every x has some y that he does not like." Write down a general formula of which this is a special case.

7. (a) $\sim(\forall x)(P(x) \wedge Q(x)) \equiv (\exists x) \sim (P(x) \wedge Q(x)) \equiv (\exists x)(\sim P(x) \vee \sim Q(x))$. Give an example.

(b) Negate $(\exists x)(P(x) \wedge Q(x))$.

(c) Negate $(\forall x)(P(x) \vee Q(x))$.

(d) Negate $(\exists x)(P(x) \vee Q(x))$.

(e) $\models \sim(\forall x)(P(x) \rightarrow Q(x)) \equiv (\exists x) \sim (P(x) \rightarrow Q(x)) \equiv (\exists x)(P(x) \wedge \sim Q(x))$. To disprove that a wealthy man is necessarily wise, we need only exhibit one wealthy man who is not wise.

(f) Negate $(\forall x)(P(x) \leftrightarrow Q(x))$.

8. (a) The negation of "For all x and for all z there exists a y such that $x + y = z$" is equivalent to "There exists an x and there exists a z such that for all y, $x + y \neq z$."

(b) Negate "Every day there is one moment when all men are quiet."

(c) Negate "There is an x such that for all y and for all z, $x + y = z$."

(d) Negate "There is an x such that for all y there is a z such that $x + y = z$."

(e) Negate "For every positive number h there is a positive number k such that for all x, $-k < x - 2 < k$ implies $-h < x^2 - 4 < h$."

(f) Negate "Every week I receive a letter from at least one friend."

9. Which of the following are equivalent?

(a) Some men are humble and powerful.

(b) Some men are humble if they are powerful.

(c) Some powerful men are humble.

(d) Some humble men are powerful.

(e) All men are humble and powerful.

(f) All men are humble if they are powerful.

(g) All powerful men are humble.

(h) All humble men are powerful.

Negate each of the preceding.

10. Discuss the following argument: $(p \rightarrow q) \vee (q \rightarrow p)$ is a tautology. Hence wealth implies happiness or happiness implies wealth.

1-6. DEFINITIONS

The purpose of a definition in mathematics is to introduce a symbol by means of a combination of others. Frequently the symbol names a class of objects. This may occur in various ways.

(1) The symbol may be familiar, but the class of objects so wide and varied that for purposes of discussion (or to avoid ambiguity) we sharply restrict the class. Thus, we defined "proposition," "=," "or."

(2) The symbol may be completely new, and the class of objects completely specified by the definition. For example, "We define a *gloop* as any whole number which is divisble by 3."

(3) The class may be completely specified and contain exactly one object, and the name assigned new. Thus "We define $k = 1,111$," or "Let $n =$ the number of possible games of tic-tac-toe." In such a case, the symbol or name is a constant. Before such a definition can be made, however, we must make quite sure of the *existence* and *uniqueness* of the object being named. If $P(x)$ is a predicate presumably describing the object, we must prove

(a) $(\exists x)\, P(x)$

and

(b) $(\forall x)(\forall y)\, [(P(x) \wedge P(y)) \rightarrow (x = y)]$.

For example, let "$P(x)$" stand for "x is a positive real number and $x^2 = 5$." after verifying (a) and (b) we may write

$$Def. \ \sqrt{5} = \text{the } x \text{ such that } P(x),$$

or

$$\sqrt{5} =_{df} \text{the } x \text{ such that } P(x).$$

The symbol "$=_{df}$" is read "equals by definition." An alternate form of the definition is

$$(x = \sqrt{5}) =_{df} P(x).$$

Strictly speaking, this defines the predicate "$x = \sqrt{5}$," but since the form of the predicate assures us that its truth set contains precisely one object, we may say that we have defined "$\sqrt{5}$" *contextually*. Operations are frequently defined contextually. Thus

$$x \oplus y =_{\mathrm{df}} x + y - xy \qquad (x, y \text{ real})$$

is a contextual definition of "$\oplus$." Our definition of "$=$" was of this type.

(4) The name and the class may be completely familiar, as in (1), but we may discover an entirely new description of the class, or a new predicate which has the class as its truth set. Thus, suppose that we have defined "rational number" as a quotient of integers, a/b, with $b \neq 0$. Later we discover that every rational number has an eventually periodic decimal expansion (like $0.54\overline{767676}\ldots$) and conversely, every number which has such an expansion is rational. We might then say "We may therefore define a rational number as a number which has an eventually periodic decimal expansion." This way of speaking should not deceive us. Whichever definition is used, we must eventually prove that the two are equivalent. However, it might be very convenient to adopt one definition, rather than the other. Frequently the same mathematical structure may be built up in different ways, so that what is a theorem in one development is a definition in another. For example, in one treatment of the integers,

$$(\forall x) \; x \text{ is an integer} \rightarrow x + 1 \text{ is an integer}$$

is a theorem, in another it is part of the definition of integer.

(5) The range of application of a symbol may be enlarged. We did this for "$\models$" and "$\equiv$," extending the range from the class of propositional functions to the class of predicates. When such an extension is made, we must check that the new meaning coincides with the old when the symbol applies to an object in the original range. Thus, it would be incorrect to extend the definition of "$+$" from the integers to the rationals by

$$\frac{a}{b} + \frac{c}{d} =_{\mathrm{df}} \frac{a + c}{b + d},$$

for if $b = d = 1$, we would get $a + c = (a + c)/2$, which is false if, for example, $a = c = 1$.

Another word of caution is in order here. When a definition is extended, it must not be assumed that all the statements which were valid in the original range will remain valid in the new one. Thus, there are extensions of addition and multiplication from the class of real numbers to a wider class (matrices) so that of the three statements

(a) $x + y = y + x$,
(b) $x(y + z) = xy + xz$,
(c) $xy = yx$,

the first two remain valid, whereas the third is invalid.

(6) The kind of object which is defined in mathematics may vary considerably. We may define numbers, number systems, functions, operations, sets (or classes), algebras, groups, rings, fields, relations, and so on. The definitions may be short or long, simple or complicated, but in a very real sense we can say that every mathematical object is of a certain type. *Every mathematical object is a set.* This may not mean very much to the student at this stage, but it indicates the degree of logical unification that has taken place in mathematics.

EXERCISES 1-7

Discuss the following:

1. For real x, $[x] =_{df}$ the greatest integer $\leq x$.

2. $\sqrt{5} =_{df}$ the real number x such that $x^2 = 5$.

3. $\sqrt{-1} =_{df}$ the real number x such that $x^2 = -1$.

4. For real x,
$$|x| =_{df} \begin{cases} x, & \text{if } x \geq 0, \\ -x, & \text{if } x < 0. \end{cases}$$

5. For real x,
$$|x| =_{df} \begin{cases} x, & \text{if } x \geq 0, \\ -x, & \text{if } x \leq 0. \end{cases}$$

6. For real x,
$$\langle x \rangle =_{df} \begin{cases} x + 1, & \text{if } x \geq 0, \\ x - 1, & \text{if } x \leq 0. \end{cases}$$

7. We extend the definition of "+" from the integers to the rationals by
$$\frac{a}{b} + \frac{c}{d} =_{df} \frac{ad + bc}{bd}.$$

8. For real a, b,
$$b - a =_{df} \text{ the } x \text{ such that } x + a = b.$$

9. For real a, b,

$$a * b =_{df} a + b + ab.$$

10. $\infty =_{df}$ the real x such that $0 \cdot x = 1$.

11. Man $=_{df}$ featherless biped.

12. $\pi =_{df}$ the ratio of the circumference of a circle to its diameter.

13. LECTURER, n. One with his hand in your pocket, his tongue in your ear and his faith in your patience. (*The Devil's Dictionary*, Ambrose Bierce.)

Chapter 2

SET THEORY

2–1. SETS

BY A SET we shall mean any well-defined collection of objects. The objects will be referred to as the *elements* of the set. For example, we may speak of the set of all cars made in Detroit during 1960, the set of all positive numbers, the set of all people alive today, the set of numbers x satisfying the equation "$x = 1 + x^2$." Synonyms often used for "set" are "aggregate," "group," "collection," "class," "family," "bunch," "heap." There is no need for the elements of a set to have any obvious connection with each other. The sun, George Washington, Pennsylvania State University, the king's gambit, and the number π make up a perfectly good set.

If b is an element of a set S, we write

$$b \in S.$$

The negation of this assertion is written "$b \notin S$." Thus "$\in$" is read "is an element of" or "belongs to," or simply "is in." Sometimes it is read "in," as in the following:

$$\forall x \in S, x < 6,$$

which means "For all x in S, $x < 6$" or "Every element of S is less than 6." Still another equivalent is

$$(\forall x)\, (x \in S \rightarrow x < 6),$$

read "For all x, if x is in S, then x is less than 6."

There are in practice two general ways to describe a set. One is simply to list names for its elements, as in the last sentence of the introductory paragraph. The other way is to prescribe a condition which is satisfied by every element of the set and by no other objects. (The other examples above are of this kind.) More precisely, if $P(x)$ is a predicate, e.g., "x is red," then we may define the set of all x such that $P(x)$. In our example

39

this would be the set of all red things. The property "redness" is possessed by all elements of this set and by nothing else. We speak of a "defining property," "defining condition," or "defining predicate" for the set. We have slightly anticipated our set-theoretic language in using the phrase "the truth set of $P(x)$" in Chapter 1.

It is customary to use the notation

$$\{ \ | \ \},$$

which may be read "the set of (all) _____ such that _____." Thus, the set of (all) x such that x is red is

$$\{x|x \text{ is red}\}.$$

The word "all" is not absolutely necessary but may be put in for emphasis. In general, if $P(x)$ is a predicate, the corresponding truth set is

$$\{x|P(x)\}.$$

Variables other than "x" may of course be used. Thus, the indicated set is the same as

$$\{y|P(y)\}.$$

Braces may also be used when a set is given by means of a list. Thus, the set consisting of the elements 1, 2, 3, 4, 5 may be written

$$\{1,2,3,4,5\}.$$

The order is not important. For example,

$$\{3,4,1,2,5\} = \{1,2,3,4,5\}.$$

Duplication of names is permitted, so that, for example,

$$\{3, 3, 4, \tfrac{6}{2}, 2 + 1, 2, 5, V, 3 - 2, 1\} = \{1, 2, 3, 4, 5\}.$$

Any listed set may also be given as the truth set of a predicate. For example, the set above may be defined by

$$\{x|(x = 1) \lor (x = 2) \lor (x = 3) \lor (x = 4) \lor (x = 5)\},$$

or by

$$\{x|(1 \leq x \leq 5) \land (x \text{ is an integer})\}.$$

Not every set defined by a predicate can be defined by a list. Thus

$$\{x|x \text{ is an integer}\}$$

cannot be listed. Even when a set is finite but has many elements, listing is cumbersome and practically impossible. Therefore the more powerful and basic method of definition by predicate (property, condition) is most often used.

Clearly, a set may be described or defined in many different ways. It is important to realize that *a set is determined completely by its elements*, not by the manner of its description. Two sets are equal iff they contain precisely the same elements. This is the *extensionality principle*. It follows that, if $P(x) \equiv Q(x)$, then

$$\{x|P(x)\} = \{x|Q(x)\},$$

and conversely. For example,

$$(x^2 - 3x + 2 = 0) \equiv ((x - 1)(x - 2) = 0)$$
$$\equiv ((x - 1 = 0) \vee (x - 2 = 0))$$
$$\equiv (x = 1 \vee x = 2).$$

Therefore

$$\{x|x^2 - 3x + 2 = 0\} = \{x|x = 1 \vee x = 2\} = \{1,2\}.$$

What we have just done is to find explicitly the truth set of the predicate

$$x^2 - 3x + 2 = 0.$$

We have "solved the equation."

⟦Sometimes equations are solved incorrectly when the transition from one predicate to the next is merely valid implication instead of valid equivalence. Consider

$$\sqrt{x - 1} = -1,$$
$$x - 1 = (-1)^2 = 1,$$
$$x = 2,$$
$$\therefore \quad \{x|\sqrt{x - 1} = -1\} = \{2\}.$$

($\sqrt{a}$ means the nonnegative square root of a.) The conclusion is incorrect. If we follow the argument carefully, we get

$$\vDash (\sqrt{x - 1} = -1) \to (x - 1 = 1),$$
$$(x - 1 = 1) \equiv (x = 2),$$
$$\therefore \quad \vDash (\sqrt{x - 1} = -1) \to (x = 2).$$

Thus, all we can deduce is that every element of $\{x|\sqrt{x - 1} = -1\}$ is also an element of $\{x|x = 2\} = \{2\}$, but not conversely.

In general, when all transitions are equivalences, the truth sets are the same. When some are implications and all others equivalences, the truth sets may be different, and careful checking is needed to "reject extraneous solutions."

Sometimes the fallacious argument works in the opposite direction. Thus: "To solve $x^2 - 1 = 0$ we observe that $x = 1$ satisfies the equation. Therefore the solution set is $\{1\}$." Translated, this reads

$$\models (x = 1) \to (x^2 - 1 = 0),$$
$$\therefore \quad \{x | x = 1\} = \{x | x^2 - 1 = 0\},$$

which is clearly incorrect, because -1 is also a solution.]

In popular usage, sets have at least two or three elements, but we shall (for convenience and consistency) allow them to have only one or even no elements. A set with exactly one element b, say, is called a *singleton*, and we may refer to it briefly as "singleton b." It is written "$\{b\}$." There is a close relationship between individual objects and their singletons. Given an object b, we can always form its singleton $\{b\}$; given a singleton B, there is a unique object b such that $B = \{b\}$. In spite of this one-to-one correspondence between objects and their singletons, it is important to distinguish between them conceptually. For example, we can multiply 17 by 3.79 but not by $\{3.79\}$; 3.79 is a number, but $\{3.79\}$ is a set of numbers.

A set with no elements also arises in many discussions. Thus, we may have the set of all 10-legged horses alive today, or the set of all integers n such that $n^2 = 2$. According to our principle that a set is determined by its elements, any two such descriptions must refer to the same set. This unique set with no elements is called the *empty set* or the *null set* and is denoted by the Danish letter "$\emptyset$" (don't try to pronounce it; just read "the empty set").

The student may feel, with some justification, that the notion of a set with no elements is unnatural. There are very good reasons for introducing this set, however. Quite often we do not know whether there are any individuals that have a given property. Thus, we would like to be able to compare different instances of the set of all students absent on a certain day, without worrying that there might not be such a set. Later, when we define certain operations on sets, it will be most convenient to know that the resultant of an operation applied to sets is also a set. The analogue of this situation is the historical admission of 0 to the realm of numbers. This permits us to say that $5 - 5$ is a number, for example. There is an operation of differencing, denoted by "$A - B$," which applies to sets, as we shall see. Can you guess how it would be defined? It will be true that the difference of two sets is always a set, provided that we admit the empty set.

The elements of a set may be of any kind: people, numbers, geometrical figures, or even sets. For example,

$$A = \{\text{Jim,Joe,Mary,Jane}\},$$
$$B = \{\{\text{Jim,Joe}\}, \{\text{Mary,Jane}\}, \varnothing\}.$$

The elements of B are the three sets listed. Another example of a set of this kind (having sets as its elements) is the set A of households in a town. The elements of A are the Smith household, the Jones household, the Miller household, and so on. Each household in turn may be regarded as a set of people. Notice that we have

$$\text{Mary Smith} \in \text{the Smith household,}$$
$$\text{the Smith household} \in A,$$

but

$$\text{Mary Smith} \notin A,$$

because the only things that belong to A are households, and Mary Smith is an individual, not a household. This is still true even if she lives alone. In that case

$$\text{the Smith household} = \{\text{Mary Smith}\}$$

and

$$\text{Mary Smith} \in \{\text{Mary Smith}\},$$

but

$$\text{Mary Smith} \neq \{\text{Mary Smith}\}.$$

We have already made this point in connection with singletons, but it is worth emphasizing again.

The extensionality principle is a very hardheaded, practical way of dealing with sets. Its direct application is frequently the best way of testing whether two given sets are equal.

EXAMPLE 2–1. Let $A =$ the set of wise men, $B =$ the set of wealthy men. Is it true that $A = B$?

Solution: Go through the list of all wise men, and for each one in turn ask whether he belongs to the set of wealthy men. Then go through the list of wealthy men, and for each one in turn ask whether he belongs to the set of wise men. If any one of the answers is "no," we may stop and assert that $A \neq B$. If all the answers are "yes," we may assert that $A = B$. Notice that we do not need to enter into complicated arguments about "the real meaning of wisdom." Of course, we must be able to determine, for each man, whether he is wise or not and whether he is wealthy or not.

EXAMPLE 2–2.   (*Detective Story*).   Let
a = the butler,
b = the person who turned out the lights,
a' = the murderer,
b' = the thief.
These need not all be distinct. For all we know, they might all be the same person. Let

$$C = \{a,b\},$$
$$D = \{a',b'\}.$$

In terms of identity of individuals, what does $C = D$ mean?
Solution: The student should verify that $C = D$ is equivalent to

$$S: (a = a' \text{ and } b = b') \text{ or } (a = b' \text{ and } b = a').$$

One way is to examine a sixteen-line truth table headed by

$a = a'$	$a = b'$	$b = a'$	$b = b'$	$C = D$	S
T	T	T	T	T	T
...	...	...	...	...	...

and to check that $C = D$ and S always have the same truth value. There are easier and more elegant methods, but this one is straightforward.

If the student has gone through Example 2–2, he has proved

(1) $[\{a,b\} = \{a',b'\}] \equiv [(a = a' \wedge b = b') \vee (a = b' \wedge b = a')]$.

As a special case, if $b' = a'$,

(2) $[\{a,b\} = \{a'\}] \equiv [a = b = a']$.

As another special case, if $a' = a$,

(3) $[\{a,b\} = \{a,b'\}] \equiv [b = b']$.

We may call $\{a,b\}$ an *unordered pair* or a *doubleton* (even though we permit $a = b$). Then Eq. (1) gives a precise condition for equality among doubletons, Eq. (2) tells when a doubleton can be a singleton, and Eq. (3) means that doubletons with a common element are equal iff the "odd" elements are equal (a kind of cancellation is involved).

There are many occasions when we wish to consider doubletons in which one element is distinguished as the "first." Thus, we might choose a committee of two, with a specified chairman. Such an object we call an *ordered pair*, written (a,b). We still allow $a = b$, however. In contrast with Eq. (1), the condition for equality of ordered pairs is

(4) $$((a,b) = (a',b')) \equiv (a = a' \wedge b = b').$$

Thus, (Jim,Joe) $\neq$ (Joe,Jim), even though $\{$Jim,Joe$\} = \{$Joe,Jim$\}$. We could use ordered pairs to indicate the proportions in a mixture. In a martini, for example, your taste will tell you that $(4,1) \neq (1,4)$.

⟦The following three paragraphs may be omitted without loss of continuity. For the inquiring student, however, they provide an example of the reduction of apparently primitive notions to others even more basic. Such reductions can be of considerable importance in the systematization of many disciplines.

We could regard Eq. (4) as an implicit or contextual definition of a new type of object (a,b), or as an embodiment of the intuitive concept of ordered pair. But we have asserted that *every* mathematical object is a set. What about (a,b)? Can we construct a set, using a, b, which behaves like (a,b) in the sense that it satisfies condition (4)? Clearly $\{a,b\}$ will not do, because Eq. (1) applies rather than Eq. (4). It was the ingenious discovery of the famous contemporary mathematician Norbert Wiener (with Kuratowski's simplification) that the set

$$\{\{a,b\}, \{a\}\}$$

does the trick. In other words, if we *define*

$$(a,b) =_{df} \{\{a,b\}, \{a\}\},$$

then we can *prove* Eq. (4) instead of postulating it. This is an excellent example of good taste or aesthetics in mathematics. It satisfies the following special case of Occam's Razor: Don't proliferate undefined concepts if you can help it.

Suppose, then, that $(a,b) = (a',b')$. Then

$$\{\{a,b\},\{a\}\} = \{\{a',b'\}, \{a'\}\}.$$

By Eq. (1), applied to the doubletons just written,

$$\{a,b\} = \{a',b'\} \wedge \{a\} = \{a'\}$$

or

$$\{a,b\} = \{a'\} \wedge \{a\} = \{a',b'\}.$$

In the first case we get $a = a'$ from the singletons, then $\{a,b\} = \{a,b'\}$ from the doubletons, and finally $b = b'$ from Eq. (3). In the second case, by a double application of Eq. (2), we get $(a = b = a') \wedge (a' = b' = a)$, which implies $a = a'$ and $b = b'$. Therefore,

$$\models (a,b) = (a',b') \rightarrow (a = a' \wedge b = b').$$

The reverse implication is even easier, and Eq. (4) is proved.

The reader may protest, with some justice, that this peculiar doubleton, whose elements are themselves sets, does not match his intuitive conception of ordered pair. If he can make explicit his intuitive feeling by writing down an additional condition which should be satisfied, we shall try to accommodate him. Or if he can suggest an alternate definition, also satisfying Eq. (4), which is simpler, we shall be happy to adopt it. If he can do neither, then we propose to adhere to Wiener's definition, taking the point of view that something that looks like bread, feels like bread, smells like bread, tastes like bread, and is as nourishing as bread will do very well until some bread comes along.

Actually, to belabor the point slightly, our definition is not really so contra-intuitive. To appoint a committee of two with chairman, one might very well write a memo saying "Joe and Jim are on the committee," a second memo saying "Joe is chairman," and then put both memos in the same envelope. There would be no misunderstanding if one modified the memos to read "Joe, Jim" and "Joe."〛

Having gone into the matter in great detail, we now absolve the reader of all obligations except to remember that (a) a set-theoretic definition of ordered pair *can* be given and (b) this definition satisfies the basic condition (4).

The notion of ordered pair is really fundamental to modern mathematics. We shall meet it again when we discuss binary relations, Cartesian products, and functions.

EXERCISES 2–1

1. List the elements in the following sets:
   (a) The set of integers greater than 0 and less than 10.
   (b) The set of integers greater than 7 and less than 9.
   (c) The set of integers n such that $n^2 + n$ is odd.
   (d) The set of ways that three distinguishable coins tossed in the air can land.
   (e) The set of ways that three indistinguishable coins tossed in the air can land.
   (f) The set of ordered pairs (a,b) with $a \in \{0,1\}$, $b \in \{2,3\}$.

(g) The set of ordered pairs (a,b) with $a \in \{0,1\}$, $b \in \{0,1\}$.

2. Find predicates of an integer variable as simple as possible for which the following are the truth sets:
    (a) $\{2,4,6,8,10\}$.
    (b) $\{-3,-2,-1,0,1,2,3\}$.
    (c) $\{1,4,9,16,25\}$.
    (d) $\{2,3,5,7,11,13,17,19,23,29\}$.
    (e) $\{1,2,3,5,6,10,15,30\}$.

3. Test whether $A = B$:
    (a) $A = \{0,1\}$, $B = \{x | x^2 - x = 0\}$.
    (b) $A = \{\text{I,II,III,IV}\}$, $B = \{4, \sqrt{4}, 4 - 1, 1\}$.
    (c) $A = \{y | y \text{ is a centaur}\}$, $B = $ the set of mermaids.
    (d) $A = 0$, $B = \{0\}$.
    (e) $A = \varnothing$, $B = \{0\}$.
    (f) $A = \varnothing$, $B = \{\varnothing\}$.

4. Use the symbols defined here and in Chapter 1 to rewrite:
    (a) 7 is in the set consisting of 1, 3, 5, 7, 9.
    (b) There is more than one element in the set of all ways to skin a cat.
    (c) Every element of A belongs to B.
    (d) Some element of A belongs to B.
    (e) A and B have no elements in common.
    (f) Every integer is either even or odd.
    (g) There are exactly two elements in A.

5. Prove that the following is a tautology:
$$[(p \vee q) \wedge (r \vee s)] \wedge [(p \vee r) \wedge (q \vee s)] \leftrightarrow (p \wedge s) \vee (q \wedge r).$$

6. Prove Eq. (1) as follows:
$$\begin{aligned} \text{Let } p \text{ stand for } a &= a', \\ q \text{ stand for } a &= b', \\ r \text{ stand for } b &= a', \\ s \text{ stand for } b &= b'. \end{aligned}$$
Then use Problem 5.

7. State whether the following are true or false:
    (a) $\{2,3\} = \{3,2\}$.
    (b) $(2,3) = (3,2)$.
    (c) $\{\text{the earth}\} = \{\text{the earth, the third planet from the sun}\}$.
    (d) $\{3,3,3\} \neq \{3\}$.
    (e) Every singleton is a doubleton.
    (f) Every element of the empty set is an odd number.
    (g) Every element of the empty set is an even number.
    (h) $\varnothing \in \{1,2\}$.
    (i) $\varnothing \in \{\varnothing, \{1,2\}\}$.

(j) If A is a set and B is a set, then
$$A = B \leftrightarrow (\forall x) (x \in A \leftrightarrow x \in B).$$
(k) $1 \in \{\{1,2\}, \{1,3\}, \{1,4\}\}$.
(l) If A is a set, then $A \neq \emptyset \leftrightarrow (\exists x) (x \in A)$.

8. List the elements of the following sets:
   (a) $\{x | x \in \{0,1,2\}\}$.
   (b) $\{(x,y) | x \in \{0,1,2\} \wedge y = x^2\}$.
   (c) $\{(y,x) | x \in \{0,1,2\} \wedge y = x^2\}$.
   (d) The set of all doubletons with elements selected from $\{Joe, John, Jim\}$.
   (e) $\{z/z$ is in your family$\}$.
   (f) The set of all numbers that belong to both $\{0,1,2\}$ and $\{1,2,3\}$.
   (g) The set of all numbers that belong to $\{0,1,2\}$ or to $\{1,2,3\}$.
   (h) The set of all numbers that belong to $\{0,1,2\}$ but not to $\{1,2,3\}$.

9. Let $P(x)$ stand for "A man starts out at a point x on the earth's surface, walks 10 miles south, 10 miles east, 10 miles north, and is back at point x." If $P(x)$ is true, what is x? A common mistake in this old chestnut is to jump to the conclusion that the truth set of $P(x)$ is a singleton. Show that this is false.

10. Below are eight sets. Notice that E and F are described in terms of previous sets in the list.
$$A = \{0\} \qquad B = \{\emptyset\} \qquad C = \emptyset \qquad D = \{1,2,3\}$$
$$E = \{D\} \qquad F = \{C\} \qquad G = \{x | x + 1 = x\} \qquad H = \{x | x + 1 = 1\}.$$
   (a) How many elements does each set contain?
   (b) Pick out all the pairs of sets which are equal to each other.

11. If $(a,b) = (b,c) = (c,d)$, what can be said about a, b, c, d?

12. Given that $\{a,b\} = \{b,c\} = \{c,d\}$, prove that $(a,b) = (c,d)$.

13. Solve the equation $x^3 - x = 0$.

2–2. SUBSET, INTERSECTION, UNION, COMPLEMENT

Just as there are relations and operations which are applicable to numbers, so too we can define significant relations and operations for sets. In this way we get an algebraic system called a Boolean algebra. Such algebras are of considerable theoretical and practical interest. In this section we shall define and illustrate the set-theoretic relations and operations.

Given a set, we are frequently interested in other sets which are included within, or contained in the given set. Thus, the set of all integers is contained in the set of all rational numbers, which in turn is contained in the set of all real numbers. Similarly, $\{1,3\}$ is contained in, or is a *subset* of, $\{1,2,3,4\}$, and $\{1\}$ is a subset of $\{1,3\}$. If A is a subset of B, then every element of A

is also an element of B. In fact, this is precisely the test—the necessary and sufficient condition—for being a subset. The notation we use is "$A \subset B$," read "A is contained in B" or "A is a subset of B." Writing down the condition symbolically, we define $A \subset B$ to mean

$$(\forall x)(x \in A \to x \in B).$$

(Notice that the small end of the horseshoe is toward the "smaller" set, just as in "$a < b$" the small end is toward the smaller number.) We also write the same statement as "$B \supset A$," just reversing the symbol, and read it as "B contains A."

Two remarks need to be made here. If we accept the definition, then we must also agree that a set is always a subset of itself. For the statement

$$x \in A \to x \in A$$

is valid, and therefore $A \subset A$ is also. Thus "$\leq$" is a better analogue of "$\subset$" than "$<$." ⟦In fact, some authors use "$\subseteq$" and reserve "$\subset$" to mean "contained in but not equal to" or "is a *proper* subset of." Since the distinction will usually not be important to us we use the simpler notation.⟧

A second consequence of the definition is that the empty set is a subset of every set. To see this, observe that

$$x \in \varnothing \to x \in B$$

is valid, since the antecedent ($x \in \varnothing$) becomes false no matter what x is replaced by, and "$p \to q$" is true when p is false. Therefore $\varnothing \subset B$ for every set B. For example, all the subsets of $\{1,2\}$ are: $\varnothing$, $\{1\}$, $\{2\}$, $\{1,2\}$.

Observe also that equality of sets may be expressed in terms of inclusion:

$$(A = B) \equiv (A \subset B \wedge B \subset A).$$

Inclusion is a *transitive* relation: If A, B, C are any sets, then

$$(A \subset B) \wedge (B \subset C) \to (A \subset C).$$

Students frequently confuse "$\subset$" and "$\in$." One important distinction between them is the transitivity of inclusion and the nontransitivity of membership. The statement "$a \in c$" does not follow from "$a \in b$" and "$b \in c$."

There is a simple pictorial device, called a *Venn diagram*, which helps us to visualize how sets are related to each other. Think of A and B as regions in a plane, which we indicate by drawing their boundaries. Then "$A \subset B$" might be represented schematically as shown in Figure 2–1. Similarly, Figures 2–2, 2–3, and 2–4 illustrate "$A \not\subset B$" ("A is not a subset of B").

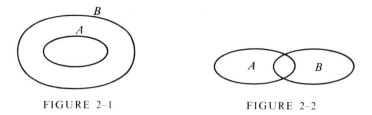

FIGURE 2-1　　　　　　　　　　　FIGURE 2-2

The operation of intersection, symbolized by "∩," is defined (contextually) by

$$A \cap B =_{df} \{x \,|\, x \in A \wedge x \in B\}.$$

The intersection of A and B is the set of all elements that they have in common. Thus,

$$\{1,2\} \cap \{2,3\} = \{2\},$$
$$\{1,2\} \cap \{3,4\} = \varnothing,$$
$$\{1,2\} \cap \{1,2,3\} = \{1,2\},$$
$$\{1,2\} \cap \{1,2\} = \{1,2\}.$$

The Venn diagram is shown in Figure 2-5. The shaded portion is $A \cap B$. In Figure 2-3, $A \cap B = B$, and in Figure 2-4, $A \cap B = \varnothing$. In this last case, when A and B have no elements in common, we say that A and B are *disjoint*.

Intersection is an *associative* operation: If A, B, C are any sets, then

(1)　　　　　　　　$(A \cap B) \cap C = A \cap (B \cap C).$

A schematic "proof," using the Venn diagrams, would proceed by building up both sides of Eq. (1) and comparing the results. Thus, starting with $A \cap B$ as in Figure 2-5, we form the cross-hatched region $(A \cap B) \cap C$, Figure 2-6. On the other side, consider first $B \cap C$, Figure 2-7. Now intersect A with $B \cap C$, Figure 2-8. Comparing Figures 2-6 and 2-8, we "see" that Eq. (1) is true. Either side of Eq. (1) may be understood as the set of all elements common to A, B, and C.

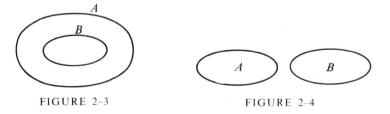

FIGURE 2-3　　　　　　　　　　　FIGURE 2-4

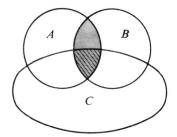

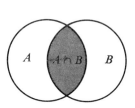

FIGURE 2-5   FIGURE 2-6

It must not be thought that we have *proved* Eq. (1) by means of the Venn diagrams, any more than we prove theorems in geometry by pointing at diagrams. We merely aid our intuition. Sometimes we are guided to a real proof, and that can be very valuable. Many mathematicians conjure up crude diagrams to help them find proofs, but they know that ultimately they must rely only on the axioms, definitions, and previously proved theorems of whatever system they are studying. It is perfectly legitimate to use a scaffolding in the erection of a building, but eventually the scaffolding must be torn down and the structure must stand by itself. The student who has learned to differentiate between handwaving and proof has come a long way.

In using Venn diagrams, we make our figures *general*, just as we do in geometry. Thus, in Figure 2-8 it would be misleading to draw A and B disjoint, or C disjoint from $A \cap B$.

A somewhat more formal proof of Eq. (1) proceeds by showing that every element of the left side is also an element of the right side and conversely. Thus, if

$$x \in (A \cap B) \cap C,$$

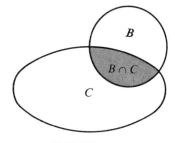

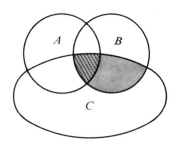

FIGURE 2-7   FIGURE 2-8

then

$$x \in A \cap B \text{ and } x \in C,$$
$$x \in A \text{ and } x \in B, \text{ and } x \in C,$$
$$x \in A, \text{ and } x \in B \text{ and } x \in C,$$
$$x \in A, \text{ and } x \in B \cap C,$$
$$x \in A \cap (B \cap C).$$

We leave it to the student to show the converse. Note that our work can be shortened by abbreviating

$$x \in A \qquad \text{by } p,$$
$$x \in B \qquad \text{by } q,$$
$$x \in C \qquad \text{by } r,$$

and translating the required set identity (1) into

$$(p \wedge q) \wedge r \leftrightarrow p \wedge (q \wedge r),$$

which is valid.

Because there is no danger of ambiguity, we shall write

$$A \cap B \cap C$$

for the set in Eq. (1). This is similar to our convention of writing "*abc*" for either side of the identity

$$(ab)c = a(bc).$$

Intersection is a *commutative* operation: If A, B are any sets, then

$$A \cap B = B \cap A.$$

This is even more obvious than associativity, but still requires proof. Prove it!

There are important applications of intersection in geometry and in algebra. We recall that the locus of a geometrical condition is the set of all points satisfying the condition. If we let x be a variable point ("x" is a variable whose domain is the set of all points in the plane, or in space) and "$P(x)$" the predicate "x satisfies the condition," then the locus is precisely $\{x|P(x)\}$. If we have a second condition imposed, it too will have a locus, say $\{x|Q(x)\}$. Then the locus of all points satisfying *both* conditions is

$$\{x|P(x) \wedge Q(x)\} = \{x|P(x)\} \cap \{x|Q(x)\}.$$

Thus we solve our problem by finding the intersection of the two loci. For example, let

$$P(x) =_{\mathrm{df}} x \text{ is equidistant from } a \text{ and } b,$$
$$Q(x) =_{\mathrm{df}} x \text{ is at distance 5 from } c,$$

where a, b, c are given points. Then $\{x|P(x)\}$ is a line (if $a \neq b$), $\{x|Q(x)\}$ is a circle, and our problem (of finding all points equidistant from two given points and at distance 5 from a given point) is solved by intersecting the line and the circle. Thus, there will be zero, one, or two solutions, depending on the relative positions of a, b, c.

In algebra we are sometimes required to solve simultaneous equations, e.g.,

$$4x - y = 7,$$
$$3x + 2y = 4.$$

What we are really being asked is to find all ordered pairs (x,y), x, y real, such that both equations hold. Thus we want the set

$$\{(x,y)|(4x - y = 7) \wedge (3x + 2y = 4)\}$$
$$= \{(x,y)|4x - y = 7\} \cap \{(x,y)|3x + 2y = 4\}.$$

Later, when we study analytic geometry, we shall see that each set on the right can be represented faithfully by a straight line in the plane. Thus the problem of solving the simultaneous equations is transformed into the problem of finding where two lines intersect, and conversely.

The operation of *union*, symbolized by "$\cup$," is defined (contextually) by

$$A \cup B =_{df} \{x|x \in A \vee x \in B\}.$$

The union of two sets is the set of all elements that are in at least one of them. Thus,

$$\{1,2\} \cup \{2,3\} = \{1,2,3\},$$
$$\{1,2\} \cup \{3,4\} = \{1,2,3,4\},$$
$$\{1,2\} \cup \{1,2,3\} = \{1,2,3\},$$
$$\{1,2\} \cup \{1,2\} = \{1,2\}.$$

The Venn diagram is given in Figure 2–9. We can easily remember the distinction between "$\cap$" and "$\cup$" by matching them with "$\wedge$" and "$\vee$," respectively. Also "$\cup$" should remind us of "*union*."

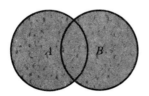

FIGURE 2–9

Union is a commutative operation: If A, B are any sets, then

(2) $A \cup B = B \cup A$.

It is also associative: If A, B, C are any sets, then

(3) $A \cup (B \cup C) = (A \cup B) \cup C$.

The student should convince himself of the truth of these set-theoretic identities before he proceeds any further. As in the case of intersection, we shall write "$A \cup B \cup C$" for the common set in Eq. (3).

Now that we have two operations at our disposal, we can form more complicated and significant expressions by combining them. This gives our language more power. For example, the ambiguous English phrase "divorced men or widowers having children" could be translated by "$D \cup (W \cap C)$" (Figure 2–10) or by "$(D \cup W) \cap C$" (Figure 2–11), each of which has an unmistakable meaning. Of course, the parentheses cannot be dropped here as above.

There are two important identities connecting the operations of intersection and union, called the *distributive* laws. If A, B, C are any sets, then

(4) $A \cap (B \cup C) = (A \cap B) \cup (A \cap C)$,
(5) $A \cup (B \cap C) = (A \cup B) \cap (A \cup C)$.

Just as Eqs. (2) and (3) can be proved by appealing to the tautologies

$$p \vee q \equiv q \vee p,$$
$$p \vee (q \vee r) \equiv (p \vee q) \vee r,$$

so can Eqs. (4) and (5) be proved by means of

$$p \wedge (q \vee r) \equiv (p \wedge q) \vee (q \wedge r),$$
$$p \vee (q \wedge r) \equiv (p \vee q) \wedge (p \vee r).$$

[See Problems 4(a) and (a') of Exercises 1–4.]

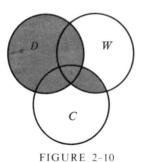

FIGURE 2–10

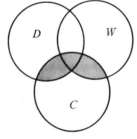

FIGURE 2–11

Another method of proof, actually more widely used and perhaps easier, is illustrated in the following proof of Eq. (4):

Let x be an arbitrary element of $A \cap (B \cup C)$. Then $x \in A$ and $x \in B$ or C. *Case 1.* $x \in B$. Then $x \in A \cap B$, so $x \in (A \cap B) \cup (A \cap C)$. *Case 2.* $x \in C$. Then $x \in A \cap C$, so $x \in (A \cap B) \cup (A \cap C)$. In either case, x is an element of the right side of Eq. (4). Since x was arbitrary, every element of $A \cap (B \cup C)$ is an element of $(A \cap B) \cup (A \cap C)$. Therefore,

(a) $A \cap (B \cup C) \subset (A \cap B) \cup (A \cap C)$.

Now let x be an arbitrary element of $(A \cap B) \cup (A \cap C)$. [*Note:* This is not necessarily the same x as the one used above; that one was released from duty when we pointed to its arbitrariness and inferred (a).] Then $x \in A \cap B$ or $x \in A \cap C$. *Case 1.* $x \in A \cap B$. Then $x \in A$ and $x \in B$, so $x \in B \cup C$, so $x \in A \cap (B \cup C)$. *Case 2.* $x \in A \cap C$. Then $x \in A$ and $x \in C$, so $x \in B \cup C$, so $x \in A \cap (B \cup C)$. In either case, $x \in A \cap (B \cup C)$. Since x was arbitrary, every element of $(A \cap B) \cup (A \cap C)$ is an element of $A \cap (B \cup C)$. Therefore,

(b) $A \cap (B \cup C) \supset (A \cap B) \cup (A \cap C)$.

Combining (a) and (b), we get Eq. (4).

The student should draw some Venn diagrams to "see" that Eqs. (4) and (5) hold. He should also carry out one or two proofs of Eq. (5).

An algebraic analogue of Eq. (4) is obtained by thinking of the letters as numbers and replacing "$\cap$" by "$\cdot$" and "$\cup$" by "$+$":

$$A \cdot (B + C) = (A \cdot B) + (A \cdot C).$$

This happens to be true always. If we do the same for Eq. (5), we get

$$A + (B \cdot C) = (A + B) \cdot (A + C),$$

which is not always true. Thus we see that there is a strong difference in structure between our algebra of sets and ordinary algebra. In the latter, one of the operations (multiplication) distributes over the other (addition), but not vice versa; in the former, each operation distributes over the other.

In many discussions it is convenient and even necessary to restrict the objects under consideration to a particular set. For example, to discuss the properties of the real numbers, we would specify in advance that all individual variables are to have the set of real numbers R as their domain. All the predicates used would contain only such variables, and all the sets obtained as truth sets for these predicates would be subsets of R. A master set of this kind is called the *universal set* or the *universe* in that discussion. Thus, if V is the universal set, and if A is any set in the discussion, then $A \subset V$.

⟦The astute student may wonder why we need to change our universe from one discussion to another. Why not select as universe "the set of all things"? Surely this would suffice for any discussion. But then, if V were the universe most natural for a given discussion, all our definitions of sets would look like $\{x|x \in V \wedge \cdots\}$. This is plainly a nuisance. Even worse, "the set of all things" turns out to be a logical monstrosity. If we allow it, or even the submonstrosity "the set of all sets," we quickly arrive at contradictions, as we shall see below. We can weasel out of this uncomfortable situation by refusing to accept these phrases as referring to a "well-defined collection," but then we'd be hard-pressed to say what phrases are acceptable, or equivalently, what collections are really "sets." Ultimately, we are driven to admit that we have not defined "set," but that the term is a primitive, undefinable one. This appears to leave our set theory in a shambles, but the situation is not really hopeless. It does force us, eventually, to construct a formal axiomatic set theory with rules that will reasonably safeguard us against monstrosities. Such theories can be constructed, but their study is highly sophisticated and technical. It would be silly for us to embark upon such a study at this stage. It is also unnecessary to do so. We can walk very well without knowing all there is to know about the physiology and mechanics of walking. We can use tools adroitly and safely without knowing how they are constructed. Thus, we shall use our intuitive set theory, admittedly incomplete, with reasonable freedom and lack of embarrassment under reasonable circumstances. A good working rule to keep us from tripping over a paradox is to avoid statements like "$A \in A$" or "$A \notin A$."

Suppose, indeed, that we disregarded the cautionary words above. Let us consider two types of set, which we shall call "self-belonging" and "not-self-belonging." They satisfy "$A \in A$" and "$A \notin A$," respectively. For example, let A be the set of all nonempty sets. Clearly A is nonempty (one element of it is $\{1,2,3\}$), so $A \in A$, and A is self-belonging. On the other hand, $D = \{1,2,3\}$ has as its only elements 1, 2, and 3, none of which is D, so $D \notin D$ and D is not-self-belonging. Now let C be the set of all not-self-belonging sets:

$$C = \{B|B \notin B\}.$$

Is C self-belonging or not-self-belonging? (It has to be one or the other.) *Case 1.* C is self-belonging, that is, $C \in C$. Therefore,

$$C \in \{B|B \notin B\}.$$

which means that C satisfies the defining condition $B \notin B$, so that $C \notin C$. This yields the contradiction: $C \in C \wedge C \notin C$. *Case 2.* C is not-self-belonging, that is, $C \notin C$. Therefore C satisfies the defining condition $B \notin B$ and

$$C \in \{B | B \notin B\},$$

The set on the right is just C, so $C \in C$. This yields the contradiction $C \notin C \wedge C \in C$. In either case we have come to grief!

The preceding two paragraphs should be regarded as merely parenthetical. Their purpose is to season our new-found knowledge about sets with the proverbial grain of salt, but the student should not permit himself to be inhibited. Remember that Lot's wife turned into a pillar of salt because she looked back.]]

Returning to the main stream of our development, let V be a universe. If A is a set (hence $A \subset V$), we define the *complement* of A, written "A'," by

$$A' =_{df} \{x | x \notin A\}.$$

Thus A' is precisely the set of all elements (of V) which are not in A. We can also say

$$x \in A' \equiv x \notin A.$$

If B is the complement of A, then

(6) $$A \cup B = V,$$

and

(7) $$A \cap B = \emptyset.$$

The student should convince himself of the truth of the preceding statement, as well as of its converse: If B is a set which satisfies Eqs. (6) and (7), then $B = A'$.

For the sake of completeness, we introduce *subtraction* of sets by the definition

$$A - B =_{df} \{x | x \in A \wedge x \notin B\}.$$

An alternate definition, in the presence of a specified universe V, is

$$A - B =_{df} A \cap B'.$$

For example, if A is the set of all integers and B the set of all real numbers greater than or equal to 0, then $A - B$ is the set of all negative integers.

The Venn diagrams for complementation and subtraction are given in Figures 2–12 and 2–13. If A is a set, then $(A')' = A$. This should be clear, but it can be proved as follows. Let x be an arbitrary element of $(A')'$. Then $x \notin A'$, so $\sim(x \in A')$, so $\sim(\sim(x \in A))$, so $x \in A$. Therefore $(A')' \subset A$. Starting with $x \in A$, we can reverse all the steps above and deduce that $x \in (A')'$. Therefore $A \subset (A')'$. Hence $(A')' = A$.

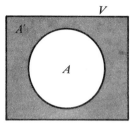

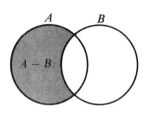

FIGURE 2–12   FIGURE 2–13

Not quite so obvious are the *de Morgan identities*: If A, B are any sets, then

(8) $$(A \cup B)' = A' \cap B',$$
(9) $$(A \cap B)' = A' \cup B'.$$

To prove Eq. (8) we use the tautology

$$\sim(p \vee q) \equiv \sim p \wedge \sim q$$

in the following sequence:

$$x \in (A \cup B)' \equiv \sim(x \in A \cup B) \equiv \sim(x \in A \vee x \in B)$$
$$\equiv \sim(x \in A) \wedge \sim(x \in B)$$
$$\equiv x \in A' \wedge x \in B'$$
$$\equiv x \in A' \cap B'.$$

Similarly, one proof of Eq. (9) is based on

$$\sim(p \wedge q) \equiv \sim p \vee \sim q.$$

An amusing alternate proof of Eq. (9) based on Eq. (8) proceeds as follows. Since A, B are arbitrary in Eq. (8), we may replace them by A', B', respectively. Thus

$$(A' \cup B')' = (A')' \cap (B')',$$
$$(A' \cup B')' = A \cap B,$$

because $(A')' = A$, $(B')' = B$. Taking complements of both sides, we get

$$((A' \cup B')')' = (A \cap B)',$$

and simplifying the left side, we obtain Eq. (9).

Roughly speaking, the de Morgan laws tell us that complementation interchanges union and intersection. How does it act on inclusion? The answer is given by the valid equivalences

(10) $A \subset B \equiv A' \supset B'$,
(11) $A \supset B \equiv A' \subset B'$.

The student should prove these, using the tautology

$$p \to q \equiv \sim q \to \sim p.$$

He should also observe the difference between (8), say, and (10). The first states the equality of two sets; the second states the equivalence of two propositions. The proofs are different, too, in that (10) involves two universal quantifications, namely,

$$[(\forall x) (x \in A \to x \in B)] \equiv [(\forall x) (x \in B' \to x \in A')].$$

The use of complementation allows us to deduce the second distributive law (5) from the first, (4). Indeed, (4) is transformed into

(4') $A' \cup (B' \cap C') = (A' \cup B') \cap (A' \cup C')$

by repeated application of the de Morgan laws. Because A, B, C were arbitrary, we can replace them in Eq. (4') by A', B', C', respectively. This has the effect of dropping the primes in Eq. (4'). The result is precisely Eq. (5).

We have just illustrated the important *principle of duality*. Given a formula involving set variables $A, B, C, \ldots$, operations $\cup$, $\cap$, ', and set constants $V, \varnothing$, we define the *dual* of the formula as the result of interchanging $\cup$ and $\cap$, V and $\varnothing$. Thus, the dual of

$$(A' \cap B) \cup (\varnothing \cup C')'$$

is

$$(A' \cup B) \cap (V \cap C')'.$$

If we know a set-theoretic identity, expressing the equality of two formulas, the duality principle allows us to assert the equality of the duals as an identity. For example, the associative law for union is

$$A \cup (B \cup C) = (A \cup B) \cup C.$$

Its dual is the associative law for intersection,

$$A \cap (B \cap C) = (A \cap B) \cap C.$$

It may happen that the original law does not explicitly assert equality of two formulas F and G but rather inclusion: $F \subset G$. Can we dualize? The answer is yes, because we can express inclusion in terms of intersection and equality:

$$(F \subset G) \equiv (F \cap G = F).$$

For example, the law

(12) $$A \cap B \subset A$$

can be written

(13) $$(A \cap B) \cap A = A \cap B.$$

The dual of Eq. (13) is

$$(A \cup B) \cup A = A \cup B.$$

This is of the form $H \cup K = H$, which is equivalent to $H \supset K$. Applying this with $H = A \cup B$, $K = A$, we get

(14) $$A \cup B \supset A,$$

the dual of (12). In general, the dual of an inclusion law is the reverse inclusion of the duals.

We shall not prove the duality principle, although the proof is not difficult. Later, when we axiomatize Boolean algebra, the duality principle will turn out to be almost trivial.

EXERCISES 2–2

1. List the elements in:
   (a) $\{1,3,5,7\} \cap \{3,4,5\}$.
   (b) $\{1,2,3\} \cup \{3,4,5\}$.
   (c) $\{x|x \text{ is an integer}\} \cap \{1,\sqrt{2},\sqrt{3},\sqrt{4}\}$.
   (d) $\{x|x \text{ is an integer} \wedge x < 3\} \cap \{x|x \text{ is a real number} \wedge x \geq -2\}$.
   (e) $\{1,3,5\} \cap \{27,91,2\}$.
   (f) $\{1,3,5,6\} \cup \{3,6\}$.
   (g) $\{3,4,5,6\} \cup \{6,7,9,8,1,2\}$.
2. List the elements in:
   (a) $(\{1,2,3\} \cup \{2,3,4\}) \cup \{1,5\}$.
   (b) $(\{1,2\} \cap \{2,4\}) \cup \{7\}$.
   (c) $(\{1,3\} \cap \{2,4\}) \cup (\{1,2\} \cap \{3,4\})$.
   (d) $(\{x|x \text{ is an even integer}\} \cup \{3,4,5\}) \cap \{x|x \text{ is an odd integer}\}$.
   (e) $((\{1,2,3\} \cap \{2,3\}) \cup \{5,6,7\}) \cap \{3,4,5\}$.
   (f) $\{\emptyset, \{1,2\}\}$.
3. List all the subsets of $\{2,3,\text{Washington}\}$.
4. List all the subsets of $\{2,3,3\}$.

5. List all the subsets of $\{1, \{2,3\}\}$.
6. If possible, find sets A, B, C such that $(A \cup B) \cap C \neq A \cup (B \cap C)$.
7. If possible, find sets A, B, C such that $(A \cup B) \cap C = A \cup (B \cap C)$.
8. If possible, find sets A, B, C such that

$$(A \cup B) \cap C \neq (A \cap C) \cup (B \cap C).$$

9. Given sets A, B, there is exactly one set C such that
   (a) $(C \supset A) \wedge (C \supset B)$, and
   (b) $(\forall D) [(D \subset A \wedge D \subset B) \rightarrow D \subset C]$.
   What is C?
10. Given sets A, B, there is exactly one set C such that
    (a) $(C \supset A) \wedge (C \supset B)$, and
    (b) $(\forall D) [(D \supset A \wedge D \supset B) \rightarrow D \supset C]$.
    What is C?
11. Suppose that $A \cup B = A \cap B$. What can you deduce about A and B?
12. Let $P(x)$, $Q(x)$ be predicates of a variable with domain V, and let $A = \{x | P(x)\}$, $B = \{x | Q(x)\}$. Write down the truth sets of the following predicates in terms of A and B:
    (a) $P(x) \vee Q(x)$.
    (b) $P(x) \wedge Q(x)$.
    (c) $\sim P(x) \vee Q(x)$.
    (d) $P(x) \rightarrow Q(x)$ [careful!].
    (e) $\sim Q(x) \rightarrow \sim P(x)$.
    (f) $P(x) \leftrightarrow Q(x)$.
    (g) $\sim P(x) \leftrightarrow \sim Q(x)$.
    (h) $\sim (P(x) \leftrightarrow Q(x))$.
    (i) $(\sim P(x) \wedge \sim Q(x)) \vee P(x)$.
13. In Problem 12 which of the sets obtained are necessarily equal to each other?
14. In Problem 12 write statements about the sets A, B which are equivalent to the universal quantification of the listed compound predicates, e.g.,

$$(\forall x) (P(x) \vee Q(x)) \equiv (A \cup B = V).$$

15. Do the same as Problem 14, with existential quantification, e.g.,

$$(\exists x) (P(x) \vee Q(x)) \equiv (A \cup B \neq \emptyset), \text{ or } (A \neq \emptyset \vee B \neq \emptyset).$$

16. Suppose that $A - B = \emptyset$. What can you deduce about A and B?
17. Suppose that $A \cap B' = \emptyset \wedge A' \cap B = \emptyset$. What can you deduce about A and B?
18. Suppose that $A \cup B' = V$. What can you deduce about A and B?
19. Simplify $[(A' \cup B') \cap (C \cup D)]'$.
20. Prove that if A, B are any sets, $[A' \cap (A \cup B)] \cup (A \cap B) = B$.
21. State and prove the dual of Problem 20.
22. Let the universe V be the set of integers $\{1, 2, \ldots, 100\}$. If A is any subset of V, let $n(A)$ be the number of elements in A. Prove that for

all $A,B \subset V$, $n(A \cup B) = n(A) + n(B) - n(A \cap B)$. What does this reduce to in case

(a) A and B are disjoint?

(b) $B = A'$?

23. In a class of 15 students, there are 7 girls, 6 honor students, and 11 students who are either boys or honor students. How many girls are honor students?

24. Two rectangles A and B have areas 6 and 10. Write an equation connecting the areas of $A \cap B$ and $A \cup B$.

25. Let $D = \{1,2,3,4,5,6\}$, $V = \{(x,y)|x \in D \wedge y \in D\}$. For $r = 1, 2, 3, \ldots, 12$, let

$$A_r = \{(x,y) \in V|x + y = r\}.$$

Make a table of the number of elements in A_r :

r	1	2	3	...	12
$n(A_r)$			2		

26. Let the universe V be the set of all real numbers and let Z be the set of all integers. State which of the following are true:

(a) $7 \in \{1,3,5\}'$.

(b) $\sqrt{3} \in Z'$.

(c) $\{x|x^2 = x\}' = \{0,1\}$.

(d) $\sqrt{4} \in Z'$.

(e) $\{3,5,7\}' \cap \{1,2,3,4,5\} = \{1,2,4\}$.

(f) $(\{1,3,5\}' \cup \{1,2,3\})' = \{5\}$.

27. [V, Z as in Problem 26.] List the elements in:

(a) $(\{1,5,17\}')'$.

(b) $\{1,2,3,4,5\} \cap \{2,4\}'$.

(c) $(\{1,2,3\} \cup \{1,17,107\}')'$.

(d) $\{x|(x - 1)(2x - 1) = 0\} - Z$.

28. Given that $(A \cup B)' = A' \cup B'$, what can you deduce about A and B?

29. Simplify:

(a) $T \cup [S \cap (T \cup S')]$.

(b) $[Q' \cup (P \cap Q')] \cup Q$.

(c) $\{1,2,3\} \cap (\{17,5,6,9\} \cup \{1,2,3\})$.

(d) $Z \cup \{x \in Z|x^{16} - 7x^3 + 2x^2 - 1 = 0\}$.

30. State which of the following are true:

(a) $3 \subset \{1,2,3\}$.

(b) $3 \in \{1,2,3\}$.

(c) $\{3\} \subset \{1,2,3\}$.

(d) $\{3\} \in \{1,2,3\}$.

(e) $\emptyset \in \{\emptyset\}$.

(f) $\emptyset \subset \{\emptyset\}$.

31. Give examples for x, y, and z such that the following situations hold:
    (a) $x \in y$, $y \in z$, and $x \notin z$.
    (b) $x \in y$, $y \in z$, and $x \in z$.
    (c) x and y are disjoint, but $x = y$.
    (d) $x \neq y$ but $x \cap y \neq \varnothing$.
32. Prove Eqs. (8) and (9) by showing that the set on the left is contained in the set on the right and vice versa. Illustrate with Venn diagrams.
33. Is set difference a commutative operation? Associative?

2–3. RELATIONS, CARTESIAN PRODUCTS

When two predicates $P(x)$ and $Q(x)$ are always true or false together, that is, when $P(x) \equiv Q(x)$, we say that they have the same *extension*. In fact, we can define the extension of a (one-place) predicate as its truth set. Thus "x is a centaur" and "x is a mermaid" have the same extension, the empty set. Nevertheless we might balk at regarding them as the same predicate. What they differ in is their *intension*. The contrast between extension and intension is roughly the same as that between denotation and connotation. There is a similar contrast between the extension and intension of two-place, three-place, ..., predicates. Thus "$xy = 0$" and "$x = 0 \vee y = 0$" are two-place predicates (of real variables) which are always true or false together, so we should say that they have the same extension. What, then, shall we define as the extension of a two-place (binary) predicate? It should be a truth set in some sense. Our first guess might be the set of all doubletons $\{x,y\}$ such that $P(x,y)$ is true. This seems to work fine for "$xy = 0$," giving us $\{0,1\}$, $\{7,0\}$, $\{0,0\}$ as acceptable doubletons. But we come to grief with the predicate "$x < y$," for the doubleton $\{0,1\}$ should be acceptable, but not $\{1,0\}$. Yet $\{0,1\} = \{1,0\}$! Clearly we need to distinguish between values of x and values of y, designating one as "first." We have a concept ready-made for this purpose—the *ordered pair* (x,y). Thus, the extension of "$x < y$" would be a set containing the elements $(0,1)$, $(3,7)$, $(-4,\pi)$, and so on, but not $(1,0)$, $(7,3)$, $(\pi,-4)$. In general, the extension of $P(x,y)$ will be the set of ordered pairs (x,y) such that $P(x,y)$ is true. For reasons that will soon be discussed, we define a (binary) *relation* as the extension of a (binary) predicate,

$$\{(x,y) | P(x,y)\}.$$

Our informal, common-sense notion of "relation" includes "is the father of," "is a son of," "is greater than," "is married to a brother of," and so on. Our mathematical usage pins these down as sets, like $\{(x,y) | x$ is the father of y}, in conformity with our dictum that every mathematical object is a set. This has the consequence that two different informal "relations" lead to the same mathematical relation precisely when the predicates are equivalent or have the same extension.

There are similar definitions for three-place relations as the extensions of three-place predicates, and so on. The elements of such relations are mathematical objects called ordered triples, quadruples,..., n-tuples. We shall see later how to define these objects in a simple way.

We have defined a relation as a set of ordered pairs, provided that it arises as the truth set of a binary predicate. Actually, this proviso is completely superfluous, for if K is any given set of ordered pairs, the truth set of the predicate $(x,y) \in K$ is precisely K. Thus we arrive at the equivalent, bare-bones definition: *A relation is a set of ordered pairs.*

In practice, the assertion that a pair (a,b) belongs to a relation R may be written in various ways: $(a,b) \in R$, $R(a,b)$, aRb, and so on. There is no harm in using familiar symbols like "$<$," "$=$," "$\subset$." Our definition can lead to weird-looking but perfectly correct statements. For example, if we (for simplicity) restrict the domains of the variables to a small set of individuals, we might write

is married to $= \{(John,Mary), (Mary,John), (Joe,Irene), (Irene,Joe)\}$,
$$< = \{(0,1), (0,2), (0,3), (1,2), (1,3), (2,3)\},$$
$$= = \{(0,0), (1,1), (2,2)\}.$$

Similarly, we could write
$$(0,1) \in <,$$
$$(1,1) \in =,$$

in place of the more familiar "$0 < 1$" and "$1 = 1$."

Given a relation R, there are two other sets associated with·it. The *domain* of R is defined as the set of all first components of pairs in R. Symbolically,

$$\text{dom } R =_{df} \{x | (\exists y) \; (x,y) \in R\}.$$

For example, if $R = \{(0,0), (1,1), (2,4), (3,9)\}$, then dom $R = \{0,1,2,3\}$.

There is a conflict in terminology between "domain of a variable" and "domain of a relation," but there is little danger of confusion. (Incidentally, some authors use "range of a variable" where we have used "domain of a variable".)

The second set associated with a relation R is the *range* of R, defined as the set of all second components of pairs in R. In symbols,

$$\text{rng } R = \{y | (\exists x) \; (x,y) \in R\}.$$

If $R = \{(1,0),\ (1,2),\ (2,1),\ (2,3),\ (3,2),\ (3,4)\}$, then $\text{rng } R = \{0,1,2,3,4\}$ and $\text{dom } R = \{1,2,3\}$.

Suppose that $\text{dom } R \subset A$ and $\text{rng } R \subset B$. If (a,b) is an arbitrary ordered pair in R, then $a \in \text{dom } R \wedge b \in \text{rng } R$. Therefore, $a \in A \wedge b \in B$. It follows that

$$R \subset \{(x,y)|x \in A \wedge y \in B\}.$$

The special set appearing on the right is called the *Cartesian product* of A and B, and is denoted by "$A \times B$." Thus

$$A \times B =_{\text{df}} \{(x,y)|x \in A \wedge y \in B\}.$$

EXAMPLE 2–3. Suppose that we can buy each car model in each of a certain set of colors. Then we may regard the set of possible car purchases as the Cartesian product of the set of models and the set of colors. One element of the Cartesian product might be (Rambler, blue).

EXAMPLE 2–4. We might classify the feelings of one person for another as friendly, neutral, or hostile. He may have a covert (hidden) feeling different from his overt (open,apparent) feeling. This leads to the concept of a "dual mood," for example, overt friendliness and covert hostility. Each dual mood can be regarded as an ordered pair. If F is the set of feelings {friendly,neutral,hostile}, then the Cartesian product $F \times F$ includes the set of all dual moods, provided that we agree on the first component as the overt feeling, the second as the covert one. In the example, the dual mood is (friendly,hostile). Not all of these dual moods are equally plausible, but it does no harm to conceptualize the entire Cartesian product.

EXAMPLE 2–5. If R is the set of real numbers, then $R \times R$ is the set of all ordered pairs (a,b) of real numbers. There is a familiar way to label each point of the plane with an ordered pair (see Figure 2–14). In the figure the point P is labeled with the pair (a,b). This labeling is the basis of analytic geometry, which was developed by René Descartes, a seventeenth-century mathematician and philosopher. It is from his name that we derive the term "Cartesian product."

We have shown that if $\text{dom } R \subset A$, and $\text{rng } R \subset B$, then $R \subset A \times B$. In particular, $R \subset \text{dom } R \times \text{rng } R$, so every relation is a subset of some Cartesian product. Conversely, every subset of a Cartesian product is a relation. Some authors use this property (being a subset of a Cartesian product) to define "relation." They are not wrong, but the student might get the erroneous impression that the Cartesian product is an essential

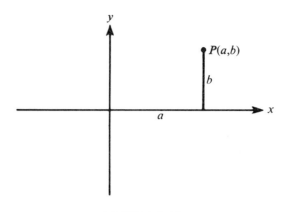

FIGURE 2–14

part of the definition, and that the relation may change if the product is changed, even though the set of pairs in the relation remains the same. This is not so. A relation is a set, so equality of two relations has precisely the same meaning as equality of the two sets.

Sometimes, however, it is convenient to mention which $A \times B$ we are regarding as containing a relation R. In this case we say that R is a relation *between* A and B. If $R \subset A \times A$, then we say briefly that R is a relation *on* A.

EXAMPLE 2–6. $R = \{(0,0), (1,2), (2,4), (3,6)\}$. R is a relation between Z (the integers) and H (the reals). It is also a relation between Z and Z, between H and H, and between H and Z. It is a relation on Z and on H, but not on $\{0,1,2,3\}$, since $R \not\subset \{0,1,2,3\} \times \{0,1,2,3\}$.

EXAMPLE 2–7. Let $A = \{0,1,2,3,4\}$, $B = \{y | y$ is a subset of $\{$Earth,Moon, Sun,Venus$\}\}$, $n(y) =$ the number of elements in y, for $y \in B$. Define $R = \{(x,y) | x \in A \wedge y \in B \wedge x = n(y)\}$. (The student should write out all the elements of R.) Then dom $R = A$, rng $R = B$, and R is a relation between A and B.

EXAMPLE 2–8. A is a set of hens, named Alice, Bessie, Cora, Dora, Emma. The pecking order on A is the relation

$$R = \{(x,y) | x \in A \wedge y \in A \wedge x \text{ pecks } y\}.$$

It might be exhibited by a table such as the one given as Table 2–1. Here x pecks y is indicated by "1," x does not peck y by "0." For example, Cora pecks everyone else and poor Emma is pecked by everyone else.

TABLE 2–1

x \ y	Alice	Bessie	Cora	Dora	Emma
Alice	0	0	0	0	1
Bessie	1	0	0	0	1
Cora	1	1	0	1	1
Dora	1	1	0	0	1
Emma	0	0	0	0	0

The systematic study of certain relations has become increasingly important in fields like philosophy, psychology, sociology, anthropology, and economics. These relations are associated with phrases such as "likes," "is afraid of," "dominates," "matches," "is preferred to," "is forbidden to speak to," "is friendly with," "is indistinguishable from," and so on.

There are three important properties that relations may have. They occur frequently in mathematics and in applications.

(1) *Reflexivity.* A relation R on A is *reflexive* (on A) iff every element of A is R-related to itself:

$$(\forall x)(x \in A \rightarrow xRx).$$

(2) *Symmetry.* A relation R is *symmetric* iff for each pair in R, the reversed pair is also in R:

$$(\forall x)(\forall y)(xRy \rightarrow yRx).$$

(3) *Transitivity.* A relation R is *transitive* iff

$$(\forall x)(\forall y)(\forall z)(xRy \wedge yRz \rightarrow xRz).$$

The pecking order given above is an example of a relation which is transitive but not reflexive and not symmetric. A relation associated with "matches" would be reflexive and symmetric, but generally not transitive. "Likes," among human beings, is unfortunately neither reflexive nor symmetric nor transitive.

R is an *equivalence relation* on A iff it is reflexive on A, symmetric, and transitive. A convenient generic symbol for an equivalence relation is "$\approx$," although others are used, such as "$\sim$," "$\cong$," "$\equiv$." Some examples are equality, congruence (of geometrical figures), equivalence (of propositions), valid equivalence (of predicate formulas), having the same direction (of lines in space). Roughly speaking, an equivalence relation expresses "equality in a certain respect."

One of the reasons for the great importance of equivalence relations is their connection with the idea of classification. Given an equivalence relation $\approx$ on a nonempty set A, we define an *equivalence class* C_a corresponding to a particular element $a \in A$ by

$$C_a =_{df} \{x \in A | x \approx a\}.$$

EXAMPLE 2–9. Let "$a \approx b$" stand for "a lives in the same house as b." This is clearly an equivalence relation. The equivalence class C_a is the set of all people living in the same house as a, that is, the household to which a belongs.

The collection of equivalence classes $\{C_a\}$ has the following properties:
(1) Each C_a is nonempty. In fact, $a \approx a$, by reflexivity, so $a \in C_a$.
(2) The union of all the C_a exhausts A: For each $b \in A$, there is at least one $a \in A$ such that $b \in C_a$. In fact, we can take $a = b$, since $b \in C_b$.
(3) If $a,b \in A$, then C_a and C_b are either identical or disjoint:

$$(C_a \cap C_b = \emptyset) \vee (C_a = C_b).$$

To see this, suppose that $C_a \cap C_b \neq \emptyset$. Then $\exists d \in A$ such that $d \in C_a \cap C_b$, that is, $d \in C_a$ and $d \in C_b$. Since $d \in C_a$, $d \approx a$, and by symmetry $a \approx d$. Since $d \in C_b$, $d \approx b$. Combining $a \approx d$, $d \approx b$ with transitivity, we have $a \approx b$. Now let x be a fixed but arbitrary element of C_a. Then $x \approx a$. Combining $x \approx a$, $a \approx b$ with transitivity, we have $x \approx b$. But this means that $x \in C_b$. Hence $(\forall x) (x \in C_a \rightarrow x \in C_b)$, which means that $C_a \subset C_b$. Similarly, by interchanging a and b in the above argument, we find that $C_b \subset C_a$. Therefore $C_a = C_b$. Thus we have proved

$$(C_a \cap C_b \neq \emptyset) \rightarrow (C_a = C_b),$$

which is of the form $\sim p \rightarrow q$. The fact that

$$(\sim p \rightarrow q) \equiv (p \vee q)$$

proves our initial assertion.

For the example of households above, properties (1), (2), and (3) take the following form:
(1) No household is empty.
(2) Everyone belongs to some household.
(3) Any two households are either identical or disjoint.

Whenever we have a collection of subsets of a set A such that (1) no subset in the collection is empty, (2) the union of all the subsets in the collection exhausts A, and (3) any two subsets in the collection are either identical or disjoint, we say that the collection is a *partition* of A. What we have just proved is that the collection of all equivalence classes corresponding to an equivalence relation $\approx$ forms a partition of A. Let us say that $\approx$ *induces* the partition.

There is also a way in which a partition of A generates an equivalence relation. Given a partition of A, an arbitrary element of A belongs to exactly one subset in the partition, as may easily be seen from (2) and (3). Therefore it makes sense to speak of *the* subset to which an element belongs. Now we define the relation E on A by

$$E = \{(x,y) | x \in A \wedge y \in A \wedge x \text{ belongs to the same subset as } y\}.$$

It is easy to verify that E is an equivalence relation on A, by checking that it is indeed reflexive on A, symmetric, and transitive. Let us say that the partition *generates* E.

Now we state, but do not prove, the basic result that, if E is any equivalence relation on A and π is any partition of A, then the following statements are equivalent: (1) E induces π and (2) π generates E. (The proof is not hard; it is merely tedious.) It follows that we can pair off each equivalence relation with a unique partition in such a way that (1) each E is paired with one and only one π and (2) each π is paired with one and only one E. This is a fine example of a one-to-one correspondence, a concept to be discussed shortly.

EXAMPLE 2–10. Let our domain be the set of integers Z, and let us define "$\approx$" by

$$\approx = \{(x,y) | x - y \text{ is even}\}.$$

Reflexivity and symmetry are easy: $x - x = 0$, which is even, and if $x - y$ is even, so is $y - x$. For transitivity, if $x - y$ and $y - z$ are even, so is $x - z = (x - y) + (y - z)$. Thus $\approx$ is an equivalence relation on Z. The corresponding partition has two equivalence classes as elements:

$$C_0 = \{x | x \text{ is even}\},$$
$$C_1 = \{x | x \text{ is odd}\}.$$

EXAMPLE 2–11. As a second example, this time from economics, let $R^+ = \{x | x \text{ is a real number} \geq 0\}$, and let $A = R^+ \times R^+$. We interpret each pair $(x,y) \in A$ as a package being offered to Joe Consumer, consisting of x pounds of meat and y pounds of cheese. Define the indifference relation

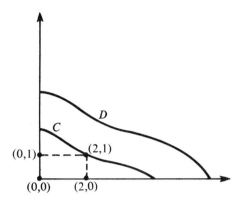

FIGURE 2–15

I on A contextually by

$(x,y)I(x',y') =_{df}$ Joe Consumer has no preference between (x,y) and (x',y').

Thus, we might have $(10,5)I(9,20)$ if Joe Consumer would just as soon have the package (10 lb meat, 5 lb cheese) as the package (9 lb meat, 20 lb cheese). I is an equivalence relation on A. To visualize the corresponding partition π of A, we represent A as a set of points in the plane (Figure 2–15). The point labeled $(2,1)$ represents the package (2 lb meat, 1 lb cheese). The curve C passing through this point represents the equivalence class containing $(2,1)$. Any two points on C represent equivalent packages. D represents another equivalence class. Notice that C and D are disjoint. The whole quarter-plane representing A is filled up with "indifference curves" C, D, and so on.

EXERCISE 2–3

Suppose that a consumer's preference is determined by total weight entirely, up to a total weight of 10 lb. Beyond that (i.e., for $x + y \geq 10$) he is "saturated" and has no preference. Sketch the indifference sets (equivalence classes) containing

   (a) $(2,1)$,
   (b) $(4,4)$,
   (c) $(6,5)$.

If R is a relation between A and B, the *inverse relation*, R^{-1}, is the relation obtained from R by interchanging the first and second components of each ordered pair in R. It is therefore a subset of $B \times A$. In symbols,

$$R^{-1} =_{df} \{(y,x)|(x,y) \in R\}.$$
$$= \{(x,y)|(y,x) \in R\}.$$

Thus, if R stands for "is a parent of," then R^{-1} stands for "is a child of." A relation R is symmetric iff $R^{-1} = R$.

If R and S are relations, it makes sense to ask whether $R \subset S$, because they are both sets. When $R \subset S$, we say that S is an *extension of* R (not to be confused with extension of a predicate). For example, "is a child of" is an extension of "is a son of." It is possible for a property of R to fail when R is extended. Thus, R might be symmetric but an extension S might not be.

EXERCISES 2–4

1. Which of the following predicates of real variables have the same extensions?
   (a) $x^2 = x$.
   (b) $y^3 - 2y^2 + y = 0$.
   (c) There can be x winners in a chess game.
   (d) $w \in \{0,1\}$.
   (e) $-xy = y^2$.
   (f) $x = 0 \vee x = 1$.
   (g) $x + y = 0$.
   (h) $(\exists y)\, y > x$.
   (i) x is a real number.
2. List the elements in $\{\text{heads,tails}\} \times \{\text{heads,tails}\}$.
3. How many elements are there in $\{1,2,3,4\} \times \{1,2,3\}$?
4. If A has m elements and B has n elements, how many elements does $A \times B$ have?
5. List all the relations between $\{1,2,3\}$ and $\{5\}$. (There are eight of them.)
6. Let $A = \{\text{England,France,Italy,Spain}\}$ and $B = \{\text{Paris,Rome,Madrid, London,Naples}\}$. Let

   $$g = \{(x,y)|x \in A \wedge y \in B \wedge y \text{ is the capital of } x\}.$$

   Then g is a relation between A and B. List the elements of g. What are dom g and rng g?
7. List the elements (as ordered pairs) of each of the following relations. Also state for each relation whether it is reflexive, whether it is symmetric, and whether it is transitive.
   (a) The relation "is greater than" on $\{1,\frac{1}{2}, -7,3\}$.
   (b) The relation "dominates" in a well-known children's game where paper dominates stone, stone dominates scissors, and scissors dominate paper.
   (c) The relation "is a descendant of" in your immediate family.

(d) The relation "has authority over" among the Secretary of State, the Secretary of Labor, the Ambassador to India, and the President.

(e) The relation "is a brother of" in your family.

8. List the elements in dom$\{(1,1), (1,2), (3,1)\}$ and those in rng$\{(1,1), (1,2), (3,1)\}$.

9. Give the domain and range for each of the relations in Problem 7.

10. Give an example of two relations f and g, both on the same set A, with rng$(f \cap g) \neq$ rng $f \cap$ rng g.

11. Which of the following relations are equivalence relations on their domains?

(a) $\{(1,3), (3,1), (3,5), (5,3), (1,5), (5,1)\}$.

(b) $\{(1,1), (3,3)\}$.

(c) $\{(1,1), (1,2), (2,1), (2,3), (3,2), (2,2), (3,3)\}$.

(d) $\{(1,1), (1,2), (2,2)\}$.

12. List all the equivalence relations on $\{\sqrt{2}, 7\}$.

13. Think of a weather map of the United States. Is the relation "has the same air pressure as" an equivalence relation? If so, what are the equivalence classes, what are they called, and how are they represented on the map?

14. Draw a rough map of some familiar area. Is the relation "has the same altitude as" an equivalence relation? If so, how can the equivalence classes be represented on the map?

15. Find out what "isotherm" means. Can two different isotherms meet?

16. Write down the inverse relation of

(a) "Loves."

(b) $\{(1,2), (2,3), (3,4)\}$.

(c) $\left\{ (x,y) \mid x > 0 \wedge y = \frac{1}{x} \right\}$.

(d) $\{(1,2), (2,3), (3,2), (2,1)\}$.

(e) $\{(x,y) \mid x \text{ is real} \wedge y = 5\}$.

17. Let E be the equality relation on a set A, and let R be an equivalence relation on A. Prove that $R \supset E$. What property of R does this express?

18. Let Z be the set of integers. For $x, y \in Z$, let "$x \equiv y$" stand for "$x - y$ is divisible by 3." Show that $\equiv$ is an equivalence relation on Z. What are the equivalence classes? If $a \equiv a'$ and $b \equiv b'$, show that $a + b \equiv a' + b'$ and $ab \equiv a'b'$.

19. Give an example of a relation S on a set A such that S is symmetric and transitive, but not reflexive on A.

20. Which of the following predicates yield equivalence relations?
(a) x differs from y by at most 0.000001.
(b) x was born in the same calendar year as y.
(c) x and y have the same shape or color.
(d) x and y are brothers.
(e) x and y like the same girl.
(f) x and y have the same shape and color.

2–4. FUNCTIONS

Let R be a relation between A and B. If distinct pairs in R necessarily have distinct first components, we say that R is a *function*. Another way of stating the condition is, if the ordered pairs (x,y) and (x,z) both belong to R, then $y = z$. For example, if

$$R = \{(0,1), (1,1), (2,3), (3,3)\},$$

then R is a function. But if

$$R = \{(1,0), (1,1), (3,4), (5,6)\},$$

then R is not a function, because the distinct pairs $(1,0)$ and $(1,1)$ have the same first component.

If R is a function and if $x \in \operatorname{dom} R$, then we know that there is one and only one y such that $(x,y) \in R$. The fact that there is at least one such y follows from the definition of domain, and that there is at most one follows from the definition of a function. The conventional way of exhibiting this state of affairs is to write: $y = R(x)$. In the first example above, we would write

$$R(0) = 1, R(1) = 1, R(2) = 3, R(3) = 3.$$

Notice that a function may have distinct pairs with the same second component.

We can think graphically of each $x \in \operatorname{dom} R$ as *determining* its *image* $R(x)$, in accordance with a diagram such as Figure 2–16. The intuitive idea of a rule by which the image $R(x)$ is determined from x is applicable here. The rule may be clumsy and uninformative, as "$R(x)$ is the second component in the unique ordered pair in R which has x as its first component," or it may be succinct, as in "$R(x) = x^2$ for each real x." This last is equivalent to $R = \{(x,y)|x \text{ is real} \wedge y = x^2\}$.

Frequently writers of mathematics are not quite so explicit as we have been, and say things like "Consider the function $y = x^2$." They may even speak of y being a function of x. It is not that they are ignorant of the

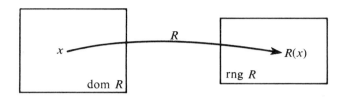

FIGURE 2-16

precise definition of function given above. It is merely that the basic idea of a function existed in men's minds long before the precise definition was formulated, and that the language of mathematics has developed its idioms over a long period. As long as we understand these idioms and can translate them accurately in our own minds, no great harm is done.

There is, however, one danger in the idiom "Consider the function $y = x^2$," and that is the omission of all mention of the domain of the function. Thus, any one of the following distinct functions has the same rule or formula "$y = x^2$":

$$\{(x,y)|x \text{ is an integer} \wedge y = x^2\},$$
$$\{(x,y)|x \text{ is a positive real} \wedge y = x^2\},$$
$$\{(x,y)|x \in \{0,1,2\} \wedge y = x^2\}.$$

A function defined by a formula is not completely specified unless we say what its domain is. Thus, we might write, in the preceding examples,

$$y = x^2 \qquad (x \text{ an integer}),$$
$$y = x^2 \qquad (x \text{ a positive real}),$$
$$y = x^2 \qquad (x = 0,1,2).$$

To verify that two functions f, g are equal, it is necessary and sufficient to check both of the following assertions:

(a) $\text{dom} f = \text{dom} g$,

(b) $f(x) = g(x) \qquad (x \in \text{dom} f)$.

Proving (b) alone is not enough. It may happen that

(a') $\text{dom} f \subset \text{dom} g$,

(b') $f(x) = g(x) \qquad (x \in \text{dom} f)$.

In this case the set of pairs constituting f is a subset of the set constituting g; that is, $f \subset g$. Then we say that g is an extension of f, or f is a restriction of g.

If $\text{dom} f = A$ and $\text{rng} f \subset B$, we say that f is a function *from* (or *on*) A *to* (or *into*) B. If $\text{rng} f = B$, we say that f is *onto* B. When f is a function from A to B, we sometimes write

$$f: A \to B$$

and say that f *maps* A into B, or f is a *mapping* of A into B. The arrow here has nothing to do with logical implication. If $\operatorname{dom} f = A$ and $D \subset A$, the *restriction of f to D*, written "$f|D$," is defined by

$$f|D = \{(x,y) \in f \,|\, x \in D\},$$

or, equivalently, by

(a) $\operatorname{dom}(f|D) = D$,
(b) $(f|D)(x) = f(x)$ $(x \in D)$.

Functions are frequently given in the form of tables. For example, the trigonometric functions, the exponential function, the error function, and the compound-interest function are all tabulated. We must bear in mind, however, that these are not complete tabulations, since the domain is too big ever to be written down completely. Instead, the values of the function are given (with a specified accuracy) corresponding to conveniently spaced values of the *independent variable*. (This is the variable whose domain is $\operatorname{dom} f$; it refers to the first component in the ordered pairs which make up f.) Along with such an incomplete table there is usually given or understood a procedure for *interpolation*—determining intermediate values, at least approximately.

Sometimes functions are defined by partitioning the domain into subsets and giving a formula for each subset. For example, part of the 1964 tax rate schedule is given in Table 2–2.

There is no need for the domain or range of a function to consist of numbers. The values of the independent variable might be geometrical figures, as in the case of the area function. The functional values might be sets, as in

$$f(x) = \{n \in Z \,|\, n - x \text{ is even}\}   (x = 0,1).$$

TABLE 2–2

If the amount on line 11d, page 1, is:	*Enter on line 12, page 1:*
Not over $1,000................	16% of the amount on line 11d.
$1,000.......$2,000..........	$160, plus 16.5%..... $1,000
$2,000...... $3,000..........	$325, plus 17.5%..... $2,000
$3,000...... $4,000..........	$500, plus 18% $3,000
$4,000...... $8,000..........	$680, plus 20% $4,000
$8,000......$12,000..........	$1,480, plus 23.5%..... $8,000
$12,000......$16,000..........	$2,420, plus 27% $12,000
$16,000......$20,000..........	$3,500, plus 30.5%.....$16,000
$20,000......$24,000..........	$4,720, plus 34% $20,000

Here,

$$f(0) = \{n \in Z | n \text{ is even}\},$$
$$f(1) = \{n \in Z | n \text{ is odd}\}.$$

(*We shall use Z consistently for the set of integers.*)

EXAMPLE 2–12

   (a) $f(x) =$ the population of x (x a town).

   (b) $f(x) =$ the color of x's eyes   (x a person).

   (c) $g(s) =$ the midpoint of s (s a line segment).

   (d) $P(E) =$ the probability of E (E an event).

   (e) $L(x) =$ the set of languages spoken by x (x a person).

   (f) $T(n) = \{m | m \in Z \wedge m \geq n\}$ ($n \in Z$).

There is one special case of the concept of function which deserves special attention. If the domain consists of ordered pairs, we speak of a function of two variables, or a (binary) *operation*. Thus

$$S(x,y) = x + y \qquad (x \text{ real, } y \text{ real})$$

defines the operation of addition. (Note that we have suppressed one pair of parentheses.) If H is the set of reals, the domain of the function S is $H \times H$. Thus we may write

$$S : H \times H \to H.$$

If the domain is of the form $A \times A$, as above, we say simply that the operation is defined on A. Much of algebra is concerned with the study of certain operations and their basic properties.

It is easy and convenient to use the notion of function to define *ordered n-tuple*. Let h be a function with dom $h = \{1,2,3, \ldots, n\}$. An example is

$$h(1) = 2, \; h(2) = 7, \; h(3) = -1, \; h(4) = 5.$$

This function may be displayed more compactly by

$$h = (2,7,-1,5),$$

and we say that h is an ordered four-tuple. In general, if we write h_k for $h(k)$, where k may be any one of $1, 2, \ldots, n$, then

$$h = (h_1, h_2, \ldots, h_n)$$

is called an *ordered n-tuple*. The element h_k is the kth *component* of h. Given the sets $B_1, B_2, \ldots, B_n$, suppose we consider the set of all ordered n-tuples $(h_1, h_2, \ldots, h_n)$ such that $h_1 \in B_1, \; h_2 \in B_2, \ldots, h_n \in B_n$. This set is called the Cartesian product of $B_1, B_2, \ldots, B_n$, and is denoted by

$$B_1 \times B_2 \times \cdots \times B_n.$$

If f is a function with

$$\operatorname{dom} f = B_1 \times B_2 \times \cdots \times B_n.$$

then we say that f is a function of n variables $x_1, x_2, \ldots, x_n$: the independent variable of f is really the ordered n-tuple $(x_1, x_2, \ldots, x_n)$.

Much of modern economics deals with functions of many variables. For example, we might wish to consider simultaneously the prices $p_1, p_2, \ldots, p_n$ of n commodities, together with the demands $d_1, d_2, \ldots, d_n$ for the same commodities. It might be convenient conceptually to regard the demand n-tuple $d = (d_1, d_2, \ldots, d_n)$ as a function of the price n-tuple $p = (p_1, p_2, \ldots, p_n)$:

$$d = f(p) \qquad (p \in P_1 \times P_2 \times \cdots \times P_n).$$

Finally, there is one kind of function of tremendous importance in mathematics and allied fields. If f is a function such that f^{-1} is also a function, then f is called a one-to-one correspondence from its domain to its range, or between its domain and range. For example, if f is defined by

$$f(n) = 2n \qquad (n \in Z),$$

then f is a one-to-one correspondence between Z (the set of all integers) and E (the set of all even integers). In terms of the pairs in f, this can be expressed by saying that two distinct pairs in f must have distinct first components and distinct second components. A one-to-one correspondence establishes a monogamous "marriage" between elements of the domain and elements of the range. Schematically, we have the diagram of Figure 2–17, with the situations shown in Figure 2–18 never arising.

A very simple example of a one-to-one correspondence is that of a primitive man keeping track of his wives by matching each one with one of his fingers (or toes, if necessary). Another one is: Suppose there are people milling around in an auditorium and you wish to know whether there are

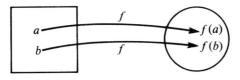

FIGURE 2-17

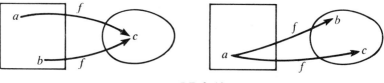

FIGURE 2-18

as many seats as people. You simply say "Sit down!" If all the seats are filled and no person is left standing, then a one-to-one correspondence has been established. We have here a concept that is even more basic than counting. A preschool child who has not yet learned the number names can still see that he has as many fingers on one hand as on the other, simply by pairing thumb with thumb, forefinger with forefinger, and so on. In fact, the process of counting is no more than setting up a one-to-one correspondence between a given set and a standard set of utterances like "un," "deux," "trois," and so forth. The last utterance made in running through the set (provided that there is a last) symbolizes the number of elements in the set. We have then "counted" the set. In the example of the auditorium above, we could have counted the people, counted the seats, and then compared the resulting final utterances, say "eighty-five" and "seventy-four," respectively. The following contrasts the two methods we have just described:

$$Joe \rightarrow Mary$$
$$John \rightarrow Irene$$
$$Harry \rightarrow Ruth$$
$$Dick \rightarrow Ann$$

or

Joe → one	one → Mary
John → two	two → Irene
Harry → three	three → Ruth
Dick → four	four → Ann

Aside from being more basic than counting, the method of one-to-one correspondence is more powerful. Thus if we define "A has as many elements as B" by "there is a one-to-one correspondence between A and B," we have a way of testing whether there are as many integers as there are even integers. The function f given by

$$f(n) = 2n \qquad (n \in Z)$$

provides us with the affirmative answer, since it shows that there exists a one-to-one correspondence between Z and E, the set of even integers. You don't have to accept this somewhat paradoxical result, if you're worried about "the whole is greater than any of its parts." But then you must also reject our proposed definition of "*A* has as many elements as *B*" and either suggest a better one or do without any. Modern mathematics has found it convenient and fruitful to adopt our definition.

Notice that we have *not* defined "the number of elements in *A*," but merely the inseparable relation "has as many elements as." This relation, denoted by "$\approx$," is called equivalence or equipotence. It is reflexive, symmetric, and transitive, so it really is an equivalence relation. The pairs (*A*,*B*) satisfy the condition that there exists *at least one* function *f*,

$$f : A \xrightarrow[\text{one-to-one}]{\text{onto}} B.$$

A word of caution is necessary. We may very well be able to set up a one-to-one correspondence between *A* and a proper subset $B_1 \subset B$. (A proper subset of *B* is one that is not equal to *B*.) This does *not* prove that *A* and *B* are inequivalent. We could have $A \approx B_1$, $A \approx B$ simultaneously, with $B_1 \subset B$ but $B_1 \neq B$. By symmetry and transitivity, $B_1 \approx B$ follows. This state of affairs occurs precisely when *B* is an infinite set. Indeed, it permits us to make an unambiguous definition of "*B* is an infinite set":

$$B \text{ is an infinite set } =_{\text{df}} \exists B_1 \subset B,\ B_1 \neq B,\ B_1 \approx B.$$

Of course, if *B* is not an infinite set, it is *finite*.

As an example, consider the solid sphere *B* with center *C*, radius 2. To each point $P \in B$ we make correspond $f(P) = $ the midpoint of the segment *CP*. Then *f* is a one-to-one correspondence between *B* and the sphere B_1 with center *C*, radius 1. It compresses *B* onto the proper subset B_1. By our definition, *B* is infinite. On the other hand, if $B = \{1,2,3\}$, then there is *no* proper subset $B_1 \subset B$ such that $B_1 \approx B$. This can be proved by examining all possibilities of mapping *B* into itself. Therefore *B* is "incompressible." By our definition, *B* is finite.

A set is *denumerable* if it is equivalent to the set $N = \{1,2,3,\ldots\}$. A set is *countable* if it is either finite or denumerable. For example, $Z(= $ the set of integers) is denumerable. Both *Z* and $\{1,2,3\}$ are countable. We should warn the student that not every infinite set is denumerable.

In the vast book of mathematics, the chapter that deals with infinite sets and their cardinality (how-manyness) is a fascinating one. We have given a mere fleeting glimpse into its pages, but enough to show that these questions can be attacked with careful reasoning rather than mystical speculation.

EXERCISES 2-5

1. In the tax example in the text, find $T(5,000)$, $T(14,000)$, $T(2,000)$, $T(4,000)$, $T(4,001)$. [$T(x)$ is the tax on x dollars.]

2. List all the functions from {Cuba,Brazil,Mexico} to {U.S.A.,U.S.S.R.}. Which of these are onto? One-to-one?

3. List all the one-to-one correspondences from {1,2,3} to itself.

4. Give two examples of each of the following:
   (a) f is a function, f^{-1} is a function.
   (b) f is a function, f^{-1} is not a function.
   (c) f is not a function, f^{-1} is a function.
   (d) f is a relation but not a function, and so is f^{-1}.

5. Let N be the set of positive integers. For $n \in N$, let $s(n) =$ the sum of the digits of n (when n is written in ordinary decimal notation). For example, $s(135) = 1 + 3 + 5 = 9$, $s(9) = 9$.
   (a) Compute $s(87,203)$, $s(20)$, $s(2)$.
   (b) Compute $s(123,454,321)$, $s(25)$, $s(7)$.
   (c) For $n = 98,979,695$, compute $s(n)$, $s(s(n))$, $s(s(s(n)))$.
   (d) For which $n \in N$ is it true that $s(n) = n$? $s(n) > n$? $s(n) < n$?
   (e) For $n \in N$, let $r(n)$ be the remainder after dividing n by 9. For all $n \in \{5, 37, 285, 764, 8,716\}$, compute $r(n) - r(s(n))$.

6. Let N be the set of positive integers, and let

   $$d = \{(m,n)|m \in N \wedge n \text{ is the number of divisors of } m\}.$$

   For example, one element of d is (4.3).
   (a) Is d a function?
   (b) Is d^{-1} a function?
   (c) What is $d(5)$? $d(7)$? $d(d(4))$?
   (d) Do you know a name for the elements of $\{m|d(m) = 2\}$?
   (e) Do you know a name for the elements of $\{m|d(m) \text{ is odd}\}$?

7. If $f = \{(x,x^2)|x \text{ is real}\}$, what is rng f? If $f = \{(x, y)|x \text{ is real} \wedge y = x^2 + 1\}$, what is rng f?

8. What are the elements of $\{3,4\} \times \varnothing$?

9. Write out the elements of $B_1 \times B_2 \times B_3$, where

   $$B_1 = \{0,1\}, B_2 = \{1,2\}, B_3 = \{2,3\}.$$

10. If B_1 has three elements, B_2 has four elements, and B_3 has five elements, how many elements will $B_1 \times B_2 \times B_3$ have? Generalize.

11. State which of the following relations are functions:
    (a) {(touchdown,6), (kicked extra point,1), (run extra point,2), (field goal,3), (safety,2), (touchback,0)}.
    (b) {(Crosby,78), (Hope,80), (Snead,71), (Jones,69), Eisenhower,93)}.

(c) {(Cleopatra,9), (Lincoln,7), (Methuselah,10), (Washington 10)}.

(d) {(1,5), (3,7), (5,9), (1,7)}.

(e) $\{(x,y)|x \text{ real} \wedge y \text{ real} \wedge x^2 + y^2 = 1\}$.

(f) $\{(x,y)|x \text{ real} \wedge y \geq 0 \wedge x^2 + y^2 = 1\}$.

12. State which of the following relations are one-to-one correspondences:

(a) {(Jack,Jacqueline), (Ike,Mamie), (Harry, Bess)}.

(b) {(Taylor,Todd), (Taylor,Hilton), (Taylor,Fisher), (Taylor,Burton), (Reynolds,Fisher)}.

(c) {(1,3), (2,9), (5,1), (4,2)}.

(d) $\{(\pi,\sqrt{2})\}$.

13. Using the relation "is husband of," express the following conditions by means of the language of functions, inverses, one-to-one correspondences, and so on:

(a) monogamy, (b) polygamy, (c) polygyny, (d) polyandry.

14. Give an example of a familiar function whose domain is A and whose range is contained in B, where

(a) A is the set of goods in a store and B is the set of real numbers.

(b) A is the set of people alive today and B is the set of integers.

(c) A is the set of people (who have ever lived) and B is the set of male people (who have ever lived).

(d) A is the set of events in history and B is the set of integers. Which of your examples are one-to-one, and which are onto B?

15. Give an example of a function h from $\{0,1,2,3,4\}$ to $\{0,1,2,3,4\}$ such that

$$h(x + y) = h(x) + h(y) \qquad (x, y \in \{0,1,2,3,4\}).$$

Are there any other examples?

16. Give an example of a function h from $\{0,1,2\}$ to $\{0,1,2\}$ such that

$$h(h(x)) = 2 \qquad \{(x \in 0,1,2\}).$$

17. Prove that f is one-to-one iff f^{-1} is one-to-one.

18. Prove that equipotence of sets is transitive:

If $A \approx B$ and $B \approx C$, then $A \approx C$.

19. Prove that there are as many squares in Z as there are odd numbers in Z.

20. Name the widest possible domain (in the reals) for the functions (to the reals) given by the formulas

(a) $y = \dfrac{1}{x}$.

(b) $y = \dfrac{1}{x(x-1)}$.

21. Toss a coin five times and exhibit the outcome as a 5-tuple.

22. If $c = (c_1, c_2, \ldots, c_n)$ is the n-tuple of unit costs for producing items $1, 2, \ldots, n$, and if $k = (k_1, k_2, \ldots, k_n)$ is the n-tuple of quantities produced, write down an expression for the total cost C. Of what variables is C a function?

23. Let

$$f(x) = x^2 - x \qquad (x \text{ real}),$$
$$g(x) = 3x^2 - 3x \qquad (x \text{ real}),$$
$$A = \{0,1\}.$$

Show that $f|A = g|A$. Are there any other subsets A of the reals for which this is true?

24. Show that $\varnothing$ is a function. What is its domain? What is its range? Is it one-to-one?

25. Give a binary operation K in the reals such that $K(x,y) \neq K(y,x)$ in general.

26. Give a relation R between Z and Z which is reflexive and symmetric but not transitive.

27. For x, y real, let $S(x,y) = x + y$, $M(x,y) = xy$. Prove that for all real x, y, z,
    (a) $M(x, M(y,z)) = M(M(x,y), z)$.
    (b) $S(x, S(y,z)) = S(S(x,y), z)$.
    (c) $M(x, S(y,z)) = S(M(x,y), M(x,z))$.

28. In a psychological experiment, the subject is given a succession of five stimuli chosen from a set of "elementary stimuli," say {red, blue, yellow}. The entire succession is called a stimulus presentation. Show that the set of stimulus presentations may be regarded as a Cartesian product. How many possible stimulus presentations are there?

*29. In *Social Choice and Individual Values* (Wiley, New York, 1951), Kenneth J. Arrow considers the set A of possible alternatives and a relation R on A, with "xRy" supposed to mean "x is preferred or indifferent to y." He then makes two basic assumptions (axioms).

Axiom 1. $(\forall x)(\forall y)\ xRy \lor yRx$.

Axiom 2. $(\forall x)(\forall y)(\forall z)\ ((xRy \land yRz) \to xRz)$.

Next he defines strict preference and indifference by

Definition 1. xPy means $\sim yRx$.

Definition 2. xIy means $xRy \land yRx$.

("xPy" is read "x is preferred to y"; "xIy" is read "x is indifferent to y.") Using only the two axioms and two definitions stated above,

prove the following assertions of Arrow. Observe that they are all intuitively self-evident from the interpretations placed on the symbols. These interpretations should not be used in the proofs, however.
(a) $(\forall x)\ xRx$.
(b) $(\forall x)(\forall y)\ xPy \rightarrow xRy$.
(c) $(\forall x)(\forall y)(\forall z)\ ((xPy \wedge yPz) \rightarrow xPz)$.
(d) $(\forall x)(\forall y)(\forall z)\ ((xIy) \wedge (yIz) \rightarrow xIz)$.
(e) $(\forall x)(\forall y)\ xRy \vee yPx$.
(f) $(\forall x)(\forall y)(\forall z)\ ((xPy \wedge yIz) \rightarrow xPz)$.
[We have modified Arrow's notation slightly.]

*30. A *cipher* is a one-to-one correspondence between the set $A = \{a,b,c,\ldots,x,y,z\}$ (the letters of the alphabet) and a set B. Frequently $B = A$, as we shall assume in this problem.
   (a) Show how you would compute the number of possible ciphers, (Don't actually compute. The number is too large.)
   (b) Construct a cipher f such that $f^{-1} = f$. (This would permit the procedures of enciphering and deciphering to be the same.)
   (c) Show that there is exactly one transitive cipher.
   (d) Is the inverse of a cipher also a cipher?
   (e) Let f and g be ciphers. Define h by
   $$h(x) = f(g(x)) \qquad (x \in A).$$
   Is h also a cipher?

31. Let R be a relation from A to A (i.e., dom $R = A$, rng $R \subset A$). If R is symmetric and transitive, show that R is an equivalence relation on A.

32. Show that a date (e.g., Sept. 15, 1964) may be regarded as an ordered triple. Is the set of all possible dates a Cartesian product?

*33. Let $A = \{1,2,3,4,5\}$, $B = \{0,1\}$, $C = B \times B \times B \times B$. For each $x \in C$, let
   $$f(x) = \text{the subset of } A \text{ consisting of those } i \in A \text{ such that } x_i = 1.$$
   For example, if $x = (0,1,1,0,1)$, then $f(x) = \{2,3,5\}$. Prove that f is one-to-one correspondence between C and the set of all subsets of A. How many subsets of A are there?

*34. Let f be a function with dom $f = A$, rng $f = B$. Prove that the collection of subsets of A of the form $\{x \mid f(x) = b\}$ (one subset for each $b \in B$) is a partition of A. What is the corresponding equivalence relation on A?

35. Show that Z, the set of all integers, is denumerable.

36. Show that $\{1,2,3\}$ is finite.

*2–5. ORDERINGS

In this section we shall discuss briefly a class of relations called *orderings*. These have become increasingly important in the social sciences, especially in psychology and economics. In the study of preference or utility, for example, our primitive intuitions are not quantitative. To say that John is twice as tall as Jim seems meaningful to us, because we can devise a simple operational test of the statement, but there is no convenient yardstick to test whether I like John twice as much as I do Jim. Lacking a natural numerical scale of preference, we must fall back on basic qualitative intuitions such as "If I prefer chess to checkers and checkers to bridge, then I prefer chess to bridge." Whether we regard such a statement as an empirical observation about the known predicate "I prefer x to y" or as a directive to use the word "prefer" only under certain conditions, it is still true that the statement is qualitative rather than quantitative.

All orderings have the property of *transitivity*, which generalizes the statement about chess, etc., made above. We repeat the definition:

Definition 2–1. A relation R is *transitive* iff

$$(\forall x)(\forall y)(\forall z)\ xRy \wedge yRz \rightarrow xRz.$$

This section is designed for quick reference by those who find that they have need for the concepts treated. For this reason there will be a minimum of motivational and expository material. The definitions will be listed in quick succession. These will be followed by tables and diagrams that should help the student to fix his ideas. For a fuller exposition, we refer him to Patrick Suppes' *Introduction to Logic* (Van Nostrand, New York, 1957), Chapter 10.

Throughout we shall assume that the relation R is contained in $A \times A$. Some properties of relations (e.g., reflexivity) make sense only in reference to A, and may change if A is changed. In such cases, A will appear explicitly in the definitions. In all cases, however, the variables will range over A.

The historical prototypes of the orderings defined here are $\leq$, $<$, $\geq$, $>$, $\subset$, $\overset{\subset}{\neq}$ ("is a proper subset of"). These, together with other examples, appear in Table 2–3. An entry "1" indicates that the relation heading the row possesses the property heading the column; "0" indicates that the relation does not have the property. In Table 2–4 "1" has the same meaning; the blank space is noncommittal. Connections between four important types of ordering are shown in Figure 2–19.

Definition 2–2. A relation R is *reflexive on* A iff

$$\forall x \in A,\ xRx.$$

TABLE 2–3

R	A	Refl.	Irrefl.	Sym.	Asym.	Antisym.	Conn.	Remarks
≤	integers	1	0	0	0	1	1	simple O.
<	integers	0	1	0	1	1	1	strict S.O.
⊂	subsets of the integers	1	0	0	0	1	0	partial O.
⊂ ≠	subsets of the integers	0	1	0	1	1	0	strict P.O.
=	integers	1	0	1	0	1	0	equiv., P.O.
Has same sign as	integers	1	0	1	0	0	0	equiv., quasi-O.
Is shorter than	people	0	1	0	1	1	0	strict P.O.
Is not taller than	people	1	0	0	0	0	1	weak O.
∅	integers	0	1	1	1	1	0	strict P.O.
∅	∅	1	1	1	1	1	1	simple O., strict S.O., equiv.

TABLE 2–4

Relation	Trans.	Refl.	Symm.	Asymm.	Antisymm.	Conn.
Quasi-O.	1	1				
Partial O.	1	1			1	
Simple O.	1	1			1	1
Weak O.	1	1				1
Strict P.O.	1			1	·	
Strict S.O.	1			1		1
Equiv.	1	1	1			

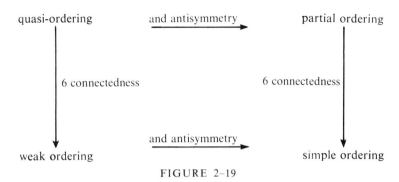

FIGURE 2–19

Definition 2–3.   A relation R is *irreflexive* iff

$$(\forall x) \sim xRx.$$

[*Note:* This is not the negation of reflexivity.]

Definition 2–4.   A relation R is *nonreflexive on A* iff

$$\exists x \in A, \sim xRx.$$

(This is the negation of reflexivity.)

Definition 2–5.   A relation R is *symmetric* iff

$$(\forall x)(\forall y)\ xRy \rightarrow yRx.$$

Definition 2–6.   A relation R is *asymmetric* iff

$$(\forall x)(\forall y)\ xRy \rightarrow \sim yRx.$$

(This is not the negation of symmetry.)

Definition 2–7.   A relation R is *antisymmetric* iff

$$(\forall y)(\forall y)\ xRy \wedge yRx \rightarrow x = y.$$

(Not yet.)

Definition 2–8.   A relation R is *nonsymmetric* iff

$$(\exists x)(\exists y)\ xRy \wedge \sim yRx.$$

(Now.)

Definition 2–9.   A relation R is *intransitive* iff

$$(\forall x)(\forall y)(\forall z)\ xRy \wedge yRz \rightarrow \sim xRz.$$

(This is not the negation of transitivity.)

Definition 2–10. A relation R is *nontransitive* iff

$$(\exists x)(\exists y)(\exists z)\ xRy \wedge yRz \wedge \sim xRz.$$

(This is the negation of transitivity.)

Definition 2–11. A relation R is *connected on A* iff

$$(\forall x \in A)\ (\forall y \in A)\ x \neq y \rightarrow xRy \vee yRx.$$

Definition 2–12. A relation R is *nonconnected on A* iff

$$(\exists x \in A)(\exists y \in A)\ x \neq y \wedge \sim xRy \wedge \sim yRx.$$

(This is the negation of connectedness.)

Definition 2–13. A relation R is *strongly connected on A* iff

$$(\forall x \in A)\ (\forall y \in A)\ xRy \vee yRx.$$

Definition 2–14. A relation is a *quasi-ordering of A* iff it is transitive and reflexive on A.

Definition 2–15. A relation is a *partial ordering of A* iff it is transitive, reflexive on A, and antisymmetric.

Definition 2–16. A relation is a *simple* (also *linear* or *total*) *ordering of A* iff it is transitive, reflexive on A, antisymmetric and connected on A.

Definition 2–17. A relation is a *weak ordering of A* iff it is transitive, reflexive on A, and connected on A.

Definition 2–18. A relation is a *strict partial ordering* iff it is transitive and asymmetric.
(This is usually not a partial ordering; "strict" is not a mere modifier of "partial ordering".)

Definition 2–19. A relation is a *strict simple ordering of A* iff it is transitive, asymmetric, and connected on A.
(This is usually not a simple ordering of A.)

Definition 2–20. A relation is an *equivalence on A* iff it is transitive, reflexive on A, and symmetric.

EXERCISES 2–6

1. Analyze the following transitive relations as in Table 2–3:
   (a) $\geq$ on Z ($=$ the set of integers).
   (b) $\{(1,1)\}$ on Z.
   (c) $\{(1,1), (1,2), (2,2)\}$ on $\{1,2\}$.

(d) $\{(1,1), (1,2), (2,2)\}$ on Z.

(e) "is preferred to" on a set of three alternatives.

2. Prove that if R is both reflexive and irreflexive on A, then $A = \emptyset$.

3. Prove that if R is both symmetric and asymmetric, then $R = \emptyset$.

4. Prove that if R is transitive, symmetric, and connected on a non-singleton A, then R is an equivalence on A.

5. Verify the following implications:

   (a) Simple ordering $\rightarrow$ partial ordering $\rightarrow$ quasi-ordering.

   (b) Simple ordering $\rightarrow$ weak ordering $\rightarrow$ quasi-ordering.

   (c) Partial ordering $\wedge$ weak ordering $\rightarrow$ simple ordering.

   (d) Strict simple ordering $\rightarrow$ strict partial ordering.

6. Prove that every strict partial ordering is irreflexive.

7. Find an example of a quasi-ordering which is not any of the other orderings in Table 2–4.

8. Find all connected equivalence relations on $\{1,2,3,4\}$.

9. Discuss the relation R defined by

$$(x,y)R(x',y') \text{ iff } x \le x' \wedge y \le y' \qquad (x, y, x', y' \in Z).$$

What is dom R?

Chapter 3

AXIOM SYSTEMS

3-1. MATHEMATICS AND REALITY

FOR CENTURIES, wise men have asked how man acquires knowledge of the world around him. They have debated and written tomes about this question. We shall not pretend that we can arrive at any final answers here, but we shall introduce the student to a few of the problems and methods of scientific inquiry. In a world where scientific discoveries are made every day, the truly educated person should inquire into and examine the processes by which these discoveries are made. We are bombarded with facts and near-facts in the daily newspapers, the weekly newsmagazines, and the monthly scientific and popular-scientific magazines. We are told about the tremendous impact that mathematics has upon other fields, such as physics, chemistry, biology, psychology, sociology, economics, and business. What is the nature of this impact on disciplines that purport to deal with the "real world"?

It is not factual information but understanding that we need. No one can hope to comprehend the flood of new results in all the sciences, but it is possible to acquire some understanding and intellectual maturity. This can be done by choosing as a model a particular field which is narrow enough so that the few facts in it can be easily absorbed, but not so narrow as to be insignificant. We can then examine in detail how the conceptual structure is built up from these facts so as to provide us with an acceptable theory, on the basis of which we can make predictions, set up experiments to verify the predictions, and confirm our theory. These are in essence the steps that we take in developing any discipline.

In this chapter we shall show how the process of conceptualization or abstraction operates at one level in the field of mathematics. It is not claimed that all scientific theories are constructed in this way.

The model that we study in this chapter is an abstract system called Boolean algebra, named after the nineteenth-century logician George

Boole, who recognized that logic could be studied as a formal algebraic structure. We choose this particular system because its axioms are rather simple, its early theorems easy to prove but nontrivial, and its applications significant.

In studying this chapter, the student should read this first section lightly, go through the remaining sections as usual, then return to the first section and read it slowly and carefully. He should also do some outside reading to deepen his understanding.

We have spoken of facts on the one hand and of concepts on the other. More generally, we may speak of the world of facts, the "real world"—whatever that may mean—and the world of concepts. The distinction between these two worlds is frequently difficult to make. For example, if we weigh two objects separately on a spring scale, we may report that one is heavier than the other. Is this to be regarded as a fact, a datum? If we examine the statement carefully, we see that a great deal of theory is involved. What we really observe is that the needle is deflected more in one case than in the other. By means of a theory about how spring scales operate, we translate this into the original statement. Also, when we perform the weighing, we observe that the needle swings back and forth several times till it comes to rest, and then we take a reading. But how do we know that this is the correct value? Perhaps this state of rest is only temporary, as were the previous swings, and there will shortly be other swings following by another state of rest giving the "correct" value. Clearly, there is an underlying theory that tells us how the needle may be expected to move. Again, how do we know that the same experiment performed a few minutes later will produce similar results?

These questions are raised, not to shake our faith in the possibility of knowing anything at all, but to emphasize that theory is indispensable in the business of acquiring knowledge, and that even the most practical, hardheaded, down-to-earth people rely heavily upon theories and assumptions, whether or not they admit it. The difference between the practical and the theoretical is not so great as one might suppose. The practical investigator accepts and uses the theories of earlier theoreticians, whereas the present theoretical investigator bases his theories on the "facts" obtained by practical experimentation. Whether we like it or not, anyone who thinks at all is using theories, crude or refined, implicit or explicit, as well as purported facts.

In constructing a new theory—and this is the task to which we shall address ourselves—we usually begin by having before us a body of "facts" which we accept as being well established, some more, some less. We leave aside the question of how these facts were arrived at, for this would lead us back and back to the very primitive foundations of knowledge. We wish to go ahead just this one step of constructing a theory to fit this particular body of facts. This jumbled, unorganized, or partly organized body of facts, which we are fairly willing to accept, we shall refer to as the "physical plane," or, following Bridgman, the "P-plane." The conceptual structure to be erected will lie in the "conceptual plane," or the "C-plane." The P-plane will certainly vary from one field of investigation to another, and the C-plane, being of our own construction, will also vary, even when the same P-plane is involved.

For example, if we are building a geometrical theory, the P plane might be taken as the collection of "facts" observed about points, lines, angles, triangles, and so on, drawn upon a huge sheet of paper. (Or we might take a collection of "facts" about material points, light rays, etc.) It is quite possible to construct different C-planes—that is, different geometries—each of which corresponds quite well with the given P-plane. One of these might be Euclidean geometry, but there certainly can be others that fit the "facts" equally well. Each of them is reasonable and self-consistent, and it may be quite difficult to decide which is most suitable. For this reason it is misleading to say, for instance, "Einstein proved that Euclid was wrong." The conceptual structure erected by Euclid is perfectly sound (after a few modifications to satisfy modern standards of rigor). The advent of non-Euclidean geometry (long before Einstein) did not invalidate the Euclidean; it simply showed that the old geometry was not the only consistent possibility. As long as it was regarded as the unique possibility, it had to be the geometry which applied to the physical world. Modern developments in physics have shown that non-Euclidean geometry is not only self-consistent but also serves as a more adequate conceptual framework for the geometry of the "real" world. Many difficulties of understanding can be erased by the clear perception of the distinctness of the real and conceptual worlds—the P-plane and the C-plane.

We begin, then, with a P-plane, and our task is to construct an adequate C-plane. Later we shall examine some of the criteria of adequacy, but now we must ask what are the materials and the mechanics of the construction. Figure 3–1 may help to guide our thinking. The P-plane is full of "facts." The C-plane is initially empty, except for more rudimentary conceptual systems from which we draw useful auxiliary ideas.

These more rudimentary conceptual systems might include logic, set theory, and whatever else we choose to regard as already well established. For example, in constructing a theory of area or volume, we would allow ourselves to use the real number system. If, however, we were building the real number system as our new theory, we might start with only logic

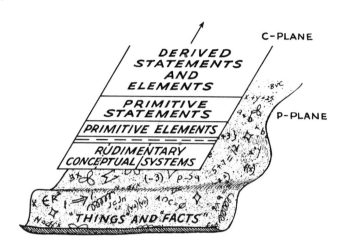

FIGURE 3–1

and set theory. If logic itself were the object of our formal study, we would still have to provide ourselves in advance with a more rudimentary, intuitive logic. In our diagram, the objects, operations, and relations in the system to be constructed are introduced above the horizontal dashed line. So far in our discussion they have not yet made their appearance.

The basic objects of our new discipline are necessarily undefined. They are "primitive elements," and it really makes no sense to demand that they be defined. They are the first on the scene. Since definitions must be in terms of concepts already introduced, the first on the scene cannot possibly be defined. For example, at the beginning of the construction of Euclidean geometry, "point," "line," and "plane" are primitive elements. Why, then, do some textbooks start out with "definitions" like "A point is that which has no dimension."? If we really took this seriously—no one does—we would have to regard truth, beauty, and honor as points. The "definition" above has no place in the logical structure of Euclidean geometry. In fact, it is never used! What function does it serve? Effectively, it says to the reader, "We are introducing a primitive concept to be called 'point,' which is intended to correspond to something in the P-plane, say a minute particle of chalk on the blackboard or a position in physical space." But it would be a serious mistake to identify "point" in the C-plane with that to which it is supposed to correspond in the P-plane and to say that they are the same.

The intended correspondence between the P-plane and the C-plane, while an important motivating factor, has no validity within the narrow confines of the C-plane. It is as though a painter made some strokes on a canvas and said, "These are the strings of a guitar." That may be the correspondence he has in mind, but we have the right to set up a different correspondence and to regard the strokes as representing prison bars, or even as entirely meaningless, uninterpreted marks. Eventually the artist may complete the picture as a coherent, consistent structure, and the interpretation he had in mind may leap out at the viewer. Nevertheless it is conceivable, and admissible, that the viewer adopt a completely different interpretation. If it was the artist's intention to make an exact representation, then we might say that he has failed if another reading of the picture is possible. Viewed as a conceptual structure in itself, however, the picture need not be regarded as a failure. In fact, the artist might have intended that there be several interpretations. The analogous situation does indeed arise in science. One example is the use of a single equation to describe the different physical processes of heat flow and gaseous diffusion. The goal achieved in this case is economy, an important consideration in scientific work.

The one point we are trying to make here is that an abstract theory stands by itself, and that there is no *logical* necessity to tie it up with anything in the physical world. The builder of the theory usually has such a connection in mind. For psychological and pedagogical reasons he may tell his readers what that connection is, and he may even use the same words in his exposition of the C-plane as occur in descriptions of the P-plane. But it is necessary to distinguish carefully between the distinct objects to which such words refer—the abstract ones in the C-plane and the concrete ones in the P-plane.

In addition to the primitive elements of our system, it is generally necessary to introduce primitive relations and operations, which are also undefined. An example of a primitive relation in geometry is "is on," as in "a point *is on* a line." As in the case of elements, these relations are usually intended to correspond to fundamental relations in the P-plane, but this intention is merely in the mind of the system builder and not a necessary part of the system. It cannot be used to deduce statements about the abstract system, even though the corresponding statements are true in the concrete system. For example, we may know, in the P-plane, that the following statement is true: "On every line there are at least two points." Suppose that we had just introduced in the C-plane the undefined terms "point" and "line" and the undefined relation "is on" between points and lines. We would not be able to *deduce* that the statement above holds in the C-plane. What we have just been saying applies equally to operations, which are after all just relations of a special kind.

How, then, can we arrive at "true" statements in the C-plane? We cannot experiment as we might in the P-plane, and we are barred from deducing results in the C-plane from facts in the P-plane. It is only from previously accepted conceptual truths that we can deduce new conceptual truths. But where do the previous ones come from? They may arise from purely logical considerations. For instance, we may assert "Every point is identical with itself" or "If a point is on a line, then it is false that the point is not on the line." But true statements of this kind are usually rather trivial and not very helpful, because their intended interpretations in the P-plane convey no information about the subject matter. We need some primitive true statements in our system to get the show on the road. They must necessarily be introduced without proof and must remain unproved. They are called "axioms" or "postulates" or "assumptions," and are fundamental to the entire system. The further statements that we prove from these fundamental ones are called *theorems*. A *proof* consists of a finite sequence of statements, each of which is either an axiom or follows from earlier statements or previous theorems by the application of a correct mode of inference. The last statement in this sequence is the theorem being proved.

Roughly speaking, theorems are like huge "if..., then ..." statements, in which the hypothesis (or antecedent) consists of all the postulates of our system and the conclusion is the usual statement of the theorem. For example, in one book there is a theorem which asserts that the sum of the angles of a triangle is 180°. Strictly, this means that if all the postulates of Euclidean geometry hold, then the sum of the angles of a triangle is 180°. This may help to explain why we can open another book and find the theorem that the sum of the angles of a triangle is less than 180°. It might be argued that both statements cannot be true simultaneously. But if we write both in the conditional form, we see that the two hypotheses are different. The postulate system assumed in the second book is different from the Euclidean one. It is no surprise, therefore, that the conclusions are different. For convenience and brevity, we usually state our postulates at the beginning of the development and agree to omit them in the statements of our theorems, although we use them in the proofs.

The older idea of an axiom as a self-evident truth has been discarded in modern mathematics. When we read "We hold these truths to be self-evident," we understand that this is a statement of faith upon which a system is to be founded. These truths are so far from being self-evident that even now there are many who do not believe them or act in accordance with them.

Once we have introduced the primitive elements, relations, and operations and stated the axioms, we are prepared to develop our conceptual system by applying the rules of correct reasoning—logic. It is as though we were given the equipment—the pieces and the board—for playing the game of chess, together with instructions which tell us what moves are legal. There are many possible directions in which the system may be developed, just as there are many possible individual chess games. It is in this multiplicity of choice that the artistry in mathematics—as in chess—comes into play. To a mind that could perceive immediately all the implications of the postulate system, all the development would appear to be trivial, as trivial as the assertion that every point is identical with itself, or as trivial as tic-tac-toe.

But the human mind is finite in its scope, and for this reason mathematics and chess will long remain as human endeavors. There are several important differences between them, however. The C-plane of chess is large but finite. Each game is finite in length (some long-suffering chess widows may doubt this) and there are only finitely many possible games. Mathematical systems usually have infinitely many possibilities, even when there are only finitely many basic objects, for the theorems are infinite in number. The P-plane of chess, if it exists at all, is vaguely and loosely connected with the C-plane, and there is no intention on the part of the players to apply in the P-plane the knowledge achieved in the C-plane. The technological advances of society bear adequate witness to the fact that mathematics is closely connected with its P-plane. Also, the mathematician is like a man who invents and plays many different games, and a good deal of the pleasure he finds is in the very process of invention. Society has accorded a greater measure of approval to the activities of the mathematician than to those of the chess player. But there is an important similarity between their activities. The mathematician proving a theorem in an axiomatic theory and the chess player playing a game both deal with intrinsically meaningless, undefined symbols in accordance with certain strict rules of procedure.

In the course of elaboration of an axiom system, it is frequently convenient to construct new elements, operations, and relations by the process of definition. For example, if distance and time have been accepted as primitives, then velocity can be defined as the ratio of distance to time. If point, line, and the relation "is on" are taken as primitives (in plane geometry), then the relation "is parallel to" between lines can be defined by "L is parallel to $M =_{df}$ there is no point P such that P is on L and P is on M." This process of definition is *logically* nothing more than convenient abbreviation; it assigns a new name to a combination of previously accepted elements and relations. But what is logically trivial may be psychologically potent. New definitions are built on old ones; new concepts are formed and suggest new theorems. Extremely complex structures arise in this way; it is doubtful that humanly created mathematics could progress very far without the condensing and idea-fixing effect of definition. Ordinary language would also be quite crude if only primitive or basic words were used.

Since we have a great deal of freedom in our choice of primitive elements, relations, operations, and statements, we must have criteria of acceptability for our system. Foremost among these is *consistency*; it must not be possible to prove within the system two propositions which contradict each other. It is often very difficult to demonstrate consistency, since that would mean showing that among the many theorems which can be proved, none of the form $p \wedge \sim p$ appears. Sometimes we content ourselves with proving *relative consistency*. This means that we assign meanings to the primitives of our system within some familiar system, thus arriving at an *interpretation* of our axiom system. If the axioms, after interpretation, become true statements in the familiar system, we say that the interpretation is a *model* of the axiom system in the familiar one. When we can construct a model, we know that a contradiction derivable in the axiom system has an interpretation, also a contradiction, which is derivable in the familiar system. Therefore if the older system is consistent, so is the new one. We may be forced to content ourselves with such a proof of relative consistency in place of absolute consistency.

Let us give a simple example of this technique. Our new system— call it S—has the following primitives: "point," "line," and the relation between points and lines, "is on." There is one axiom: "For every two distinct points P and Q, there is one and only one line L such that P is on L and Q is on L." Our familiar system—call it N—will consist of the set of positive integers. We shall construct an interpretation S' of S in N as follows. The numbers 2, 3, and 5 will serve as "points," and the numbers 6, 10, and 15 will serve as "lines." A "point" P "is on" a "line" L if and only if P divides L. Thus 2 is on 6, 3 is on 15, and 5 is not on 6. We can show, by direct examination of all possible cases, that the one axiom of S, when interpreted in S', is true. For example, if $P = 2$ and $Q = 3$, then there is one and only one line L, namely $L = 6$, such that P is on L and Q is on L. We have therefore demonstrated that S is consistent relative to N, because we have constructed S', a model of S, in N. It is amusing to diagram our miniature geometry, Figure 3–2.

Our use of the term "model," to denote an interpretation in which the axioms become true statements, is a rather technical and specialized one. In the social sciences it has become fashionable to speak of model construction. This means, in our language, that a C-plane is constructed to

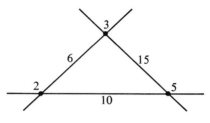

FIGURE 3–2

correspond with certain features of a given *P*-plane. The *C*-plane is then called a mathematical model of the *P*-plane. With our technical meaning of "model" we would say that the *P*-plane is a model of the *C*-plane. We shall not quarrel about terminology.

Let us mention briefly some other desirable qualities of an axiom system. It should be reasonably simple, powerful enough to produce the required results, and economical. To understand this last quality, think of the primitive elements, relations, operations, and statements (axioms) as costs or inputs. Include among the costs the effort involved in making definitions and in proving theorems. Think of the quantity, quality, and applicability of the body of theorems as revenues or outputs. Then in a very crude sense we would measure the economy or efficiency of the axiom system by the revenue/cost or output/input ratio.

Thus, suppose among the axioms there is one that can be proved easily from the others. Deleting it from the axioms and adding it to the theorems would increase output and lower input, with very little increase of effort. If an axiom cannot be derived from the others, we call it *independent*, and if every axiom is independent, we say that we have an *independent system*. One way to show that an axiom is independent of all the others is to find a model that satisfies all the others and not the given one. Fortunately, independence is not an essential requirement, for it may be very difficult to prove that a particular axiom follows from the others, and this difficulty must be counted as a heavy cost. We need to be guided by our esthetic feelings in making such judgments. There is a text of Euclidean geometry that has close to fifty postulates strewn through it, many of them easily derivable from the others. Clearly this violates mathematical good taste.

Once we have constructed an axiom system that is supposed to incorporate some or all of the essential features of a given *P*-plane, how can we use it? That depends. If we really feel that the process of abstraction (going from *P*-plane to *C*-plane) has been performed reasonably and adequately, then we can develop the body of theorems in the *C*-plane and apply them in the *P*-plane by the inverse process of interpretation. This is usually the situation when the *P*-plane lies in mathematics itself or in the more highly developed and exact sciences like physics or chemistry, and it is in these cases that the construction of mathematical models has scored its greatest successes. Even when the applicability of a particular set of axioms is subject to question, it may very well be possible to set up several different systems and to develop them to the point where crucial experiments can be devised to choose among them the most appropriate.

As we move away from the exact sciences in the direction of the behavioral sciences, it becomes more and more difficult to establish adequate mathematical models. The number of relevant independent variables tends to increase, and the investigator is forced to steer a dangerous course between the Scylla of oversimplification and the Charybdis of unwieldy complexity. The task, we hope, is not an impossible one, but it imposes heavy requirements on the researcher. He must be thoroughly familiar with the methodology of model construction. He must know enough mathematics to develop his model significantly, at least to the point where he can formulate problems for the mathematician to solve. Finally, he must know enough probability and statistics to design and carry out experiments to test his models. This is all in addition to having sufficient knowledge of his own field. It is small wonder that the social and behavioral sciences have been making greater mathematical demands on their students. Even to read the literature in a field like psychology requires considerable mathematical sophistication nowadays. An excellent exposition of some of the problems encountered in psychology appears in the introduction to Bush and Mosteller, *Stochastic Models for Learning* (Wiley, New York, 1955).

Powerful as it is, the axiomatic method is not a panacea in any science. At its best, it can produce startling results; at its worst, it can reduce to sterile axiom chopping. We have gone into it in considerable detail in this section and will illustrate it in the rest of the chapter so that the student may understand its power as well as its limitations. Armed with familiarity, he can exercise enlightened contempt where it is appropriate, or appreciate a job well done, without excessive fear or awe.

EXERCISES 3–1

1. In the following axiom system the primitive elements are "hearts" and "arrows" and a primitive relation "pierces" between the set of arrows and the set of hearts. There is one axiom:

Axiom. If *P* and *Q* are distinct hearts, there is one and only one arrow *L* such that *L* pierces *P* and *L* pierces *Q*.

Definition. The *common target* of the arrows L and $M = {}_{df}$ the set of hearts P such that L pierces P and M pierces P.

(a) Prove the following theorem:

Theorem. The common target of two distinct arrows is either empty or a singleton.

(b) Is the following necessarily true? If the set of hearts has exactly two elements, then the set of arrows is a singleton. Either prove this or give an interpretation in which the Axiom is true but this statement isn't.

2. In the following axiom system the primitives are "acts," "the null act," and "is the resultant of." There are three axioms.

Axiom 1. If x and y are acts, there is one and only one act z such that z is the resultant of x and y.

Axiom 2. If x is an act, then the resultant of x and the null act is x.

Axiom 3. If x is an act, then the resultant of the null act and x is x.

(a) Prove the following theorems.

Theorem 1. If z is an act such that for all acts x the resultant of x and z is x, then z is the null act.

Theorem 2. If z is an act such that for all acts x the resultant of x and z is x, then for all acts x the resultant of z and x is x.

(b) Is the following necessarily true? If x and y are acts, then the resultant of x and y is the same as the resultant of y and x. Either prove this or give a model in which it is false.

(c) Give several interpretations of the primitives that make the axioms true.

3–2. THE AXIOMS OF BOOLEAN ALGEBRA

We select for our P-plane the collection of all subsets of a universal set V, together with the operations of union and intersection. We denote this collection by B_1, or, if we wish to be explicit about its dependence on V, by $B_1(V)$. In Chapter 2 we derived a number of set-theoretic identities. We shall choose a few basic identities to serve as prototypes for the axioms in the C-plane. The reason for the curious numbering of the identities will be explained later. In the statements that follow, the domain of all variables will be B_1, *not* V. It is the subsets of V that are of interest here, not the elements of V.

0. $(\forall a)(\forall b)\, a \cup b \in B_1$.   0'. $(\forall a)(\forall b)\, a \cap b \in B_1$.

1. $(\forall a)(\forall b)\, a \cup b = b \cup a$.   1'. $(\forall a)(\forall b)\, a \cap b = b \cap a$.

  2. $(\forall a)(\forall b)(\forall c)\, a \cap (b \cup c) = (a \cap b) \cup (a \cap c)$.

  2'. $(\forall a)\, (\forall b)(\forall c)\, a \cup (b \cap c) = (a \cup b) \cap (a \cup c)$.

3. $(\forall a)\, a \cup \emptyset = a$.   3'. $(\forall a)\, a \cap V = a$.

  4. $(= 4')(\forall a)(\exists b)$ such that $(\alpha)\, a \cup b = V$ and $(\alpha')\, a \cap b = \emptyset$.

The student should have no difficulty in verifying these identities, if he has not already done so.

Now we strip the symbols B_1, $\cup$, $\cap$, V, $\varnothing$ of all meaning and restate these properties of B_1 as axioms. In this process of abstraction we select for the corresponding symbols B, $+$, $\cdot$, 1, 0. B will denote an arbitrary collection; 1 and 0 will be fixed elements of B. All variables will have B as domain.

BOOLEAN ALGEBRA

Primitives: B, a set.

   $+$, $\cdot$, operations,

   1, 0, elements of B.

Axioms:

Axiom 0. $(\forall a)(\forall b)\ a + b \in B$.   Axiom 0'. $(\forall a)(\forall b)\ a \cdot b \in B$.

Axiom 1. $(\forall a)(\forall b)\ a + b = b + a$.   Axiom 1'. $(\forall a)(\forall b)\ a \cdot b = b \cdot a$.

   Axiom 2. $(\forall a)(\forall b)(\forall c)\ a \cdot (b + c) = (a \cdot b) + (a \cdot c)$.

   Axiom 2'. $(\forall a)(\forall b)(\forall c)\ a + (b \cdot c) = (a + b) \cdot (a + c)$.

Axiom 3. $(\forall a)\ a + 0 = a$.   Axiom 3'. $(\forall a)\ a \cdot 1 = a$.

   Axiom 4. $(= \text{Axiom } 4')$ $(\forall a)(\exists b)$ *such that*

   $(\alpha)\ a + b = 1$ and $(\alpha')\ a \cdot b = 0$.

Essentially these axioms are due to E. V. Huntington. They are arranged in *dual* pairs $(0,0')$, $(1,1')$, $(2,2')$, $(3,3')$, $(4,4')$, with Axiom 4 self-dual. If we have any statement which is expressible in terms of the primitives, its *dual* is the statement obtained by interchanging $+$ and $\cdot$, 1 and 0. For example, the dual of

(1) $(\forall a)(\forall b)(\forall c)\ a + (b + c) = (a + b) + c$,

which is *not* one of the axioms, is

(1') $(\forall a)(\forall b)(\forall c)\ a \cdot (b \cdot c) = (a \cdot b) \cdot c$.

The dual of every axiom is also an axiom. Suppose that we can prove a statement, say Eq. (1), using only the axioms. Then the dual statement (1') can also be proved, and the steps in the proof of (1') may be taken to be the duals of the steps in the proof of (1). Thus, *the dual of every theorem is also a theorem.* This is the *principle of duality.* Our theorems will also be numbered Theorem n and Theorem n'. We shall carry out the dual proofs for a little while, but once the idea is clear, we shall merely state the dual theorem without proof.

For convenience we shall adopt the usual algebraic conventions about $+$ and $\cdot$. Thus,

$$ab = a \cdot b,$$
$$a + bc = a + (b \cdot c),$$
$$ab + cd = (a \cdot b) + (c \cdot d),$$

and so on. Actually, this amounts to stating definitions of the expressions appearing on the left. But Eq. (1) above is *not* a convention. It is a theorem. Once we have proved it, we can make the definition

$$a + b + c = a + (b + c),$$

if we wish. It will then follow that

$$a + b + c = (a + b) + c.$$

Now we shall discuss the axioms briefly. Axiom 0 asserts that + is an operation on B into B. The resultant $a + b$ is uniquely defined for all a, $b \in B$, and it is also an element of B. The operation + cannot take us out of B. The door is closed, so to speak. For this reason, we say that B *is closed with respect to* +. For example, the set of even integers is closed with respect to ordinary addition and multiplication, and the set of odd integers is closed with respect to multiplication but not with respect to addition. The set $\{1,2\}$ is not closed with respect to either. Axiom 0' asserts multiplicative closure of B. Actually, closure statements are not always included among the axioms of algebraic systems, but may be mentioned when the primitives are stated. Thus, we might have written

Primitives: B, a set.
    +, ·, operations on B into B,
    1, 0, elements of B.

In our proofs we shall not explicitly refer to the closure axioms but shall use them as blanket permissions to form sensible combinations of symbols with the operations. Thus, in the course of a proof, we might introduce $a + b(c + d)$ and use it as an element of B without going through the tedious step-by-step proof that it belongs to B (if a, b, c, d do, of course). Actually, this is relevant to the interesting question, "When is a proof?" The answer depends on the level of our audience. We can give complete proofs, dotting every i and crossing every t, or we can skip easy steps in the interest of brevity. The ultimate in brevity is

Proof: Obvious.

The term "obvious" is rather common in mathematical discourse. Because of human frailty, it is all too often translatable by "false." It is excellent to use in a proof by intimidation. Synonyms are "trivial," "clear," "easy to see," and so on. There is an apocryphal story about the mathematician Hardy. While lecturing to a class, he pointed to an equation and said, "This is obvious. . . . Hmmm, is it obvious?" After staring at the blackboard for five minutes, he ran out of the room and across the courtyard to his office, where he could be seen poring feverishly over several reference books.

A half-hour later he returned to his patient class and announced trium-phantly, "Yes, it's obvious!"

Axioms 1 and 1' assert the *commutativity* of addition and multiplication (+ and ·). This structural property is a great convenience, but there are important systems which do not possess it.

Distributivity of multiplication over addition, Axiom 2, is no surprise, but its dual, Axiom 2', may be a shock to the unsophisticated algebra student. Up to this point the axioms would become true statements in the interpretation

$$B \Rightarrow \text{the set of real numbers,}$$
$$+ \Rightarrow + \text{(ordinary addition),}$$
$$\cdot \Rightarrow \cdot \text{(ordinary multiplication),}$$
$$1 \Rightarrow 1 \text{(ordinary),}$$
$$0 \Rightarrow 0 \text{(ordinary).}$$

But addition is *not* distributive over multiplication in this interpretation. Thus, the real number system is not a model of Boolean algebra.

Axioms 3 and 3' assert that 0 and 1 are additive and multiplicative *identities*. They would become true in the above interpretation.

Axiom 4, which is self-dual, tells us that every element has at least one *complement*. In the model $B_1(V)$, the set-theoretic complement $V - A$ serves as a Boolean algebra complement. In fact, if C is a set such that

$$(\alpha) \ A \cup C = V, \qquad (\alpha') \ A \cap C = \emptyset,$$

then we can prove that $C = V - A$. For if $x \in C$, then (α') tells us that $x \notin A$; if $x \notin A$, then (α) tells us that $x \in C$. Therefore

$$C = \{x | x \in C\} = \{x | x \notin A\} = V - A.$$

It is interesting that we can prove the uniqueness of the Boolean algebra complement, purely from the axioms. It follows that we could give a proof of this result without explicit use of the membership relation $\in$. The student might amuse himself by attempting such a proof now.

There are a great many theorems which can be proved in Boolean algebra, and naturally we cannot state them all. To set ourselves a reason-able goal, we shall aim at a proof of the *associative laws*:

$$(\forall a)(\forall b)(\forall c) \ a + (b + c) = (a + b) + c,$$
$$(\forall a)(\forall b)(\forall c) \ a(bc) = (ab)c.$$

We shall also prove *de Morgan's laws*:

$$(\forall a)(\forall b) \ (a + b)' = a'b',$$
$$(\forall a)(\forall b) \ (ab)' = a' + b'.$$

The corresponding set-theoretic identities are easy to prove. It may surprise the reader that these basic and important laws are not assumed as axioms. There is nothing logically wrong with doing that, and it is done in some treatments. But why assume something when you can prove it? The effort involved is not too great, the intervening theorems are significant and interesting, and the entire sequence provides an excellent illustration of C-plane construction in its early stages.

EXERCISES 3–2

1. Let $V = \{\text{sun,moon}\}$. What are the elements of $B_1(V)$?
2. Let $V = \{\text{sun,moon,earth}\}$. What are the elements of $B_1(V)$?
3. Write out the $\cup$ and $\cap$ tables for $B_1(V)$, with $V = \{\text{May,June}\}$. Verify the two distributive laws for a few cases.
4. With V as in Problem 2, how many cases would you need to consider to verify completely the commutativity of $\cap$?

3–3. TRUTH FUNCTIONS

Before launching into the systematic development of Boolean algebra, we shall exhibit two more P-planes which will serve as models. The first of these is the algebra (or calculus) of *truth functions*. These arise naturally when we try to determine whether a given propositional function is a tautology. To solve this problem we do not need to know the precise form of the function. All we need is its truth table. Consider, for example, the truth table given as Table 3–1. We have deliberately omitted the heading in the third column. What the table gives us is a resultant value for each ordered pair, where the components of the pair may be T or F independently. The collection of such pairs may be written in terms of the set $B_0 = \{T,F\}$:

$$\{(x,y)|x \in B_0 \wedge y \in B_0\}.$$

TABLE 3–1

p	q	
T	T	T
T	F	F
F	T	T
F	F	T

But this is precisely the Cartesian product $B_0 \times B_0$. The table assigns a value to each pair in $B_0 \times B_0$, and the value is an element of B_0. The table is therefore nothing more or less than a *function* from $B_0 \times B_0$ into B_0. It is an example of a truth function, so called because the independent variables have as domains the set of truth values $\{T,F\} = B_0$, and the functional values also are elements of B_0.

For brevity, let us write B_0^n instead of $B_0 \times B_0 \times \cdots \times B_0$ (n factors). Then the general definition is: A *truth function* is any function from B_0^n into B_0. The number n may be any positive integer. The special function which always assigns the value T is denoted by 1. The one which always assigns the value F is denoted by 0. If a given propositional function A has the truth function a, then A is a tautology precisely when $a = 1$. Similarly, if we have two propositional functions A and C, with truth functions a and c, then $A \equiv C$ iff $a = c$. This is virtually the definition of tautological equivalence by equality of truth tables.

Let us denote by B_2 the collection of truth functions. We can introduce two operations in B_2, which we shall call addition, $+$, and multiplication, $\cdot$. They are defined by the schemes of Table 3–2. These schemes are to be interpreted as follows. Choose an arbitrary set of values for all the variables which appear in either a or b. Then the value of a is determined as T or F, and so is the value of b. If both are T, the scheme tells us that we assign the value T to $a + b$. If the value of a is T and the value of b is F, then we assign T to $a + b$, and so on. In this way we assign a truth value to $a + b$ corresponding to each set of values for all the variables; that is, we have defined a truth function of the combined variables and called it $a + b$. Similarly, the truth function $a \cdot b$ is defined by the second scheme.

The operations thus defined are closely related to, but not identical with, the operations $\vee$ and $\wedge$. If A and B are propositional functions with associated truth functions a and b, then the truth function associated with $A \vee B$ is $a + b$, and the one associated with $A \wedge B$ is $a \cdot b$.

TABLE 3–2

a	b	$a + b$
T	T	T
T	F	T
F	T	T
F	F	F

a	b	$a \cdot b$
T	T	T
T	F	F
F	T	F
F	F	F

We now have a set B_2 with operations $+$ and $\cdot$ on B_2 into B_2 and with two special elements 1 and 0. We assert that *this system* $(B_2, +, \cdot, 1, 0)$ *is a model of Boolean algebra*, with the obvious interpretations

$$B \Rightarrow B_2,$$
$$+ \Rightarrow +,$$
$$\cdot \Rightarrow \cdot,$$
$$1 \Rightarrow 1,$$
$$0 \Rightarrow 0.$$

The symbols on the right refer to truth functions, while those on the left are the abstract ones of Boolean algebra. We choose them the same deliberately, so that the interpretations are easily remembered. It would have been safer to use different symbols—say, by putting circles around $+$, $\cdot$, 1, 0—but there is little danger of confusion if we keep in mind the systems to which they apply. In much the same way it would be safer to use "point" in physical geometry and "punta" in axiomatic geometry. In fact, there is much more danger of confusion in the case of the two geometries than in the case of the two algebras.

The verification in B_2 of the axioms for Boolean algebra is fairly routine. Closure and commutativity are obvious (are you properly intimidated?) and distributivity follows from the tautologies

$$A \wedge (B \vee C) \equiv (A \wedge B) \vee (A \wedge C),$$
$$A \vee (B \wedge C) \equiv (A \vee B) \wedge (A \vee C),$$

by passing over to the associated truth functions. Finally, the complementation axiom is verified as follows. If a is a given truth function, define a' as that truth function which takes the value F whenever a takes the value T, and vice versa. It follows directly from the definitions that

$$(\alpha) \ a + a' = 1, \qquad (\alpha') \ a \cdot a' = 0.$$

Thus a' satisfies the required conditions for the b of Axiom 4.

To apply the algebra of truth functions to the propositional calculus we need to translate from the latter to the former. We do so by means of a dictionary, Table 3–3. The letters $p, q, r, \ldots$ are supposed to be independent propositional variables on the left. On the right we use the same letters to indicate the associated truth functions, Table 3–4. The reason for $A \to B$ being translated as $a' + b$ is that

$$A \to B \equiv \sim A \vee B.$$

Similarly, the tautology

$$A \leftrightarrow B \equiv (A \wedge B) \vee (\sim A \wedge \sim B)$$

gives us $ab + a'b'$ as the translation of $A \leftrightarrow B$.

TABLE 3-3

Propositional calculus	Algebra of truth functions
$p, q, r, \ldots, A, B, \ldots$	$p, q, r, \ldots, a, b, \ldots$
$A \vee B$	$a + b$
$A \wedge B$	ab
$\sim A$	a'
$A \rightarrow B$	$a' + b$
$A \leftrightarrow B$	$ab + a'b'$
$A \equiv B$	$a = b$
$\models A$	$a = 1$
$\models \sim A$	$a = 0$

To illustrate how Boolean algebra can be used to solve problems in the propositional calculus, consider

$$A = [(p \vee r) \wedge (q \vee s)] \wedge [(p \vee s) \wedge (r \vee q)],$$

and suppose that we wish to reduce it to a simpler equivalent form. Using Table 3–3 we see that the associated truth function is

$$a = [(p + r)(q + s)][(p + s)(r + q)].$$

Now assume that the theory of Boolean algebra has been developed to the point where the associative laws have been proved. Their interpretations must be true in B_2, so we can write

$$\begin{aligned}
a &= \{[(p + r)(q + s)](p + s)\}(r + q) \\
&= \{(p + s)[(p + r)(q + s)]\}(r + q) \\
&= \{[(p + s)(p + r)](q + s)\}(q + r) \\
&= [(p + s)(p + r)][(q + s)(q + r)].
\end{aligned}$$

We have used the associative law for multiplication and the two commutative laws. Now an application of the second distributive law, Axiom 2′, yields

$$\begin{aligned}
(p + s)(p + r) &= p + sr, \\
(q + s)(q + r) &= q + sr,
\end{aligned}$$

TABLE 3-4

p			q	
T	T		T	T
F	F		F	F

so

$$a = (p + sr)(q + sr)$$
$$= (sr + p)(sr + q)$$
$$= sr + pq$$
$$= pq + rs,$$

again by commutativity and Axiom 2'. Going back to Table 3–3 we see that we have proved the tautology

$$[(p \lor r) \land (q \lor s)] \land [(p \lor s) \land (r \lor q)] \equiv (p \land q) \lor (r \land s).$$

Another example is the proof of

$$p \land (p \to q) \equiv p \land q.$$

Translated, it reads

$$p(p' + q) = pq.$$

Now

$$p(p' + q) = pp' + pq = 0 + pq = pq,$$

which is probably simpler than a proof by truth tables.

EXERCISES 3–3

Let us consider all functions of independent variables $p, q, r, \ldots$ such that the domains of the variables are the set $K = \{0,1\}$ (the ordinary numbers 0 and 1) and such that the ranges of the functions are also in K. For example, the function f given by

$$f(p,q) = 1 - p + pq \qquad (p,q \in K)$$

is of this type, but the function g given by

$$g(p,q) = p + q \qquad (p,q \in K)$$

is not, since $g(1,1) = 2$, and $2 \notin K$. All functions of this special type we call arithmetic truth functions (a.t.f.'s). The set of them will be called Y. The function which always takes the value 1 we call 1, and that which always takes the value 0 we call 0. If a, b are elements of Y(a.t.f.'s), define $\oplus$, $\odot$ as operations on Y by

$$a \oplus b = a + b - ab,$$
$$a \odot b = ab,$$

where the operations on the right are those of ordinary arithmetic. Thus Y becomes an algebraic system.

1. Prove that Y is a model of Boolean algebra, with the interpretations

$$B \Rightarrow Y,$$
$$+ \Rightarrow \oplus,$$
$$\cdot \Rightarrow \odot,$$
$$1 \Rightarrow 1,$$
$$0 \Rightarrow 0.$$

2. Prove that Y is a model of Boolean algebra, with the interpretations

$$B \Rightarrow Y,$$
$$+ \Rightarrow \odot,$$
$$\cdot \Rightarrow \oplus,$$
$$1 \Rightarrow 0,$$
$$0 \Rightarrow 1.$$

3. Show that problems of tautology in the propositional calculus can be translated into problems in Y [using interpretation (1)] by means of Table 3–5.

4. Prove that in Y, for all a, b, ...,
   (a) $a \oplus a = a$.
   (b) $a \odot a = a$.
   (c) $a \oplus 1 = 1$.
   (d) $a \odot 0 = 0$.
   (e) $a \oplus (b \oplus c) = (a \oplus b) \oplus c$.
   (f) $a \odot (b \odot c) = (a \odot b) \odot c$.
   (g) $1 - (a \oplus b) = (1 - a) \odot (1 - b)$.
   (h) $1 - (a \odot b) = (1 - a) \oplus (1 - b)$.
   (i) $a \odot (1 - a + ab) = a \odot b$.

5. Set up a "reasonable" one-to-one correspondence between $(B_2, +, \cdot, 1, 0)$ and $(Y, \oplus, \odot, 1, 0)$. State explicitly why your correspondence is "reasonable."

TABLE 3–5

Propositional calculus	Arithmetic truth functions
$p, q, r, \ldots, A, B, C, \ldots$	$p, q, r, \ldots, a, b, c, \ldots$
$A \vee B$	$a \oplus b$
$A \wedge B$	$a \odot b$
$\sim A$	$1 - a$
$A \rightarrow B$	$1 - a + ab$
$A \leftrightarrow B$	$1 - a - b + 2ab$
$A \equiv B$	$a = b$
$\models A$	$a = 1$

6. Let Y_1 be the subset of Y consisting of 0, 1, f, g, where

$$f(p) = p \qquad (p \in K),$$
$$g(p) = 1 - p \qquad (p \in K).$$

Prove that $(Y_1, \oplus, \odot, 1, 0)$ is a model of $(B, +, \cdot, 1, 0)$.

7. Let Y_2 be any subset of Y containing exactly three elements, including 0 and 1. Prove that $(Y_2, \oplus, \odot, 1, 0)$ is not a model of $(B, +, \cdot, 1, 0)$.

3–4. SWITCHING CIRCUITS

An important and rather surprising application of Boolean algebra is in the analysis and design of electrical switching circuits. The well-known contemporary applied mathematician Claude Shannon as a young man showed that such circuits can be studied algebraically. The strength of this discovery is that it allows a circuit designer to remove unnecessary costly relays or switches with a minimum of laboratory work or diagram chasing. When circuits are produced in the tens of thousands, an extra switch in each one can be very expensive. Not all the problems in this field have been solved. The switching department at the Bell Telephone Laboratories has spent and will continue to spend hundreds of thousands of dollars on techniques for simplifying the design of circuits. Other companies in the communications and computer field are also deeply interested in these problems of logical design.

Let us imagine that we have a source of electrical energy connecting two terminals T_1 and T_2, and a conducting wire joining them, Figure 3–3. Then a current will flow in this circuit, and we shall say that it is "on." If we interrupt the circuit somewhere along the wire and insert a two-way switch, denoted by p, then in one position of p the circuit is on and in the other it is off:

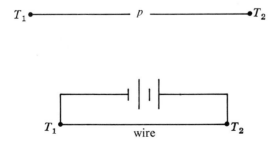

FIGURE 3–3

TABLE 3–6	
(switch)p	(circuit)p
on	on
off	off

TABLE 3–7	
(switch)p	(circuit)$\sim p$
on	off
off	on

In this figure we have omitted the power source, which will always be assumed present. This simple circuit will also be denoted by p. Thus we have the trivial table, Table 3–6.

It is possible to connect two physically different switches in the same circuit so that they are on or off simultaneously. In this case we shall use the same symbol for both. Similarly, it is possible to connect two switches so that each one is on when the other is off. Then we shall call one p, say, and the other $\sim p$. Thus, the circuit

$$T_1' \bullet \!\!-\!\!-\!\!-\!\!-\!\!-\!\!-\!\!-\!\!-\!\!-\!\!-\!\!\sim p \!-\!\!-\!\!-\!\!-\!\!-\!\!-\!\!-\!\!-\!\!-\!\!-\!\!\bullet T_2'$$

would have the table given as Table 3–7. We are not interested in hardware here, but this might be accomplished by having a spring contact which, in normal position, closes the $T_1'-T_2'$ circuit, but which is pulled out of position when the T_1-T_2 circuit p is on, thus breaking contact. Undoubtedly there are better ways of accomplishing the same result.

Given two circuits A and B, we can form a new circuit $A \wedge B$ by connecting them in *series*, Figure 3–4. This circuit will be on precisely when both A and B are on, in accordance with Table 3–8.

Given two circuits A and B, we can form the new circuit $A \vee B$ by connecting them in *parallel*, Figure 3–5. If either A or B is on, then current will flow, and $A \vee B$ will be on. The table will be the one given as Table 3–9.

TABLE 3–8		
A	B	$A \wedge B$
on	on	on
on	off	off
off	on	off
off	off	off

TABLE 3–9		
A	B	$A \vee B$
on	on	on
on	off	on
off	on	on
off	off	off

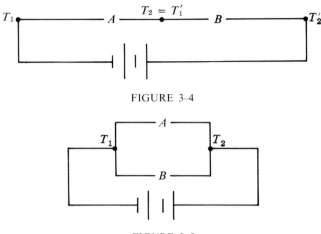

FIGURE 3–4

FIGURE 3–5

Starting with a collection of switches $p, q, r, \ldots$, we can now form a large number of complicated circuits by using the *opposite* switches $\sim p$, $\sim q$, $\sim r, \ldots$, together with parallel and series connections.

Every circuit will have associated with it a *circuit function* which gives the condition of the circuit as a function of the conditions of the switches. For example, the circuit A, Figure 3–6, will have the circuit function given by Table 3–10.

For design purposes we are interested only in the circuit function. Two circuits A and B are *equivalent* iff they have the same circuit function, in which case we write $A \equiv B$. For example, the circuit B given by Figure 3–7 is equivalent to the above circuit A (Figure 3–6). The same purpose is being accomplished with four fewer physical switches.

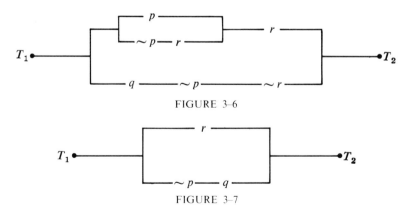

FIGURE 3–6

FIGURE 3–7

TABLE 3-10

p	q	r	A
on	on	on	on
on	on	off	off
on	off	on	on
on	off	off	off
off	on	on	on
off	on	off	on
off	off	on	on
off	off	off	off

The analogy between circuits and propositional functions should be apparent to the student. We have chosen our notation so as to make this clear. In fact, we have something much stronger than an analogy. We have an almost perfect correspondence. We say "almost" because we have not shown how to construct an opposite to any given circuit, whereas any propositional function A has a negation $\sim A$. We could have postulated an opposite for any circuit just as we did for switches, but it really was not necessary. Given any circuit A, we can *construct* a circuit B which is on when A is off and conversely. Indeed, given any circuit function whatsoever, we can design a circuit which responds in accordance with it. For example, if the given function is as in Table 3–11, we would construct a circuit with three branches successively in parallel, one for each row of the table in which C is "on." In each branch we use p or $\sim p$ according as p is "on" or "off" in that row, and similarly for q. Thus, for the first row we use

$$T_1 \bullet\!\!-\!\!-\!\!-\!\!-\!\!- p -\!\!-\!\!-\!\!- q -\!\!-\!\!-\!\!-\!\!-\bullet T_2$$

for the third,

$$T_1 \bullet\!\!-\!\!-\!\!-\!\!-\!\!- \sim p -\!\!-\!\!-\!\!- q -\!\!-\!\!-\!\!-\!\!-\bullet T_2$$

and for the fourth,

$$T_1 \bullet\!\!-\!\!-\!\!-\!\!-\!\!- \sim p -\!\!-\!\!-\!\!- \sim q -\!\!-\!\!-\!\!-\!\!-\bullet T_2$$

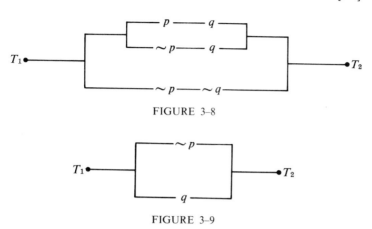

FIGURE 3-8

FIGURE 3-9

Putting them together in parallel, we get the required circuit, Figure 3–8. There happens to be a simpler one that works, Figure 3–9. The technique illustrated above applies equally well to any circuit function of $p, q, r, \ldots$

To see how this applies to finding a circuit opposite to a given one, consider a table opposite to that of C above, Table 3–12. There is only one row in which opp. C is on, the second. The required circuit is therefore

$$T_1 \bullet \!\!\!\!\!\!\!\!\!\!\!\!\!\!\!\!\!\! p \!\!\!\!\!\!\!\!\!\!\!\! \sim q \!\!\!\!\!\!\!\!\!\!\!\! \bullet T_2$$

As remarked above, it is the collection of circuit functions that interests us. For every circuit there is a unique circuit function; for every circuit function there are many associated circuits. (We showed above that there is at least one, and once we have one we can construct many.) We can make the collection B_3 of circuit functions into an algebra by the following definitions. If a, b are elements of B_3 corresponding to circuits A, B, then

TABLE 3–11

p	q	C
on	on	on
on	off	off
off	on	on
off	off	on

TABLE 3–12

p	q	Opp. C
on	on	off
on	off	on
off	on	off
off	off	off

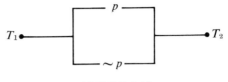

FIGURE 3–10

$$a \vee b =_{df} \text{ the circuit function for } A \vee B,$$
$$a \wedge b =_{df} \text{ the circuit function for } A \wedge B,$$
$$1 =_{df} \text{ the "always-on" circuit function,}$$
$$0 =_{df} \text{ the "always-off" circuit function.}$$

The circuit of Figure 3–10 has the function 1. A circuit for the function 0 is

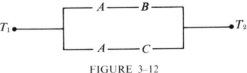

We assert that this system B_3 is a model of Boolean algebra, with the interpretations

$$B \Rightarrow B_3,$$
$$+ \Rightarrow \vee,$$
$$\cdot \Rightarrow \wedge,$$
$$1 \Rightarrow 1,$$
$$0 \Rightarrow 0.$$

We leave the verification of our assertion to the student. The distributive law can be proved, for example, by considering the circuit of Figure 3–11, which has the circuit function $a \wedge (b \vee c)$, and the circuit of Figure 3–12, which has the circuit function $(a \wedge b) \vee (a \wedge c)$. One then proves that these circuits are equivalent. To verify Axiom 4, we take as a complement of a the opposite function $\sim a$, which is on when a is off and conversely.

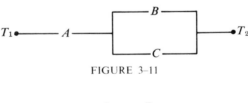

FIGURE 3–11

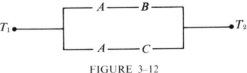

FIGURE 3–12

TABLE 3–13

Circuits	Circuit functions B_3
$p, q, r, \ldots, A, B, \ldots$	$p, q, r, \ldots, a, b, \ldots$
$A \vee B$ (parallel)	$a \vee b$
$A \wedge B$ (series)	$a \wedge b$
$A \equiv B$	$a = b$
A is always on	$a = 1$
A is always off	$a = 0$
opp. A	$\sim a$

There is a dictionary (Table 3–13) going from the collection of circuits to the algebra B_3, just as there was one from the propositional calculus to the algebra of truth functions.

Given a problem in circuit theory, we translate it into a problem in B_3. Then, since B_3 is a model of Boolean algebra, we can apply all the theorems of B. Finally, if we can solve the translated problem, we translate the solution back to circuit theory.

As an illustration, consider the circuit of Figure 3–13, with the purpose of simplification. Translated to B_3, we have the circuit function

$(*)$ $\qquad \{[(p \wedge q) \vee (r \wedge p)] \wedge (s \vee q)\} \vee \{(q \vee r) \wedge [(s \wedge r) \vee (q \wedge s)]\}.$

In the following sequence we shall be deliberately laborious and explicit about the steps, using only the axioms of B, the associative laws, which are theorems, and the *idempotent law* $(\forall s)\ ss = s$, which is Theorem 5. The element $(*)$ corresponds, in B, to

$(pq + rp)(s + q) + (q + r)(sr + qs)$
$= (pq + pr)(s + q) + (q + r)(sq + sr)$ (comm.)
$= [p(q + r)](q + s) + (q + r)[s(q + r)]$ (comm. and distr.)
$= p[(q + r)(q + s)] + [(q + r)s](q + r)$ (assoc.)
$= p(q + rs) + [s(q + r)](q + r)$ (distr. and comm.)
$= p(q + rs) + s[(q + r)(q + r)]$ (assoc.)
$= p(q + rs) + s(q + r)$ (idem.)
$= p(q + rs) + (sq + sr)$ (distr.)
$= p(q + rs) + (sq + (ss)r)$ (idem.)
$= p(q + rs) + (sq + s(sr))$ (assoc.)
$= p(q + rs) + (sq + s(rs))$ (comm.)
$= p(q + rs) + s(q + rs)$ (distr.)
$= (p + s)(q + rs).$ (distr.)

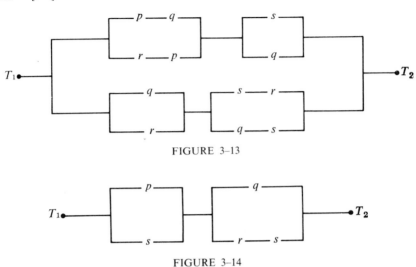

FIGURE 3–13

FIGURE 3–14

Translating our result to B_3, we get

$$(p \lor s) \land (q \lor (r \land s)),$$

which is the function for the circuit of Figure 3–14.

Naturally, as we become more familiar with the laws of Boolean algebra, we can shorten the sequence by skipping "obvious" steps. Also, we could have avoided the need to translate from the $\land, \lor$ notation to the $+, \cdot$ notation

TABLE 3–14

p	q	r	c
yes	yes	yes	yes
yes	yes	no	yes
yes	no	yes	yes
yes	no	no	no
no	yes	yes	yes
no	yes	no	no
no	no	yes	no
no	no	no	no

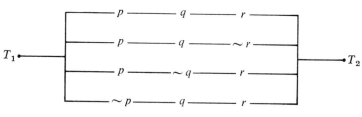

FIGURE 3–15

and back again, by adopting the $+$, $\cdot$ notation in the first place. These short-cuts are desirable and permissible as soon as the danger of confusion is past.

It is possible to design voting circuits for a given number of people, with given conditions. Each person has a switch of his own, which he presses or not according as his vote is "yes" or "no," and a light is sup-posed to go on iff the outcome is favorable to the question. For instance, a majority-rule circuit for three voters would have the circuit function of Table 3–14. One formula for c, obtained by our standard method, is

$$(p \wedge q \wedge r) \vee (p \wedge q \wedge \sim r) \vee (p \wedge \sim q \wedge r) \vee (\sim p \wedge q \wedge r).$$

(We have used associativity to give unambiguous meaning to $p \wedge q \wedge r$, and so on.)

A possible circuit is shown in Figure 3–15. The corresponding formula in B is

$$
\begin{aligned}
pqr &+ pqr' + pq'r + p'qr \\
&= (pqr + pqr') + (pqr + pq'r) + (pqr + p'qr) \\
&= pq(r + r') + p(q + q')r + (p + p')qr \\
&= pq + pr + qr \\
&= p(q + r) + qr.
\end{aligned}
$$

Thus, a simpler circuit is the one shown in Figure 3–16. In this derivation we have used the existence of a unique complement, associativity, and the additive idempotent law $(\forall a)\ a + a = a$.

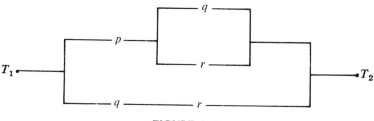

FIGURE 3–16

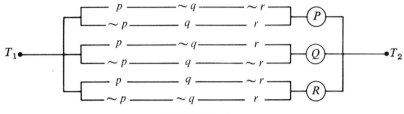

FIGURE 3-17

In the preceding discussion the outcome has always been "on" or "off," "yes" or "no." In many cases more than two outcomes will be required. Consider, for example, the game called "odd man wins," played by three persons. Each makes a "yes" or "no" choice by pressing or not pressing his own switch. There are four possible outcomes: One player wins if his choice is different from the other two, or no one wins. One way to represent the outcomes is to have three lights P, Q, and R which go on whenever the corresponding player wins. The circuit would be as shown in Figure 3-17.

We know, however, that we also get four possible outcomes if two lights are on or off independently. Let us therefore have two lights A and B, and set up the code given in Table 3-15. Now we see that A is on iff $P \vee R$, and B is on iff $Q \vee R$. But (using the Boolean algebra notation)

$$P = pq'r' + p'qr,$$
$$Q = pq'r + p'qr',$$
$$R = pqr' + p'q'r.$$

TABLE 3-15

A	B	Winner
on	off	P
off	on	Q
on	on	R
off	off	none

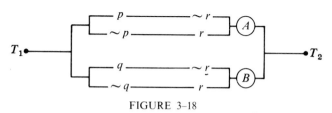

FIGURE 3-18

Hence

$$A = P + R$$
$$= pq'r' + p'qr + pqr' + p'q'r$$
$$= pr'(q' + q) + p'r(q + q')$$
$$= pr' + p'r.$$

Similarly,

$$B = Q + R$$
$$= pq'r + p'qr' + pqr' + p'q'r$$
$$= (p + p')q'r + (p' + p)qr'$$
$$= q'r + qr'.$$

Hence our circuit may be simplified to the one given in Figure 3–18.

If we prefer not to burden our memory with a code, we could let A and B represent yellow and blue (wideband) filters interposed between a source of white light and an observer. Then the outcomes are

Yellow: P wins,
Blue: Q wins,
Green: R wins,
White: no one wins.

EXERCISES 3–4

(The student may use any of the theorems proved in Section 3-5.)

1. Verify that B_3 is a model of Boolean algebra.

2. Design a circuit which is on iff switches p and q have the same setting. (Such a circuit could be used to control a hall light from two different switches.)

3. Simplify the circuit of Figure 3–19.

4. Simplify the circuit of Figure 3–20.

5. Design a circuit corresponding to

$$\sim[(p \wedge \sim q) \vee (q \wedge \sim r)] \wedge (p \wedge q).$$

Use as few (physical) switches as possible.

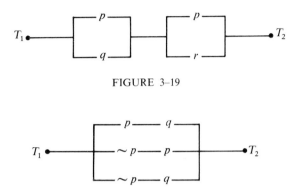

FIGURE 3–19

FIGURE 3–20

6. Assign a reasonable circuit meaning to $A \rightarrow B$; also to $A \leftrightarrow B$.

7. Design a circuit for majority rule in a committee of four, except that the chairman's vote prevails in case of a tie. (He votes in all cases.)

8. In a committee of five, the chairman votes only in case of a tie. Design a decision-making circuit. Compare this situation with majority rule, the chairman always voting.

9. Show that the opposite of a series circuit is equivalent to the parallel circuit of the opposites:

$$\sim(P \wedge Q \wedge R \wedge \cdots) \equiv \sim P \vee \sim Q \vee \sim R \vee \cdots$$

What about the opposite of a parallel circuit?

10. How many distinct, inequivalent circuits can be designed using one switch p, which may be duplicated or negated? Two switches p, q? Three switches p, q, r?

11. Discuss the relationships among B, B_2, B_3.

12. Design a circuit to control a hall light from three different switches.

13. How many lights would you use for a circuit with 30 possible outcomes? How many outcomes would n lights allow?

3–5. DEVELOPMENT OF BOOLEAN ALGEBRA

In Section 3–2 we introduced the axiom system B of Boolean algebra and showed that $B_1(V)$, the collection of subsets of a given universal set V, is a model of B. In Sections 3–3 and 3–4 we presented two other models: B_2, the algebra of truth functions, and B_3, the algebra of circuit functions. As we develop the theorems of Boolean algebra, the student should keep these models in mind and interpret the theorems in each one. In many cases the interpretation is easier to prove in the model than in B, but our treatment has the advantage of presenting in logical sequence a previously unorganized collection of results. Our goals in this section will be the proofs of the associative laws and the de Morgan laws, which in B_1 take the form

$$(\forall a)(\forall b)(\forall c)\, a \cup (b \cup c) = (a \cup b) \cup c,$$
$$(\forall a)(\forall b)(\forall c)\, a \cap (b \cap c) = (a \cap b) \cap c,$$
$$(\forall a)(\forall b)\, (a \cup b)' = a' \cap b',$$
$$(\forall a)(\forall b)\, (a \cap b)' = a' \cup b'.$$

For convenience of reference, the student should write out the axioms and have them before him. He should also read again the remarks on duality in Section 3–2.

Now to work!

Our first theorem is preparatory to the definition of *the* complement of any given element. By *a* complement of an element, say c, we mean any element b such that

$$\text{(a)} \quad c + b = 1, \qquad \text{(a')} \quad cb = 0.$$

Axiom 4 is an *existence* assertion for a complement. Theorem 1 is a *uniqueness* assertion, saying that there is at most one complement of any given element. Taken together, they assert that there is exactly one complement, *the* complement. We then have the right to assign a symbol c' to it.

Theorem 3–1. For each a, if b_1 and b_2 are elements satisfying

$$\text{(a)} \quad a + b_1 = 1, \qquad \text{(a')} \quad ab_1 = 0,$$
$$\text{(b)} \quad a + b_2 = 1, \qquad \text{(b')} \quad ab_2 = 0,$$

then $b_1 = b_2$.

Proof:

(1)　　　$b_1 = b_1 \cdot 1$　　　　　(Axiom 3'),
(2)　　　$b_1 \cdot 1 = b_1(a + b_2)$　　　(Hypothesis b),
(3) $b_1(a + b_2) = b_1 a + b_1 b_2$　　(Axiom 2),
(4)　　　$b_1 a = ab_1$　　　　(Axiom 1'),
(5)　　　$ab_1 = 0$　　　　　(Hypothesis a'),
(6)　　$\therefore\ b_1 = 0 + b_1 b_2$　　(steps 1, 2, 3, 4, 5),

(7) $0 + b_1b_2 = b_1b_2 + 0$ (Axiom 1),
(8) $b_1b_2 + 0 = b_1b_2$ (Axiom 3),
(9) $\therefore \quad b_1 = b_1b_2$ (steps 6, 7, 8).

Since the hypotheses are symmetric in b_1 and b_2, we can go through steps (1) to (9) with b_1 and b_2 interchanged. Therefore

(10) $b_2 = b_2b_1$ (symmetry in b_1, b_2),
(11) $b_2b_1 = b_1b_2$ (Axiom 1'),
(12) $\therefore \quad b_1 = b_2$ (steps 9, 10, 11).

This completes the detailed proof of uniqueness. An abbreviated proof might be:

$$b_1 = b_1 \cdot 1 = b_1(a + b_2) = b_1a + b_1b_2 = ab_1 + b_1b_2$$
$$= 0 + b_1b_2 = b_1b_2 + 0 = b_1b_2.$$

Similarly,

$$b_2 = b_2b_1 = b_1b_2 = b_1.$$

Even shorter proofs are available, depending on what is "obvious" to the audience.

Definition 3-1. If a is any element, then a', the complement of a, is the unique element satisfying

(*) $(a + a' = 1) \wedge (aa' = 0)$.

Every proposition involving the operation of complementation can be written without the symbol "'" by means of the definition. To dualize such a proposition, we observe that a' will be changed into itself, because (*) is self-dual. Thus, the rule remains as before: Interchange + and ·, 1 and 0.

EXAMPLE 3-1.   Dualize $(ab' = 0) \rightarrow (a = ab)$. [$a$ and b are any fixed elements.]

Solution: The given statement is equivalent to

$$(\forall c) (c = b' \wedge ac = 0) \rightarrow a = ab.$$

This in turn is equivalent to

$$(\forall c) (c + b = 1 \wedge cb = 0 \wedge ac = 0) \rightarrow (a = ab),$$

with "'" eliminated. The dual of this last statement is

$$(\forall c) (cb = 0 \wedge c + b = 1 \wedge a + c = 1) \rightarrow (a = a + b).$$

(Note the interchange of $cb = 0$ and $c + b = 1$.) This is equivalent to

$$(\forall c)\,(c = b' \wedge a + c = 1) \rightarrow (a = a + b),$$

and finally to

$$(a + b' = 1) \rightarrow (a = a + b).$$

This illustrates the extended rule given above.

EXERCISES 3–5

Dualize:

1. Theorem 3–1.
2. $(ab)' = a' + b'$.
3. $(a')' = a$.
4. $a + a = a$.
5. $0' = 1$.
6. $a \cdot 0' = a$.
7. $a + 1 = 1$.
8. $a + (b + c) = (a + b) + c$.
9. $(ab' = 0) \wedge (a'b = 0) \rightarrow (a = b)$.
10. $(a + b)' = a'b'$.

(Suitably universally quantified, these are all true.)

Theorem 3–2. $(\forall a)\,(a')' = a$.

Proof: Let $c = (a')'$. By Definition 3–1, c is the unique solution of

(1) $$a' + c = 1 \wedge a'c = 0.$$

Also by definition,

$$a + a' = 1 \wedge aa' = 0.$$

By commutativity (Axiom 1, Axiom 1'),

$$a' + a = 1 \wedge a'a = 0.$$

Therefore a satisfies the conditions imposed on c in Eq. (1). By Theorem 3–1, $a = c = (a')'$.

Theorem 3–3. $0' = 1$.

Proof: $0 + 1 = 1 + 0 = 1$, and $0 \cdot 1 = 0$. By Definition 3–1 (with $a = 0$), $0' = 1$.

Theorem 3–3′. $1′ = 0$.
Proof #1: $1′ = (0′)′$ (by Theorem 3–3)
        $= 0$ (by Theorem 3–2).
Proof #2: $1 + 0 = 1$, and $1 \cdot 0 = 0 \cdot 1 = 0$. By Definition 3–1 (with $a = 1$), $1′ = 0$.
Proof #3: Theorem 3–3 and duality.

Our next theorem gives us a useful tool for proving that two elements are equal.

Theorem 3–4. $(\forall a)(\forall b) (ab′ = 0) \wedge (a′b = 0) \rightarrow (a = b)$.
Proof: Let a and b satisfy $ab′ = 0$ and $a′b = 0$. Then

$$a = a \cdot 1 = a(b + b′) = ab + ab′ = ab + 0 = ab,$$
$$b = b \cdot 1 = b(a + a′) = ba + ba′ = ab + a′b = ab + 0 = ab,$$
$$\therefore \quad a = b.$$

Theorem 3–4′. $(\forall a)(\forall b) (a + b′ = 1) \wedge (a′ + b = 1) \rightarrow (a = b)$.
Proof #1: Theorem 3–4 and duality.
Proof #2: Let a and b satisfy $a + b′ = 1$ and $a′ + b = 1$. Then

$$a = a + 0 = a + bb′ = (a + b)(a + b′) = (a + b) \cdot 1 = a + b,$$
$$b = b + 0 = b + aa′ = (b + a)(b + a′)$$
$$= (a + b)(a′ + b) = (a + b) \cdot 1 = a + b,$$
$$\therefore \quad a = b.$$

Note that every step is the dual of the corresponding step in the proof of Theorem 3–4.

Theorem 3–5. $(\forall a) aa = a$.
Proof: $a = a \cdot 1 = a(a + a′) = aa + aa′ = aa + 0 = aa$.

Theorem 3–5′. $(\forall a) a + a = a$.
Proof: Left to student.

Theorem 3–6. $(\forall a) a \cdot 0 = 0$.
Proof: $a \cdot 0 = a \cdot 0 + 0 = a \cdot 0 + aa′ = a(0 + a′) = a(a′ + 0)$
        $= aa′ = 0$.

Theorem 3–6′. $(\forall a) a + 1 = 1$.
Proof: Left to student.

Theorem 3–7. $(\forall a)(\forall b) (a + b = 0) \rightarrow (a = 0) \wedge (b = 0)$.

Proof: Suppose that $a + b = 0$. Then

$$ab' = ab' + 0 = ab' + bb' = b'a + b'b$$
$$= b'(a + b) = b' \cdot 0 = 0.$$

By commutativity and symmetry, $ba' = 0$, so $a'b = 0$.

$$\therefore \quad a = b \text{ (by Theorem 3–4)}.$$
$$\therefore \quad a + a = 0.$$
$$\therefore \quad a = 0 \text{ (by Theorem 3–5')}.$$
$$\therefore \quad b = 0.$$

Theorem 3–7'. $(\forall b)(\forall b)\,(ab = 1) \to (a = 1) \wedge (b = 1)$.
Proof: Left to student.

Theorem 3–8. $(\forall a)(\forall b)(\forall c)\,a + (b + c) = (a + b) + c$.
Proof: Let $x = a + (b + c)$, $y = (a + b) + c$. Then

$$0 = yy' = y'y = y'[(a + b) + c] = y'(a + b) + y'c.$$
$$\therefore \quad (y'(a + b) = 0) \wedge (y'c = 0) \qquad \text{(by Theorem 3–7)}.$$
$$\therefore \quad (y'a + y'b = 0) \wedge (y'c = 0).$$
$$\therefore \quad (y'a = 0) \wedge (y'b = 0) \wedge (y'c = 0) \qquad \text{(Why?)}$$

Now

$$xy' = y'x = y'[a + (b + c)] = y'a + y'(b + c)$$
$$= 0 + y'(b + c) = y'(b + c) = y'b + y'c = 0.$$

Similarly, the student may prove that

$$(x'a = 0) \wedge (x'b = 0) \wedge (x'c = 0),$$
$$x'y = 0.$$
$$\therefore \quad (xy' = 0) \wedge (x'y = 0).$$
$$\therefore \quad x = y \qquad \text{(by Theorem 3–4)}.$$
$$\therefore \quad a + (b + c) = (a + b) + c.$$

Theorem 3–8'. $(\forall a)(\forall b)(\forall c)\,a(bc) = (ab)c$.
Proof: Left to student.

Once we have proved the associative laws, Theorems 3–8 and 3–8', we may define

$$a + b + c =_{df} a + (b + c),$$
$$abc =_{df} a(bc),$$

and we know then that

$$a + b + c = (a + b) + c,$$
$$abc = (ab)c.$$

Similarly, we may define

$$a + b + c + d =_{df} a + (b + c + d),$$
$$abcd =_{df} a(bcd),$$

and so on.

EXERCISE 3–6

Prove that $a + b + c + d = (a + b + c) + d$; also that $abcd = (ad)(bc)$.

We are now in a position to prove *de Morgan's laws*:

Theorem 3–9. $(\forall a)(\forall b)\,(a + b)' = a'b'.$

Theorem 3–9'. $(\forall a)(\forall b)\,(ab)' = a' + b'.$

Proof of Theorem 3–9: Let $c = a'b'.$ Then

$$(a + b) + c = (a + b) + a'b'$$

$$= [(a + b) + a'][(a + b) + b'] \quad \text{(by Axiom 2')}$$

$$= [(b + a) + a'][(a + b) + b']$$

$$= [b + (a + a')][a + (b + b')] \quad \text{(by Theorem 3–8)}$$

$$= (b + 1)(a + 1)$$

$$= 1 \cdot 1 \quad \text{(by Theorem 3–6')}$$

$$= 1.$$

Also,

$$(a + b)c = c(a + b) = ca + cb$$

$$= (a'b')a + (a'b')b$$

$$= b'(aa') + a'(bb') \quad \text{(Why?)}$$

$$= b' \cdot 0 + a' \cdot 0$$

$$= 0 + 0 \quad \text{(Why?)}$$

$$= 0.$$

Thus c satisfies the two conditions that are necessary and sufficient for it to be the complement of $(a + b)$. Therefore

$$a'b' = c = (a + b)'.$$

Proof of Theorem 3–9': Theorem 3–9 and duality. However, there is an amusing alternate proof using Theorems 3–9 and 3–2. In Theorem 3–9 replace a by a' and b by b' throughout. This may be done, since Theorem 3–9 holds for any pair of elements, including a', b'. Thus

$$(a' + b')' = (a')'(b')'$$

$$= ab \qquad \text{(by Theorem 3–2)}.$$

$$\therefore \quad (ab)' = [(a' + b')']' = a' + b'.$$

EXAMPLE 3–2.   Prove that $(a + bc)' = a'(b' + c')$.
Solution: $(a + bc)' = a'(bc)'$ (by Theorem 3–9)
$\qquad\qquad\quad = a'(b' + c')$ (by Theorem 3–9').

EXERCISES 3–7

(All the theorems in the text may be used.)
1. Prove that $(ab' + c'd')' = (a' + b)(c + d)$.
2. Show that

$$\sim[(p \wedge \sim q) \vee (\sim r \wedge \sim s)] \leftrightarrow (\sim p \vee q) \wedge (r \vee s)$$

is a tautology.
3. Show that the circuits of Figure 3–21 are opposites.
4. Design a circuit opposite to that of Figure 3–22.
5. Prove $(\forall a)(\forall b)(ab = a + b) \rightarrow (a = b)$. [*Hint:* Multiply the given equation first by a', then by b'.]
6. Two circuits yield equivalent circuits when connected in series or in parallel. Prove that the two given circuits are equivalent.

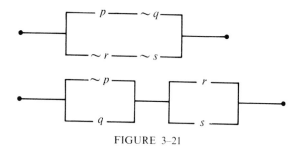

FIGURE 3–21

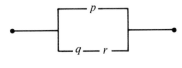

FIGURE 3–22

7. Consider a system containing two elements N and A, with two operations $*$ and Δ, defined by

$$N * N = N, \qquad N \, \Delta \, N = N,$$
$$N * A = N, \qquad N \, \Delta \, A = A,$$
$$A * N = N, \qquad A \, \Delta \, N = A,$$
$$A * A = A, \qquad A \, \Delta \, A = A.$$

Show that this system is a model of Boolean algebra, with the interpretation

$$B \Rightarrow \{N,A\},$$
$$+ \Rightarrow \Delta,$$
$$\cdot \Rightarrow *,$$
$$0 \Rightarrow N,$$
$$1 \Rightarrow A.$$

8. Consider the system containing just the two circuit functions 0 and 1. Write down all possible equations like $0 \wedge 0 = 0$, $0 \vee 1 = 1$, and compare with the system in Problem 7. Discuss.

9. In Problem 7, try the following interpretation:

$$B \Rightarrow \{N,A\},$$
$$+ \Rightarrow *,$$
$$\cdot \Rightarrow \Delta,$$
$$0 \Rightarrow N,$$
$$1 \Rightarrow A.$$

Is the system a model with this interpretation? Is the interpretation given in Problem 7 the only one that works?

10. Suppose that in the circuit function interpretation of Boolean algebra, we restrict ourselves to the set of circuit functions which depend on p, q, r only. Do we still get a (model of) Boolean algebra? Give reasons.

11. Give arguments for and against the statement "All Boolean algebras look alike."

12. Let z be an element of a Boolean algebra such that

$$(\forall a)\, a + z = a.$$

Prove that $z = 0$. Dualize.

13. Suppose that C is a Boolean algebra in which $0 = 1$. Prove that $C = \{0\}$.

14. Construct, if possible, Boolean algebras with (a) three elements, (b) four elements, and (c) five elements.

15. In Boolean algebra, define $\leq$ by

$$(\forall a)(\forall b)\, [a \leq b \leftrightarrow_{df} ab = a].$$

Prove:

(a) $(\forall a)(\forall b)(\forall c)\, a \leq b \wedge b \leq c \rightarrow a \leq c.$
(b) $(\forall a)(\forall b)\, a \leq b \wedge b \leq a \rightarrow a = b.$
(c) $(\forall a)(\forall b)(\forall c)\, a \leq b \wedge a \leq c \rightarrow a \leq bc.$
(d) $(\forall a)(\forall b)(\forall c)\, b \leq a \wedge c \leq a \rightarrow b + c \leq a.$
(e) $(\forall a)(\forall b)\, a \leq b \rightarrow b' \leq a'.$
(f) $(\forall a)(\forall b)(\forall c)\, a \leq b \rightarrow ca \leq cb.$
(g) $(\forall a)(\forall b)(\forall c)\, a \leq b \rightarrow c + a \leq c + b.$
(h) $(\forall a)\, 0 \leq a \wedge a \leq 1.$

16. In Boolean algebra define Δ by

$$(\forall a)(\forall b)\, a \,\Delta\, b =_{df} ab' + a'b.$$

Prove:

(a) $(\forall a)(\forall b)\, a \,\Delta\, b = b \,\Delta\, a.$
(b) $(\forall a)(\forall b)(\forall c)\, a \,\Delta\, (b \,\Delta\, c) = (a \,\Delta\, b) \,\Delta\, c.$
(c) $(\forall a)(\forall b)\, a \,\Delta\, b = 0 \leftrightarrow a = b.$
(d) $(\forall a)(\forall x)(\forall c)\, a \,\Delta\, x = c \leftrightarrow x = a \,\Delta\, c.$
(e) $(\forall a)(\forall b)(\forall c)\, a(b \,\Delta\, c) = (ab) \,\Delta\, (ac).$
(f) $(\forall a)\, a \,\Delta\, a' = 1.$
(g) $(\forall a)(\forall b)\, (a \,\Delta\, b)' = a' \,\Delta\, b.$
(h) $(\forall a)(\forall b)\, a' \,\Delta\, b' = a \,\Delta\, b.$

3–6. ISOMORPHISM

In this section we introduce the powerful concept of *isomorphism*, which is tremendously important in mathematics, science, and philosophy. The word is derived from the Greek roots iso-, meaning *equal*, and morph-, meaning *form*. We shall merely give a rough description, together with a few illustrations, rather than a formal definition. The student should therefore regard this section as a road sign indicating that a certain kind of mathematical territory lies ahead, and not as a detailed map of that territory. As he meets examples of this concept its meaning will become clearer.

Two models of the same axiom system (e.g., two Boolean algebras) are abstractly equivalent or isomorphic if their structures are so much alike that one may be regarded as a mere re-labeling of the other.

EXAMPLE 3–3.   Let us define an abstract single-operational system as follows:

Primitives: S, a set.

     $*$, an operation.

Axioms: (1) $(\forall x)(\forall y)\ x \in S \wedge y \in S \rightarrow x * y \in S$.

The single axiom (1) merely asserts that S is closed with respect to $*$.

Consider $S_1 = \{0,1\}$, with the operation $\cdot$ (ordinary multiplication). $(S_1, \cdot)$ is a model of $(S, *)$ under the interpretation

$$S \Rightarrow S_1,$$

(1)

$$* \Rightarrow \cdot.$$

Similarly, let $S_2 = $ the set of subsets of $V = \{\text{sun}\}$, with the operation $\cup$ (ordinary union). The elements of S_2 are $\varnothing$ and V. $(S_2, \cup)$ is a model of $(S, *)$ with the interpretation

$$S \Rightarrow S_2$$

(2)

$$* \Rightarrow \cup.$$

Now we set up a one-to-one correspondence f between S_1 and S_2:

$$f(0) = V,$$

(3)

$$f(1) = \varnothing.$$

This correspondence shows that S_1 and S_2 are equivalent as sets, but it does much more. It carries the $\cdot$ table in S_1 onto the $\cup$ table in S_2, Table 3–16. Notice that as soon as we fill in the headings (row and column) in each table, all the entries are determined by the definitions of $\cdot$ and $\cup$. The elements which correspond by Eq. (3) are put in the same positions as headings. Now we can check that the similarly placed entries within the table also correspond by Eq. (3). We say that "f carries $\cdot$ into $\cup$." A more

TABLE 3–16

·	0	1
0	0	0
1	0	1

$\xrightarrow{f}$

$\cup$	V	$\varnothing$
V	V	V
$\varnothing$	V	$\varnothing$

$$f : \begin{cases} 0 \to V, \\ 1 \to \varnothing. \end{cases}$$

precise way of expressing this is

(4) $\qquad\qquad \forall a, b \in S_1, \ f(a \cdot b) = f(a) \cup f(b).$

Observe that $\cdot$ and $\cup$ arise from $*$ by the interpretations (1) and (2). Thus, we may say that f carries the interpretation of $*$ in S_1 into the interpretation of $*$ in S_2. Everything "fits."

Suppose that instead of f we had chosen the one-to-one correspondence g defined by

(5)
$$g(0) = \varnothing,$$
$$g(1) = V.$$

Then it would not be true that g carries $\cdot$ into $\cup$. For

$$g(0 \cdot 1) = g(0) = \varnothing,$$
$$g(0) \cup g(1) = \varnothing \cup V = V,$$

so

$$g(0 \cdot 1) \neq g(0) \cup g(1).$$

Therefore g is not an isomorphism, whereas f is one.

EXAMPLE 3–4. Let $S_3 = \{1, -1\}$, $\cdot =$ ordinary multiplication. The table for $(S_3, \cdot)$ is Table 3–17. Although there are two possible one-to-one correspondences between S_3 and S_1, neither is an isomorphism between $(S_3, \cdot)$ and $(S_1, \cdot)$. Both systems are models of $(S, *)$ and they have the same number of elements, but they do not have the same structure as single-operational systems.

EXAMPLE 3–5. Let $S_4 = \{1, 0, -1\}$, $\cdot =$ ordinary multiplication. $(S_4, \cdot)$ is a model of $(S, *)$, but it is not isomorphic with any of the systems in Examples 3–3 and 3–4. That the basic sets have the same number of elements is a necessary condition for isomorphism, though not a sufficient one.

TABLE 3–17

·	1	−1
1	1	−1
−1	−1	1

EXAMPLE 3–6.   Let S_5 = the set of real numbers, + = ordinary addition. Let S_6 = the set of all positive real numbers, · = ordinary multiplication. Then $(S_5,+)$ and $(S_6,·)$ are isomorphic single-operational systems. One correspondence that works is f, given by

(6) $f(x) = 2^x$ $(x \in S_5)$.

The analogue of Eq. (4) is

(7) $\forall a,b \in S_5, f(a + b) = f(a) \cdot f(b)$.

The student should recognize Eq. (7) as one of the "laws of exponents":

$$2^{a+b} = 2^a \cdot 2^b \qquad (a,b \in S_5).$$

EXAMPLE 3–7.   Let us define an abstract transitive single-relation system as follows:

Primitives: A, set.

$<$, relation on A.

Axioms: (1) $\forall a,b,c \in A, a < b \wedge b < c \rightarrow a < c$.

(This means that $<$ is transitive.)

Let $S_7 = \{0,1,2\}$, and let $\leq$ have its ordinary meaning on S_7. Let $S_8 = \{6,10,12\}$, and let $\geq$ have its ordinary meaning on S_8. We exhibit $(S_7,\leq)$ and $(S_8,\geq)$ as yes-no tables, Table 3–18. The correspondence

$$0 \rightarrow 6$$

$$1 \rightarrow 10$$

$$2 \rightarrow 12$$

is one-to-one but not an isomorphism between the transitive single-relation systems $(S_7,\leq)$ and $(S_8,\geq)$. But

$$f: \begin{cases} 0 \rightarrow 12 \\ 1 \rightarrow 10 \\ 2 \rightarrow 6 \end{cases}$$

TABLE 3–18

≤	0	1	2	≥	6	10	12
0	yes	yes	yes	6	yes	no	no
1	no	yes	yes	10	yes	yes	no
2	no	no	yes	12	yes	yes	yes

is an ismorphism between them. The student may verify this by rearranging the right side of Table 3–18 appropriately.

EXAMPLE 3–8. Let $<$ denote ordinary "less than" for S_5 and S_6 (see Example 3–6). Then $(S_5, <)$ and $(S_6, <)$ are isomorphic models of $(A, <)$. The correspondence (6) will work.

Mathematical systems may have more than one primitive set, operation, or relation. To have isomorphisms between models of such abstract systems, we must have one-to-one correspondences between the primitive sets that carry the other primitives (constants, operations, relations) of one model into the appropriate primitives of the other model. By "appropriate," of course, we mean "interpreting the same primitives of the abstract system." We illustrate these ideas for the case of Boolean algebras.

EXAMPLE 3–9. Let $V = \{1,2\}$, $W = \{6,8\}$. The set $B_1(V)$ of all subsets of V yields a model of Boolean algebra, with the interpretation

$$B \Rightarrow B_1(V),$$
$$+ \Rightarrow \cup,$$
(8)
$$\cdot \Rightarrow \cap,$$
$$0 \Rightarrow \emptyset,$$
$$1 \Rightarrow V.$$

Also, $B_1(W)$ is a model of Boolean algebra with the interpretation

$$B \Rightarrow B_1(W),$$
$$+ \Rightarrow \cup,$$
(9)
$$\cdot \Rightarrow \cap,$$
$$0 \Rightarrow \emptyset,$$
$$1 \Rightarrow W.$$

Let us define the one-to-one correspondence f from $B_1(V)$ to $B_1(W)$ by

(10) $$f: \begin{cases} \varnothing \to \varnothing, \\ \{1\} \to \{8\}, \\ \{2\} \to \{6\}, \\ V \to W, \end{cases}$$

[Because $\varnothing$ in $B_1(V)$ and $B_1(W)$ are interpretations of the same primitive constant 0 [from (8) and (9)], they are appropriate for matching by (10). Similarly, V and W are interpretations of the same primitive constant 1 [from (8) and (9)], and they do match by (10). The two remaining primitives, $+$ and $\cdot$, are operations. Their interpretations are

$$+ : \cup \text{ in } B_1(V), \ \cup \text{ in } B_1(W),$$
$$\cdot \ : \cap \text{ in } B_1(V), \ \cap \text{ in } B_1(W).$$

Therefore, if f is to be an isomorphism, we must have

(11) $$\forall a,b \in B_1(V), f(a \cup b) = f(a) \cup f(b),$$
(12) $$\forall a,b \in B_1(V), f(a \cap b) = f(a) \cap f(b).$$

In this case, where f carries $\cup$ into $\cup$ (and $\cap$ into $\cap$), we say that f *preserves* $\cup$ (and $\cap$). The student should exhibit the tables for $\cup$ and $\cap$ in $B_1(V)$ and $B_1(W)$ to show that Eqs. (11) and (12) are true.

The correspondence f is not the only one that works. What is another one?

EXERCISE 3–8

Show that $B_1(V)$ is isomorphic with itself (as a Boolean algebra) by means of the correspondence: $g(\varnothing) = \varnothing$, $g(\{1\}) = \{2\}$, $g(\{2\}) = \{1\}$, $g(V) = V$.

Among models of the same axiom system, the relation "is isomorphic with" is an equivalence relation: It is reflexive, symmetric, and transitive.

It may happen that any two models of an axiom system S are isomorphic. In this case we say that S is *categorical*. When we wish to capture the essence of a given concrete system, or P-plane, it is useful to have the corresponding abstract system (C-plane) categorical. An example of a categorical system is obtained by adjoining to the axioms of Boolean algebra the further axiom that the number of elements in B is 4. The number 4 may be replaced by any positive integer n, and the system is still categorical. This follows from a rather deep theorem, which characterizes finite Boolean algebras as being isomorphic with $B_1(V)$ for some finite universe V. This theorem will be proved in the next section. An interesting byproduct is that the number of elements in a finite Boolean algebra must be a power of 2, since the number of subsets of V is 2^k when V has k elements.

The fact that a system is categorical does not necessarily mean that it is unfruitful or inapplicable to many situations. The conclusion that any two models are isomorphic may be deep, difficult, and important, for it may reveal a structural similarity between two concrete systems which were previously thought to be unrelated.

At the other end of the scale, there are axiom systems with many non-isomorphic models. They are quite flexible and have many essentially distinct applications. For example, Boolean algebra is very flexible. The models $B_1(V)$ and $B_1(W)$ are nonisomorphic whenever V and W are not equivalent as sets (i.e., they do not have the same number of elements). Moreover, there are Boolean algebras which are not isomorphic with any $B_1(V)$.

Flexibility is desirable from the standpoint of economy of effort. Every theorem proved in the system S yields many true propositions when interpreted in all the models of S.

EXERCISES 3–9

1. Consider the following axiom system:

Primitives: K, a set.

Axioms: None.

What does isomorphism reduce to for models of this system?

2. Prove that any two Boolean algebras with four elements are isomorphic.

3. Discuss the schematic representation of ismorphism given as Figure 3–23. (Explain what the arrows and double arrow represent.)

4. Let

$$f(n) = n + 1 \qquad (n \in Z).$$

(Z = the set of all integers.)

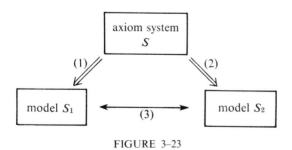

FIGURE 3–23

(a) Is f a one-to-one correspondence?
(b) Is f a mapping from Z onto Z?
(c) Does f preserve addition?
(d) Does f preserve multiplication?
(e) Does f preserve $<$?

5. The same as Problem 4, for $f(n) = 2n$ $(n \in Z)$.
6. The same as Problem 4, for $f(n) = -n$ $(n \in Z)$.
7. Let $f(n) = n + 1$ $(n \in Z)$. Find a definition for $\otimes$ such that

$$f(mn) = f(m) \otimes f(n) \qquad (m,n \in Z).$$

Is $(Z,\otimes)$ isomorphic with $(Z,\cdot)$?

8. Define $\oplus$ by

$$m \oplus n = m + n + mn \qquad (m,n \in Z).$$

Show that $(Z,\oplus)$ and $(Z,\cdot)$ are isomorphic, with the mapping $f : n \to n - 1$ from $(Z, \cdot)$ to $(Z,\oplus)$.

EXERCISES 3–10

A *group* $(G,*)$ is defined as a set G with an operation $*$ satisfying:

Axiom 1. $\forall x,y \in G, \ x * y \in G$ 　　(closure).

Axiom 2. $\forall x,y,z \in G, \ x * (y * z) = (x * y) * z$ 　　(associativity).

Axiom 3. $\exists e \in G$ such that $\forall x \in G, \ e * x = x * e = x$. ($e$ is an *identity* element.)

Axiom 4. $\forall x \in G, \ \exists y \in G$ such that $x * y = y * x = e$. (y is an *inverse of* x.)

A group $(G,*)$ is *commutative* iff it satisfies

Axiom 5. $\forall x,y \in G, \ x * y = y * x$.

1. Prove that there is only one identity element.

2. Prove that for each $x \in G$ there is only one inverse y. We usually designate it as x^{-1}.

3. Suppose that $x, y, z \in G$ and that $x * y = x * z$. Compute $x^{-1} * (x * y)$ and $x^{-1} * (x * z)$. What conclusion do you obtain?

4. Satisfy yourself that the following are commutative groups. In each case name the identity element and give a formula for the inverse of an arbitrary element x.
　　(a) The real numbers under addition.
　　(b) The nonzero real numbers under multiplication.
　　(c) The integers under addition.
　　(d) The even integers under addition.
　　(e) The positive rational numbers under multiplication.

5. Let $P = R \times R$, the set of all pairs of real numbers (a,b), and let $+$ be the operation on P defined by

$$(a_1,b_1) + (a_2,b_2) = (a_1 + a_2, b_1 + b_2).$$

Show that $(P,+)$ is a commutative group. What is the identity? What is the inverse of (a,b)?

6. Let $K = R \times R - \{(0,0)\}$ and let $\cdot$ be the operation on K defined by

$$(a_1,b_1) \cdot (a_2,b_2) = (a_1 a_2 - b_1 b_2, a_1 b_2 + a_2 b_1).$$

Show that $(K,\cdot)$ is a commutative group. What is the identity? What is the inverse of (a,b)?

7. Let G be the set of all pairs of real numbers (a,b) such that $a \neq 0$, and let $*$ be the operation on G defined by

$$(a_1,b_1) * (a_2,b_2) = (a_1 a_2, a_1 b_2 + b_1).$$

Show that $(G,*)$ is a group. Is it commutative? What is the identity? What is the inverse of (a,b)?

8. Let H be the set of all functions f given by

$$f(x) = ax + b \qquad (x \in R),$$

where a and b are real and $a \neq 0$. Let $\circ$ denote the operation of composition of functions:

$$(f \circ g)(x) = f(g(x)) \qquad (x \in R).$$

Show that $(H,\circ)$ is a group. Is it commutative? What is the identity? What is the inverse of $f \in H$? How is $(H,\circ)$ related to $(G,*)$ of Problem 7?

9. Let A denote the set of real numbers with 0 and 1 removed. We define six transformations (mappings, functions) of A onto A by

$$T_1(x) = x, \qquad T_4(x) = 1 - \frac{1}{x},$$

$$T_2(x) = 1 - x, \qquad T_5(x) = \frac{1}{1-x},$$

$$T_3(x) = \frac{1}{x}, \qquad T_6(x) = \frac{x}{x-1}.$$

Let $T = \{T_1, T_2, T_3, T_4, T_5, T_6\}$, and let $\circ$ denote the operation of composition of functions, as in Problem 8. Write out the "$\circ$ table," giving all the resultants like $T_2 \circ T_4 = T_3$. Show that $(T,\circ)$ is a group. What is the identity? Express every element as a product of T_2's and T_3's.

10. Let V be a set, G the collection of all subsets of V. Define the operation Δ on G by
$$A \,\Delta\, B = (A - B) \cup (B - A).$$
Show that (G, Δ) is a commutative group. What is the identity? What is the inverse of A?

11. Construct all groups with two elements, up to isomorphism; i.e., regard two isomorphic groups as "the same." [*Hint:* Write out the group table.]

12. Construct all groups with three elements, up to isomorphism.

*13. Construct all groups with four elements, up to isomorphism.

14. Let $(G, \cdot)$ be a group such that $a^2 = e$ for every $a \in G$ ($a^2 =_{\text{df}} a \cdot a$). Show that $(G, \cdot)$ is commutative. [*Hint:* Consider $(xy)^2$ for any $x, y \in G$.]

*15. If a finite group has an even number of elements, show that there is at least one element $a \neq e$ such that $a^2 = e$. (*Hint:* Show that the number of elements b such that $b \neq b^{-1}$ is even.)

*16. Let G be the set of all permutations of $S = \{1,2,3\}$ (i.e., all one-to-one correspondences between S and S). A typical element of G is written
$$A = \begin{pmatrix} 1 & 2 & 3 \\ a & b & c \end{pmatrix},$$
meaning that 1 goes into a, 2 into b, 3 into c ($A: 1 \to a, 2 \to b, 3 \to c$). We "multiply" two permutations A, B, to get $A \circ B$, by performing first B, then A on the result. For example,
$$\begin{pmatrix} 1 & 2 & 3 \\ 3 & 1 & 2 \end{pmatrix} \circ \begin{pmatrix} 1 & 2 & 3 \\ 2 & 1 & 3 \end{pmatrix} = \begin{pmatrix} 1 & 2 & 3 \\ 1 & 3 & 2 \end{pmatrix}.$$
Label the six elements of G and write out the $\circ$ table for G. Show that $(G, \circ)$ is a group. Give a simple rule for finding the inverse of any element. Compare $(G, \circ)$ with $(T, \circ)$ of Problem 9.

17. Let $(G, *)$ and $(H, \cdot)$ be groups, and let f be a function from G into H such that
$$f(a * b) = f(a) \cdot f(b) \qquad (a, b \in G).$$
Such a function is called a *homomorphism* of G into H. Prove:
   (a) rng $f[\ = \{y \in H | \exists a \in G, y = f(a)\}]$ is a group under $\cdot$.
   (b) $\{a \in G | f(a) = e\}$ is a group under $*$ [e = identity in $(H, \cdot)$].

*18. Let A be a set and R a relation on A. Let P be the set of all permutations f of A which preserve R, i.e.,
$$aRb \leftrightarrow f(a)Rf(b) \qquad (a, b \in A).$$
Prove that P is a group under composition.

3–7. FINITE BOOLEAN ALGEBRAS

The main achievement of our development in Section 3–5 has been to derive certain important properties of Boolean algebras, such as associativity, idempotence, and the de Morgan identities, from a very economical system of axioms. These properties are so important that they are frequently assumed as axioms. In a sense we have engaged in an intellectual exercise proving that our axiom system is adequate to ensure a structure of the type we had in mind all along. Indeed, if it were not adequate we should have changed it. Thus we can say that we have not yet gone beyond the fundamentals of the subject.

In this section we propose and solve the important problem of classifying all finite Boolean algebras. We want to be able to answer questions like "Are there any Boolean algebras with 200 elements, and if so, what do they look like?" or "We know that there is a Boolean algebra with eight elements, namely $B_1(V)$, the algebra of all subsets of $V = \{1,2,3\}$. Is every eight-element Boolean algebra isomorphic to this one, or are there some which are essentially different in structure?"

Initially our attack will be frankly experimental. For a few integers n we shall exhaust all the possibilities for an n-element Boolean algebra. After recording the results we shall examine them and try to formulate a hypothesis consistent with them. We shall derive some consequences of our hypothesis and see if these consequences are true. Finally, when enough consequences have been verified, we shall reverse the deductive process and attempt to prove the hypothesis true.

$n = 1$. There is obviously only one possibility for the $+$ and $\cdot$ tables, Table 3–19. This is clearly what we would get for $B_1(V)$, where $V = \varnothing$.

$n = 2$. B must consist of the two distinct elements 0 and 1. (If $0 = 1$, then the second element a must satisfy $a = a \cdot 1 = a \cdot 0 = 0$, a contradiction.) The tables are uniquely determined, Table 3–20. Thus there is only one possible structure for a Boolean algebra with two elements. *Any two two-element Boolean algebras are isomorphic.* All of them are therefore isomorphic to $B_1(V)$, where $V = \{1\}$, a one-element set.

$n = 3$. As we saw above, 0 and 1 are distinct. Let a be the third element. In any Boolean algebra, for all $x \in B$,

$$0 + x = x + 0 = x,$$

$$0 \cdot x = x \cdot 0 = 0,$$

$$1 + x = x + 1 = 1,$$

$$1 \cdot x = x \cdot 1 = x,$$

TABLE 3–19

+	0		·	0
0	0		0	0

so the only combinations not yet determined are $a + a$ and $a \cdot a$. But these are both a, by the idempotent laws (Theorems 3–5 and 3–5′). The tables are uniquely determined, Table 3–21. Thus there is *at most* one possible structure for a Boolean algebra with three elements. *Any two three-element Boolean algebras are isomorphic.* In this case, however, there is no concrete model $B_1(V)$, for the number of elements in $B_1(V)$ is 2^k if $V = \{1, 2, \ldots, k\}$. An attempt to construct a model by means of truth functions or circuit functions also fails, for much the same reason. Can we use the set $\{0, 1, a\}$ with the concretely given tables below as a model? We certainly have an interpretation, but to see that it is a model we must show that all the axioms are satisfied. Checking them we find that Axioms 0, 0′, 1, 1′, 2, 2′, 3, 3′ are indeed satisfied. But what is the complement of a? If $a' = 0$, then $a = 1$, which is false. If $a' = 1$, then $a = 0$, which is false. If $a' = a$, then $a = a \cdot a = a \cdot a' = 0$, so $a = 0$, which is false. This proves that *there are no three-element Boolean algebras.*

We could have shortened our discussion by looking for the complement of a immediately, but it was worthwhile to bring out the logical point that the uniqueness of a proposed mathematical structure does not imply its existence.

$n = 4$. As above, we must have distinct elements 0, 1, a, a'. The tables must be as given in Table 3–22. Once the headings of these tables are given, we have no choice in filling in the entries. The student should go through all 32 entries and give a reason for each one. We have therefore proved that *any two four-element Boolean algebras are isomorphic.* All of them are therefore isomorphic to $B_1(V)$, where $V = \{1, 2\}$, a two-element set.

$n = 5$. As in the case $n = 4$, we must have the distinct elements 0, 1, a, and a'. Let the fifth element be b. Then $b' \neq 0, 1, a, a'$ (why?). Therefore

TABLE 3–20

+	0	1		·	0	1
0	0	1		0	0	0
1	1	1		1	0	1

TABLE 3-21

+	0	1	a		·	0	1	a
0	0	1	a		0	0	0	0
1	1	1	1		1	0	1	a
a	a	1	a		a	0	a	a

$b' = b$. But this implies $b = b \cdot b = b \cdot b' = 0$, which is false. Hence *there are no five-element Boolean algebras.* By default, *any two five-element Boolean algebras are isomorphic.*

We could go along in this way, examining in turn the cases $n = 6, 7, 8$, and so on. At first glance, this appears to provide us with an inexhaustible supply of research problems. Each individual case can (at worst) be settled by trying all possibilities. Let us tabulate the results for a few cases, Table 3–23.

The cases $n = 6, \ldots, 10$ we may regard as exercises, or accept as proved. The results appear to be of two kinds:

(1) If n is of the form 2^k for some nonnegative integer k, then a Boolean algebra B with n elements is isomorphic to $B_1(V)$, where V is a set with k elements.

(2) If n is not of the form 2^k, then there is no Boolean algebra with n elements. Both assertions are subsumed under the following

Hypothesis. If B is a Boolean algebra with n elements then $n = 2^k$ for some nonnegative integer k, and B is isomorphic to $B_1(V)$, where V is a set with k elements.

TABLE 3-22

+	0	1	a	a'		·	0	1	a	a'
0	0	1	a	a'		0	0	0	0	0
1	1	1	1	1		1	0	1	a	a'
a	a	1	a	1		a	0	a	a	0
a'	a'	1	1	a'		a'	0	a'	0	a'

TABLE 3–23

n	Models
1	$B_1(V)$, where $V = \phi$
2	$B_1(V)$, where $V = \{1\}$
3	none
4	$B_1(V)$, where $V = \{1,2\}$
5	none
6	none
7	none
8	$B_1(V)$, where $V = \{1,2,3\}$
9	none
10	none

Now suppose that B is an n-element Boolean algebra. According to the Hypothesis, there is a set V and an isomorphism under which

$$B \to B_1(V),$$

$$+ \to \cup,$$

$$\cdot \to \cap,$$

$$0 \to \varnothing,$$

$$1 \to V.$$

If v is an element of V, then $\{v\}$ is an element of $B_1(V)$, so there must correspond to $\{v\}$ an element b of B having the same algebraic properties in B as the singleton $\{v\}$ has in $B_1(V)$. What are these algebraic properties? It is easy to see that if X is any subset of V (element of $B_1(V)$), then $\{v\} \cap X = \varnothing$ (if $v \notin X$), or $\{v\} \cap X = \{v\}$ (if $v \in X$). Also, of course, $\{v\} \neq \varnothing$. Conversely, if A is a nonempty subset of V such that $A \cap X = \varnothing$ or $A \cap X = A$ for all $X \subset V$, then A is necessarily a singleton. (The student should prove this.) This characteristic property of indivisibility for singletons may be translated into the following definition in an arbitrary Boolean algebra.

Definition 3–2. An *atom* of a Boolean algebra B is a nonzero element a of B such that

$$\forall x \in B, \; ax = 0 \vee ax = a.$$

It is an interesting fact, which we shall not prove here, that there are Boolean algebras ($\neq \{0\}$) without any atoms. Obviously they are not isomorphic to any $B_1(V)$. One consequence of the Hypothesis is that a Boolean algebra B with n elements ($n = 2,3,4,\ldots$) must have some atoms. We can be more specific. Suppose that c is a nonzero element of B. It corresponds, via the isomorphism, to a nonempty subset C of V. Let $v \in C$, and define $D = \{v\}$. Then $C \cap D$ is a singleton. If d is the element of B which corresponds to D, then the statement

$$C \cap D \text{ is a singleton}$$

corresponds to

$$cd \text{ is an atom.}$$

Therefore, *if the Hypothesis is true*, so is the following.

Theorem 3–10. In a Boolean algebra B with a finite number of elements, for every $c \neq 0$ there is an element d such that cd is an atom.

If we can prove Theorem 3–10 independently of the Hypothesis, then we have a partial verification of the Hypothesis. This we now do.

Proof of Theorem 3–10: Let $b_1 = c$. If possible, let $b_2 \neq b_1$ be such that $b_1 b_2 \neq 0$. Then, if possible, let $b_3 \neq b_1$, b_2 be such that $b_1 b_2 b_3 \neq 0$. Continue in this way as long as possible, till at some stage a nonzero product $b_1 \cdots b_j$ is reached such that every $x \neq b_1, \ldots, b_j$ satisfies

$$b_1 \cdots b_j x = 0$$

Now if x is any one of $b_1, \ldots, b_j$, say b_2, then

$$b_1 b_2 b_3 \cdots b_j x = b_1 b_2 b_3 \cdots b_j b_2$$
$$= b_1 (b_2 b_2) b_3 \cdots b_j$$
$$= b_1 b_2 b_3 \cdots b_j.$$

Thus, if we let $a = b_1 b_2 b_3 \cdots b_j$, then

$$ax = 0 \qquad (x \neq b_1, b_2, \ldots, b_j),$$
$$ax = a \qquad (x = b_1, b_2, \ldots, b_j).$$

Therefore a is an atom. Furthermore it is a multiple of $c = b_1$. This completes the proof.

EXERCISE 3–11

Where does the proof of Theorem 3–10 break down if B is not finite?

Our next theorem corresponds to the statement that distinct singletons in $B_1(V)$ have an empty intersection.

Theorem 3–11. Let a_1, a_2 be atoms in a Boolean algebra. Then

$$a_1 a_2 = 0 \vee a_1 = a_2.$$

Proof: Suppose that $a_1a_2 \neq 0$. Since a_1 is an atom, $a_1a_2 = a_1$. Since a_2 is an atom, $a_2a_1 = a_2$. Therefore $a_1 = a_2$.

In $B_1(V)$, the union of all the singletons in V is clearly V. If our Hypothesis is true, the corresponding statement for finite Boolean algebras is also true. We prove it without appealing to the Hypothesis, so that we have a further verification.

Theorem 3–12. Let $\{a_1, a_2, \ldots, a_k\}$ be the set of all atoms in a finite Boolean algebra B. Then

$$a_1 + a_2 + \cdots + a_k = 1.$$

Proof: Let $c = (a_1 + a_2 + \cdots + a_k)' = a_1'a_2' \cdots a_k'$. Assume that $c \neq 0$. By Theorem 3–10 there is a $d \in B$ such that cd is an atom, say a_1:

$$a_1 = a_1'a_2' \cdots a_k'd.$$

Multiply both sides by a_1:

$$a_1 = a_1a_1 = a_1(a_1'a_2' \cdots a_k'd)$$
$$= (a_1a_1')(a_2' \cdots a_k'd)$$
$$= 0.$$

This contradicts the fact that a_1 is an atom, which is nonzero by definition. Hence our assumption $c \neq 0$ is false. But from $c = 0$ we get

$$a_1 + a_2 + \cdots + a_k = c' = 1.$$

Theorem 3–12 is a special case of the following one. As so often happens, the special case may be used to prove the general theorem.

Theorem 3–13. In a finite Boolean algebra B, every element b is the sum of all the atoms a_i such that $ba_i \neq 0$.

Proof: Using the notation of Theorem 3–12, we have

$$1 = a_1 + a_2 + \cdots + a_k.$$

Multiply both sides by b:

$$b = ba_1 + ba_2 + \cdots + ba_k.$$

Let $S_b = \{i | ba_i \neq 0\}$. For $i \in S_b$, $ba_i = a_i$. For $i \notin S_b$, $ba_i = 0$, and all these zeros may be omitted from the sum. Therefore

$$b = \sum_{i \in S_b} a_i.$$

The notation indicates the sum of all those a_i such that $i \in S_b$; that is, $ba_i \neq 0$. If S_b is the empty set, the sum is 0, of course.

Corollary. In a finite Boolean algebra B, with distinct atoms a_1, a_2, $\ldots, a_k$, let S_b denote the set of all $i = 1, 2, \ldots, k$ such that $ba_i \neq 0$. Then for all $b, c \in B$,

$$S_b = S_c \leftrightarrow b = c.$$

Proof: Clearly $b = c \to S_b = S_c$. Conversely, if $S_b = S_c$, then by Theorem 3–13,

$$b = \sum_{i \in S_b} a_i = \sum_{i \in S_c} a_i = c.$$

Therefore $S_b = S_c \to b = c$.

We now have a way of associating with each $b \in B$ a subset of $V = \{1, 2, \ldots, k\}$, namely, S_b. In mathematical language we have a function f defined on B by

$$f(b) = S_b \qquad (b \in B).$$

The corollary just proved asserts that f is one-to-one. The range of f is contained in $B_1(V)$. Our next result is that rng $f = B_1(V)$.

Theorem 3–14. In a finite Boolean algebra B, with distinct atoms $a_1, \ldots, a_k$, the correspondence $f: B \to B_1(V)$ given by $f(b) = S_b$ $(b \in B)$ [where S_b is the set of all $i \in V = \{1, \ldots, k\}$ such that $ba_i \neq 0$] is one-to-one from B onto $B_1(V)$.

Proof: Let S and T be any subsets of V (whether of the form S_b or not), and suppose that

(1) $$\sum_{i \in S} a_i = \sum_{j \in T} a_j.$$

If some index, say q, belongs to S but not to T, then

$$a_q \sum_{i \in S} a_i = a_q(\cdots + a_q + \cdots) = a_q,$$

but by Theorem 3–11,

$$a_q \sum_{j \in T} a_j = \sum_{j \in T} a_q a_j = 0,$$

since a_q and a_j are distinct atoms for all $j \in T$. This contradiction shows that

$$(\forall_q)q \in S \to q \in T,$$

that is, $S \subset T$. Similarly we see that $T \subset S$. Hence Eq. (1) implies that $S = T$.

Now, to prove the theorem, we need only show that for every $S \subset V$ there exists an element $b \in B$ such that $f(b) = S$; that is, $S = S_b$. Given S, define

$$b = \sum_{i \in S} a_i.$$

By Theorem 3–13,

$$b = \sum_{j \in S_b} a_j.$$

From the preceding paragraph, $S = S_b$, as required.

Corollary. If B is a finite Boolean algebra with n elements, then for some nonnegative integer k, $n = 2^k$.

Proof: By Theorem 3–14, B has as many elements as $B_1(V)$, for some $V = \{1, 2, \ldots, k\}$. To every $S \subset V$ we make correspond an ordered k-tuple $(x_1, x_2, \ldots, x_k)$, where the x_i are determined by

$$x_i = 1 \qquad (i \in S),$$

$$x_i = 0 \qquad (i \notin S).$$

As S runs through all the subsets of V, the corresponding k-tuple runs through the set of all possible k-tuples of 0's and 1's. This set is precisely $T \times T \times \cdots \times T$ (k factors), where $T = \{0, 1\}$. The correspondence is one-to-one, and the number of elements in the Cartesian product is 2^k. Therefore $n = 2^k$.

It remains to show that the function f of Theorem 3–14 is an isomorphism between B and $B_1(V)$.

Theorem 3–15. With the hypotheses and notation of Theorem 3–14, f is an isomorphism between the Boolean algebras $(B, +, \cdot, 1, 0)$ and $(B_1(V), \cup, \cap, V, \emptyset)$. Explicitly, for all $b, c \in B$,

(a) $f(b + c) = f(b) \cup f(c)$,
(b) $f(bc) = f(b) \cap f(c)$,
(c) $f(0) = \emptyset$,
(d) $f(1) = V$.

Proof: Given $b, c \in B$, by Theorem 3–13,

$$b + c = \sum_{i \in S_b} a_i + \sum_{j \in S_c} a_j.$$

If $q \in S_b - S_c$ or $q \in S_c - S_b$, then a_q appears exactly once in the sum. If $q \in S_b \cap S_c$, the sum contains $a_q + a_q = a_q$. If $q \notin S_b$ and $q \notin S_c$, then a_q does not appear in the sum. Therefore,

$$b + c = \sum_{q \in S_b \cup S_c} a_q.$$

But by Theorem 3–13,

$$b + c = \sum_{i \in S_{b+c}} a_i.$$

By the proof of Theorem 3–14 $[(1) \to S = T]$,

$$S_b \cup S_c = S_{b+c},$$

which is equivalent to (a).

Similarly, we have

$$bc = \sum_{i \in S_b} a_i \cdot \sum_{j \in S_c} a_j.$$

A typical term in the product of these two sums is $a_i a_j$, where $i \in S_b$ and $j \in S_c$. By Theorem 3–11 the only terms $a_i a_j$ which are nonzero are those for which $i = j$. Such a common index belongs to both S_b and S_c, that is, to $S_b \cap S_c$. Therefore,

$$bc = \sum_{i \in S_b \cap S_c} a_i.$$

But

$$bc = \sum_{i \in S_{bc}} a_i.$$

As above, therefore,

$$S_b \cap S_c = S_{bc},$$

which is equivalent to (b).

Finally, it is obvious from definition that $S_0 = \emptyset$ and $S_1 = V$; that is, (c) and (d) hold.

EXERCISE 3–12

Prove that for all $b \in B, f(b') = f(b)'$.

Chapter 4

THE REAL NUMBERS

4–1. INTRODUCTION

UP TO NOW we have been using the real numbers as though we knew all about them. We have been accepting their properties as "facts." For example, we "know" that if s and t are real numbers, then $s + t = t + s$ and $st = ts$. We "know" that if a, b, c are real numbers such that $a < b$, then $c + a < c + b$. We "know" many "facts" in a rather haphazard, disconnected way. Just as long as the "facts" we use are so elementary and obvious, there is no great harm in leaving them in a somewhat disorganized state. Soon, however, we shall need to develop and use a number of nontrivial results about the real number system, and it would be dangerous to do so without a firm conceptual foundation.

This state of affairs is a perfect example of the ideas presented in Section 3–1. We have before us the "reality" or P-plane consisting of the number system that we have been using from childhood on. Many of the properties of the system are deeply ingrained in our minds and now seem very obvious to us, so obvious that we are likely to regard as silly any attempt to establish them anew. But this (and more) is what we must do now. We must construct a C-plane to correspond to our familiar number system. We must perform the important task of distilling our knowledge, *abstracting* it, so that we have a firm basis on which to build further knowledge. To show how necessary this is, we ask the student—with his present intuitive background—to think about, discuss with his colleagues, and prove, if he can, the following statement:

$$.999\ldots = 1.$$

(The three dots signify that the 9's continue without end.) We might also ask him to think about the following problems:

(1) What is the sum of $.\overparen{434343}\ldots$ and $.\overparen{899899899}\ldots$? What is their product?

148

(2) Is there a number x between 1 and 2 which satisfies the equation $x^6 = x + 1$?

(3) Is there a number b greater than 0 for which $b < 1$ and $2b < 1$ and $3b < 1$ and ... ? (That is, for every positive integer n, $nb < 1$.)

These examples are intended to show how quickly we reach the boundaries of our intuitive understanding. Even if the student arrives at answers to them, he is likely to have the uneasy feeling that he really does not understand what an infinite decimal represents, nor what facts about real numbers he can accept as fundamental. Thus he will not be sure that he has devised an adequate proof, since the basic rules of the game have not been spelled out for him.

In this respect the development of mathematical maturity in an individual imitates (or should imitate) the same process in the mathematical community. Three or four centuries ago mathematicians took for granted the foundations of their discipline and were busy discovering or inventing new results. They were like bright, impatient children intent on discovery, with whole new worlds opening up to them. Standards of proof were not as high as they are now. Along with the deep and significant advances there were many proofs that we would today regard as invalid and some results that were wrong. Even then voices, such as that of Bishop Berkeley, were raised in protest against the almost mystical practices of some mathematicians. Later, the foundations of mathematics came to be scrutinized more closely by its practitioners. Within the last century or so we have arrived at a deeper understanding and have attained a higher degree of sophistication than ever before. This is not to say that our standards have reached the highest possible level. It may well be that our own proofs will be found wanting a hundred years from now. But sufficient to the day is the rigor thereof.

Fortunately, the path from naiveté to maturity is not so thorny for the present-day student as it was for those who first cleared it. He is merely asked to set foot upon and follow the well-blazed trail, and to appreciate the need for the journey. He need not be deterred by fear of "sophisticated" material. After all, is it better to be a naive or a sophisticated investor? Consumer? Student of current events?

Granted, then, that we are prepared to axiomatize the real number system. Our purpose is not to question or destroy the foundations of our knowledge, but merely to make them quite explicit. Because this particular P-plane is so important to us, the axiom system we construct will be categorical. That is, it will be strong enough to characterize our ordinary number system completely. Any two concrete systems that satisfy the axiom system will necessarily be isomorphic—have precisely the same structure.

For this reason we may speak about *the* real number system, meaning any one of the isomorphic models.

Before proceeding to Section 4–2, write down as many fundamental properties as you can for the real numbers as you know them. In the interest of economy, omit any property which you can prove from the others you have written down.

4–2. THE ADDITION AXIOMS

We remind the student that we have a certain amount of freedom in our choice of axioms. The particular set that we choose should be readily acceptable to him on intuitive grounds. The axioms will be grouped and discussed in the following order:

A1 to 5. Addition axioms.
M1 to 5. Multiplication axioms.
D.   Distributive axiom.
O1 to 4. Order axioms.
O5.   Least-upper-bound axiom.

As we progress through this sequence we shall pause occasionally to examine the type of system already achieved. The theorems and problems at any stage will depend only on the axioms adopted previous to that stage.

Primitives: R, a set.

0, 1, distinct elements of R.

$+, \cdot$, operations.

$<$, a relation.

Unless otherwise indicated, all variables range over R.

Addition Axioms:

A1. $\forall x,y,\ x + y \in R$ (*additive closure*).

A2. $\forall x,y,z,\ x + (y + z) = (x + y) + z$ (*associativity of addition*).

A3. $\forall x,y,\ x + y = y + x$ (*commutativity of addition*).

A4. $\forall x,\ x + 0 = x$ (*additive identity*).

A5. $\forall x, \exists y$ such that $x + y = 0$ (*additive inverse*).

Any system satisfying Axioms A1 to A5 is called a *commutative group* (see Exercises 3–10). Thus, the next four theorems, which depend on the addition axioms only, hold for any commutative group.

Theorem 4–1   (*Additive Cancellation*)

$$\forall a,x,y,\ (x + a = y + a) \to (x = y).$$

Proof: Suppose that $x + a = y + a$. By Axiom A5, $\exists b$ such that $a + b = 0$. Then

$$(x + a) + b = (y + a) + b,$$
$$x + (a + b) = y + (a + b),$$
$$x + 0 = y + 0,$$
$$x = y.$$

(The student should supply the reasons.)

Corollary. $\forall a,x,y, (a + x = a + y) \rightarrow (x = y)$.

Theorem 4–2 (*Uniqueness of Additive Inverse*)

$$\forall x,y,z, (x + y = 0 \wedge x + z = 0) \rightarrow (y = z).$$

Proof: If $x + y = 0$ and $x + z = 0$, then $x + y = x + z$, so $y = z$ by the corollary.

Definition 4–1. The unique additive inverse of x guaranteed by Axiom A5 and Theorem 4–2 is called the *negative of* x and is written $-x$.

Theorem 4–3. $\forall x, -(-x) = x$.
Proof: Given $x \in R$, $x + (-x) = 0$, so $(-x) + x = 0$. By Definition 4–1, this means that x is the additive inverse of $-x$, i.e., $x = -(-x)$.

Theorem 4–4. $\forall a,b$, there is a unique element x satisfying $a + x = b$.
Proof: If x satisfies $a + x = b$, then

$$(-a) + (a + x) = (-a) + b,$$
$$(-a + a) + x = (-a) + b,$$
$$0 + x = (-a) + b,$$
$$x + 0 = (-a) + b,$$
$$x = (-a) + b.$$

Therefore, a solution, *if it exists*, is unique. It is easy to see that $a + ((-a) + b) = b$, and the theorem is proved.

Definition 4–2. $b - a =_{df}$ the unique solution of $a + x = b$.

EXERCISES 4-2

1. Simplify: (a) $-(-2)$. (b) $-(-(-2))$. (c) $-(-(-(-2)))$.
2. For $x \in R$, define $f(x) = -x$. Prove:
   (a) $\forall x,y, (f(x) = f(y)) \rightarrow (x = y)$.

TABLE 4–1

+	0	k
0	0	k
k	k	0

(b) $\forall x, \exists y$ such that $f(y) = x$.
What is dom f? rng f? Is f one-to-one?

3. Prove $\forall a,b,\; b - a = b + (-a)$.

4. Prove $\forall a,b,\; b - (-a) = b + a$.

5. Prove $\forall a,\; 0 - a = -a$.

6. Consider the system $(G,+,0)$ defined as follows: $G = \{0,k\}$, $k \neq 0$, with the addition table, Table 4–1.

    (a) Prove that $(G, +, 0)$ is a commutative group, that is, that it satisfies Axioms A1 to A5.

    (b) What is -0?

    (c) What is $-k$?

    (d) On the basis of Axioms A1 to A5 *alone*, can you prove that the only element of R which is its own negative is 0?

7. Construct a commutative group $(H,+,0)$ for which H has three distinct elements $0, k, r$.

8. Supply all the reasons in the proof of Theorem 4–1.

9. Prove the corollary of Theorem 4–1.

4–3. THE MULTIPLICATION AXIOMS

There are five axioms for multiplication.

M1. $\forall x,y,\; xy \in R$ (*multiplicative closure*).

M2. $\forall x,y,z,\; x(yz) = (xy)z$ (*associativity of multiplication*).

M3. $\forall x,y,\; xy = yx$ (*commutativity of multiplication*).

M4. $\forall x,\; x \cdot 1 = x$ (*multiplicative identity*).

M5. $\forall x \neq 0,\; \exists y$ such that $xy = 1$ (*restricted multiplicative inverse*).

(Note that we sometimes write xy for $x \cdot y$.)

There is an obvious similarity between the addition and multiplication axioms, but there is also one very important difference. In Axiom A5 there is no restriction on x, so that every element has an additive inverse. In Axiom M5 every element x *different from* 0 has a multiplicative inverse. Nothing whatsoever is asserted about 0. Later, after the distributive axiom is stated, we can prove that 0 does not have a multiplicative inverse. Let us see now what we can prove about multiplication on the basis of Axioms M1 to M5.

Theorem 4–5 (*Restricted Multiplicative Cancellation*)

$$\forall a \neq 0, \forall x,y, (xa = ya) \to (x = y).$$

Proof: Suppose that $a \neq 0$ and $xa = ya$. By Axiom M5, $\exists b$ such that $ab = 1$. Then

$$(xa)b = (ya)b,$$
$$x(ab) = y(ab),$$
$$x \cdot 1 = y \cdot 1,$$
$$x = y.$$

(The student should supply the reasons.)

   Corollary. $\forall a \neq 0, \forall x,y, (ax = ay) \to (x = y).$

Theorem 4–6 (*Restricted Uniqueness of Multiplicative Inverse*)

$$\forall x \neq 0, \forall y,z, (xy = 1) \wedge (xz = 1) \to (y = z).$$

Proof: If $xy = 1$ and $xz = 1$, then $xy = xz$, so $y = z$ by the corollary, since $x \neq 0$.

Definition 4–3. For $x \neq 0$, the unique multiplicative inverse of x guaranteed by Axiom M5 and Theorem 4–6 is called the *inverse of x* or the *reciprocal of x* and is written x^{-1}.

Theorem 4–7. $\forall x \neq 0$, x^{-1} has a unique multiplicative inverse, which we shall denote by $(x^{-1})^{-1}$, and $(x^{-1})^{-1} = x$.

Proof: Given $x \neq 0$, let $y = x^{-1}$. Then, since $yx = xy = 1$, y has at least one multiplicative inverse (namely, x). Suppose that z is a multiplicative inverse of y. Then $yz = 1$, and

$$z = z \cdot 1 = 1 \cdot z = (xy)z$$
$$= x(yz) = x \cdot 1 = x.$$

This proves the theorem.

Theorem 4–8. $\forall a \neq 0$, $\forall b$, there is a unique element x satisfying $ax = b$.

Proof: Given a and b, with $a \neq 0$, we know that a^{-1} exists. Define $x = a^{-1}b$. Then

$$ax = a(a^{-1}b) = (aa^{-1})b = 1 \cdot b = b \cdot 1 = b.$$

Thus x is a solution. If y is a solution, then $ay = b$, so $ax = ay$, and $x = y$ by the corollary of Theorem 4–5. Thus there is exactly one solution.

Definition 4–4.   For $a \neq 0$, $b/a =_{df}$ the unique solution of $ax = b$. Thus we can write $1/a$ for a^{-1}, and frequently we do.

We should take careful note that division by 0 is not permitted by this definition. The inscription "$b/0$" is completely meaningless to us so far. We could, if we wished, assign a meaning to it. For example, we could define $b/0 = 17$ for every b. This would be most unwise, however, for then almost every statement made about b/a would have to be split into two cases: one for $a \neq 0$, one for $a = 0$. The only sensible definition would be one that makes $x = b/a$ equivalent to $ax = b$, and this is possible only if a unique solution exists. Later, after introducing one more axiom, we shall see that $0 \cdot x = 0$ for all x. From this it follows that if $b \neq 0$, $0 \cdot x = b$ has no solution, and that if $b = 0$, $0 \cdot x = b$ has all of R as its solution set. Thus, the equation $0 \cdot x = b$ *never* has a unique solution, no matter what b is. We shall therefore not assign any meaning to "$b/0$." Nor are we under any compulsion to assign a meaning. The fact that we—or anyone else— can make certain pencil scratches on a piece of paper does not force us to ascribe mathematical meaning to those scratches. To help the student remember that division by zero is not defined by us, we submit the following immortal verse:

Ode to the Impossible

Said Nero unto Julius Caesar,
"This problem really should be easier."

Said Julius Caesar unto Nero,
"You never can divide by zero!"

In spite of all our protestations, however, there will be some students drawn, as a moth to the flame, to the mystical "infinity" as a value for $b/0$. It is true that the symbol "∞" is used in various contexts in mathematics, but always with precisely defined meanings. There is no point in discussing those uses here, since we are interested in the real number system R. No matter what else "∞" is used for, it cannot be an element of R.

EXERCISES 4–3

1. Simplify, assuming that $2(=_{df} 1 + 1)$ is not equal to 0:
   (a) $(2^{-1})^{-1}$.
   (b) $((2^{-1})^{-1})^{-1}$.
   (c) $(((2^{-1})^{-1})^{-1})^{-1}$.

2. For $x \in R$, $x \neq 0$, define $g(x) = x^{-1}$. Prove

$$\forall x \neq 0, \forall y \neq 0, (g(x) = g(y)) \to (x = y).$$

3. Prove $\forall a \neq 0, \forall b, b/a = ba^{-1}$.

4. Prove $\forall a \neq 0, \forall b, (a^{-1} \neq 0) \to (b/a^{-1} = ba)$.

*5. On the basis of Axioms A1 to A5 and M1 to M5 *alone*, can you prove that the reciprocal of a nonzero element is also nonzero?

6. Supply all the reasons in the proof of Theorem 4–5.

7. Prove the corollary of Theorem 4–5.

8. How do the proofs of Theorems 4–4 and 4–8 differ?

9. Discuss the meaning of "$\sqrt{+-}$."

10. Discuss: The only solution of $x^2 = 2x$ is 2, because $\{x|x^2 = 2x\} = \{x|x = 2\} = \{2\}$.

11. Prove: For all a and c, and for all $b \neq 0$, $d \neq 0$, if $bd \neq 0$, then

$$\left(\frac{a}{b}\right) \cdot \left(\frac{c}{d}\right) = \left(\frac{ac}{bd}\right).$$

4–4. THE DISTRIBUTIVE AXIOM

So far we have not postulated any connection between the operations of addition and multiplication. Without such a connection, many results about the real numbers cannot be proved to be true. In fact, we can construct a very simple system which satisfies Axioms A1 to A5 and M1 to M5, but in which $0 \cdot 0 \neq 0$. This system H has exactly two elements, 0 and 1, and the two operations are given explicitly by Table 4–2. It is an easy exercise to prove that $(H, +, \cdot)$ satisfies Axioms A1 to A5 and M1 to M5. Another example is the system K, with three elements 0, 1, 2 and with Table 4–3. Such examples are quite easy to construct, but hardly worthwhile, except to illustrate our point, that a bi-operational system is rather uninteresting unless the two operations are strongly connected with each other. The distributive law provides the needed tie-up.

TABLE 4–2

+	0	1		·	0	1
0	0	1		0	1	0
1	1	0		1	0	1

TABLE 4–3

+	0	1	2
0	0	1	2
1	1	2	0
2	2	0	1

·	0	1	2
0	2	0	1
1	0	1	2
2	1	2	0

The Distributive Axiom:

D. $\forall x,y,z,\ x(y + z) = xy + xz$.

Once Axiom D is adjoined to Axioms A and M, there arises a rich and intricate structure called a *field*. Most of the usual algebraic facts can now be obtained with comparative ease. We shall prove a few of the important ones.

Theorem 4–9. $\forall x,\ 0 \cdot x = 0$.

Proof: For any x, $0 + 0 \cdot x = 0 \cdot x = (0 + 0)x = 0 \cdot x + 0 \cdot x$. By additive cancellation, $0 = 0 \cdot x$. (The student should supply the reasons for all steps.)

Theorem 4–10. *There is no solution to the equation* $0 \cdot x = 1$.

Proof: For every $x,\ 0 \cdot x = 0 \neq 1$.

At this point the student should review our previous remarks and convince himself that division by zero is impossible in any field.

Theorem 4–11. $\forall x,\ (-1)x = -x$.

Proof: For any x,

$$x + (-1)x = 1 \cdot x + (-1)x$$
$$= (1 + (-1))x$$
$$= 0 \cdot x$$
$$= 0.$$

By the definition of $-x$ as the unique solution y of

$$0 = x + y,$$

we see that

$$-x = (-1)x.$$

Theorem 4–12. $(-1)(-1) = 1$.
Proof: By Theorem 4–3, $1 = -(-1)$. By Theorem 4–11 (with $x = -1$),

$$(-1)(-1) = -(-1).$$

Therefore

$$1 = (-1)(-1).$$

Theorem 4–13. $\forall a,b,\ (-a)(-b) = ab$.
Proof: For all a and b,

$$\begin{aligned}
(-a)(-b) &= ((-1)a)((-1)b) \\
&= (-1)[a((-1)b)] \\
&= (-1)[(a(-1))b] \\
&= (-1)[((-1)a)b] \\
&= (-1)[(-1)(ab)] \\
&= [(-1)(-1)](ab) \\
&= 1 \cdot (ab) \\
&= ab.
\end{aligned}$$

(The student should supply the reasons for all steps.)

The following important theorem asserts, in words, that the product of two nonzero elements is also nonzero. It is true in every field, of course, since only the field axioms A, M, and D are used in the proof.

Theorem 4–14. $\forall x,y,\ (x \neq 0 \wedge y \neq 0) \rightarrow (xy \neq 0)$.
Proof: Suppose that x and y are elements which make the hypothesis true but not the conclusion: $x \neq 0$, $y \neq 0$, but $xy = 0$. Then x has a reciprocal (multiplicative inverse) x^{-1}, and

$$\begin{aligned}
y = 1 \cdot y &= (x^{-1}x)y \\
&= x^{-1}(xy) \\
&= x^{-1} \cdot 0 \\
&= 0 \cdot x^{-1} \\
&= 0,
\end{aligned}$$

which contradicts our assumption that $y \neq 0$.

⟦The student may be a little mystified by the succession of equalities in the preceding proof. Although he undoubtedly can supply a reason for every step, he may very well not see the motivations for the steps nor how we came to think of them. For this reason, we offer the following somewhat more natural proof:

Given $x \neq 0$, $y \neq 0$, but $xy = 0$, we wish to "solve for y" in the equation $xy = 0$. This is done by dividing both sides by the coefficient of y, which is x. The division is possible, since $x \neq 0$. Dividing by x is equivalent to multiplying by x^{-1}. Thus,

$$x^{-1}(xy) = x^{-1} \cdot 0 = 0 \cdot x^{-1} = 0.$$

But

$$x^{-1}(xy) = (x^{-1}x)y = 1 \cdot y = y.$$

Therefore $y = 0$, which is the required contradiction.

If we read the second string of equalities backward, then connect with the first string read forward, we arrive at the original short proof. Of course, we can give even shorter proofs if we are willing to omit some "obvious" steps.

In studying mathematical proofs the student—as well as the mature mathematician—will sometimes be baffled by a seeming lack of motivation. The individual steps are clear, but the key ideas, the driving mechanism of the proof, may be hidden. Some mathematicians are more prone to such tours de force than others, and seem to delight in the "bolt from the blue." It is really not their intention to mystify the reader. They merely strive for economy and perfection. The great mathematician Gauss, whose motto was "pauca sed matura" ("few but ripe"), felt that after a building was erected the scaffolding should be removed. He desired to make his works perfectly flawless gems, without any superfluous accretions to mar their brilliance. Many important discoveries of his (including non-Euclidean geometry) were unpublished during his lifetime because he had not perfected them to his satisfaction.

It is a common experience that a lecturer presents his material in such a smooth and polished manner that the audience is unaware of the difficulties he had to overcome. Only those who have tried to surmount the same obstacles can fully appreciate his efforts. In this respect the partially unprepared lecturer, who knows the general idea of the proof but must work out the details as he goes, may be the more illuminating instructor. But there is also a moral for the student here. Before studying the proof of a theorem, let him try to prove it himself. If he is successful, so much the better. If he is only partly successful, then he will have taken some of the steps, at least, and will have a greater appreciation of the finished product. Reading, especially in mathematics, should be a cooperative enterprise.]

An alternate form of Theorem 4–14 is the following.

Theorem 4–15. $\forall x,y,\ (xy = 0) \to (x = 0 \vee y = 0)$.
The proof follows from Theorem 4–14 and the tautological equivalence of

$$(\sim p \wedge \sim q) \to \sim r$$

and

$$r \to (p \vee q).$$

Theorem 4–16. $\forall a,b,c,\ a(b - c) = ab - ac$.
Proof: For all a, b, c,

$$
\begin{aligned}
a(b - c) &= a(b + (-c)) \\
&= ab + a(-c) \\
&= ab + a((-1)c) \\
&= ab + (a(-1))c \\
&= ab + ((-1)a)c \\
&= ab + (-1)(ac) \\
&= ab - ac.
\end{aligned}
$$

EXERCISES 4–4

1. Prove $\forall a,b,\ -(a + b) = -a - b$.
2. Prove $\forall a,b,\ -(a - b) = b - a$.
3. Prove $\forall a,b,\ (a + b)(a - b) = a^2 - b^2$. ($a^2$ means $a \cdot a$, of course.)
4. Find the flaw in the following argument: Let $a = b = 1$. Then $a^2 - b^2 = a - b$. Therefore $(a + b)(a - b) = a - b$. Therefore $a + b = 1$. Therefore $2 = 1 + 1 = a + b = 1$.
5. Prove $\forall a,b,c$, if a/c has meaning, then

$$\frac{a}{c} + \frac{b}{c} = \frac{a + b}{c}.$$

6. Prove $\forall a,c,\ \forall b \neq 0,\ \forall d \neq 0,\ (a/b)(c/d) = ac/bd$.
7. Prove $\forall a,\ \forall b \neq 0,\ \forall c \neq 0,\ ac/bc = a/b$.
8. Prove $\forall a,c,\ \forall b \neq 0,\ \forall d \neq 0,\ (a/b) + (c/d) = (ad + bc)/bd$.
9. Prove $\forall a,b,c,\ (abc = 0) \to (a = 0) \vee (b = 0) \vee (c = 0)$.
10. Find the solution set of $x(x - 2) = x$.
11. Find the set of all pairs (x,y) for which $xy = 0$.
12. Find the solution set of $(x - 5)^2 = 0$.
13. Prove that $\forall a \neq 0,\ \forall b \neq 0$, dividing by a/b is equivalent to multiplying by b/a.

TABLE 4-4

+	0	1		0	1
0	0	1	0	0	0
1	1	0	1	0	1

TABLE 4-5

+	0	1	2		0	1	2
0	0	1	2	0	0	0	0
1	1	2	0	1	0	1	2
2	2	0	1	2	0	2	1

14. Discuss $\forall x$, $x/x = 1$.

15. Can you prove, on the basis of the axioms for a field, that $1 + 1 \neq 0$?

16. Show that system F given by Table 4–4 is a field: $F = \{0.1\}$.

17. Show that the systems H and K in Tables 4–2 and 4–3 are not fields.

*18. Show that system G, given by Table 4–5, is a field: $G = \{0,1,2\}$.

19. Recall that $2 =_{df} 1 + 1$. Let J be a field in which $2 = 0$ (there are many). Prove:

　(a) $\forall x,y \in J$, $(x + y)^2 = x^2 + y^2$.

　(b) $\forall x,y \in J$, $(x + y)^4 = x^4 + y^4$.

20. Let L be a field in which $3 = 0$ ($3 =_{df} 2 + 1$). Prove $\forall x,y \in L$, $(x + y)^3 = x^3 + y^3$.

21. Let M be a field in which $6 = 0$. Prove that M is of type J or of type L (Problems 19 and 20) but not both.

22. Memorize the last line of "Ode to the Impossible."

4-5. THE ORDER AXIOMS

As we have seen, there are many essentially different (nonisomorphic) systems which satisfy Axioms A, M, and D. In order to narrow down the field we now introduce four axioms pertaining to a primitive order relation "$<$," which we interpret as "is less than." The first two deal only with this relation, the third connects it with addition, and the fourth connects it with multiplication.

Order Axioms:

O1. $\forall x,y$, *one and only one of the following holds:*

(a) $x < y$, (b) $x = y$, (c) $y < x$ *(trichotomy).*

O2. $\forall x,y,z, (x < y) \wedge (y < z) \rightarrow (x < z)$ *(transitivity).*

O3. $\forall a,x,y, (x < y) \rightarrow (a + x < a + y)$.

O4. $\forall b,x,y, (0 < b) \wedge (x < y) \rightarrow (bx < by)$.

Any field which satisfies Axioms O1 to O4 is called an *ordered field.* These axioms are very effective in limiting the range of possibilities. For example, it can be proved that no ordered field has a finite number of elements. We shall not pause to carry out the proof here, but the interested student could convince himself that a field with three elements, say, cannot be ordered.

At this point it is convenient to introduce some notation which is undoubtedly familiar to the student.

Definition 4–5. For all x,y,

(a) $(x > y) \leftrightarrow (y < x)$.

(b) $(x \le y) \leftrightarrow (x < y) \vee (x = y)$.

(c) $(x \ge y) \leftrightarrow (y \le x)$.

Definition 4–6. *For all* x,

(a) x *is positive* $\leftrightarrow x > 0$.

(b) x *is negative* $\leftrightarrow x < 0$.

(c) x *is nonnegative* $\leftrightarrow x \ge 0$.

EXERCISE 4–5

Prove that the sum of two positive numbers is positive.

A few significant theorems can now be stated and proved.

Theorem 4–17. For all x,

$$x \text{ is positive} \leftrightarrow -x \text{ is negative,}$$

and

$$x \text{ is negative} \leftrightarrow -x \text{ is positive.}$$

Proof: Suppose that x is positive. By Definition 4–6(a), $x > 0$, and by Definition 4–5(a), $0 < x$. Using Axiom O3 to add $-x$ to both sides, we get $-x < 0$. By Definition 4–6(b), this means that $-x$ is negative. We leave the rest of the proof to the student.

Theorem 4–18. $1 > 0$.

Proof: By Axiom O1, we have exactly one of

$$\text{(a) } 0 < 1, \text{ (b) } 0 = 1, \text{ (c) } 1 < 0.$$

Now (b) is ruled out, since 0 and 1 are distinct elements. Suppose (c) holds. This means that 1 is negative, so -1 is positive, by Theorem 4–17, that is, $0 < -1$. In Axiom O4, take $b = -1$, $x = 0$, $y = -1$. Then $(-1) \cdot 0 < (-1)(-1)$. But $(-1) \cdot 0 = 0$ and $(-1)(-1) = 1$ (why?). Therefore $0 < 1$, which is (a). This contradicts Axioms O1. The only remaining possibility is (a), which is equivalent to $1 > 0$. This completes the proof.

Corollary. $-1 < 0$.

Theorem 4–19. Let p, q be positive, m, n, negative. Then
(a) pq is positive.
(b) pn is negative.
(c) mn is positive.
Proof: In Axiom O4, take $b = p$, $x = 0$, $y = q$. Then $p \cdot 0 < p \cdot q$. But $p \cdot 0 = 0$, so $0 < pq$, and pq is positive. This proves (a). Next, since n is negative, $n < 0$. Multiplying by the positive number p and using Axiom O4, we get $pn < p \cdot 0 = 0$. This proves (b). Finally since m, n are both negative, $-m$ and $-n$ are both positive. Therefore $mn = (-m)(-n)$ is also positive. This proves (c).

Notice that we have proved the usual rule of signs for multiplication. We can summarize it by Table 4–6.

It is worthwhile to warn the student here that a symbol such as "$-a$" does not necessarily represent a negative number. Thus, if $a = -1$, then $-a = 1 > 0$; if $a = 0$, then $-a = 0$; if $a = 1$, then $-a < 0$. Similarly, $+a \, [=_{df} a]$ is not necessarily positive.

Theorem 4–20. Let p be positive, n negative. Then

(a) $\dfrac{1}{p}$ is positive.   (b) $\dfrac{1}{n}$ is negative.

TABLE 4–6

	pos.	neg.
pos.	pos.	neg.
neg.	neg.	pos.

Proof: If $1/p = 0$, then $1 = p \cdot (1/p) = p \cdot 0 = 0$, which is false. If $1/p$ is negative, then $1 = p \cdot (1/p) = (\text{positive}) \cdot (\text{negative}) = \text{negative}$, which is false. The only remaining possibility is (a). The proof of (b) is left to the student.

Theorem 4–21.   Let p, q be positive, with $p > q$. Then $1/p < 1/q$.
Proof: By Theorem 4–20, $1/p$ and $1/q$ are positive, so $(1/p)(1/q)$ is positive. Multiplying both sides of $p > q$ by this positive number (Axiom O4), we get $1/q > 1/p$, which is equivalent to the conclusion.

Theorem 4–22. $\forall x, x^2 \geq 0$.
Proof: Left to student.

EXAMPLE 4–1.   Let $f(x) = x^2 - 2x$ $(x \in R)$. Show that f assumes a minimum value. What is that value?
Solution:

$$f(x) = x^2 - 2x$$
$$= (x^2 - 2x + 1) - 1$$
$$= (x - 1)^2 - 1.$$

By Theorem 4–22, $(x - 1)^2 \geq 0$, so for all $x \in R, f(x) \geq -1$. But $f(1) = -1$, so $f(x) \geq f(1)$ $(x \in R)$. Thus, the minimum of f is $f(1) = -1$.

EXAMPLE 4–2.   Let $a \in R$, $f(x) = x^2 - ax$ $(x \in R)$. Show that f assumes a minimum value. What is that value, and for what x is it assumed?
Solution:

$$f(x) = x^2 - ax$$
$$= x^2 - ax + \frac{a^2}{4} - \frac{a^2}{4}$$
$$= (x - a/2)^2 - a^2/4.$$

By Theorem 4–22, $(x - a/2)^2 \geq 0$, so

$$f(x) \geq -\frac{a^2}{4}.$$

But $f(a/2) = -a^2/4$, so

$$f(x) \geq f\left(\frac{a}{2}\right) \qquad (x \in R).$$

Thus, the minimum of f is $f(a/2) = -a^2/4$.

EXAMPLE 4–3.　Let $a,b \in R, f(x) = x^2 + ax + b \, (x \in R)$. Show that f assumes a minimum value. What is that value, and for what x is it assumed?

Solution: The minimum of f is $f(-a/2) = b - (a^2/4)$.

EXERCISES 4–6

1. Suppose that $a < b < c < d$. Prove $c - b < d - a$.
2. Suppose that $a < b < 0$. Prove $a^2 > b^2$.
3. Given $a > 0, b > 0$. Prove $a^2 > b^2 \leftrightarrow a > b$.
4. Given $a > 0, b > 0$. Prove $a^3 > b^3 \leftrightarrow a^2 > b^2$.
5. Prove that there is no largest number.
6. Prove in detail that 3 is positive.
7. Prove $\forall x,y,z, (x \leq y) \wedge (y \leq z) \rightarrow (x \leq z)$.
8. Complete the proof of Theorem 4–17.
9. Prove Theorem 4–22.
10. Find the minimum of $3x^2 - 4x + 7 \, (x \in R)$.
11. Carry out the solution of Example 4–3.
*12. Let $a_1,a_2,a_3,a_4 \in R$, and let

$$f(x) = (x - a_1)^2 + (x - a_2)^2 + (x - a_3)^2 + (x - a_4)^2 \qquad (x \in R).$$

Show that the minimum of f is attained at $x = \bar{a}$, where $\bar{a} = \frac{1}{4}(a_1 + a_2 + a_3 + a_4)$, and that $f(\bar{a}) = a_1^2 + a_2^2 + a_3^2 + a_4^2 - 4\bar{a}^2$. Also, prove that

$$[\tfrac{1}{4}(a_1 + a_2 + a_3 + a_4)]^2 \leq \tfrac{1}{4}(a_1^2 + a_2^2 + a_3^2 + a_4^2).$$

13. Let $a,b \in R$. Prove $ab \leq \frac{1}{2}(a^2 + b^2)$.
14. Prove $\forall x > 0, x + (1/x) \geq 2$.
15. Let $a > 0, b > 0$. Prove

(a) $2 \leq \dfrac{b}{a} + \dfrac{a}{b}$.

(b) $4 \leq (a + b)\left(\dfrac{1}{a} + \dfrac{1}{b}\right)$.

(c) $\dfrac{2}{(1/a) + (1/b)} \leq \dfrac{a + b}{2}$.

*16. Let $a,b,c,d \in R$.　Prove $abcd \leq \frac{1}{4}(a^4 + b^4 + c^4 + d^4)$. [Hint: Use Problem 13 a few times.]

17. Another way of introducing order in a field is to take as primitive a set P (intended as the set of positive numbers) and to take as axioms the

following:

P1. $\forall x$, *one and only one of the following holds:*

(a) $x \in P$, (b) $x = 0$, (c) $-x \in P$.

P2. $\forall x,y$, $(x \in P) \wedge (y \in P) \rightarrow (x + y \in P)$.

P3. $\forall x,y$, $(x \in P) \wedge (y \in P) \rightarrow (x \cdot y \in P)$.

Then one *defines* $x < y$ to mean $y - x \in P$.

On the basis of the above, Axioms O1 to O4 are *theorems*. Prove them.

EXERCISES 4–7

The following exercises deal with the absolute value function, defined by $|x| = x$ for $x \geq 0$, $|x| = -x$ for $x < 0$. This will be of importance in later chapters.

Prove the following:

1. $|x|^2 = x^2$ $(x \in R)$.

2. $-|x| \leq x \leq |x|$ $(x \in R)$.

3. $|xy| = |x| \cdot |y|$ $(x,y \in R)$.

4. $|a| \leq |b| \leftrightarrow a^2 \leq b^2$ $(a,b \in R)$.

5. $|x + y| \leq |x| + |y|$ $(x,y \in R)$. [*Hint*: Put $x + y = a$, $|x| + |y| = b$ in Problem 4 and then use Problems 1, 2, and 3.]

6. $|x - y| \leq |x| + |y|$ $(x,y \in R)$.

7. (a) $|a| - |b| \leq |a - b|$,

   (b) $-|a - b| \leq |a| - |b|$,

   (c) $||a| - |b|| \leq |a - b|$ $(a,b \in R)$.

8. $|x| < c \leftrightarrow -c < x < c$ $(x,c \in R)$.

9. Show that $\{x|5 < x < 9\} = \{x||x - 7| < 2\}$. In general, show that for $a,b \in R$,

$$\{x|a < x < b\} = \left\{ x \left| \left| x - \frac{a + b}{2} \right| < \frac{b - a}{2} \right. \right\}.$$

4–6. THE NATURAL NUMBERS AND MATHEMATICAL INDUCTION

We have not yet completed the axiom system for the reals, but it is worthwhile to call a temporary halt. We shall show how in every ordered field we can find a set N of elements which act just like the familiar natural numbers $1, 2, 3, \ldots$. Once this is done, we can establish the important *principle of mathematical induction*.

Given an ordered field F, how do we single out the "natural numbers" in F? Certainly we should include 1, which is given to us by the axiom system as one of the primitives. Next, of course, we want $1 + 1$, to which we assign the symbol "2."

Thus

$$2 =_{df} 1 + 1.$$

This we can follow by

$$3 =_{df} 2 + 1,$$
$$4 =_{df} 3 + 1,$$
$$5 =_{df} 4 + 1,$$

and so on. The set that we have defined in this way is the one we want.

This sounds easy, and is probably acceptable to most readers. Unfortunately, this procedure leaves a great deal to be desired. The trouble is that we have *not* defined a set at all. If we try to write down the supposed definition, we get something like

$$N =_{df} \{x \in F | x = 1 \lor x = 2 \lor x = 3 \lor x = 4 \lor x = 5 \lor and\ so\ on\},$$

or

$$N =_{df} \{x \in F | x = 1 \lor x = 2 \lor x = 3 \lor x = 4 \lor x = 5 \lor \cdots\},$$

or

$$N =_{df} \{1,2,3,4,5,\ldots\}.$$

These inscriptions are adequate enough on the intuitive level to indicate our meaning. Indeed we spoke, in the preceding paragraph, about the "familiar natural numbers 1, 2, 3, ..." But then we were discussing informally the counting numbers that we have used since childhood. *We were operating in the P-plane.* The task that we have set ourselves is to make precise this very idea of the counting numbers or natural numbers and to incorporate this idea in the C-plane. The three attempts above involve nonmathematical language such as "and so on" or "...". They are not satisfactory definitions in the C-plane.

At this point the reader may quite understandably lose patience and say, "Well, I know what I mean by '*and so on*,' and so do you. Then why all this fuss about something that we both understand?" The answer is that if we truly understand, we should be able to state what we mean in the mathematical language that we have fashioned, or else admit that that language is not good enough—in which case we should improve it. The alternative is to throw up our hands in despair and continue to operate in the P-plane. Fortunately we do not need to give up nor to change our mathematical language. All that we need is a little perseverance. The effort to find a solution will be amply rewarded by a deeper understanding than we had before.

Let us make a fresh start. Certainly we want N to be a subset of F. Certainly we want N to contain 1. Certainly we want to be able to add 1 to any element of N and still get an element of N. This much, at least, we can formalize. Let us define a σ-*set* ("σ" to indicate "successor") as a set S in F satisfying

(a) $1 \in S$,

(b) $\forall x, x \in S \to x + 1 \in S$.

Thus, we can say briefly that we want N to be a σ-set.

Does this capture the idea? Not quite, for there are many σ-sets. For example, F itself is a σ-set. So also are the following:

$$\{x \in F \mid x \geq 0\},$$
$$\{x \in F \mid x \geq 1\},$$
$$\{1\} \cup \{x \in F \mid x \geq 2\}.$$

Among all the σ-sets available to us, how do we single out N? Clearly, the ones we have mentioned fail because they have superfluous elements. None of them appears to lack any of the elements we do want. After experimenting with a few more, this conclusion seems to be borne out: Every σ-set we can construct contains the elements that we are trying to characterize. Turn this statement around: The elements that we are trying to characterize belong to every σ-set. But this is practically the definition we seek! Let us try:

Definition 4–7. $N =_{\mathrm{df}} \{x \mid \forall S, S \text{ is a } \sigma\text{-set} \to x \in S\}$.

In words, N is defined as *the intersection of all σ-sets*.

A slight worry arises, but is quickly dispelled. Is N itself a σ-set, as we would hope and demand? First, N is clearly a subset of F. Next, since 1 is an element of every σ-set, $1 \in N$ by the definition of N. Therefore N satisfies (a). Finally, suppose that $x \in N$. If S is any σ-set, $x \in S$, again by the definition of N. But if $x \in S$ then $x + 1 \in S$, by (b). This holds for every σ-set, that is,

$$\forall S, S \text{ is a } \sigma\text{-set} \to x + 1 \in S.$$

By the definition of N, $x + 1 \in N$. Thus,

$$\forall x, x \in N \to x + 1 \in N,$$

and (b) is satisfied by N. Since N is a subset of F satisfying (a) and (b), it is a σ-set. In fact, it is the smallest possible σ-set:

(*) $\forall S, S \text{ is a } \sigma\text{-set} \to N \subset S$.

Our definition appears to be quite successful. We wanted N to contain *all* those elements and *only* those elements which arise from 1 by unlimited addition of 1. The *"all"* is taken care of by the fact that N is a σ-set, the *"only"* by the fact that it is the smallest one. Furthermore, the definition can be used effectively to prove results about the natural numbers.

EXAMPLE 4–4.   Prove that $\forall n \in N, n \geq 1$.
Solution: $S = \{x \mid x \geq 1\}$ is a σ-set, so $N \subset S$.

EXAMPLE 4–5.   Prove that $\forall n \in N, n = 1 \vee n \geq 2$.
Solution: $S_1 = \{x \mid x = 1 \vee x \geq 2\}$ is a σ-set, so $N \subset S$.

EXAMPLE 4–6.   Prove that $\forall n \in N, n = 1 \vee n - 1 \in N$.
Solution: Let $T = \{x \in N \mid x = 1 \vee x - 1 \in N\}$. Clearly $1 \in T$. If $x \in T$, then $(x + 1) - 1 \in N$, so $x + 1 \in T$. Therefore T is a σ-set and $N \subset T$.

EXAMPLE 4–7.   Prove that there is no natural number n such that $2 < n < 3$.
Solution: Assume that $\exists n \in N, 2 < n < 3$. Then $n \neq 1$, so by Example 4–6, $n - 1 \in N$. But $1 < n - 1 < 2$, contradicting Example 4–5. Therefore, $\sim(\exists n \in N, 2 < n < 3)$.

EXAMPLE 4–8.   Prove that $\forall k \in N$, there is no natural number n such that $k < n < k + 1$.
Solution: Let $S = \{k \in N \mid \sim(\exists n \in N, k < n < k + 1)\}$. By Example 4–5, $1 \in S$. Suppose that $k \in S$ but $k + 1 \notin S$. Then $\exists n \in N, k + 1 < n < k + 2$. Now $n > k + 1 \geq 1 + 1 > 1$, by Example 4–4, so $n \neq 1$, and by Example 4–6, $n - 1 \in N$. But $k < n - 1 < k + 1$, contradicting the fact that $k \in S$. Therefore, $\forall k, k \in S \rightarrow k + 1 \in S$. This shows that S is a σ-set and therefore $N \subset S$.

Logical note: The mode of inference used in the preceding proof is

$$\frac{(P \wedge \sim Q) \rightarrow \sim P}{\therefore \quad P \rightarrow Q}$$

The student may verify that the truth table for $(p \wedge \sim q) \rightarrow \sim p$ is the same as that for $p \rightarrow q$.

Corollary 1. $\forall n, k \in N, k \leq n \vee k \geq n + 1$.
Corollary 2. $\forall n, k \in N, k > n \rightarrow k \geq n + 1$.
Corollary 3. $\forall n, k \in N, k < n + 1 \rightarrow k \leq m$.
Corollary 4.   For $k \in N$, define $I_k = \{n \in N \mid 1 \leq n \leq k\}$. Then $\forall k \in N$, $I_{k+1} = I_k \cup \{k + 1\}$.

Corollary 5. For $k \in N$, let D be a nonempty subset of I_k. Then D contains a largest element.

Let us now make an easy but profoundly important observation. Suppose that S is a subset of N and that S is a σ-set. Then $N \subset S$, by (∗). Since $S \subset N$, we conclude that $S = N$. Somewhat more explicitly, suppose that
(1) $S \subset N$,
(2) $1 \in S$,
(3) $\forall x, x \in S \rightarrow x + 1 \in S$.
Then S is a σ-set contained in N, so
(4) $S = N$.
The fact that (1), (2), and (3) together imply (4) is one form of the principle of mathematical induction.

Another form, which may be more familiar, is the following. Let $P(n)$ be a predicate of the variable n ranging over N [loosely, $P(n)$ is a "statement depending on $n \in N$"]. Suppose that
(A) $P(1)$ is true.
(B) $\forall n \in N, P(n) \rightarrow P(n + 1)$.
Then
(C) $\forall n \in N, P(n)$ is true.
To see that (A) and (B) imply (C), let

$$S = \{ n \in N | P(n) \text{ is true} \}.$$

Then
(1) $S \subset N$.
By (A),
(2) $1 \in S$.
By (B),
(3) $\forall x, x \in S \rightarrow x + 1 \in S$.
Thus S satisfies (1), (2), (3) above, and (4) follows: The truth set S of $P(n)$ is all of N. This means that (C) holds. That

$$(A) \wedge (B) \rightarrow (C)$$

is the usual form of the principle of mathematical induction.

EXERCISES 4-8

1. Prove that for all $n \in N$,

$$1 + 2 + 3 + \cdots + n = \tfrac{1}{2}n(n + 1).$$

2. Prove that for all $n \in N$,

$$1 + 3 + 5 + \cdots + (2n - 1) = n^2.$$

3. Prove that for all $n \in N$, $n^2 - n$ is even.
4. Prove that for all $n \in N$, $n^3 - n$ is divisible by 3.

We now state and prove a theorem which can frequently be used instead of the principle of mathematical induction.

Theorem 4–23. Every nonempty subset of N contains a least element. *Proof:* Let A be a nonempty subset of N, and let k be an element of A. Define D as the set of all $n \in N$ which are less than *every* element of A:

$$D = \{n \in N | \forall a \in A, n < a\}.$$

Clearly D is a subset of $I_k = \{n \in N | 1 \le n \le k\}$. If $D = \emptyset$, then $1 \in A$, and 1 is the least element in A. If $D \sim \emptyset$, then by Corollary 5 of Example 4–8, D has a largest element d. Every $a \in A$ satisfies $a > d$, so by Corollary 2, $a \ge d + 1$. Also $d + 1 \in A$, for if not, $d + 1$ would be an element of D larger than d. Therefore $d + 1$ is the least element in A.

Mathematical induction can be used to discover results as well as to verify them.

EXAMPLE 4–9.   We already know that

$$(\forall n) \; 1^0 + 2^0 + 3^0 + \cdots + n^0 = n,$$
$$(\forall n) \; 1 + 2 + 3 + \cdots + n = \tfrac{1}{2}n^2 + \tfrac{1}{2}n.$$

Let us guess that the sum of the first n squares

$$S_n = 1^2 + 2^2 + 3^2 + \cdots + n^2$$

is a polynomial in n of degree 3, say,

$$f(n) = An^3 + Bn^2 + Cn + D,$$

where A, B, C, D are undetermined constants. We shall determine the constants in such a way that induction works, that is, statements (A) and (B) above hold, with $P(n)$ standing for $S_n = f(n)$. For (A) to hold, $P(1)$ must be true:

  (a) $1 = S_1 = f(1) = A + B + C + D.$
For (B) to hold, we need

$$(\forall n) \; S_n = f(n) \rightarrow S_{n+1} = f(n + 1).$$

This will be true if

$$S_{n+1} - S_n = f(n + 1) - f(n) \qquad (n \in N),$$

that is, if

$$(n + 1)^2 = f(n + 1) - f(n)$$

$$= A(n + 1)^3 + B(n + 1)^2 + C(n + 1) + D$$

$$- An^3 - Bn^2 - Cn - D$$

$$= A(n^3 + 3n^2 + 3n + 1) + B(n^2 + 2n + 1) + C(n + 1)$$

$$- An^3 - Bn^2 - Cn,$$

$$n^2 + 2n + 1 = 3An^2 + (3A + 2B)n + (A + B + C) \qquad (n \in N).$$

This, in turn, will be true if the coefficients of n^2, n, 1 on both sides are equal:

(b) $1 = 3A$,

(c) $2 = 3A + 2B$,

(d) $1 = A + B + C$.

Thus, the induction will go through if (a), (b), (c), and (d) all are true. From (a) and (d), $D = 0$ (as we might have suspected). From (b), $A = \frac{1}{3}$, and then from (c), $B = \frac{1}{2}$. Finally, from (d), $C = 1 - A - B = \frac{1}{6}$. Therefore,

$$S_n = \tfrac{1}{3}n^3 + \tfrac{1}{2}n^2 + \tfrac{1}{6}n$$

$$= \tfrac{1}{6}(2n^3 + 3n^2 + n)$$

$$= \tfrac{1}{6}n(n + 1)(2n + 1) \qquad (n \in N).$$

The first three or four values of n should be checked.

There is still one important matter to be settled. We have shown how to define a certain subset N of an ordered field F and we have had the temerity to call the elements of N "the natural numbers." Suppose, however, we had started with a different ordered field F^* and constructed in it a set N^* in the same way, by means of the σ-sets in F^*. Since these may be very different from the σ-sets in F, it is possible that N^* is very different from N. Which would we then choose to represent the natural numbers of the P-plane? Fortunately the problem does not arise. It can be shown that there is a one-to-one correspondence between N and N^* which makes 1 in N correspond to $1 \in N^*$, addition in N to addition in N^*, multiplication in N to multiplication in N^*, and order in N to order in N^*. This iso-morphism between any two sets of "natural numbers" obtained in this way allows us to assert that there is "essentially" only one N, and that all others can be gotten from it by a faithful, slavish re-naming or copying procedure. If it is not already clear to the student how the elements of N mirror the counting numbers of the P-plane, we can spell it out quite explicitly.

For each $n \in N$, consider the set $I_n = \{m \in N | 1 \leq m \leq n\}$. Then if A is any set which can be put in one-to-one correspondence with I_n, we shall say that A is an n-element set, or that the *cardinal number* of A is n, or that the number of elements in A is n. For example, since we can match John with 1, Joe with 2, Jim with 3, we can establish a one-to-one correspondence between $A = \{\text{John,Joe,Jim}\}$ and $\{1,2,3\} = I_3$, and we can say that A is a 3-element set. Thus we come full circle to the most primitive ideas of counting. A (nonempty) *finite* set can be defined as one with cardinal number n for some $n \in N$. Similarly we can now make precise the idea of a sequence. Where previously we spoke of the finite sequence $a_1, a_2, a_3, \ldots, a_n$, using "$\ldots$" loosely as "and so on," we can now speak of a function defined on I_n. The infinite sequence $a_1, a_2, a_3, \ldots$ is simply a function defined on N. Thus, as we promised, we have deepened our understanding by learning how to interpret mathematically the loose phrase "and so on."

It should be clearer to the student now why the first three proposed definitions of N were not adequate. One would be hard pressed to give proofs of the kind illustrated above using "handwaving" definitions. A good definition helps us to advance the theory by proving significant results.

EXERCISES 4–9

1. An element of N is *even* or *odd* according as it is of the form $2k$ or $2k - 1$, respectively, for some $k \in N$. Prove by induction that every element of N is either even or odd.

2. Prove $\forall n \in N, (n > 2) \rightarrow (n - 2 \in N)$.

*3. Prove $\forall n, k \in N, (n > k) \rightarrow (n - k \in N)$.

*4. Prove $\forall n, k \in N, n + k \in N$.

*5. Prove $\forall n, k \in N, nk \in N$.

6. Prove $\forall n \in N, (n(n + 1))/2 \in N$.

*7. For $n, k \in N$, show that $\{n \in N | k + 1 \leq m \leq k + n\}$ is an n-element set.

*8. For $n, k \in N$, let A and F be disjoint sets with cardinal numbers n, k, respectively. Prove that $A \cup B$ is an $(n + k)$-element set.

9. Prove that

$$1^3 + 2^3 + 3^3 + \cdots + n^3 = (1 + 2 + 3 + \cdots + n)^2 \qquad (n \in N).$$

10. Prove that for all $n \in N$, the number of subsets of $I_n = \{1, 2, \ldots, n\}$ is 2^n.

[*Hint:* In the induction step (B), consider separately those subsets of I_{n+1} that contain $n + 1$ and those that do not.]

11. (a) Frame a careful definition of "uninteresting natural number."

(b) Let U be the set of uninteresting natural numbers, according to your definition. Is U empty? If not, name one element.

(c) If U is nonempty, does it have a first element? Is the first uninteresting natural number interesting?

12. We build an exponential tower

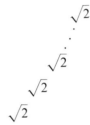

by defining $a_1 = \sqrt{2}$, $a_2 = \sqrt{2}^{a_1}$, $a_3 = \sqrt{2}^{a_2}$, and in general,

$$a_{n+1} = \sqrt{2}^{a_n} \qquad (n \in N).$$

Do you think a_n is greater than 5 for some n? Greater than 50? Greater than 5,000?

Let "$P(n)$" stand for "$a_n < 2$." Is $P(1)$ true? If $P(n)$ is true for some n, what can you say about a_{n+1}? What do you conclude?

13. Prove that for all $n \in N$,

$$\frac{1}{2} + \frac{1}{4} + \frac{1}{8} + \cdots + \frac{1}{2^n} = 1 - \frac{1}{2^n}.$$

14. Let $0 \le h \le 1$. Prove that $\forall n \in N$, $h^n \le h$.

15. Prove by induction: If $h > -1$, then

$$\forall n \in N, (1 + h)^n \ge 1 + nh.$$

16. Call a natural number *acceptable* if it is possible to dissect a square into n squares (not necessarily all of the same size); e.g., 4 and 6 are acceptable:

   (a) Prove that 7 and 8 are acceptable.

   (b) Prove that if n is acceptable, then so is $n + 3$.

   (c) Prove that all natural numbers greater than 5 are acceptable.

 *(d) Prove that 2, 3, and 5 are not acceptable.

17. Prove that for all $n \in N$, $n > 1$,

$$\frac{1}{1 \cdot 2} + \frac{1}{2 \cdot 3} + \frac{1}{3 \cdot 4} + \cdots + \frac{1}{(n-1)n} = 1 - \frac{1}{n}.$$

18. Prove

$$\frac{1}{\sqrt{1} + \sqrt{2}} + \frac{1}{\sqrt{2} + \sqrt{3}} + \frac{1}{\sqrt{3} + \sqrt{4}} + \cdots + \frac{1}{\sqrt{99} + \sqrt{100}} = 9.$$

[*Hint:* $(\sqrt{n+1} + \sqrt{n})(\sqrt{n+1} - \sqrt{n}) = 1.$]

19. Evaluate

$$\left(1 + \frac{1}{1}\right)\left(1 + \frac{1}{2}\right)\left(1 + \frac{1}{3}\right) \cdots \left(1 + \frac{1}{n}\right) \qquad (n \in N).$$

   20. Prove by induction that if $f(B)$ is the number of elements in the finite set B, then

$$f(B_1 \times B_2 \times B_3 \times \cdots \times B_n) = f(B_1)f(B_2)f(B_3) \cdots f(B_n).$$

   21. Discuss the following argument: If "$P(n)$" stands for "n calories a day is a starvation diet," then

      (A) $P(1)$ is true,

      (B) $\forall n \in N$, $P(n) \to P(n + 1)$.

      $\therefore$ $\forall n \in N$, $P(n)$.

   22. Define the sequence (a_n), $n \in N$, by

$$a_1 = 5,$$
$$a_2 = 13,$$
$$a_{n+2} = 5a_{n+1} - 6a_n \qquad (n \in N).$$

For example, $a_3 = 5a_2 - 6a_1 = 65 - 30 = 35$. Prove

$$\forall n \in N, \ a_n = 3^n + 2^n.$$

23. Two sequences (a_n), (b_n), $n \in N$, satisfy

$$\text{(1) } a_{n+1} = 2a_n + 1 \qquad (n \in N),$$

$$\text{(2) } b_{n+1} = 2b_n + 1 \qquad (n \in N).$$

(a) Prove that if $a_1 = b_1$, then $a_n = b_n$ $(n \in N)$.
(b) Prove that the sequence $(2^n A - 1)$, $n \in N$, satisfies (1), no matter what constant A is.
(c) Solve (1) for the case $a_1 = 1$. Is the solution unique?

24. (a) Prove that any two sequences that satisfy

$$\text{(1) } a_{n+2} = 2a_{n+1} - a_n \qquad (n \in N)$$

and that agree for $n = 1$ and $n = 2$ must agree for all $n \in N$.
(b) Prove that $(A + Bn)$ satisfies (1), no matter what constants A and B are.
(c) Find a solution of (1) for the case $a_1 = 1$, $a_2 = 3$. Is the solution unique?
(d) Find a solution of (1) for the case $a_1 = 5$. Is the solution unique?

25. Let (a_n), (b_n), $n \in N$, be sequences satisfying

$$a_{n+1} = 3a_n - 4b_n,$$

$$b_{n+1} = -2a_n + 3b_n \qquad (n \in N).$$

Prove that

$$a_n^2 - 2b_n^2 = a_1^2 - 2b_1^2 \qquad (n \in N).$$

26. Let $u_1 = u_2 = 1$,

$$u_{n+2} = u_{n+1} + u_n \qquad (n \in N).$$

For example, $u_3 = 2$, $u_4 = 3$, $u_5 = 5$, $u_6 = 8$.
(a) For what $n \in N$ is u_n even? (Guess, then prove.)
(b) Prove

$$u_{n+2} = 1 + u_n + u_{n-1} + \cdots + u_1 \qquad (n \in N).$$

*(c) Let $d_n = u_n^2 - u_{n-1}u_{n+1}$ $(n \geq 2)$. Tabulate d_n for $n = 2, 3, \ldots, 7$. Guess a formula for d_n, then prove it.

27. Prove $\forall n \in N$, $2^n > n$.
28. Prove $\forall n \in N$, $3^n > 2n$.
29. Let $0 \leq h \leq 1$. Prove that

$$(1 + h)^n \leq 1 + (2^n - 1)h \qquad (n \in N).$$

4-7. THE RATIONAL NUMBERS

Having defined the set of natural numbers N in an ordered field F, we proceed to define a set $Z \subset F$ which behaves like the system of ordinary whole numbers (in the P-plane) $\{\ldots, -3, -2, -1, 0, 1, 2, \ldots\}$.

Definition 4-8. $Z =_{df} N \cup \{0\} \cup \{-n|n \in N\}$.

The elements of Z are called *integers*. It can be shown that Z is a commutative group with respect to addition, that is, that it satisfies Axioms A1 to 5. It is closed with respect to multiplication but not division (by nonzero elements). To remedy this situation, we now define the set of *rational numbers*.

Definition 4-9. $Q =_{df} \left\{ \dfrac{m}{n} \,\middle|\, m, n \in Z, n \neq 0 \right\}$.

It is not difficult to show that Q is an ordered field. Every ordered field F contains a faithful copy of Q, i.e., an isomorphic system. In particular, the real number system R contains the rationals, and we have

$$N \subset Z \subset Q \subset R.$$

Is it possible that Q is an adequate conceptual image of our "ordinary" number system? In other words, should we just postulate that $R = Q$? For a time the ancient Greeks thought that the rational numbers would serve quite well for all geometrical measurements, until they discovered that the diagonal of a square of unit side had a length which was not rational. This is equivalent to the assertion that there is no element of Q whose square is 2. Let us now prove this celebrated result.

Theorem 4-24. For all $m, n \in N$,

$$\left(\frac{m}{n} \right)^2 \neq 2.$$

Proof: Let us call $n \in N$ acceptable if there is an $m \in N$ such that $m^2 = 2n^2$, and let A be the set of acceptable elements of N. We wish to prove that A is empty. If not, then by Theorem 4-23 A has a least element, say n. Let m be the associated element. If m is odd, then so is m^2, and we reach the contradiction that the odd number m^2 is equal to the even number $2n^2$. (We assume here some elementary facts about oddness and evenness.) Therefore m is even, say $m = 2k$, $k \in N$. Substituting, we get $2n^2 = m^2 =$

$(2k)^2 = 4k^2$, so $n^2 = 2k^2$. Therefore k is acceptable: $k \in A$. But $k < n$, contradicting the definition of n. This contradiction shows that A is empty, and the theorem is proved.

EXERCISES 4-10

1. Prove that $\sqrt{3}$ is not rational.
2. Let m, n be defined as in the proof of Theorem 4-24. Let

$$m' = 3m - 4n, \quad n' = 3n - 2m.$$

Prove: (a) $n' > 0$, (b) $n' < n$, (c) $m'^2 = 2n'^2$.
Show that these three statements yield another proof of Theorem 4-24.

3. An excellent device for approximating $\sqrt{a}$ ($a > 0$) is the following. Start with some approximation x_1, and define, successively,

$$x_2 = \frac{1}{2}\left(x_1 + \frac{a}{x_1}\right),$$

$$x_3 = \frac{1}{2}\left(x_2 + \frac{a}{x_2}\right),$$

$$x_4 = \frac{1}{2}\left(x_3 + \frac{a}{x_3}\right),$$

and so on. Apply this method to $a = 2$ and $a = 3$.

4. Find three nonempty subsets of Q which satisfy Axioms A1 to A5.
5. Let A be a subset of Q containing 0 and 1 and satisfying Axioms A1 to A5 and M1 to M5. Prove that $A = Q$.
6. Let $A = \{n \in N | n \text{ is even}\}$, $B = \{1/m | m \in N\}$, $C = \{pq | p \in A \wedge q \in B\}$. Show that C satisfies Axioms M1 to M5.
7. Let $A = \{n \in N | n \text{ is odd}\}$, $B = \{1/m | m \in N\}$, $C \in \{pq | p \in A \wedge q \in B\}$. Show that C satisfies Axioms M1 to M4 but not M5.
8. Find at least three subsets of Q which satisfy Axioms O1 to O4.

4-8. THE LEAST-UPPER-BOUND AXIOM

From the preceding section we expect that R should be properly larger than Q. There is some danger, on the other hand, of making R too large. For example, we should not like to have in R an element greater than every natural number. So far our axioms A, M, D, and O do not guarantee that such huge elements do not exist. In fact, it is possible to construct ordered fields which do contain such elements. By taking reciprocals, we would get "very small" positive elements, smaller than any positive rational.

How do we avoid these two dangers of making R too small or too large? It is remarkable that both purposes can be served by introducing a single axiom. This last axiom of our system completes the task of characterizing the real number field. It is known as the *least-upper-bound axiom* or the *completeness axiom*. It could also be called the *calculus axiom*, since it provides an essential tool for the development of the differential and integral calculus. In spite of its great power, it is quite simple to state and comprehend. We begin with some needed definitions.

Definition 4–10. If A is a subset of R, b an element of R, then b is *an upper bound of A* iff

$$\forall x \in A, \, x \leq b.$$

EXERCISES 4–11

1. Formulate the analogous definition of *lower bound*.
2. Show that every element of R is an upper bound of the empty set.
3. Show that
   (a) 1 is an upper bound of $A = \{x | x < 0\}$.
   (b) 0 is an upper bound of A.
   (c) No negative number is an upper bound of A.
   (d) 3 is an upper bound of $\{1, \frac{1}{2}, 2, 3\}$.
   (e) An upper bound of B may or may not be an element of B (give examples of both situations).
   (f) 1 is a lower bound of $\{x | x^2 > 2 \wedge x \text{ is positive}\}$.
4. Assume in this exercise that every positive element $x \in R$ has a positive square root $\sqrt{x}$ in R.

   (a) Show that if $0 \leq x \leq 2$, then $0 \leq \sqrt{2 + x} \leq 2$.

   (b) Define $x_1 = \sqrt{2}$, $x_2 = \sqrt{2 + x_1}$, $x_3 = \sqrt{2 + x_2}$, and in general, $x_{n+1} = \sqrt{2 + x_n}$. Show that 2 is an upper bound of $C = \{x_n | n \in N\}$.
   (c) Show that $2 - x_{n+1} = (2 - x_n)/(2 + x_{n+1})$ for all $n \in N$.
   (d) Show that $2 - x_{n+1} \leq \frac{1}{2}(2 - x_n)$ for all $n \in N$.
   (e) Show that $0 \leq 2 - x_n \leq (\frac{1}{2})^{n-1}$ for all $n \in N$.

Definition 4–11. If A is a subset of R, b an element of R, then b is *the least upper bound of A* iff

   (a) b is an upper bound of A,

and

(b) $\forall c$, c is an upper bound of $A \to b \leq c$.

A paraphrase of this definition is that b is an upper bound of A which is less than every other upper bound of A. Notice that we speak of *the* least upper bound. The student should convince himself that a set can have at most one least upper bound.

It may happen that a set has no least upper bound simply because it has no upper bound. For example, N has no upper bound. But even if A has an upper bound, it may have no least upper bound. For example, the empty set has every number as an upper bound. If we were operating solely within Q, we could find other examples of this phenomenon. Thus, if $A = \{x \in Q \mid x^2 < 2\}$, then A has upper bounds in Q (e.g., 3) but no element *of* Q is the least upper bound of A. The proof of this can be made to depend on the following facts:

(a) $\forall x \in Q$, $x^2 < 2 \to \exists n \in N$, $\left(x + \dfrac{1}{n}\right)^2 < 2$.

(b) $\forall x \in Q$, $x^2 > 2 \to \exists n \in N$, $\left(x - \dfrac{1}{m}\right)^2 > 2$.

(c) $\forall x \in Q$, $x^2 \neq 2$.

Proposition (c) is Theorem 4–24, of course, and (a) asserts that if $x^2 < 2$, we can add a small enough number $1/n$ to x so that $(x + (1/n))^2$ is still less than 2.

EXERCISES 4–12

1. Assuming (a), (b), (c), prove that no element of Q is the least upper bound of A.

2. If $p, q \in N$ and $(p/q)^2 < 2$, show that

$$\left(\frac{p}{q} + \frac{1}{n}\right)^2 < 2$$

for $n = 4pq$. [*Hint:* If $p^2/q^2 < 2$, then $(p^2 + 1)/q^2 \leq 2$. Therefore it is enough to show that

$$\left(\frac{p}{q} + \frac{1}{n}\right)^2 < \frac{p^2 + 1}{q^2}.\,]$$

3. Formulate a definition of *greatest lower bound* of a set A in R.

The difficulty with Q that we have just observed—that a subset with an upper bound in Q need not have a least upper bound in Q—is one that we wish to eliminate from R. The empty set must necessarily play a special role, and is explicitly ruled out in the following axiom.

Axiom O5. *The Least-Upper-Bound Axiom.* Every nonempty subset of R which has an upper bound also has a least upper bound.

EXAMPLE 4–10.   Let $A = \{x|x \leq 1\}$. The least upper bound of A is 1; it is an element of A.

EXAMPLE 4–11.   Let $B = \{x|x < 1\}$. The least upper bound of B is 1; it is not an element of B.

EXAMPLE 4–12.   Let $C = \{(1 + x)^2|x > 0\}$. Show that the greatest lower bound of C is 1.

Solution: If $x > 0$, then $(1 + x)^2 > 1$, so 1 is a lower bound of C. Suppose that $b > 1$. We shall show that b is not a lower bound of C by finding an element of C which is less than b. In other words, we shall find an $x > 0$ such that

$$(1 + x)^2 < b,$$

$$1 + 2x + x^2 < b.$$

We must satisfy

$$2x + x^2 < b - 1.$$

If we agree in advance to choose x so that $0 < x < 1$, then $x^2 < x$, so

$$2x + x^2 < 3x.$$

Thus, it is sufficient for us to solve

$$3x < b - 1,$$

$$x < \frac{b - 1}{3}.$$

This gives us our answer: Any positive x which is less than the smaller of 1 and $(b - 1)/3$ will do.

EXAMPLE 4–13.   Let $D = \{(1 - x)^2|0 < x < 1\}$. Show that the least upper bound of D is 1.

Solution: Left to student.

Theorem 4–25. $\forall x \in R, \exists n \in N$ such that $n > x$.

Proof: Let us suppose that the theorem is false. Its negation is

$$\exists x \in R, \forall n \in N, n \le x.$$

Let x be such an element. Then x is an upper bound of N. By Axiom O5, N has a least upper bound b. Therefore $b - 1$ is not an upper bound of N: $\exists n \in N, n > b - 1$. Adding 1, we get $n + 1 > b$. Since $n + 1 \in N$, b is not an upper bound of N. This contradiction proves the theorem.

Theorem 4–26.　$\forall a > 0,\ \exists n \in N$ such that $na > 1$.

Proof: Given $a > 0$, we have $1/a \in R$. By Theorem 4–25 there is an $n \in N$ such that $n > 1/a$. Multiplying by $a\ (> 0)$, we get $na > 1$, as desired.

Theorem 4–26 is sometimes referred to as the Archimedean axiom. It has the geometrical interpretation that, given any two line segments, it is possible to lay off enough copies of one segment (end to end) to cover the other.

Corollary.　$\forall a > 0, \forall b,\ \exists n \in N$ such that $na > b$.

Theorem 4–27.　Suppose that $a \ge 0$ and $\forall n \in N, na \le 1$. Then $a = 0$.

Proof: Suppose $a \ne 0$. Then $a > 0$. By Theorem 4–26 there is an $n \in N$ such that $na > 1$, contradicting the hypothesis. Hence $a = 0$.

Corollary 1.　Suppose that $a \in R$ and $\forall n \in N, 0 \le a \le 1/n$. Then $a = 0$.

Corollary 2.　Suppose that $a \in R$ and $\forall n \in N,\ -(1/n) \le a \le 1/n$. Then $a = 0$.

Proof: If $a \ge 0$, apply Corollary 1 to a; if $a \le 0$, apply Corollary 1 to $-a$.

These ideas and results are extremely useful. They can be made the basis of many proofs. One type of application is the following. We wish to prove that two numbers b, c, defined in different ways, are actually equal. Define $a = b - c$ and show that the hypothesis of Corollary 2 are satisfied. Then $a = 0$ and $b = c$. Actually the scheme is to show that b is not much greater than c (if at all) and that c is not much greater than b (if at all). Of course, the phrase "not much greater" must be interpreted properly. Another variation arises in the determination of the area of a region K. By judicious choice of regions containing and contained in K, we obtain upper and lower approximations to the area of K. If L is the set of lower approximations, U the set of upper approximations, then the area of K is an upper bound of L and a lower bound of U:

$$\forall x,y,\; x \in L \wedge y \in U \to (x \le \text{area of } K \le y).$$

If b is the least upper bound of L, B the greatest lower bound of U, then

$$b \le \text{area of } K \le B.$$

In the best cases, we can show that $b = B$, and of course the common value is the area of K. In any case, if $x \in L$ and $y \in U$, we can assert that we know the area of K approximately, with an error of at most $y - x$. Clearly, if we can choose our approximating regions so that their areas are close together, our error will be small. This "squeezing" process was used by the Greeks to compute the area of a circle. It is essentially the "exhaustion" process of Archimedes, and forms the basis for the integral calculus.

We shall write *l.u.b.* A for the least upper bound of A, *g.l.b.* A for the greatest lower bound of A. We shall also abbreviate upper bound and lower bound as *u.b.* and *l.b.*

EXERCISES 4–13

1. Give examples of the following:
   (a) A set with a g.l.b. but no l.u.b.
   (b) A set with no g.l.b. and no l.u.b.
   (c) A set with the same g.l.b. and l.u.b.
2. Let $H = \{(1 + x)^3 | x > 0\}$. Prove that g.l.b. $H = 1$.
3. Suppose that l.u.b. $K = 5$. Prove that there is an element $k \in K$ such that $4.999 < k \le 5$.
4. Suppose that l.u.b. $K = c$. Prove that for every $h > 0$, there is an element $k \in K$ such that

$$c - h < k \le c.$$

5. Let (a_n), $n \in N$, be a bounded sequence such that $a_n \le a_{n+1}$ $(n \in N)$. Let $c = $ l.u.b. $\{a_n | n \in N\}$. Prove that for every $h > 0$ there is an $n_0 \in N$ such that

$$c - h < a_n \le c \qquad (n = n_0 + 1, n_0 + 2, \ldots).$$

*6. Let $c = $ l.u.b. $\{x | x^2 < 2\}$. Prove that $c^2 = 2$.
7. Prove that a nonempty subset A of R which has a lower bound also has a greatest lower bound. [*Hint:* Consider $B = \{-x | x \in A\}$.]

4-9. DECIMAL REPRESENTATIONS

We are all familiar with the representation of certain numbers by terminating decimals. Thus

$$1.23 =_{df} 1 + \frac{2}{10} + \frac{3}{10^2},$$

$$24.078 =_{df} 2 \cdot 10 + 4 + \frac{0}{10} + \frac{7}{10^2} + \frac{8}{10^3},$$

$$360.415 =_{df} 3 \cdot 10^2 + 6 \cdot 10 + 0 + \frac{4}{10} + \frac{1}{10^2} + \frac{5}{10^3}.$$

Nonterminating (or infinite) decimals are quite a different matter, however. If we tried to imitate the definitions above, we would have no definition at all, since the expression appearing to the right of "$=_{df}$," say

$$\frac{a_1}{10} + \frac{a_2}{10^2} + \frac{a_3}{10^3} + \cdots,$$

has not been defined. It is possible, of course, to develop the theory of infinite series, but we do not need it for the present purpose. Instead, we shall use an elementary but important theorem of analysis.

Definition 4–12. For $a \leq b$, the *closed interval*

$$[a,b] = \{x|a \leq x \leq b\}.$$

The *length* of the interval is $b - a$.

Definition 4–13. If (J_n), $n \in N$, is a sequence of closed intervals such that $J_1 \supset J_2 \supset J_3 \supset \cdots$, it is called a *nested sequence of closed intervals.*
Of course, the meaning of "$\cdots$" in Definition 4–13 is

$$\forall n \in N, J_n \supset J_{n+1}.$$

The next theorem should appear "obvious" to the student, and its proof is not too difficult.

Theorem 4–28. If (J_n), $n \in N$, is a nested sequence of closed intervals, there is a closed interval $J = [a,b]$ such that $J \subset J_n$ for all $n \in N$. In particular, there is a number common to all the J_n.
Proof: Let $J_n = [a_n, b_n]$ $(n \in N)$. It follows from our hypothesis that

(1) $$a_m \leq b_n \qquad (m,n \in N).$$

In this inequality regard n as fixed:

$$(\forall m)\ a_m \leq b_n.$$

Thus $A = \{a_m | m \in N\}$ is bounded above by b_n. By the l.u.b. axiom, $a = $ l.u.b. A exists, and since b_n is an u.b. of A,

$$a \leq b_n \qquad (n \in N).$$

Similarly, $B = \{b_n | n \in N\}$ is bounded below by a, so $b = $ g.l.b. B exists, and $a \leq b$. It is now an easy matter to verify that the interval $J = [a,b]$ is contained in every J_n. Indeed, since $a = $ l.u.b. A, we have $a_n \leq a\ (n \in N)$. Similarly $b \leq b_n\ (n \in N)$. Thus

(2) $$a_n \leq a \leq b \leq b_n \qquad (n \in N)$$

which is equivalent to $J \subset J_n$ for all $n \in N$. This completes the proof.

It is important for us to know when the interval $[a,b]$ of Theorem 4–28 degenerates to a single point, that is, when $a = b$. From (2) in the proof, we have

$$b - a \leq b_n - a_n \qquad (n \in N),$$

so $b - a$ is a l.b. of $\{b_n - a_n | n \in N\}$. Therefore

$$b - a \leq \text{g.l.b. } \{b_n - a_n | n \in N\} = c,$$

say.

We wish to prove that the inequality also goes in the opposite direction. For this purpose it is sufficient to show that c is "not much larger" than $b - a$, if at all. Let k be an arbitrary element of N. Since $a - (1/2k)$ is not an upper bound of A, there exists $n \in N$ such that $a_n > a - (1/2k)$. Similarly, since $b + (1/2k)$ is not a lower bound of B, there exists $m \in N$ such that $b_m < b + (1/2k)$. Therefore

$$a - \frac{1}{2k} < a_n \leq b_m < b + \frac{1}{2k}.$$

Let r be an element of N greater than both n and m. Then

$$a - \frac{1}{2k} < a_n \leq a_r \leq b_r \leq b_m < b + \frac{1}{2k},$$

$$a - \frac{1}{2k} < a_r \leq b_r < b + \frac{1}{2k}.$$

From this it follows that

$$b_r - a_r < \left(b + \frac{1}{2k}\right) - \left(a - \frac{1}{2k}\right),$$

$$b_r - a_r < (b - a) + \frac{1}{k}.$$

Since c is a l.b. of $\{b_n - a_n | n \in N\}$, we have

$$c \leq b_r - a_r < (b - a) + \frac{1}{k},$$

$$(b - a) \leq c < (b - a) + \frac{1}{k}.$$

Subtracting $(b - a)$ throughout and recalling that k was arbitrary, we conclude that

$$0 \leq c - (b - a) < \frac{1}{k} \qquad (k \in N).$$

By Corollary 1 of Theorem 4–27,

$$c = b - a.$$

The special case we want, $b - a = 0$, is therefore equivalent to $c = 0$. We have proved the following important result.

Theorem 4–29. Under the conditions of Theorem 4–28, there is a unique real number common to all the J_n if and only if the g.l.b. of their lengths is 0.

We are now ready to give a meaning to nonterminating decimals. Suppose we have given a sequence of digits (d_n), $n \in N$:

$$d_n \in \{0,1,2,3,4,5,6,7,8,9\}.$$

Define

$$a_n = .d_1 d_2 \cdots d_n,$$

$$b_n = a_n + \frac{1}{10^n} \qquad (n \in N).$$

For example, if $d_1 = 3$, $d_2 = 0$, $d_3 = 9$, $d_4 = 6$, and so on, then

$$a_1 = .3 \qquad b_1 = .4,$$

$$a_2 = .30 \qquad b_2 = .31,$$

$$a_3 = .309 \qquad b_3 = .310,$$

$$a_4 = .3096 \qquad b_4 = .3097.$$

It is clear that

$$a_1 \le a_2 \le a_3 \le \cdots,$$

but it is not so clear that

$$b_1 \ge b_2 \ge b_3 \ge \cdots.$$

To see this, consider that for all $n \in N$,

$$b_n - b_{n+1} = a_n - a_{n+1} + \frac{1}{10^n} - \frac{1}{10^{n+1}}$$

$$= \frac{9}{10^{n+1}} - (a_{n+1} - a_n)$$

$$= \frac{9}{10^{n+1}} - \frac{d_{n+1}}{10^{n+1}}$$

$$= \frac{9 - d_{n+1}}{10^{n+1}}$$

$$\ge 0.$$

Using the fact that $a_n < b_n$ $(n \in N)$, we see that the intervals $J_n = [a_n, b_n]$ form a nested sequence. In fact, suppose that $m \ge n$. Then

$$a_n \le a_m < b_m \le b_n,$$

so $J_m \subset J_n$. Finally,

$$\text{g.l.b. } \{b_n - a_n | n \in N\}$$

$$= \text{g.l.b. } \left\{ \frac{1}{10^n} | n \in N \right\}$$

$$= 0.$$

By Theorem 4–29, there is a unique real number common to all the J_n. *It is this number which is represented by the infinite decimal*

$$.d_1 d_2 d_3 \cdots.$$

The numbers so represented lie in the interval [0,1]. If we prefix a positive integer n (with its usual decimal representation), we mean

$$n + .d_1d_2d_3 \cdots$$

of course.

We have just shown that we can assign a unique nonnegative number to every infinite decimal. Is it true that every nonnegative number has a representation by an infinite decimal? The answer is *yes*, but for some numbers the representation is not unique. These are precisely the numbers which are representable by terminating decimals. For example,

$$\tfrac{1}{2} = .5 = .5000 \cdots$$

also has the representation

$$.4999 \cdots .$$

For this, the sequence (d_n) is given by

$$d_1 = 4,$$

$$d_n = 9 \qquad (n \geq 2).$$

Thus

$$a_n = \underbrace{.499 \cdots 9}_{n} \qquad (n \in N),$$

$$b_n = \underbrace{.500 \cdots 0}_{n} \qquad (n \in N).$$

Since .5 is common to all the J_n, it is the unique number represented by $.4999 \cdots$.

We shall not prove here all the facts stated in the preceding paragraph. Suffice it to say that the representation of a given number $x \geq 0$ as an infinite decimal is obtained by a "squeezing" process in which we find intervals

$$J_n = \left[\frac{k_n}{10^n}, \frac{k_n + 1}{10^n} \right]$$

in each of which x lies, and such that

$$J_1 \supset J_2 \supset J_3 \supset \cdots$$

It is exactly when x coincides with one of the endpoints that we get the ambiguity.

There is an interesting way to characterize the rationals by their decimal representations. If we divide one positive integer p by another, q, using the familiar algorithm to obtain the decimal expansion of the ratio p/q, after a certain point the remainders start to repeat and so do the digits in the quotient. Thus, every rational number is represented by an ultimately repeating decimal. For example,

$$\frac{12}{7} = 1.\overline{714285},$$

the bar indicating the repeating pattern. Conversely, every ultimately repeating decimal represents a rational number. We shall not prove this, but merely indicate by an example how to find the corresponding rational.

EXAMPLE 4–14. Evaluate $b = .24\overline{3}$.

Solution: $100b = 24.3\overline{43}$,

$$b = \quad .24\overline{3}.$$

$$\therefore \quad 99b = 24.1 = \frac{241}{10},$$

$$b = \frac{241}{990}.$$

EXERCISES 4–14

1. Write down the first few intervals J_n for $.\overline{761}$.
2. Evaluate $.04\overline{512}$.
3. Add $.4\overline{12}$ and $1.\overline{234}$.
4. Multiply $.\overline{7}$ by $.\overline{5}$.
5. Find the decimal expansions of $n/7$ ($1 \le n \le 6$).
6. Prove that $.41 = .4\overline{10}$.
7. Prove that $.\overline{9} = 1$ directly from the definition of $.d_1 d_2 d_3 \cdots$.
*8. Prove that $10(.d_1 d_2 d_3 \cdots) = d_1.d_2 d_3 \cdots$.
*9. Prove that $10^2(.d_1 d_2 d_3 \cdots) = d_1 d_2.d_3 \cdots$.
10. State the general rule for multiplying an infinite decimal by a power of 10 (positive or negative).
11. State a necessary and sufficient condition that $[a,b] \cap [c,d] = \emptyset$.
12. State a necessary and sufficient condition that $[a,b] \subset [c,d]$.
13. Is the decimal expansion of $\sqrt{2}$ ultimately repeating? Give your reasons.
14. Prove that $(\forall n)\, a_n \le 7$ implies

$$\text{l.u.b.} \{a_n | n \in N\} \le 7.$$

15. Prove that $(\forall n)\ a_n < 7$ does not imply

$$\text{l.u.b. } \{a_n | n \in N\} < 7.$$

16. Let $J_n = \{x | 0 < x < 1/n\}$ for $n \in N$. Is there a number common to all the J_n? Give reasons. Does this contradict Theorem 4–28?

17. Let $A = \{2 + 3/n + 4/n^2 | n \in N\}$. Find (a) l.u.b. A and (b) g.l.b. A.

18. Let $A_k = \left\{ \left(1 + \dfrac{1}{n}\right)^2 \middle| n \in N,\ n \geq k \right\}$, for $k \in N$, and let $a_k = $ g.l.b. A_k, $b_k = $ l.u.b. A_k. Find

(a) l.u.b. $\{a_k | k \in N\}$.

(b) g.l.b. $\{a_k | k \in N\}$.

(c) l.u.b. $\{b_k | k \in N\}$.

(d) g.l.b. $\{b_k | k \in N\}$.

*19. Carry out the development of this section for base two instead of base ten.

Chapter 5

LINEAR ALGEBRA

5-1. REAL n-TUPLES AND VECTOR SPACES

IN DESCRIBING COMPLICATED PHENOMENA or objects quantitatively, it is frequently necessary to use more than one number in the description. For example, to give the position of a point in a plane, we could first draw two reference lines L_1, L_2 perpendicular to each other in the plane, Figure 5–1. The point θ where these lines meet is called the origin. If we proceed from there 5 units in the positive L_1 direction (to the right in our diagram) and 2 units in the positive L_2 direction (upward in our diagram), we arrive at the point P, which is then assigned the label or name (5,2). Similarly, the point Q would have the label $(5,-2)$, the point S would be labeled $(-2,1)$, and the point T would be labeled $(-2,-1)$.

This way of assigning ordered pairs of real numbers to points in the plane is the basis of analytic geometry, which we shall study later. What we really do is set up a one-to-one correspondence between the points in the plane and the ordered pairs (x_1,x_2), with $x_1 \in R$, $x_2 \in R$. (Here, and throughout, R denotes the set of all real numbers.) We recall that the set of all such ordered pairs has been denoted by $R \times R$. To denote points in space in a similar fashion, we would use ordered triples of real numbers. The set of all such triples (x_1,x_2,x_3) is denoted by $R \times R \times R$.

There are many types of objects that require more than three numbers to describe them. An event, for instance, would be given by an ordered quadruple (4-tuple) (x_1,x_2,x_3,x_4), where the first three components would refer to the position in space of the event and x_4 would refer to the time. The set of all such quadruples is denoted by $R \times R \times R \times R$. To abbreviate, we write R^2 for $R \times R$, R^3 for $R \times R \times R$, R^4 for $R \times R \times R \times R$, and in general, if n is any natural number, R^n for $R \times R \times \cdots \times R$ (n factors). Thus R^n is the set of all n-tuples $(x_1,x_2,\ldots,x_n)$, where each component x_i ($i = 1$ or 2 or $\cdots$ or n) is a real number. In particular, if $n = 1$, $R^1 = R$. By analogy with the cases $n = 1, 2, 3$, we speak of the "space" of all real n-tuples.

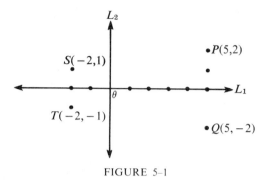

FIGURE 5-1

Many of the concepts and results which are applicable for $n = 1, 2, 3$ can be carried over to the cases $n > 3$, and we can develop an n-dimensional Euclidean geometry. It is for this reason that our discussions of sets of n-tuples sometimes use geometrical terminology. Linear programming, for example, has to do with maximizing certain functions defined on regions in n-dimensional space. We do not, however, expect the student to *perceive* geometrical configurations in n dimensions, but it may help him to try to *conceive* of them, by analogy. He should not despair, though, if these conceptions are beyond him. They are not at all necessary to his understanding of what follows.

Our use of ordered n-tuples is not limited to geometry. To describe a production schedule in a steel company which produces 12 grades of steel, we could number the grades from 1 to 12 in a particular order, and then let x_i denote the amount (in tons, say) of grade i steel to be produced $(i = 1, 2, \ldots, 12)$. Then $(x_1, x_2, \ldots, x_{12})$ is an ordered 12-tuple which gives the production schedule unambiguously. It is an element of R^{12}. Similarly, we could describe the price schedule for these grades by the 12-tuple $(p_1, p_2, \ldots, p_{12})$, where p_i is the price (in dollars) per ton of the ith grade.

A few remarks about notation and language are in order here. It is worthwhile to think of an n-tuple as a single entity (being, thing, object) having components in a certain order, and it is desirable to choose our notation accordingly. Thus, if b is an n-tuple, its first component would be b_1, its second component $b_2, \ldots$, its nth component b_n. We use the letter b with a subscript 1, 2, and so on, just as members of a family have part of their names in common—the family name—and are differentiated from each other by their given names. The Romans would sometimes use the names Primus, Secundus, Tertius, and so on, as given names for their children in the same way as we propose to use subscripts. We should not confuse subscripts with exponents: "b_1" is read as "b sub one," "b_2" as

"b sub two," "b_n" as "b sub n," whereas "b^2" is read as "b squared," "b^n" as "b to the nth." Sometimes subscripts and exponents appear together, as in "b_1^2," which is read as "b sub one, squared" or "the square of b sub one."

One advantage of our subscript notation is that we save ourselves the trouble of stating each time what the components of an n-tuple are to be called. All we need do is name the n-tuple itself. Thus, if we say "Let x, y be n-tuples," we understand that $x = (x_1, x_2, \ldots, x_n)$, $y = (y_1, y_2, \ldots, y_n)$.

A second advantage is that we can express sums in a very compact form, using the summation symbol Σ. Thus, to express

$$x_1 + x_2 + x_3 + \cdots + x_n,$$

we would first write down the name x_i of a typical component of the n-tuple $(x_1, x_2, \ldots, x_n)$, then write the Σ before it to indicate that elements of the form x_i are to be summed, and finally indicate the values of i which are involved in the summation by writing $i = 1$ below the Σ, n above it. The final form is

$$\sum_{i=1}^{n} x_i,$$

read "summation x_i, i from 1 to n" or "the sum of x_i, i from 1 to n."

EXAMPLE 5–1

(a) $\displaystyle\sum_{i=3}^{8} y_i = y_3 + y_4 + y_5 + y_6 + y_7 + y_8.$

(b) $\displaystyle\sum_{i=4}^{7} 2^i = 2^4 + 2^5 + 2^6 + 2^7.$

(c) $\displaystyle\sum_{j=1}^{k} a_j = a_1 + a_2 + a_3 + \cdots + a_k.$

(d) $\displaystyle\sum_{n=1}^{m} c_n = c_1 + c_2 + \cdots + c_m.$

(e) $\displaystyle\sum_{k=1}^{5} f(x_k) = f(x_1) + f(x_2) + f(x_3) + f(x_4) + f(x_5).$

Note that the summation index is i in Example 5–1(a) and (b), j in (c), n in (d), k in (e). Any convenient letter may be used, without changing the meaning of the sum. Thus, we could write the sum in Example 5–1(b) as

$$\sum_{j=4}^{7} 2^j = 2^4 + 2^5 + 2^6 + 2^7.$$

The letter j does not appear on the right. It is a "dummy-index." We may think of it as a bound variable, with its domain specified by the "$j = 4$" below the summation sign and the "7" above it. The domain of a summation variable is sometimes called "the range of summation." If the range of summation is easily understood from the context, indication of it may be omitted. For example, if x_i is the examination grade of the ith student in a class of n students, then the average grade is

$$\bar{x} = \frac{1}{n}\sum x_i = \frac{1}{n}(x_1 + x_2 + \cdots + x_n).$$

A measure of the spread of the grades from the average is the standard deviation. The standard deviation σ of sequence of grades, x_i, $i = 1, \ldots, n$ is obtained from the formula

$$\sigma^2 = \frac{1}{n}\sum (x_i - \bar{x})^2$$

$$= \frac{1}{n}[(x_1 - \bar{x})^2 + (x_2 - \bar{x})^2 + \cdots + (x_n - \bar{x})^2].$$

Sometimes the entries in a sum depend on several subscripts. For example, if the steel producer mentioned above had five plants, numbered 1 to 5, then we might denote by x_{ij} the number of tons of grade i steel to be produced in plant j. The total production of grade i steel would be

$$x_i = \sum_{j=1}^{5} x_{ij} \qquad (i = 1, 2, \ldots, 12).$$

The total production of steel in the jth plant would be y_j, say:

$$y_j = \sum_{i=1}^{12} x_{ij} \qquad (j = 1, 2, 3, 4, 5).$$

The grand total of all grades in all plants is

$$\sum_{i=1}^{12} x_i = \sum_{i=1}^{12} \sum_{j=1}^{5} x_{ij}$$

or, equally,

$$\sum_{j=1}^{5} y_j = \sum_{j=1}^{5} \sum_{i=1}^{12} x_{ij}.$$

Notice that in

$$\sum_{j=1}^{5} x_{ij} = x_{i1} + x_{i2} + x_{i3} + x_{i4} + x_{i5}$$

we sum over the index j, but i remains as a free index. In

$$\sum_{i=1}^{12} x_{ij} = x_{1j} + x_{2j} + \cdots + x_{12,j}$$

we sum over i, and j is the free index. In the grand total we sum over both i and j.

We can express the identity

$$(x_1 + x_2 + \cdots + x_n) + (y_1 + y_2 + \cdots + y_n)$$
$$= (x_1 + y_1) + (x_2 + y_2) + \cdots + (x_n + y_n)$$

in shorter form by

$$\sum_{i=1}^{n} x_i + \sum_{i=1}^{n} y_i = \sum_{i=1}^{n} (x_i + y_i).$$

Similarly, the identity

$$c(x_1 + x_2 + \cdots + x_n) = cx_1 + cx_2 + \cdots + cx_n$$

could be written

$$c \sum_{i=1}^{n} x_i = \sum_{i=1}^{n} cx_i.$$

If all the entries x_i in a sum are equal, say $x_1 = x_2 = \cdots = x_n = b$, then

$$\sum_{i=1}^{n} x_i = \sum_{i=1}^{n} b = nb.$$

Once the student gets enough practice in the use of the summation abbreviation, he will find it very convenient.

EXERCISES 5–1

1. Write out the following without the $\sum$:

(a) $\displaystyle\sum_{k=5}^{10} 3k.$

(b) $\displaystyle\sum_{i=1}^{n} (2i - 1).$

(c) $\displaystyle\sum_{j=2}^{7} c_{jk}.$

(d) $\displaystyle\sum_{k=1}^{4} c_{jk}.$

(e) $\displaystyle\sum_{j=1}^{3} \sum_{k=1}^{4} c_{jk}.$

(f) $\displaystyle\left(\sum_{j=1}^{3} b_j \right)\left(\sum_{k=1}^{3} b_k \right).$

(g) $\displaystyle\sum_{j=1}^{3} \sum_{k=1}^{3} b_j b_k.$

(h) $\displaystyle\sum_{i=1}^{n} (n - i + 1).$

(i) $\displaystyle\sum_{i=1}^{n} i.$

2. Use the Σ to express the following:
   (a) $4 + 6 + 8 + 10 + 12.$
   (b) The sum of all the odd numbers from 1 to 49.
   (c) $a_1 + a_2 + a_3 + \cdots + a_k.$
   (d) $a_{11} + a_{12} + a_{13} + \cdots + a_{1k}.$
   (e) $a_{11} + a_{21} + a_{31} + \cdots + a_{k1}.$
   (f) $p_1 x_1 + p_2 x_2 + p_3 x_3 + \cdots + p_n x_n.$
   (g) $a_{11} x_1 + a_{12} x_2 + a_{13} x_3 + \cdots + a_{1n} x_n.$
   (h) $n + (n - 1) + (n - 2) + \cdots + 2 + 1.$
   (i) $1 + 2 + 2^2 + 2^3 + \cdots + 2^{10}.$
   (j) $2 + 2^2 + 2^3 + \cdots + 2^{11}.$

3. Show that the sums in Problems 1(f) and 1(g) are equal.

4. Let

$$A = \sum_{i=1}^{n} i, \quad B = \sum_{i=1}^{n} (n - i + 1).$$

   (a) Show that $A = B.$
   (b) Show that $A + B = \displaystyle\sum_{i=1}^{n} (n + 1).$
   (c) Show that $A = \frac{1}{2} n(n + 1).$

5. Let

$$S = 1 + 2 + 2^2 + 2^3 + \cdots + 2^{10},$$

$$T = 2 + 2^2 + 2^3 + \cdots + 2^{11}.$$

   (a) Show that $T = 2S.$
   (b) Show that $T = S + 2^{11} - 1.$
   (c) Show that $S = 2^{11} - 1.$
   (d) Find a formula for $\displaystyle\sum_{i=0}^{n} 2^i.$
   (e) Find a formula for $\displaystyle\sum_{i=0}^{n} r^i \quad (r \neq 1).$

6. When are the ordered n-tuples x and y equal?

7. If we multiply out, we get an identity

$$(1 + x)^n = \sum_{k=0}^{n} C_{nk} x^k \quad (n = 1, 2, 3, 4, \cdots).$$

List the numerical values of

(a) C_{1k} $(k = 0,1)$.

(b) C_{2k} $(k = 0,1,2)$.

(c) C_{nk} $(3 \le n \le 6;\ \ 0 \le k \le n)$.

(d) C_{n1} $(1 \le n \le 10)$.

8. (a) Mr. Jones invests in General Motors stock by buying 100 shares on the first trading day of each month, for n months. If p_i $(i = 1,2,\ldots,n)$ is the price of a single share on the ith purchase, show that Mr. Jones' average price is

$$\frac{1}{n} \sum_{i=1}^{n} p_i.$$

(b) Mr. Smith invests in General Motors' stock by buying \$10,000 worth at the same times and the same prices as Mr. Jones. Show that Mr. Smith's average price (total cost divided by total number of shares) is

$$\frac{1}{\dfrac{1}{n} \displaystyle\sum_{i=1}^{n} \dfrac{1}{p_i}}.$$

(This method of investing is called dollar-averaging. It is a mathematical theorem that Mr. Smith's average price is no greater than Mr. Jones'. This is reasonable, since Smith buys more shares at lower prices, fewer at higher prices. Try to prove it for $n = 2$.)

We now define an operation of *addition* for n-tuples. Given the n-tuples $x,y \in R^n$, we define $x + y$ as that n-tuple $z \in R^n$ whose components z_i satisfy $z_i = x_i + y_i$ $(i = 1, 2, \ldots, n)$. Written out in full, this means that

$$(x_1,x_2,\ldots,x_n) + (y_1,y_2,\ldots,y_n) =_{df} (x_1 + y_1, x_2 + y_2,\ldots, x_n + y_n).$$

For example, with $n = 4$,

$$(3,-1,2,0) + (4,2,7,3) = (7,1,9,3).$$

Observe that R^n is closed with respect to the operation of addition. The sum of two real n-tuples is again a real n-tuple. In our example of the steel plant, if x denotes this week's production schedule, u next week's, then $x + u$ would be the combined production schedule for both weeks.

There is also an operation called *multiplication by scalars* between real numbers and real n-tuples. If $t \in R$ and $x \in R^n$, then $t \cdot x$ or simply tx is defined as the n-tuple $z \in R^n$ whose components z_i satisfy $z_i = tx_i$ $(i = 1,2, \ldots, n)$. That is,

$$tx = t(x_1,x_2,\ldots,x_n) =_{df} (tx_1,tx_2,\ldots,tx_n).$$

Each component x_i of x is multiplied by the *scalar* t. (When we are considering n-tuples and real numbers simultaneously, the real numbers are called scalars.) For example,

$$2(3, -1, 2, 0) = (6, -2, 4, 0).$$

If x denotes a production schedule, then $1.25x$ would represent a 25 per cent increase in production across the board.

There are certain rules which interrelate the addition and scalar multiplication just defined. All these rules follow from the definitions and from well-known properties of the real numbers. For instance, we shall prove that if $t \in R$, $x \in R^n$, $y \in R^n$, then $t(x + y) = tx + ty$.

Proof:

$$x + y = (x_1, \ldots, x_n) + (y_1, \ldots, y_n) = (x_1 + y_1, \ldots, x_n + y_n),$$

$$t(x + y) = t(x_1 + y_1, \ldots, x_n + y_n) = (t(x_1 + y_1), \ldots, t(x_n + y_n)),$$

$$tx = t(x_1, \ldots, x_n) = (tx_1, \ldots, tx_n),$$

$$ty = t(y_1, \ldots, y_n) = (ty_1, \ldots, ty_n),$$

$$tx + ty = (tx_1 + ty_1, \ldots, tx_n + ty_n).$$

The first component of $t(x + y)$ is $t(x_1 + y_1)$. Here t, x_1, y_1 are ordinary real numbers, the $+$ between x_1 and y_1 is ordinary addition, and the multiplication between t and $(x_1 + y_1)$ is ordinary multiplication. We know that $t(x_1 + y_1) = tx_1 + ty_1$. This is the first component of the n-tuple $tx + ty$. Similarly, the ith component of $t(x + y)$ is $t(x_i + y_i) = tx_i + ty_i$, for each $i = 1, 2, \ldots, n$. But this is precisely the ith component of $tx + ty$. Since two n-tuples are equal if and only if the corresponding components are all equal, we have proved that $t(x + y) = tx + ty$.

We now give a list of some of the rules or properties which hold for R^n together with its addition and multiplication by scalars. The student should check some of the following statements:

R^n is a nonempty set.

Closure $(+)$: $+$ is a binary operation on R^n into R^n.

Closure $(\cdot)$: $\cdot$ is a binary operation between R and R^n into R^n.

1. $\forall x, y, z \in R^n$, $x + (y + z) = (x + y) + z$.
2. $\forall a, b \in R^n$, $\exists x \in R^n$, $a + x = b$.
3. $\forall x, y \in R^n$, $x + y = y + x$.
4. $\forall t \in R$, $\forall x, y \in R^n$, $t(x + y) = tx + ty$.
5. $\forall s, t \in R$, $\forall x \in R^n$, $(s + t)x = sx + tx$.
6. $\forall s, t \in R$, $\forall x \in R^n$, $s(tx) = (st)x$.
7. $\forall x \in R^n$, $1 \cdot x = x$.

The student must have observed that the preceding set of statements looks very much like an axiom system. This is not accidental. The statements were formulated in such a way that they would constitute an axiom system if R^n were replaced throughout by V. If V is any set with operations $+, \cdot$ satisfying the axiom system, we say that $(V, +, \cdot)$ is a (real) *vector space.* The elements of V are then called *vectors* and the elements of R are called *scalars.* Since R^n with its operations does satisfy the axiom system, $(R^n, +, \cdot)$ is a vector space, and its elements, the n-tuples, are vectors. Thus $(R^n, +, \cdot)$ is a model of (real) vector space, with the interpretations

$$V \Rightarrow R^n,$$

$$+ \Rightarrow +\ \text{(addition of } n\text{-tuples)},$$

$$\cdot \Rightarrow \cdot\ \text{(multiplication by scalars)}.$$

The concept of vector space is one of the most natural and useful in mathematics and its applications. There are many nonisomorphic models of vector space, so we have great flexibility. Even the set of all R^n's, with $n = 1, 2, 3, \ldots$ does not exhaust all the possible models. There are models which are not isomorphic with any R^n. We shall meet some of them later, but for the present our concern is with R^n.

EXERCISES 5-2

1. Compute:
   (a) $(1,7) + (2,3)$.
   (b) $(1,9,3) + (4,-1,0)$.
   (c) $(1,4) + 2(9,3) + (7,1)$. (Because of Axiom 1 this is unambiguous.)
   (d) $(1,5,3,6) + (-7)(0,0,4,3)$.
   (e) $2(1,0,6,3,4) + 7(4,2,1,5,0) + 3(1,6,0,4,5)$.
2. Find a vector r such that

$$2r + (7,1,0,1,-6,\tfrac{1}{3}) = (0,0,0,0,0,0).$$

3. Find a vector x such that

$$5x + 2 \cdot (1,4,3) = (9,-1,-7).$$

4. Find real numbers s and t such that

$$s(1,6) + t(-1,4) = (6,10).$$

5. Compute

$$\sum_{i=1}^{5} (i, 2i - 1, 4).$$

6. Suppose $0 \in R^5$ and that $\forall x \in R^5 : x + 0 = x$. Prove that

$$0 = (0,0,0,0,0).$$

7. Give an example of two vectors x, y in R^2 such that

$$\forall a \in R^2, \; \exists s,t \in R \text{ with } a = sx + ty.$$

Let us examine in detail one of the statements about R^n (number 2). If $a = (a_1,a_2,\dots,a_n)$ and $b = (b_1,b_2,\dots,b_n)$ are given, we must produce an $x = (x_1,x_2,\dots,x_n)$ such that

$$(a_1,a_2,\dots,a_n) + (x_1,x_2,\dots,x_n) = (b_1,b_2,\dots,b_n).$$

Using the definition of addition, we see that this is equivalent to

$$(a_1 + x_1, a_2 + x_2,\dots, a_n + x_n) = (b_1,b_2,\dots,b_n).$$

Now two n-tuples are equal if and only if corresponding components are all equal, so $a + x = b$ is equivalent to

and
$$a_1 + x_1 = b_1$$

and
$$a_2 + x_2 = b_2$$

$$a_3 + x_3 = b_3$$

and
$$\cdot \quad \cdot \quad \cdot$$

$$a_n + x_n = b_n.$$

The conjunction of all these equations could have been written in one fell swoop as

$$a_i + x_i = b_i \qquad (i = 1,2,\dots,n).$$

Since each of them has exactly one solution

$$x_i = b_i - a_i \qquad (i = 1,2,\dots,n).$$

we see that the equation $a + x = b$ has exactly one solution:

$$x = (b_1 - a_1, b_2 - a_2,\dots, b_n - a_n).$$

We have therefore proved somewhat more than was required. In addition to proving the existence of a solution, we proved its uniqueness. This gives us the right to assign a symbol to it which shows its dependence on a and b. We write

$$b - a =_{\text{df}} (b_1 - a_1, b_2 - a_2,\dots, b_n - a_n).$$

Since this uniqueness result is an important property of R^n, why did we not include it in our list, so that it might become an axiom after the process of abstraction? The answer is that it is a consequence of the other axioms. *Every* vector space possesses the property that the solution of $a + x = b$ guaranteed by Axiom 2 is unique. Uniqueness is a theorem of the abstract system. Together with the existence assertion of Axiom 2, it will permit us to define $b - a$ as *the* solution of $a + x = b$. Our proof for R^n used the special form of the elements. The proof for an arbitrary vector space uses only the primitive assertions of the axiom system. Leading up to this theorem (Theorem 5–3, which follows), we state two others. None of the theorems of this section will be proved here. The first five are not difficult.

Theorem 5–1.　There is a unique element θ in V which satisfies

$$\forall x \in V,\ x + \theta = x.$$

Theorem 5–1 asserts the existence and uniqueness of an identity with respect to addition. In our R^n model it is easy to exhibit the additive identity. It is

$$0_n =_{\mathrm{df}} (0,0,\ldots,0).$$

Clearly, for all $x \in R^n$ we have $x + 0_n = x$.

Theorem 5–2.　$\forall a,x,y \in V,\ a + x = a + y \to x = y$. This cancellation theorem is easily verified for R^n.

Theorem 5–3.　Given $a,b \in V$, there exists a unique $x \in V$ such that $a + x = b$.

We may now define $b - a$ as the unique solution of $a + x = b$. Furthermore, we may define

$$-a =_{\mathrm{df}} \theta - a.$$

Thus,

$$a + (-a) = \theta,$$

and $-a$ is the unique solution of

$$a + x = \theta.$$

The element $-a$ is called the *additive inverse of a*, or the *negative of a*. In R^n,

$$-a = (-a_1, -a_2, \ldots, -a_n).$$

But also, by definition of multiplication by scalars in R^n,

$$(-1)a = ((-1)a_1, (-1)a_2, \ldots, (-1)a_n)$$
$$= (-a_1, -a_2, \ldots, -a_n).$$

Therefore, *for* R^n, $(-1)a = -a$ for every $a \in R^n$. Is this true in an arbitrary vector space? The answer is given in the affirmative by the following two theorems:

Theorem 5–4. $\forall a \in V, 0 \cdot a = 0$.

Theorem 5–5. $\forall a \in V, (-1)a = -a$.

So far, one might be led to think that to every result for R^n there is a corresponding theorem for V, an arbitrary vector space. This is definitely false, as we shall soon see.

Let V and W be vector spaces. A function f from V into W is called a *linear mapping* if it preserves the operations of addition and multiplication by scalars. Explicitly, this means that

(1) $$f(x + y) = f(x) + f(y) \qquad (x, y \in V),$$
(2) $$f(tx) = tf(x) \qquad (t \in R, x \in V).$$

EXAMPLE 5–2.   Let $V = R^2$, $W = R^1$. For $x = (x_1, x_2) \in R^2$, define

$$f(x) = 2x_1 + x_2.$$

To test Eqs. (1) and (2) above, we compute

$$f(x + y) = 2(x_1 + y_1) + (x_2 + y_2)$$
$$= (2x_1 + x_2) + (2y_1 + y_2)$$
$$= f(x) + f(y).$$

Also, for $t \in R$,

$$f(tx) = 2(tx_1) + (tx_2)$$
$$= t(2x_1 + x_2)$$
$$= tf(x).$$

Therefore f is a linear mapping of V into W. Actually it is onto W, but it is not one-to-one. For example, $f((0,6)) = 6$, $f((3,0)) = 6$.

Properties (1) and (2) above are very natural and easy to accept. In fact, beginning students in algebra are sometimes too willing to accept them [especially (1)] as applying to all functions. For example, they will write, *incorrectly*,

$$(a + b)^2 = a^2 + b^2,$$
$$\sqrt{a + b} = \sqrt{a} + \sqrt{b}.$$

The functions which satisfy Eqs. (1) and (2) are of a very special kind. For example, if f is a linear mapping of R^n into R^1, it can be proved that there are constants $a_1, a_2, \ldots, a_n$ such that

$$f(x) = a_1 x_1 + a_2 x_2 + \cdots + a_n x_n \qquad (x \in R^n).$$

A *one-to-one* linear mapping of V *onto* W is an *isomorphism*. Isomorphic vector spaces are essentially indistinguishable.

EXAMPLE 5–3.   Let $V = \{ y \in R^3 | y_2 = 0 \}$. A typical element of V is $(y_1, 0, y_3)$. With the addition and multiplication by scalars inherited from R^3, V is a vector space. Let us define the mapping f from V to R^2 by

$$f((y_1, 0, y_3)) = (y_1, y_3) \qquad (x \in V).$$

We leave it to the student to show that f is an isomorphism of V onto R^2.

EXERCISE 5–3

Let $V = \{ x \in R^3 | x_1 + x_2 + x_3 = 0 \}$. Show that V is a vector space isomorphic with R^2.

Some vector spaces can be built up out of a small number of elements by using the two fundamental operations. For example, in R^2 every element (x_1, x_2) may be expressed as a combination of $e^{(1)} = (1,0)$ and $e^{(2)} = (0,1)$:

$$(x_1, x_2) = x_1(1,0) + x_2(0,1).$$

In general, a vector space V may contain n elements $v^{(1)}, v^{(2)}, \ldots, v^{(n)}$ such that every $x \in V$ is expressible as a linear combination:

$$x = t_1 v^{(1)} + t_2 v^{(2)} + \cdots + t_n v^{(n)}.$$

If this is true, then the smallest n for which it is true is called the *dimension* of V, abbreviated *dim V*. By special courtesy, the trivial vector space with only one element θ is assigned dimension 0. Not all vector spaces are finite-dimensional. The others are called *infinite-dimensional*.

The following theorems show how important R^n is in the theory of vector spaces.

Theorem 5–6. R^n is an n-dimensional vector space.

Theorem 5–7.   Every n-dimensional vector space is isomorphic with R^n.

Suppose that W is a vector space and that $V \subset W$. If V becomes a vector space when endowed with the same operations as in W—i.e., if

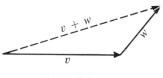

FIGURE 5–2

V is nonempty and closed with respect to the two operations in W—we say that V is a (linear) *subspace* of W.

Theorem 5–8.   If W is an n-dimensional vector space and if V is a subspace of W, then dim $V \leq n$.

Theorems 5–6, 5–7, and 5–8 are far from trivial and would need careful proof in a thorough treatment of vector spaces.

According to Theorem 5–7, we may think of R^n as providing us with a set of names or labels for the elements of an n-dimensional vector space V, so that the operations $+$ and $\cdot$ can be carried out on the labels to give correct results. This setting up of a perfect dictionary to translate from V to R^n and back again can be very useful, particularly when the elements of V and the operations are originally presented in an unfamiliar way.

In physics, forces, velocities, and accelerations are represented by vectors. They are usually drawn as arrows with direction and magnitude. Two arrows represent the same vector if they have the same direction and magnitude (we do not care where the arrows start). To find the sum (or resultant) of two physical vectors v and w we use Figure 5–2. The initial point of w is placed at the terminal point of v without changing the magnitude or direction of w. Then $v + w$ completes the triangle, as indicated. If t is a positive number, then tv is the vector with the same direction as v, but t times as large (Figure 5–3). If t is negative, we reverse the direction of

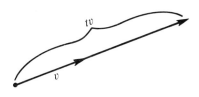

FIGURE 5–3

FIGURE 5–4

v and multiply its magnitude by the numerical value of t to get tv (Figure 5–4).

With these geometrical definitions of the operations we obtain a vector space. To see this we would of course have to verify the seven axioms. The student might amuse himself by proving (or at least diagramming) the corresponding geometrical theorems. This vector space is three-dimensional, so it is isomorphic with R^3. Accordingly, the vectors can be represented by ordered triples, and geometrical problems can be reduced to algebraic ones. For example, the theorem that the medians of a triangle are concurrent becomes an algebraic triviality. The fact that several forces applied at the same point are in equilibrium is expressed simply by saying that the sum of the corresponding vectors is the zero vector.

EXERCISES 5–4

1. Compute:
   (a) $7 \cdot (6,4)$.
   (b) $(4,3,1) + (0,2,1)$.
   (c) $5(1,2) - 7(3,-1)$.
   (d) $(1,3,7) - (2,4,1)$.
   (e) $(2,1) + (7,3) - (1,4)$.
   (f) $\sum_{i=1}^{4} (i, i + 1)$.

2. Find a vector r such that

$$5r + (1,7,3) = (2,1,4).$$

3. Given a vector $a = (a_1, a_2)$, find real numbers s and t such that

$$a = s(1,3) + t(3,1).$$

4. Let V be the set of all functions from $\{5,7\}$ to R. For f, $g \in V$, define $f + g$ as that function h with

$$h(5) = f(5) + g(5),$$
$$h(7) = f(7) + g(7).$$

For $t \in R$ and $f \in V$, define tf as that function k with

$$k(5) = tf(5),$$
$$k(7) = tf(7).$$

Show that we now have a vector space. Exhibit an isomorphism between this vector space and R^2.

5. Let V be the set of all functions from R to R. Define $+$ and $\cdot$ in a manner similar to the definitions in Problem 4. Show that $(V,+,\cdot)$ is a vector space.

6. Prove that in any vector space,

$$(\forall a)(\forall b)\ b - a = b + (-1)a.$$

7. Let V be the subset of R^2 consisting of all (x_1,x_2) satisfying $x_2 = 5x_1$. Prove:

(a) $(V,+,\cdot)$ is a subspace of R^2.

(b) $(V,+,\cdot)$ is one-dimensional.

8. Prove that R^2 is not isomorphic with R^1.

*9. Prove that isomorphism of vector spaces is an equivalence relation.

10. Let f be a linear mapping from V into W (V and W are vector spaces).

(a) Prove that

$$S = \{f(x)|x \in V\}$$

is a subspace of W.

(b) Prove that

$$T = \{x|f(x) = \theta\}$$

is a subspace of V.

(c) Prove that f is one-to-one iff $T = \{\theta\}$.

11. Which of the following functions f are linear mappings of R^2 into R^1? Give reasons. (In each case, $x \in R^2$.)

(a) $f(x) = 2x_1 + 3x_2$.

(b) $f(x) = 7$.

(c) $f(x) = 0$.

(d) $f(x) = (x_1 + x_2)^2$.

(e) $f(x) = x_1^2 + x_2^2$.

(f) $f(x) = x_1$.

(g) $f(x) = 3x_2$.

12. Suppose there is a sales tax of 5 per cent on commodity 1, 3 per cent on commodity 2, 1 per cent on commodity 3, and no tax on commodity 4. Is the total tax on a purchase (x_1,x_2,x_3,x_4) given by a linear mapping of R^4 into R^1? Write down a formula for the total tax.

13. There are five examinations in a course. The final numerical grade is obtained by giving equal weights to the first four and double weight to the last. Find a function from R^5 into R^1 such that when the grades are substituted for the x's, the functional value is the final grade. Is the function that you get a linear mapping?

5-2.   MATRICES

The equation

$$f(x) = a_1 x_1 + a_2 x_2 + \cdots + a_n x_n \qquad (x \in R^n)$$

defines a linear mapping of R^n into R^1, as we have seen in the preceding section. Two such mappings coincide if and only if the n-tuples of coefficients $(a_1, a_2, \ldots, a_n)$ coincide. Every n-tuple leads to a linear mapping, and every linear mapping comes from an n-tuple. This correspondence is one-to-one, and enables us to make concrete the concept of linear mapping from R^n to R^1.

Similarly, the pair of equations

$$f_1(x) = a_{11} x_1 + a_{12} x_2 + \cdots + a_{1n} x_n \qquad (x \in R^n),$$

$$f_2(x) = a_{21} x_1 + a_{22} x_2 + \cdots + a_{2n} x_n \qquad (x \in R^n)$$

defines a linear mapping of R^n into R^2, the image of $x \in R^n$ being the ordered pair $(f_1(x), f_2(x)) \in R^2$. Conversely, it can be proved that every linear mapping of R^n into R^2 comes from a pair of n-tuples

$$(a_{11}, a_{12}, \ldots, a_{1n}),$$

$$(a_{21}, a_{22}, \ldots, a_{2n}).$$

To think of this pair of n-tuples as a single object, we put them under the same roof, so to speak:

$$\begin{pmatrix} a_{11} & a_{12} & \cdots & a_{1n} \\ a_{21} & a_{22} & \cdots & a_{2n} \end{pmatrix}$$

The mathematical object just named above is called a *matrix*, or, when specifying its shape, a $2 \times n$ matrix. We always give the number of rows first, then the number of columns. A $1 \times n$ matrix is called a row vector, and an $n \times 1$ matrix is called a column vector. An element of R^n may be thought of as yielding either a row vector or a column vector.

An $m \times n$ matrix is exhibited as a rectangular array of numbers a_{ij}, where i ranges over $1, 2, \ldots, m$ and j ranges over $1, 2, \ldots, n$:

$$
i\text{th row} \rightarrow
\begin{pmatrix}
a_{11} & a_{12} & \cdots & a_{1j} & \cdots & a_{1n} \\
a_{21} & a_{22} & \cdots & a_{2j} & \cdots & a_{2n} \\
\vdots & \vdots & & \vdots & & \vdots \\
a_{i1} & a_{i2} & \cdots & a_{ij} & \cdots & a_{in} \\
\vdots & \vdots & & \vdots & & \vdots \\
a_{m1} & a_{m2} & \cdots & a_{mj} & \cdots & a_{mn}
\end{pmatrix}
$$

jth column

For example, with $m = 4$, $n = 3$,

$$
A =
\begin{pmatrix}
a_{11} & a_{12} & a_{13} \\
a_{21} & a_{22} & a_{23} \\
a_{31} & a_{32} & a_{33} \\
a_{41} & a_{42} & a_{43}
\end{pmatrix}
$$

is a 4×3 matrix.

To specify an $m \times n$ matrix, we must assign the element in the ith row and jth column. Thus, we must define a real-valued function on the set of pairs (i,j), where $i \in \{1,2,\ldots,m\}$, $j \in \{1,2,\ldots,n\}$. It is sometimes fruitful to think of the $m \times n$ matrix above as a column of row vectors or as a row of column vectors.

We introduced matrices above as arising from linear mappings of R^n to R^m (with $m = 1, 2$). The generalization to an arbitrary natural number m should be clear. Although this application of matrices is the most important one and motivates the definitions of the matrix operations which follow, it is not the only possible application. They may be useful wherever two-way classifications or arrays appear. Mathematically, a matrix is merely a function defined on a Cartesian product.

Two matrices of the same shape ($m \times n$) are added by adding corresponding components. For example,

$$
\begin{pmatrix}
4 & 3 \\
-1 & 2 \\
0 & -3
\end{pmatrix}
+
\begin{pmatrix}
2 & 1 \\
1 & 5 \\
3 & 0
\end{pmatrix}
=
\begin{pmatrix}
6 & 4 \\
0 & 7 \\
3 & -3
\end{pmatrix}.
$$

For row or column vectors, matrix addition reduces to vector addition of the corresponding n-tuples. Observe that addition of differently shaped matrices is not defined. The set of $m \times n$ matrices is closed under addition: The resultant is again of the same shape.

An $m \times n$ matrix A may be multiplied by a real number t, by multiplying each component of A by t. The resultant is again an $m \times n$ matrix and is denoted by tA. For example,

$$3 \begin{pmatrix} 1 & 0 & -2 \\ 4 & -1 & 5 \end{pmatrix} = \begin{pmatrix} 3 & 0 & -6 \\ 12 & -3 & 15 \end{pmatrix}.$$

For row or column vectors, multiplication by t reduces to multiplication of the corresponding n-tuples by the scalar t.

For fixed m and n, the set of all $m \times n$ matrices, endowed with the two operations of addition and multiplication by scalars just defined, becomes a vector space. The student should verify this fact. This vector space is isomorphic with R^{mn}; its dimension is mn.

We shall now define a third operation, matrix multiplication, which is more complicated. The reason for this particular definition will be given later.

Let A be an $m \times p$ matrix with elements a_{ik} $(i = 1, \ldots, m; k = 1, \ldots, p)$, and let B be a $p \times n$ matrix with elements b_{kj} $(k = 1, \ldots, p; j = 1, \ldots, n)$. Then the product of A and B, written AB, is the $m \times n$ matrix with elements c_{ij} $(i = 1, \ldots, m; j = 1, \ldots, n)$, where

(I) $$c_{ij} = \sum_{k=1}^{p} a_{ik}b_{kj} \qquad (i = 1, \ldots, m; j = 1, \ldots, n).$$

Written without the Σ, the (i,j)th element of the product is

$$c_{ij} = a_{i1}b_{1j} + a_{i2}b_{2j} + \cdots + a_{ip}b_{pj}.$$

Notice that the row index i of the elements of A and the column index j of the elements of B are kept fixed in the sum. Thus c_{ij} is a sort of product of the ith row of A and the jth column of B. In fact, according to our definition,

$$(a_{i1} \quad a_{i2} \quad \cdots \quad a_{ip}) \begin{pmatrix} b_{1j} \\ b_{2j} \\ \vdots \\ b_{pj} \end{pmatrix} = (c_{ij}).$$

Thus, matrix multiplication is *row-by-column* multiplication.

EXAMPLE 5–4

(a) $\quad (2 \quad 3 \quad -1) \begin{pmatrix} 5 \\ 1 \\ -1 \end{pmatrix} = ((2)(5) + (3)(1) + (-1)(-1)) = (14).$

(b) $\quad (2 \quad 3 \quad -1) \begin{pmatrix} 5 & x \\ 1 & y \\ -1 & z \end{pmatrix} = (14 \quad 2x + 3y - z).$

(c) $\quad \begin{pmatrix} 2 & 3 & -1 \\ 4 & 0 & 1 \end{pmatrix} \begin{pmatrix} 5 \\ 1 \\ -1 \end{pmatrix} = \begin{pmatrix} 14 \\ 19 \end{pmatrix}$

(d) $\quad \begin{pmatrix} 2 & 3 & -1 \\ 4 & 0 & 1 \end{pmatrix} \begin{pmatrix} 5 & 3 & 5 & 1 \\ 1 & 0 & -1 & 2 \\ -1 & 4 & -1 & 3 \end{pmatrix} = \begin{pmatrix} 14 & 2 & 8 & 5 \\ 19 & 16 & 19 & 7 \end{pmatrix}$

It should be clear from the definition that it is not always possible to form the product AB, since the inner dimensions might not be right. A convenient device for remembering how the dimensions work out in a product is

$$(m \times \mathbf{p}) \cdot (\mathbf{p} \times n) \Rightarrow (m \times n).$$

A and B must fit together according to the following scheme:

$$\overset{\leftarrow p \rightarrow}{\underset{m}{\uparrow} \binom{A}{}} \quad \overset{\leftarrow n \rightarrow}{\binom{B}{}} \underset{p}{\overset{\uparrow}{\downarrow}} = \overset{\leftarrow n \rightarrow}{\underset{m}{\uparrow} \binom{AB}{}}$$

If A is 3×2 and B is 4×5, then AB has no meaning. If A is 3×2 and B is 2×5, then AB is defined, but BA has no meaning. Even when AB and BA are defined, as when A is 3×2 and B is 2×3, the products are in general different. For AB is 3×3 and BA is 2×2, so $AB \neq BA$. (Two matrices are equal, of course, iff they are of the same shape and all corresponding components are equal.) Finally, even when both A and B are $n \times n$, so that AB and BA are defined and also $n \times n$, it may still happen that $AB \neq BA$. For example,

$$\begin{pmatrix} 1 & 2 \\ 3 & 4 \end{pmatrix} \begin{pmatrix} 1 & -1 \\ 0 & 2 \end{pmatrix} = \begin{pmatrix} 1 & 3 \\ 3 & 5 \end{pmatrix}$$

but

$$\begin{pmatrix} 1 & -1 \\ 0 & 2 \end{pmatrix}\begin{pmatrix} 1 & 2 \\ 3 & 4 \end{pmatrix} = \begin{pmatrix} -2 & -2 \\ 6 & 8 \end{pmatrix}.$$

There are several types of matrices that play special roles with respect to addition and multiplication. If m and n are natural numbers, we write $0_{m \times n}$ (or simply 0) for the $m \times n$ matrix composed entirely of zeroes: $a_{ij} = 0$ $(i = 1, \ldots, m; j = 1, \ldots, n)$. It is the additive identity or 0 in the vector space of all $m \times n$ matrices; if A is any $m \times n$ matrix, then $A + 0 = A$. We write I_n (or simply I) for the square matrix, with n rows and n columns, that has 1's down the main diagonal (upper left to lower right) and 0's elsewhere:

$$I_n = \begin{pmatrix} 1 & 0 & 0 & \cdots & 0 \\ 0 & 1 & 0 & \cdots & 0 \\ 0 & 0 & 1 & \cdots & 0 \\ \vdots & \vdots & \vdots & & \vdots \\ 0 & 0 & 0 & \cdots & 1 \end{pmatrix}.$$

I_n acts as a multiplicative identity for all matrices A for which either AI_n or $I_n A$ is defined. Thus, if A is $m \times n$, then $AI_n = A$; if A is $n \times m$, then $I_n A = A$. For example,

$$\begin{pmatrix} 1 & 0 \\ 0 & 1 \end{pmatrix}\begin{pmatrix} 3 & 4 & x \\ 2 & 5 & y \end{pmatrix} = \begin{pmatrix} 3 & 4 & x \\ 2 & 5 & y \end{pmatrix}.$$

The set M_n of all $n \times n$ matrices is a fascinating and rich algebraic structure. It is equipped with three important operations: scalar multiplication, addition, and matrix multiplication. It is closed under each of these operations. Most of the rules of ordinary arithmetic hold for M_n. For example, the associative law for multiplication holds:

$$A(BC) = (AB)C \qquad (A,B,C \in M_n).$$

The distributive laws hold:

$$A(B + C) = AB + AC,$$

$$(B + C)A = BA + CA.$$

The commutative law *for addition* holds:

$$A + B = B + A.$$

However, the commutative law for *multiplication* fails (for $n > 1$). For each $n > 1$, we can exhibit matrices $A,B \in M_n$ for which $AB \neq BA$. M_n is a significant example of a noncommutative algebra. It is a proper generalization of the real number system R, since M_1 is isomorphic, as an algebra, with R.

The laws stated above, and others, hold for all matrices, provided that the products and sums mentioned are defined. For example, if A is $m \times p$, B is $p \times q$, and C is $q \times n$, then $A(BC) = (AB)C$. These laws will be illustrated in the following exercises.

EXERCISES 5-5

1. State whether the following are defined. If they are, compute them:

(a) $\begin{pmatrix} 1 & -1 \\ 2 & 0 \end{pmatrix} + \begin{pmatrix} 3 & 4 & 5 \\ -1 & 1 & -1 \end{pmatrix}$.

(b) $\begin{pmatrix} 1 & -1 \\ 2 & 0 \end{pmatrix} \begin{pmatrix} 3 & 4 & 5 \\ -1 & 1 & -1 \end{pmatrix}$.

(c) $\begin{pmatrix} 3 & 4 & 5 \\ -1 & 1 & 1 \end{pmatrix} \begin{pmatrix} 1 & -1 \\ 2 & 0 \end{pmatrix}$.

(d) $\begin{pmatrix} 1 & 3 \\ 2 & 0 \end{pmatrix} + 6 \begin{pmatrix} \frac{1}{2} & \frac{1}{3} \\ \frac{1}{3} & \frac{1}{6} \end{pmatrix}$.

(e) $\begin{pmatrix} 5 & -1 \\ 2 & 1 \end{pmatrix} \begin{pmatrix} 0 & 3 \\ -1 & 2 \end{pmatrix}$.

(f) $\begin{pmatrix} 0 & 3 \\ -1 & 2 \end{pmatrix} \begin{pmatrix} 5 & -1 \\ 2 & 1 \end{pmatrix}$.

(g) $\begin{pmatrix} a & b \\ c & d \end{pmatrix} \begin{pmatrix} 1 \\ 3 \end{pmatrix} + \begin{pmatrix} 1 \\ 3 \end{pmatrix} \begin{pmatrix} a & b \\ c & d \end{pmatrix}$.

(h) $\begin{pmatrix} 1 & 1 \\ 0 & 1 \end{pmatrix} \begin{pmatrix} 1 \\ 3 \end{pmatrix} - (1 \quad 3) \begin{pmatrix} 1 & 1 \\ 0 & 1 \end{pmatrix}$.

(i) $\begin{pmatrix} 1 & x \\ 0 & 1 \end{pmatrix}\begin{pmatrix} 1 & y \\ 0 & 1 \end{pmatrix}$.

(j) $\begin{pmatrix} 3 & 2 & 1 \\ 1 & 2 & 3 \end{pmatrix}\left[\begin{pmatrix} 1 & 1 & 2 \\ 0 & 1 & 5 \\ -1 & 0 & 3 \end{pmatrix} - 3\begin{pmatrix} 1 & 0 & 0 \\ 0 & 1 & 0 \\ 0 & 0 & 1 \end{pmatrix}\right]$.

(k) $\begin{pmatrix} 3 & 2 & 1 \\ 1 & 2 & 3 \end{pmatrix}\begin{pmatrix} 1 & 1 & 2 \\ 0 & 1 & 5 \\ -1 & 0 & 3 \end{pmatrix} - 3\left[\begin{pmatrix} 3 & 2 & 1 \\ 1 & 2 & 3 \end{pmatrix}\begin{pmatrix} 1 & 0 & 0 \\ 0 & 1 & 0 \\ 0 & 0 & 1 \end{pmatrix}\right]$.

(l) $\begin{pmatrix} 1 & 3 \\ 5 & 0 \end{pmatrix}\left[\begin{pmatrix} 1 & 7 \\ 5 & 1 \end{pmatrix}\begin{pmatrix} 2 & 2 \\ 1 & 3 \end{pmatrix}\right]$.

(m) $\left[\begin{pmatrix} 1 & 3 \\ 5 & 0 \end{pmatrix}\begin{pmatrix} 1 & 7 \\ 5 & 1 \end{pmatrix}\right]\begin{pmatrix} 2 & 2 \\ 1 & 3 \end{pmatrix}$.

(n) $I_2\begin{pmatrix} 1 & 1 \\ 2 & 3 \end{pmatrix} - \begin{pmatrix} 1 & 1 \\ 2 & 3 \end{pmatrix}$

2. Compute:

(a) $\begin{pmatrix} 1 & -1 \\ 1 & 2 \end{pmatrix}\left[5\begin{pmatrix} 2 & 1 & -1 & 4 \\ 3 & 2 & -1 & 3 \end{pmatrix}\right]$.

(b) $\left[5\begin{pmatrix} 1 & -1 \\ 1 & 2 \end{pmatrix}\right]\begin{pmatrix} 2 & 1 & -1 & 4 \\ 3 & 2 & -1 & 3 \end{pmatrix}$.

(c) $5\left[\begin{pmatrix} 1 & -1 \\ 1 & 2 \end{pmatrix}\begin{pmatrix} 2 & 1 & -1 & 4 \\ 3 & 2 & -1 & 3 \end{pmatrix}\right]$.

3. Prove that if A and B are of the same shape, then $A + B = B + A$.

4. Compute and compare:

(a) $\begin{pmatrix} 3 & 0 & 0 \\ 0 & 1 & 0 \\ 0 & 0 & 1 \end{pmatrix}\begin{pmatrix} 1 & 2 & -1 \\ 4 & 2 & 3 \\ -2 & 1 & 7 \end{pmatrix}$.

(b) $\begin{pmatrix} 1 & 2 & -1 \\ 4 & 2 & 3 \\ -2 & 1 & 7 \end{pmatrix} \begin{pmatrix} 3 & 0 & 0 \\ 0 & 1 & 0 \\ 0 & 0 & 1 \end{pmatrix}.$

(c) $\begin{pmatrix} 1 & 0 & 0 \\ 0 & 3 & 0 \\ 0 & 0 & 1 \end{pmatrix} \begin{pmatrix} 1 & 2 & -1 \\ 4 & 2 & 3 \\ -2 & 1 & 7 \end{pmatrix}.$

(d) $\begin{pmatrix} 1 & 2 & -1 \\ 4 & 2 & 3 \\ -2 & 1 & 7 \end{pmatrix} \begin{pmatrix} 1 & 0 & 0 \\ 0 & 3 & 0 \\ 0 & 0 & 1 \end{pmatrix}.$

5. Compute and compare:

(a) $\begin{pmatrix} 1 & 2 \\ 5 & 7 \end{pmatrix} \left[\begin{pmatrix} 1 & 0 \\ 5 & 5 \end{pmatrix} + \begin{pmatrix} 2 & 7 \\ 0 & 1 \end{pmatrix} \right].$

(b) $\begin{pmatrix} 1 & 2 \\ 5 & 7 \end{pmatrix} \begin{pmatrix} 1 & 0 \\ 5 & 5 \end{pmatrix} + \begin{pmatrix} 1 & 2 \\ 5 & 7 \end{pmatrix} \begin{pmatrix} 2 & 7 \\ 0 & 1 \end{pmatrix}.$

6. Find, if possible, a matrix A such that

$$A \begin{pmatrix} 0 & 1 \\ 2 & -1 \end{pmatrix} = I_2.$$

[*Hint:* A must be 2×2, say $\begin{pmatrix} x & y \\ z & w \end{pmatrix}$. Solve for the unknowns.]

7. Find, if possible, a matrix B such that

$$B \begin{pmatrix} 0 & 1 \\ 2 & -1 \end{pmatrix} = \begin{pmatrix} 2 & 1 \\ -1 & 0 \end{pmatrix}.$$

8. Find, if possible, a matrix C such that

$$C \begin{pmatrix} 1 & 2 \\ 2 & 4 \end{pmatrix} = I_2.$$

9. Find, if possible, a matrix D such that

$$\begin{pmatrix} 1 & 2 \\ 0 & 1 \end{pmatrix} \left[D \begin{pmatrix} 1 & 3 \\ 0 & 1 \end{pmatrix} \right] = I_2.$$

10. Find, if possible, nonzero column vectors $\begin{pmatrix} x_1 \\ x_2 \end{pmatrix}$ such that

(a) $\begin{pmatrix} 2 & 4 \\ 0 & 3 \end{pmatrix}\begin{pmatrix} x_1 \\ x_2 \end{pmatrix} = 2\begin{pmatrix} x_1 \\ x_2 \end{pmatrix}$.

(b) $\begin{pmatrix} 2 & 4 \\ 0 & 3 \end{pmatrix}\begin{pmatrix} x_1 \\ x_2 \end{pmatrix} = 3\begin{pmatrix} x_1 \\ x_2 \end{pmatrix}$.

(c) $\begin{pmatrix} 2 & 4 \\ 0 & 3 \end{pmatrix}\begin{pmatrix} x_1 \\ x_2 \end{pmatrix} = 10\begin{pmatrix} x_1 \\ x_2 \end{pmatrix}$.

(Three separate problems.)

11. Find, if possible, numbers a, b, c, d such that

$$a\begin{pmatrix} 2 \\ 1 \end{pmatrix} + b\begin{pmatrix} 5 \\ 3 \end{pmatrix} = \begin{pmatrix} 1 \\ 0 \end{pmatrix},$$

$$c\begin{pmatrix} 2 \\ 1 \end{pmatrix} + d\begin{pmatrix} 5 \\ 3 \end{pmatrix} = \begin{pmatrix} 0 \\ 1 \end{pmatrix}.$$

Express the conjunction of these two conditions as a single matrix equation.

12. Let A be a 2×2 matrix, x and y two-dimensional column vectors, and t a real number. Prove:

(a) $A(x + y) = Ax + Ay$.

(b) $A(tx) = t(Ax)$.

Interpret these results in terms of linear mappings.

*13. Given

$$z_1 = y_1 + 2y_2, \qquad y_1 = x_1 - x_2,$$

$$z_2 = 3y_1 + 4y_2, \qquad y_2 = 6x_1 + 5x_2,$$

express z_1, z_2 directly in terms of x_1, x_2, as

$$z_1 = ax_1 + bx_2,$$

$$z_2 = cx_1 + dx_2.$$

Now compare the matrix $\begin{pmatrix} a & b \\ c & d \end{pmatrix}$ with $\begin{pmatrix} 1 & 2 \\ 3 & 4 \end{pmatrix}\begin{pmatrix} 1 & -1 \\ 6 & 5 \end{pmatrix}$. Using this example (and others, possibly), try to guess a general theorem.

5–3. LINEAR MAPPINGS AND MATRICES

We have already indicated that matrices are related to linear mappings. In this section we shall make the connection more explicit.

First we shall commit the small mathematical error of identifying two objects which are really distinct. To every $x \in R^n$ there corresponds a column vector

$$\begin{pmatrix} x_1 \\ x_2 \\ \cdot \\ \cdot \\ \cdot \\ x_n \end{pmatrix}$$

with the same components as x. Under this one-to-one correspondence, addition and scalar multiplication are preserved, so the two vector spaces are isomorphic. To simplify our language, we shall regard them as the same.

Now suppose that A is an $m \times n$ matrix and that $x \in R^n$. Then (with the above identification) the product Ax is defined and is an element of R^m. Therefore the function f given by

(1) $$f(x) = Ax \qquad (x \in R^n)$$

is a mapping (function) from R^n to R^m. Because

(2) $$A(x + y) = Ax + Ay \qquad (x, y \in R^n),$$

(3) $$A(tx) = t(Ax) \qquad (x \in R^n, t \in R),$$

it follows that f is a linear mapping. In this way, *to every $m \times n$ matrix there corresponds a linear mapping of R^n into R^m*.

Conversely, *every linear mapping f of R^n into R^m corresponds to an $m \times n$ matrix A satisfying* Eq. (1). The proof will be omitted, although it is not difficult. This correspondence is also one-to-one.

It is possible to define quite naturally the operations of multiplication by scalars and addition for mappings (not necessarily linear) of R^n into R^m. If $t \in R$ and $f: R^n \to R^m$, then tf is defined by

(4) $$(tf)(x) = t[f(x)] \qquad (x \in R^n).$$

Let us make quite clear what the definition tells us. We start with an arbitrary $x \in R^n$. The mapping f carries x to the element $f(x) \in R^m$. To this element we then apply multiplication by the scalar t, and we end up

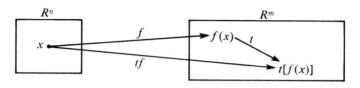

FIGURE 5–5

with $t[f(x)]$. The mapping directly from x to $t[f(x)]$ so defined we call tf. A way of picturing the situation is shown in Figure 5–5.

EXAMPLE 5–5. Let f be the mapping from R^2 to R^3 defined by $f:(x_1,x_2) \to (x_1,7,x_2)$. Then $3f$ is the mapping from R^2 to R^3 defined by $3f:(x_1,x_2) \to (3x_1,21,3x_2)$. Notice that neither f nor $3f$ is linear.

Next let f and g be mappings (not necessarily linear) from R^n to R^m. Then $f + g$ is defined as the mapping from R^n to R^m given by

(5) $$(f + g)(x) = f(x) + g(x) \qquad (x \in R^n).$$

The diagram for this situation is given as Figure 5–6.

Let us now restrict our attention to the set, say L_{nm}, of all *linear* mappings of R^n into R^m. If $f \in L_{nm}$ and $t \in R$, then also $tf \in L_{nm}$. If $f,g \in L_{nm}$, then also $f + g \in L_{nm}$. Thus, the set L_{nm} is closed under scalar multiplication and addition. It is routine to show that L_{nm}, endowed with these two operations, is a vector space.

We have already seen that M_{mn}, the set of all $m \times n$ matrices, is a vector space under the matrix operations of scalar multiplication and addition. Also, there is a one-to-one correspondence between L_{nm} and M_{mn}. It should come as no surprise to the student that this correspondence is in fact an isomorphism between the two vector spaces. This isomorphism allows us to treat the rather abstract linear mapping as a very concrete object—

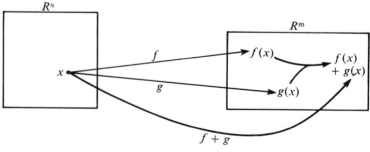

FIGURE 5–6

namely, a matrix. Calculations with linear mappings can be carried out by performing the corresponding calculations with the corresponding matrices.

EXAMPLE 5–6. Let f and g be the mappings from R^3 to R^2 defined by

$$f: \begin{pmatrix} x_1 \\ x_2 \\ x_3 \end{pmatrix} \rightarrow \begin{pmatrix} 2x_1 - 3x_2 + x_3 \\ 2x_2 - x_3 \end{pmatrix},$$

$$g: \begin{pmatrix} x_1 \\ x_2 \\ x_3 \end{pmatrix} \rightarrow \begin{pmatrix} 4x_1 + x_2 \\ x_1 - x_2 + x_3 \end{pmatrix}.$$

The matrices corresponding to f and g are

$$A = \begin{pmatrix} 2 & -3 & 1 \\ 0 & 2 & -1 \end{pmatrix}, \quad B = \begin{pmatrix} 4 & 1 & 0 \\ 1 & -1 & 1 \end{pmatrix},$$

respectively. The matrix corresponding to $3f - 2g$ is $3A - 2B$:

$$3A - 2B = \begin{pmatrix} 2 & -11 & 3 \\ -2 & 8 & -5 \end{pmatrix}.$$

Therefore $3f - 2g$ is given by

$$(3f - 2g): \begin{pmatrix} x_1 \\ x_2 \\ x_3 \end{pmatrix} \rightarrow \begin{pmatrix} 2x_1 - 11x_2 + 3x_3 \\ -2x_1 + 8x_2 - 5x_3 \end{pmatrix}.$$

EXAMPLE 5–7. Let $e^{(1)}, e^{(2)}, e^{(3)}$ denote the unit vectors in R^3:

$$e^{(1)} = \begin{pmatrix} 1 \\ 0 \\ 0 \end{pmatrix}, \quad e^{(2)} = \begin{pmatrix} 0 \\ 1 \\ 0 \end{pmatrix}, \quad e^{(3)} = \begin{pmatrix} 0 \\ 0 \\ 1 \end{pmatrix}.$$

Suppose that f is a linear mapping from R^3 to R^2 such that

$$f(e^{(1)}) = \begin{pmatrix} 3 \\ 1 \end{pmatrix}, \quad f(e^{(2)}) = \begin{pmatrix} 0 \\ 2 \end{pmatrix}, \quad f(e^{(3)}) = \begin{pmatrix} 1 \\ -1 \end{pmatrix}.$$

What is the matrix corresponding to f?

Solution: If $x \in R^3$, then

$$x = x_1 e^{(1)} + x_2 e^{(2)} + x_3 e^{(3)}.$$

Hence

$$f(x) = f(x_1 e^{(1)} + x_2 e^{(2)} + x_3 e^{(3)})$$

$$= x_1 f(e^{(1)}) + x_2 f(e^{(2)}) + x_3 f(e^{(3)})$$

$$= x_1 \begin{pmatrix} 3 \\ 1 \end{pmatrix} + x_2 \begin{pmatrix} 0 \\ 2 \end{pmatrix} + x_3 \begin{pmatrix} 1 \\ -1 \end{pmatrix}$$

$$= \begin{pmatrix} 3x_1 + 0 \cdot x_2 + x_3 \\ x_1 + 2x_2 - x_3 \end{pmatrix}.$$

Therefore the matrix corresponding to f is

$$\begin{pmatrix} 3 & 0 & 1 \\ 1 & 2 & -1 \end{pmatrix}.$$

A third operation involving mappings is only slightly more complicated than the other two. In some respects it is simpler, since it involves no special properties of vector spaces. The following definition is therefore framed for arbitrary sets and mappings between them.

Let X, Y, Z be sets. Let g be a mapping from X into Y, and let f be a mapping from Y into Z. Then $f \circ g$ is the mapping from X into Z given by

$$(f \circ g)(x) = f[g(x)] \qquad (x \in X).$$

The mapping $f \circ g$ is called the *composition* of f and g. The relevant diagram is given in Figure 5-7.

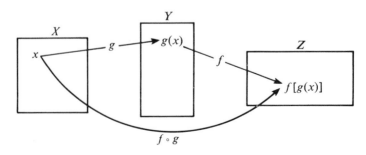

FIGURE 5-7

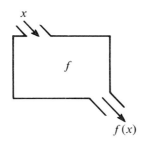

FIGURE 5-8

Notice the apparent reversal of order of the letters f and g. This is because of our convention of writing the function symbol to the left of the variable. The important fact to remember is that the mapping symbol closest to the variable is the one we apply first, so that $f \circ g$ means: Apply g first, then f, in accordance with the defining equation above. Starting with x, we work from the inside out.

We can think of mappings or functions as machines, Figure 5–8. If the input of the "machine" f is x, then the output is $f(x)$. If we connect two "machines" f and g so that the output of g is the input of f, the composite "machine" is $f \circ g$, Figure 5–9.

An important property of composition is that it is *associative* whenever

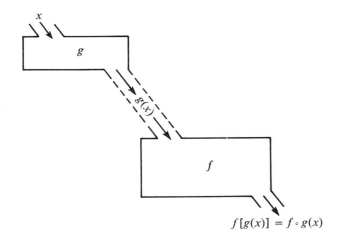

$$f[g(x)] = f \circ g(x)$$

FIGURE 5-9

the spaces and the mappings fit together properly. Suppose that f, g, h are mappings as indicated:

$$X \xrightarrow{h} Y \xrightarrow{g} Z \xrightarrow{f} W.$$

The domain of h is X, the domain of g is Y, and the domain of f is Z. If x is any element of X, then by definition

$$[f \circ (g \circ h)] (x) = f[(g \circ h)(x)]$$
$$= f[g[h(x)]]$$
$$= (f \circ g)[h(x)]$$
$$= [(f \circ g) \circ h](x).$$

Since this is true for every $x \in X$,

$$f \circ (g \circ h) = (f \circ g) \circ h.$$

We are therefore free to omit the parentheses and to write $f \circ g \circ h$ for the common mapping.

EXAMPLE 5–8.   Let $p_i (i = 1, \ldots, m)$ denote the mapping from R^m to R defined by $p_i(x) = x_i (x \in R^m)$. Let f be a mapping from R^n to R^m. Then $p_i \circ f$ is simply the ith component of f. It is a mapping from R^n to R.

EXAMPLE 5–9.   Let g be a mapping from R^n into R^p, and let f be a mapping from R^p into R^m. Then $f \circ g$ is defined. What is the ith component of $f \circ g$?
   Solution:

$$(f \circ g)_i = p_i \circ (f \circ g)$$
$$= (p_i \circ f) \circ g$$
$$= f_i \circ g.$$

In words, the ith component of (f following g) is the same as (the ith component of f) following g.

The composition $g \circ f$ may not be defined even if $f \circ g$ is defined. Even if both are defined, they need not be equal. For example, let f and g be given by

$$f(x) = x^2 \qquad (x \in R),$$
$$g(x) = x + 1 \qquad (x \in R).$$

Then, for all $x \in R$,

$$(f \circ g)(x) = f[g(x)] = f(x + 1) = (x + 1)^2,$$
$$(g \circ f)(x) = g[f(x)] = g(x^2) = x^2 + 1.$$

Thus, composition is not commutative in general.

We now show that the composition of two linear mappings is linear, provided that it is defined. Let g be a linear mapping from R^n into R^p, and let f be a linear mapping from R^p into R^m. Then $f \circ g$ is defined. To test its linearity, let $t \in R$, $x \in R^n$. Then

$$(f \circ g)(tx) = f[g(tx)] \quad \text{(def. of } f \circ g)$$
$$= f[tg(x)] \quad \text{(linearity of } g)$$
$$= tf[g(x)] \quad \text{(linearity of } f)$$
$$= t(f \circ g)(x) \quad \text{(def. of } f \circ g).$$

Next, let $x, y \in R^n$. Then

$$(f \circ g)(x + y) = f[g(x + y)] \quad \text{(why?)}$$
$$= f[g(x) + g(y)] \quad \text{(why?)}$$
$$= f[g(x)] + f[g(y)] \quad \text{(why?)}$$
$$= (f \circ g)(x) + (f \circ g)(y) \quad \text{(why?)}.$$

Thus $f \circ g$ passes both tests of linearity. This completes the proof.

EXAMPLE 5–10. Let f and g be the linear mappings from R^2 to R^2 corresponding to the matrices

$$A = \begin{pmatrix} 1 & 2 \\ 3 & 4 \end{pmatrix}, \quad B = \begin{pmatrix} a & b \\ c & d \end{pmatrix},$$

respectively. Then $f \circ g$ is linear. What is the corresponding matrix?

Solution: For $x \in R^2$, we have

$$g(x) = Bx$$
$$= \begin{pmatrix} a & b \\ c & d \end{pmatrix}\begin{pmatrix} x_1 \\ x_2 \end{pmatrix}$$
$$= \begin{pmatrix} ax_1 + bx_2 \\ cx_1 + dx_2 \end{pmatrix}.$$

Now

$$(f \circ g)(x) = f[g(x)]$$
$$= A(g(x))$$
$$= \begin{pmatrix} 1 & 2 \\ 3 & 4 \end{pmatrix}\begin{pmatrix} ax_1 + bx_2 \\ cx_1 + dx_2 \end{pmatrix}$$

$$= \begin{pmatrix} (a + 2c)x_1 + (b + 2d)x_2 \\ (3a + 4c)x_1 + (3b + 4d)x_2 \end{pmatrix}.$$

Therefore the required matrix is

$$\begin{pmatrix} a + 2c & b + 2d \\ 3a + 4c & 3b + 4d \end{pmatrix}.$$

Observe, in Example 5–10, that the answer is exactly the matrix product AB. This is no accident, of course, and the result is quite general. In fact the matrix product was defined in such a way as to make the result true. If we accept this result—we shall not prove it here—then the associativity of matrix multiplication follows readily. For if A, B, C are matrices that "fit" in the products $A(BC)$ and $(AB)C$, and if f, g, h are the corresponding linear mappings, then BC corresponds to $g \circ h$ and $A(BC)$ to $f \circ (g \circ h)$. Similarly, $(AB)C$ corresponds to $(f \circ g) \circ h$. But we have seen that $f \circ (g \circ h) = (f \circ g) \circ h$, so $A(BC)$ and $(AB)C$ correspond to the same linear mapping $f \circ g \circ h$. They must be equal, because the correspondence is one-to-one: $A(BC) = (AB)C$.

The student may wish to amuse himself by proving the associativity of matrix multiplication directly from its definition. Actually, such a proof is not very difficult, but requires a proper choice of notation and an adroit interchange of the order of summation in a double sum.

We may have occasion to use the *identity mapping* j_n from R^n to R^n defined by

$$j_n(x) = x \qquad (x \in R^n).$$

Clearly j_n is linear, and its corresponding matrix is the identity matrix I_n.

EXERCISES 5–6

1. Let f, g be the mappings from R^2 to R^2 defined by

$$f(x) = (x_1 + x_2, x_1 - x_2) \qquad (x \in R^2),$$
$$g(x) = (3x_1 + x_2, -x_1 - x_2) \qquad (x \in R^2).$$

Let $h = f + g, q = f \circ g, p = g \circ f$.
  (a) Are f, g, h, q, p linear?
  (b) Compute $h((9,3))$, $q((2,1))$, $p((2,1))$, $h(p((1,3)))$, $f(g((2,1)))$, $(f + 7g)((1,3))$, and $(2q + 3p)((1,3))$.

2. Let $f: R^3 \to R^3$ be defined by

$$f(x) = (-x_3, x_2, -x_1) \qquad (x \in R^3).$$

Prove that $f \circ f = j_3$. Write down the matrix A corresponding to f, and compute $A^2 (= AA)$.

3. Let f, g be the mappings from R^3 to R^3 defined by

$$f(x) = (2x_1 - x_3, x_1 + x_2, x_1 - x_3) \quad (x \in R^3),$$
$$g(x) = (x_1, x_1 + x_2, x_1 + x_2 + x_3) \quad (x \in R^3).$$

Compute $f \circ g((1,5,0))$, $g \circ f((1,5,0))$, $(f + g)((1,5,0))$, $(f \circ g + g \circ f)((1, \sqrt{2}, \sqrt{3}))$, $(g \circ f \circ g)((1,2,1))$, $f \circ g(x)$ and $g \circ f(x)$ for $x \in R^3$.

4. Let

$$\left. \begin{array}{l} z_1 = y_1 + 7y_2 + 5y_3 \\ z_2 = 2y_1 \qquad\quad + 7y_3 \end{array} \right\} \quad (y_1, y_2, y_3 \in R),$$

$$\left. \begin{array}{l} y_1 = x_1 + 3x_2 + 7x_3 + 2x_4 \\ y_2 = \qquad\quad 5x_2 + x_3 + 2x_4 \\ y_3 = x_1 \qquad\quad - x_3 + 3x_4 \end{array} \right\} \quad (x_1, x_2, x_3, x_4 \in R).$$

Express z_1, z_2 in terms of x_1, x_2, x_3, x_4. (This problem can be worked in two ways. Do both.)

5. A company sells n items at unit prices k_j ($j = 1, \ldots, n$). There are m purchasers; the ith one buys b_{ij} units of item j ($i = 1, \ldots, m$; $j = 1, \ldots, n$). The total cost to the ith purchaser is c_i ($i = 1, \ldots, m$).

(a) Write equations expressing the c_i in terms of the b_{ij} and the k_j.
(b) Write these equations in compact matrix notation.
(c) Write in matrix notation the total cost to all purchasers.

6. Let A be an $r \times s$ matrix, B an $m \times n$ matrix. Write down necessary and sufficient conditions on r, s, m, n for each of the following to be defined (five separate problems):

(a) $A + B$.   (d) $AB + BA$.
(b) AB.   (e) $A(A + B)$.
(c) BA.

7. Let A, B, C be matrices such that $A(B + C)$ is defined. Show that $AB + AC$ is defined and that $A(B + C) = AB + AC$.

8. Let A, B, C be matrices such that $(A + B)C$ is defined. Show that $AC + BC$ is defined and that $(A + B)C = AC + BC$.

9. Let $f: R^n \to R^m$ be linear. Let a and $b \neq 0$ be fixed elements of R^n. By *the line through a in the direction b* we mean the set

$$L = \{z | z = a + tb \text{ for some } t \in R\}.$$

Show that the image of L under f,

$$\{f(z)|z \in L\},$$

is the line through $f(a)$ in the direction $f(b)$. (This is the reason for the term "linear mapping"). To be precise, we must assume $f(b) \neq 0$.

10. Let $A = \begin{pmatrix} 1 & 3 \\ 0 & 1 \end{pmatrix}$. Compute A^2, A^3, A^4, A^5. If n is a positive integer, what is A^n?

11. Let $B = \begin{pmatrix} 3 & 0 \\ 0 & 2 \end{pmatrix}$. Compute B^2, B^3, B^4, B^5. If n is a positive integer, what is B^n?

12. Let $C = \begin{pmatrix} 1 & 1 \\ 0 & 1 \end{pmatrix}$, $D = \begin{pmatrix} 1 & -1 \\ 0 & 1 \end{pmatrix}$, $B = \begin{pmatrix} 3 & 0 \\ 0 & 2 \end{pmatrix}$. Show that

(a) $CD = DC = I_2$.

(b) $CBD = \begin{pmatrix} 3 & -1 \\ 0 & 2 \end{pmatrix}$.

(c) $\begin{pmatrix} 3 & -1 \\ 0 & 2 \end{pmatrix}^2 = (CBD)(CBD) = CB^2D = ?$

(d) $\begin{pmatrix} 3 & -1 \\ 0 & 2 \end{pmatrix}^3 = CB^3D = ?$

(e) $\begin{pmatrix} 3 & -1 \\ 0 & 2 \end{pmatrix}^{100} = CB^{100}D = \begin{pmatrix} 3^{100} & 2^{100} - 3^{100} \\ 0 & 2^{100} \end{pmatrix}$.

13. Suppose that V and W are vector spaces and $f: V \to W$ is linear. Let θ, $\bar{\theta}$ be the additive identities in V, W, respectively. Let

$$N = \{x \in V | f(x) = \bar{\theta}\}.$$

N is called the *null space* of f. Prove that N is closed under addition and scalar multiplication. This means that $(N, +, \cdot)$ is itself a vector space, if N is not empty. Prove that N is not empty.

14. With the notation of Problem 13, show that

(a) $\forall x, x' \in V$, $x - x' \in N \to f(x) = f(x')$.

(b) $\forall x, x' \in V$, $f(x) = f(x') \to x - x' \in N$.

(c) If f is one-to-one, then $N = \{\theta\}$.

(d) If $N = \{\theta\}$, then f is one-to-one.

15. With the notation of Problem 13, let H be the range of f:

$$H = \{y \in W | \exists x \in V, f(x) = y\}.$$

Prove that H is a subspace of W.

*16. Suppose that V and W are vector spaces, f is a linear mapping from V into W, and g is a mapping from W into V such that $g \circ f = j$, where $j(x) = x \ (x \in V)$. Prove that:

    (a) g is *onto* V (i.e., the range of g is V).

    (b) f is *one-to-one* $[\forall x, x' \in V, f(x) = f(x') \to x = x']$.

    (c) If $h = f \circ g$, then $h \circ h = h$.

    (d) If $h = f \circ g$, then $g \circ h \circ f = j$.

17. Given a linear mapping f of R^2 into R^1 such that

$$f\left(\begin{pmatrix}1\\0\end{pmatrix}\right) = 7, \quad f\left(\begin{pmatrix}0\\1\end{pmatrix}\right) = 3,$$

    (a) Find $f\left(\begin{pmatrix}2\\5\end{pmatrix}\right)$.

    (b) Find $f\left(\begin{pmatrix}x_1\\x_2\end{pmatrix}\right)$, $\quad x_1, x_2 \in R$.

    (c) Find the matrix corresponding to f.

18. Given a linear mapping f of R^2 into R^1 such that

$$f\left(\begin{pmatrix}1\\0\end{pmatrix}\right) = 4, \quad f\left(\begin{pmatrix}1\\1\end{pmatrix}\right) = 11,$$

find $f(x)$ $(x \in R^2)$. $\left[Hint: \begin{pmatrix}1\\1\end{pmatrix} - \begin{pmatrix}1\\0\end{pmatrix} = \begin{pmatrix}0\\1\end{pmatrix}; \text{ what is } f\left(\begin{pmatrix}0\\1\end{pmatrix}\right)?\right]$ What is the matrix corresponding to f?

19. Let $A = \begin{pmatrix}2 & 1 & 3\\4 & 2 & 6\end{pmatrix}$. Compute $y = Ax$ if

$$x = \begin{pmatrix}1\\0\\0\end{pmatrix}, \begin{pmatrix}0\\1\\0\end{pmatrix}, \begin{pmatrix}0\\0\\1\end{pmatrix}, \begin{pmatrix}2\\3\\4\end{pmatrix}, \begin{pmatrix}4\\-1\\0\end{pmatrix}, \begin{pmatrix}x_1\\x_2\\x_3\end{pmatrix}.$$

Write an equation connecting y_1 and y_2. Can you find an x such that $Ax = \begin{pmatrix}1\\1\end{pmatrix}$?

20. Chemical ingredients numbered $i = 1, 2, 3, 4, 5$ go into the manufacture of products numbered $j = 1, 2, 3$. Let x be the production vector, y the corresponding required ingredient vector.

(a) If x, x' are production vectors, show that the ingredient vector for their sum is the sum of their ingredient vectors.

(b) If t is a positive real, x a production vector, show that the ingredient vector for tx is t times the ingredient vector for x.

(c) Is there a linear mapping f such that $y = f(x)$? If so, from where to where?

(d) If we represent f by a matrix A, what do the columns of A tell us?

(e) What do the individual elements a_{ij} of A represent?

(f) Write out in full the system of equations of which $y = Ax$ is an abbreviation.

(g) Write out in summation notation the system in part (f).

(h) Let $c = (c_1 \; c_2 \; c_3 \; c_4 \; c_5)$ be a row vector representing the unit costs of the ingredients. What does $cy = cAx$ represent? What does cA represent?

21. Compute:

(a)
$$\begin{pmatrix} 1 & 7 & 3 & 0 \\ 2 & 1 & 4 & 1 \\ 9 & 2 & 1 & 1 \\ 0 & 0 & 1 & -1 \end{pmatrix} \begin{pmatrix} 1 \\ 2 \\ 3 \\ 2 \end{pmatrix}.$$

(b)
$$\begin{pmatrix} 1 & 2 & 4 & 7 \\ 3 & 1 & 5 & 0 \\ -1 & 1 & 2 & 4 \end{pmatrix} \begin{pmatrix} 1 \\ 0 \\ 2 \\ 4 \end{pmatrix}.$$

(c)
$$\begin{pmatrix} 1 & -1 & 6 \\ 2 & 0 & 1 \\ 4 & -1 & 4 \\ 0 & 3 & 0 \end{pmatrix} \begin{pmatrix} 1 \\ 2 \\ 3 \end{pmatrix}.$$

22. Let A be a 3×3 matrix. What is the effect of multiplying A on the right by

$$B = \begin{pmatrix} 1 & 0 & 0 \\ 0 & 1 & 0 \\ 0 & 0 & 5 \end{pmatrix}?$$

What about BA?

5–4. THE SOLUTION OF EQUATIONS

In elementary algebra we learn quite early how to solve equations of the form $ax = b$. In our present study of linear algebra we shall learn how, given y, to solve for x:

(1) $f(x) = y,$

where f is a linear mapping of R^n into R^m. Before entering into the details, we shall examine the problem from a general, semiqualitative standpoint, to discover what sort of answer we may expect.

For the purpose of this discussion, it does no harm to be somewhat general, and it may do some good. Let X and Y be sets, and let f be a mapping (or function) from X into Y. Thus, dom $f = X$ and rng $f \subset Y$. There are at least four problems that we may pose with regard to f:

Problem 1. What is the range of f?
Problem 2. Given $y \in Y$, does there exist $x \in X$ such that $f(x) = y$?
Problem 3. Given $y \in Y$, for how many $x \in X$ is it true that $f(x) = y$?
Problem 4. Given $y \in Y$, find all $x \in X$ such that $f(x) = y$.

We can organize our thinking about these problems by considering the solution set $S(y)$ of Eq. (1). This is merely the truth set of (1):

(2) $S(y) = \{x \in X \,|\, f(x) = y\}$ $(y \in Y)$.

In terms of solution sets, our problems become:

Problem 1. What is $\{y \in Y \,|\, S(y) \ne \varnothing\}$?
Problem 2. Given $y \in Y$, is $S(y) \ne \varnothing$?
Problem 3. Given $y \in Y$, what is the cardinality of $S(y)$ [i.e., the number of elements in $S(y)$]?
Problem 4. Given $y \in Y$, find $S(y)$.

In theory, Problem 1 is solvable as soon as f is given. All we need do is run through all the elements $x \in$ dom $f\,[= X]$ and record all the functional values $f(x)$. If we recall that f is a set of ordered pairs, we see that the range of f is just the set of all second components of the pairs. In practice, we frequently cannot perform this feat of recording all functional values, and must devise some other scheme for solving Problem 1.

EXAMPLE 5–11. $X = Y = R$; $f(x) = x^2 + 1$ $(x \in R)$. What is rng f?
   Solution: For all $x \in R$, $x^2 \ge 0$, so $x^2 + 1 \ge 1$. Therefore,

$$\text{rng } f \subset \{y \,|\, y \ge 1\}.$$

Given $y \ge 1$, can we find an x such that

$$x^2 + 1 = y?$$

If so, then

$$x^2 = y - 1.$$

Now $y \geq 1$, so $y - 1 \geq 0$. Every nonnegative number c has exactly one nonnegative square root, $\sqrt{c}$. Thus, we suspect that

$$x = \sqrt{y - 1}$$

is a solution. Testing this value, we have

$$f(x) = \left(\sqrt{y - 1}\right)^2 + 1$$
$$= y - 1 + 1$$
$$= y.$$

Therefore every $y \geq 1$ belongs to rng f, and

$$\operatorname{rng} f = \{ y | y \geq 1 \}.$$

We have solved Problem 1. This also solves Problem 2, for if y is given, we need only check whether $y \geq 1$. We have not solved Problems 3 or 4. With a little more care, we could have done so and found

$$S(y) = \varnothing \qquad\qquad (y < 1),$$

(3) $\qquad\qquad S(y) = \{0\} \qquad\qquad (y = 1),$

$$S(y) = \left\{ \sqrt{y - 1}, -\sqrt{y - 1} \right\} \qquad (y > 1).$$

The cardinality of $S(y)$ turns out to be 0, 1, and 2 in these cases, respectively.

Actually, Problem 4, the solution of which gives us the most information, is a somewhat nebulous one. We could, with some justice, say that it is answered by Eq. (2). The difficulty stems from our use of the weasel word "find." When can we say that we have "found" a set? Presumably what we have in mind is a very explicit description of the elements, or a listing of them if possible, as in the example above. Both

$$S(y) = \{x \in R | x^2 + 1 = y\} \qquad (y \in Y)$$

and the explicit listings in Eq. (3) are solutions, but every sensible person would regard (3) as more desirable and useful. The same considerations apply, of course, to the other problems stated above.

What we should keep in mind is our search for explicit descriptions of the solution sets $S(y)$. A general method is to transform our problem to an equivalent one, that is, one with the same solution set. *We change the question but not the answer.* This method will be illustrated when we discuss the solution of systems of linear equations.

EXERCISES 5–7

1. Answer Problems 1 through 4 of the text for

$$X = R, \; Y = R, \text{ and } f(x) = 2 - x^2 \qquad (x \in R).$$

2. Let $X = \left\{2,7,9,\sqrt{2}\right\}$, $Y = \{7,1,3,6,5\}$, $f(2) = 7$, $f(7) = 1$, $f(9) = 1$, $f\left(\sqrt{2}\right) = 5$. Answer Problems 1 through 4.

3. Let both X and Y denote the set of integers. Let $f(x) = 2x$ for all positive $x \in X$, and let $f(x) = -2x$ for all $x \in X$ with $x \le 0$. Then for example, $f(3) = 6$, $f(2) = 4$, $f(-5) = (-2)(-5) = 10$, $f(-1) = 2$. Answer Problems 1 through 4.

4. Let $X = Y = R$, $f(x) = ax$ $(x \in R)$. Answer Problems 1 through 4. (Your answers will depend on the value of a. Discuss the relevant cases.)

5. Discuss the equation

$$x_1 + x_2 = y \qquad (x \in R^2, \; y \in R^1).$$

6. Discuss the system

$$\left. \begin{array}{l} x_1 + x_2 = 0 \\ x_1 + ax_2 = 0 \end{array} \right\} \qquad (x \in R^2).$$

Consider relevant cases for the value of the parameter a.

5–5. SIMULTANEOUS LINEAR EQUATIONS

Consider the system of m linear equations in n unknowns $x_1, \ldots, x_n$:

$$\begin{aligned} a_{11}x_1 + a_{12}x_2 + \cdots + a_{1n}x_n &= y_1, \\ a_{21}x_1 + a_{22}x_2 + \cdots + a_{2n}x_n &= y_2, \\ &\cdots \\ a_{m1}x_1 + a_{m2}x_2 + \cdots + a_{mn}x_n &= y_m, \end{aligned}$$

(1)

or, in compact form,

(2) $$\sum_{j=1}^{n} a_{ij}x_j = y_i \qquad (i = 1, \ldots, m).$$

We may regard this system as defining a linear mapping f from R^n to R^m, with

(3) $$f(x) = y \qquad (x \in R^n).$$

The $m \times n$ matrix corresponding to f is of course $A = (a_{ij})$. The matrix form of Eqs. (1), (2), and (3) is

(4) $$Ax = y \qquad (x \in R^n).$$

We are interested in finding the solution set

(5) $$S(y) = \{x \in R^n | f(x) = y\} \qquad (y \in R^m).$$

It may happen that $S(y)$ is empty. For example, the system

$$x_1 - x_2 = 1,$$

$$x_1 - x_2 = 4,$$

clearly has no solution, for that would imply the contradiction $1 = 4$. In such a case we call the system *inconsistent*.

Suppose, however, that the system (1) does have a solution, say $\bar{x}$. The problem of finding all solutions can then be reduced to a somewhat simpler one. For if x is any solution, we have

(6) $$f(x) = y,$$

(7) $$f(\bar{x}) = y.$$

Subtracting, we get

$$f(x) - f(\bar{x}) = \theta',$$

where θ' is the zero in R^m, $\theta' = 0_m$. Because f is linear,

$$f(x - \bar{x}) = f(x) - f(\bar{x}) = \theta'.$$

Therefore $x - \bar{x} = w$ is a solution of the *homogeneous* equation

(8) $$f(w) = \theta'.$$

Let us denote by $N(f)$ the set of all solutions of Eq. (8):

(9) $$N(f) = \{w \in R^n | f(w) = \theta'\}.$$

$N(f)$ is called the *null space* of f. It is an easy exercise to show that $N(f)$ is a linear subspace of R^n. It is never empty, for it always contains the zero $\theta = 0_n$ of R^n. It follows that *every solution x is the sum of the particular solution $\bar{x}$ and an element of the null space*:

(10) $$x = \bar{x} + w \qquad (w \in N(f)).$$

Conversely, *every such sum is a solution*:

$$f(x) = f(\bar{x} + w)$$
$$= f(\bar{x}) + f(w)$$
$$= y + \theta'$$
$$= y.$$

Symbolically, we may write

(11) $$S(y) = \bar{x} + N(f)$$
$$= \{\bar{x} + w \,|\, w \in N(f)\}.$$

Application 1. The linear mapping f is one-to-one if and only if $N(f) = \{\theta\}$.

A vector space that contains an element $w \neq \theta$ must contain all scalar multiples of w. These are all distinct, so the space has infinitely many elements. In particular, if the original system has two distinct solutions (at least), then $N(f) \neq \{\theta\}$, so $N(f)$ has infinitely many elements, and so does the solution set. Therefore there are only three possibilities for $S(y)$: It is empty, or a singleton, or infinite. In the latter case, cardinality is too crude a measure of the size of $S(y)$. Instead, we classify according to the dimension of $N(f)$. It is customary to refer to dim $N(f)$ as the *number of degrees of freedom* of the problem.

EXAMPLE 5–12. Let

$$f(x) = \begin{pmatrix} x_1 + x_2 \\ x_1 - x_2 \end{pmatrix} \qquad (x \in R^2).$$

To find $N(f)$, we must solve

$$x_1 + x_2 = 0,$$
$$x_1 - x_2 = 0.$$

If x is a solution, then by addition we get $2x_1 = 0$, $x_1 = 0$, and by subtraction $2x_2 = 0$, $x_2 = 0$. Therefore $x = \theta$, and $N(f) = \{\theta\}$. There are 0 degrees of freedom, and f is one-to-one.

EXAMPLE 5–13. Let

$$f(x) = \begin{pmatrix} x_1 + 2x_2 \\ 3x_1 + 6x_3 \end{pmatrix} \qquad (x \in R^2).$$

To find $N(f)$, we solve

$$x_1 + 2x_2 = 0,$$

$$3x_1 + 6x_2 = 0.$$

Now any solution of the first equation also satisfies the second, for

$$x_1 + 2x_2 = 0 \rightarrow 3(x_1 + 2x_2) = 0 \qquad (x \in R^2).$$

To solve the first equation, let $x_2 = t$. Then $x_1 = -2t$. Therefore,

$$x = \begin{pmatrix} -2t \\ t \end{pmatrix} = t \begin{pmatrix} -2 \\ 1 \end{pmatrix},$$

and

$$N(f) \subset \left\{ t \begin{pmatrix} -2 \\ 1 \end{pmatrix} \middle| t \in R \right\}.$$

Conversely, every vector of the form $t \begin{pmatrix} -2 \\ 1 \end{pmatrix}$ is a solution. Hence

$$N(f) = \left\{ t \begin{pmatrix} -2 \\ 1 \end{pmatrix} \middle| t \in R \right\}.$$

Thus $N(f)$ is one-dimensional; the problem has one degree of freedom.

EXERCISE 5–8

Show that the number of degrees of freedom for

$$f(x) = x_1 + x_2 + x_3 \qquad (x \in R^3)$$

is two, by showing that

$$N(f) = \left\{ s \begin{pmatrix} 1 \\ 0 \\ -1 \end{pmatrix} + t \begin{pmatrix} 0 \\ 1 \\ -1 \end{pmatrix} \middle| s,t \in R \right\}.$$

Let us now consider the range of the mapping,

(12) $$\text{rng } f = \{ y \in R^m | \exists x \in R^n, f(x) = y \}.$$

From the linearity of f it follows readily that rng f is a linear subspace of R^m. For if $y \in \text{rng } f$ and $t \in R$, then $y = f(x)$ for some $x \in R^n$, so $ty = tf(x) = f(tx)$, and $ty \in \text{rng } f$. Similarly, if $y,y' \in \text{rng } f$, then $y = f(x)$ and $y' = f(x')$ for some $x,x' \in R^n$, so

$$y + y' = f(x) + f(x') = f(x + x'),$$

and $y + y' \in \text{rng } f$.

EXAMPLE 5–14. What is dim rng f, if

$$f(x) = \begin{pmatrix} x_1 + x_2 \\ x_1 + 2x_2 \\ x_1 - x_2 \end{pmatrix} \qquad (x \in R^2)?$$

Solution: Every $y \in$ rng f is of the form

$$y = x_1 \begin{pmatrix} 1 \\ 1 \\ 1 \end{pmatrix} + x_2 \begin{pmatrix} 1 \\ 2 \\ -1 \end{pmatrix} \qquad (x_1, x_2 \in R).$$

Therefore rng f is generated by the two vectors

$$a = \begin{pmatrix} 1 \\ 1 \\ 1 \end{pmatrix}, \quad b = \begin{pmatrix} 1 \\ 2 \\ -1 \end{pmatrix}.$$

Would a smaller number of vectors suffice to generate rng f? If so, then there would be a single vector, say

$$y = \begin{pmatrix} y_1 \\ y_2 \\ y_3 \end{pmatrix},$$

and the two vectors a and b above would be scalar multiples of y:

$$\begin{pmatrix} 1 \\ 1 \\ 1 \end{pmatrix} = s \begin{pmatrix} y_1 \\ y_2 \\ y_3 \end{pmatrix},$$

$$\begin{pmatrix} 1 \\ 2 \\ -1 \end{pmatrix} = t \begin{pmatrix} y_1 \\ y_2 \\ y_3 \end{pmatrix}.$$

We leave it to the student to show that this is impossible. Therefore dim rng $f = 2$.

Verify the result of Example 5–14 by showing that $N(f) = \{\theta\}$, so that f is one-to-one and

$$f : R^2 \to \text{rng } f$$

is an isomorphism.

There is a useful connection between the three integers

$$\dim \text{dom } f, \ \dim N(f), \ \dim \text{rng } f.$$

Theorem 5–9. If f is a linear mapping from one vector space to another, then

$$\dim \text{dom } f = \dim N(f) + \dim \text{rng } f.$$

The dimension theorem is illustrated by the examples given above:

(Example 5–12.) $\dim \text{dom } f = 2$, $\dim N(f) = 0$, $\dim \text{rng } f = 2$.
(Example 5–13.) $\dim \text{dom } f = 2$, $\dim N(f) = 1$, $\dim \text{rng } f = 1$.

$$\text{rng } f = \left\{ s \binom{1}{3} \middle| s \in R \right\}.$$

(Exercise 5–8.) $\dim \text{dom } f = 3$, $\dim N(f) = 2$, $\dim \text{rng } f = 1$.

$$\text{rng } f = R^1.$$

(Example 5–14.) $\dim \text{dom } f = 2$, $\dim N(f) = 0$, $\dim \text{rng } f = 2$.

Application 2. A system of m linear equations in n unknowns, with $n > m$, has infinitely many solutions if it has any.

Proof: We may regard the system

$$\sum_{j=1}^{n} a_{ij} x_j = y_i \qquad (i = 1, \ldots, m)$$

as defining a linear mapping f from R^n to R^m. By the dimension theorem,

$$n = \dim \text{dom } f = \dim N(f) + \dim \text{rng } f$$

$$\leq \dim N(f) + m.$$

$$\therefore \quad \dim N(f) \geq n - m > 0.$$

Hence $N(f) \neq \{\theta\}$ and f is not one-to-one. Our proof even gives us a lower bound $n - m$ for the number of degrees of freedom in a nonempty solution set.

EXAMPLE 5–15. The system

$$x_1 + 2x_2 - x_3 = 0,$$
$$3x_1 + 4x_2 + x_3 = 4$$

has infinitely many solutions, since it has the solution $x_1 = 1, x_2 = 0,$ $x_3 = 1.$

The system

$$x_1 + 2x_2 - x_3 = 0,$$
$$3x_1 + 6x_2 - 3x_3 = 3$$

has no solutions, for if it did, we could multiply the first equation by 3 and find the contradiction $3 \cdot 0 = 3.$

Application 3. If $A = (a_{ij})$ is an $m \times n$ matrix with $n < m$, then there is at least one $y \in R^m$ such that the system of m linear equations in n unknowns,

$$\sum_{j=1}^{n} a_{ij}x_j = y_i \qquad (i = 1, \ldots, m)$$

has no solution.

Proof: For the corresponding mapping $f: R^n \to R^m$,

$$n = \dim \operatorname{dom} f = \dim N(f) + \dim \operatorname{rng} f$$
$$\geq \dim \operatorname{rng} f.$$
$$\therefore \quad \dim \operatorname{rng} f \leq n < m = \dim R^m.$$

Therefore $\operatorname{rng} f$ is a proper subset of R^m, and there is a $y \in R^m$ such that $f(x) = y$ has no solution.

EXAMPLE 5–16. Let

$$A = \begin{pmatrix} 1 & 2 \\ 3 & 4 \\ 5 & 6 \end{pmatrix}.$$

Then for some $y \in R^3$, the system

$$x_1 + 2x_2 = y_1,$$
$$3x_1 + 4x_2 = y_2,$$
$$5x_1 + 6x_2 = y_3$$

has no solution. The system is "overdetermined."

In the special case of n linear equations in n unknowns, we have $f: R^n \to R^n$. If f is *onto* R^n (i.e., $\text{rng} f = R^n$), the dimension theorem tells us that $N(f) = \{\theta\}$, so f is *one-to-one*. Conversely, if f is one-to-one, then $N(f) = \{\theta\}$, $\dim N(f) = 0$, and by the dimension theorem, $\dim \text{rng} f = n$. Therefore $\text{rng} f$ is an n-dimensional subspace of R^n. In this case it is true, although we have not proved it, that $\text{rng} f = R^n$. In other words, a proper linear subspace of a finite-dimensional vector space has a strictly smaller dimension. It follows that

$$f \text{ is onto } R^n \leftrightarrow f \text{ is one-to-one.}$$

Application 4.   Let $A = (a_{ij})$ be an $n \times n$ matrix. For the system

$$\sum_{j=1}^{n} a_{ij}x_j = y_i \qquad (i = 1, \ldots, n)$$

consisting of n linear equations in n unknowns, we have the following alternatives:

(I) For every $y \in R^n$, there is one and only one solution $x \in R^n$.

(II) For some vectors $y \in R^n$, there are no solutions. For all others, there are infinitely many solutions. For no $y \in R^n$ is there one and only one solution. There exists an $x \neq \theta$ such that $Ax = \theta$.

EXAMPLE 5–17.   Let

$$A = \begin{pmatrix} 1 & -2 & 1 \\ 3 & 1 & -4 \\ -5 & 3 & 3 \end{pmatrix}.$$

Clearly $A\theta = \theta$. But also

$$A\begin{pmatrix} 1 \\ 1 \\ 1 \end{pmatrix} = \theta.$$

It follows that for the system

$$\begin{aligned} x_1 - 2x_2 + x_3 &= y_1, \\ 3x_1 + x_2 - 4x_3 &= y_2, \\ -5x_1 + 3x_2 + 2x_3 &= y_3, \end{aligned}$$

there are vectors y for which there are no solutions, and that for all vectors which have solutions, there are infinitely many.

EXERCISES 5–10

1. Let

$$f(x) = \begin{pmatrix} 2x_1 + x_2 \\ 4x_1 + 2x_2 \end{pmatrix} \qquad (x \in R^2).$$

(a) What is the range of f? (Solve by any method whatsoever.)

(b) Does there exist $x \in R^2$ with $f(x) = \begin{pmatrix} 3 \\ 1 \end{pmatrix}$?

(c) For how many $x \in R^2$ is it true that $f(x) = \begin{pmatrix} 4 \\ 8 \end{pmatrix}$?

(d) Find all $x \in R^2$ such that $f(x) = \theta$.

2. Discuss fully the system

$$x_1 - x_2 = y_1,$$

$$x_1 + 2x_2 = y_2.$$

3. Discuss fully the system

$$2x_1 \qquad - x_3 = y_1,$$

$$x_1 + x_2 \qquad = y_2.$$

4. Let V and W be vector spaces and let $f: V \to W$ be linear. For $x, x' \in V$, define $x \equiv x'$ to mean $x - x' \in N(f)$. Show that $\equiv$ is an equivalence relation. What are the equivalence classes?

5. Table 5–1 gives the main content, in conveniently chosen units, of three foods. What possible diets will give a total of 1.5 units of carbohydrates, 1.6 units of fat, and 1.3 units of protein?

6. Give an example of a linear mapping $f: R^2 \to R^1$ with

$$N(f) = \left\{ \begin{pmatrix} s \\ 4s \end{pmatrix} \Big| s \in R \right\}.$$

TABLE 5–1

	Food I	Food II	Food III
Carbohydrates	0.1	0.5	0
Fat	0.3	0	0.1
Protein	0.1	0.4	0

7. List all the possible pairs of the form (dim rng f, dim $N(f)$) if f is a linear mapping from R^3 to R^4. Do the same for $f: R^4 \to R^3$.

8. Let $A = \begin{pmatrix} 1 & 1 \\ 1 & 1 \end{pmatrix}$. Define f by

$$f(x) = Ax \qquad (x \in R^2).$$

Is f one-to-one? Is f onto R^2? Determine rng f and $N(f)$.

9. Complete the solution of Example 5–14.

10. In Example 5–16 find a vector y such that the system is inconsistent. Do the same for Example 5–17.

*11. We define R^∞ as the set of all infinite sequences

$$x = (x_1, x_2, x_3, \ldots) \qquad (x_i \in R, i \geq 1).$$

We make R^∞ a vector space by defining

$$tx =_{df} (tx_1, tx_2, tx_3, \ldots) \qquad (t \in R, x \in R^\infty),$$

and

$$x + y =_{df} (x_1 + y_1, x_2 + y_2, \ldots) \qquad (x, y \in R^\infty).$$

(a) What is the additive identity θ in R^∞?

(b) Define $f: R^\infty \to R^\infty$ by

$$f(x_1, x_2, x_3, \ldots) = (0, x_1, x_2, \ldots) \qquad (x \in R^\infty).$$

Show that f is linear. Determine rng f and $N(f)$. Is f one-to-one? Is f onto R^∞?

(c) Show that R^∞ is isomorphic with a proper subspace of itself. Can this happen for a finite-dimensional vector space?

5–6. THE MECHANICS OF SOLUTION

After our discussion of the solution of linear systems in general terms, we are prepared to study the technique of actual solution. Given a system of m linear equations in n unknowns,

(1) $$\sum_{j=1}^{n} a_{ij}x_j = y_i \qquad (i = 1, \ldots, m),$$

we are interested in finding the solution set

(2) $$S(y) = \{x \in R^n \mid f(x) = y\} \qquad (y \in R^m),$$

where, of course, f is the associated linear mapping from R^n to R^m, given by

$$f_1(x) = \sum_{j=1}^{n} a_{1j}x_j,$$

$$f_2(x) = \sum_{j=1}^{n} a_{2j}x_j,$$

(3)

$$\vdots$$

$$f_m(x) = \sum_{j=1}^{n} a_{mj}x_j.$$

The first important step is to recognize that $S(y)$ can be expressed as the intersection of m sets,

(4) $$\{x \in R^n | f_i(x) = y_i\} \qquad (i = 1, \ldots, m),$$

where f_i is the ith component of f. This is no surprise, of course. To say that x satisfies all the equations in (1) is no more or less than to say that x belongs to all the solution sets (4), that is, to their intersection.

Let us denote the ith set in Eq. (4) by the symbol $[f_i; y_i]$. The reason for this choice of notation is that we wish to exhibit the dependence of the set on f_i and y_i. Then we have

(5) $$S(y) = [f_1; y_1] \cap [f_2; y_2] \cap \cdots \cap [f_m; y_m].$$

Our plan, as we have stated earlier, is to change the problem but not the answer. There are three simple types of change that do this, and they will be more than enough to solve our problem completely. We say "more than enough" because one of them, the first, is a matter of convenience rather than necessity.

The first change (or operation, in a nontechnical sense) on the system is the interchange of any two of the sets $[f_i; y_i]$. Because intersection is commutative and associative, this operation does not alter $S(y)$. All it amounts to is a decision as to the order of the equations in (1).

The next operation is to replace one of the sets, say $[f_k; y_k]$, by $[tf_k; ty_k]$, where t is a nonzero scalar. That is, we "multiply through by t" in the equation

(6) $$f_k(x) = y_k$$

to get

(7) $$tf_k(x) = ty_k.$$

Clearly, if x satisfies Eq. (6), then it satisfies Eq. (7). Conversely, if x satisfies Eq. (7), then it satisfies

$$\frac{1}{t}(tf_k(x)) = \frac{1}{t}(ty_k),$$

which is equivalent to Eq. (6). (It is at this point that we use our assumption $t \neq 0$, to ensure the existence of $1/t$.) Therefore, the two solution sets are the same.

The third operation involves two of the solution sets, say, $[f_k;y_k]$ and $[f_r;y_r]$, with $k \neq r$. In

$$\cdots \cap [f_k;y_k] \cap \cdots \cap [f_r;y_r] \cap \cdots$$

of Eq. (5) we replace $[f_r;y_r]$ by $[f_r - tf_k;y_r - ty_k]$ to get

$$\cdots \cap [f_k;y_k] \cap \cdots \cap [f_r - tf_k; y_r - ty_k] \cap \ldots,$$

where t is any scalar at all ($t = 0$ is possible but useless, since no change takes place). The $\cdots$'s indicate the other $[f_i;y_i]$, with $i \neq k, r$. They do not change. Thus, we must show that

$$[f_k;y_k] \cap [f_r;y_r] = [f_k;y_k] \cap [f_r - tf_k; y_r - ty_k].$$

Suppose that x belongs to the set on the left. Then

$$f_k(x) = y_k,$$
$$f_r(x) = y_r.$$
$$\therefore \quad f_r(x) - tf_k(x) = y_r - ty_k.$$

That is, x belongs to the set on the right. Conversely, suppose that x belongs to the set on the right. Then

$$f_k(x) = y_k,$$
$$f_r(x) - tf_k(x) = y_r - ty_k.$$
$$\therefore \quad f_r(x) = y_r.$$

That is, x belongs to the set on the left. Notice that $[f_k;y_k]$ acts as a catalyst: It has to be there to help the change take place, but it itself does not change.

Let us summarize the "permissible" operations on a system of linear equations, permissible in the sense that the solution set of the resultant system is the same as the solution set of the original:

(I) We may interchange any two of the equations.

(II) We may multiply any equation through by a nonzero scalar.

(III) We may subtract from any equation a scalar multiple of any other equation.

Ordinarily, when we solve complicated problems, the method is slightly different. If A is the required solution set, we prove something like

$$(\forall x)\ x \in A \to x \in B.$$

That is, we find another set B such that $A \subset B$. Then, if B is sufficiently simple, we test its elements and discard all those not in A. In the present case we are careful to replace the given system by another with precisely the same solution set. If we have performed the operations correctly, there is no need to test the answers. It is not a bad idea to do so, however, in order to catch any arithmetical mistakes.

Let us now illustrate the use of our permissible operations in a simple example.

EXAMPLE 5–18. Solve:

$$(1) \qquad 3x_2 = 4,$$
$$(2)\ 2x_1 - x_2 = 6.$$

Solution: Interchange Eq. (1) and Eq. (2):

$$(2)\ 2x_1 - x_2 = 6,$$
$$(1) \qquad 3x_2 = 4.$$

Multiply Eq. (2) by $\frac{1}{2}$:

$$(3) \quad x_1 - \tfrac{1}{2}x_2 = 3,$$
$$(1) \qquad 3x_2 = 4.$$

Multiply Eq. (1) by $\frac{1}{3}$:

$$(3) \quad x_1 - \tfrac{1}{2}x_2 = 3,$$
$$(4) \qquad x_2 = \tfrac{4}{3}.$$

Add $\frac{1}{2}$ times Eq. (4) to Eq. (3) [i.e., subtract $-\frac{1}{2}$ times Eq. (4) from Eq. (3)]:

$$(5) \quad x_1 \qquad = \tfrac{11}{3}$$
$$(4) \qquad x_2 = \tfrac{4}{3}.$$

Thus, the solution set consists of the single vector $\begin{pmatrix} 11/3 \\ 4/3 \end{pmatrix}$.

Let us consider another example.

EXAMPLE 5–19.   Solve:

$$(1) \quad x_1 + 3x_2 + 5x_3 = 2,$$
$$(2) \quad 2x_1 + 3x_3 - x_2 = 1,$$
$$(3) \quad 3x_1 + 2x_2 + 8x_3 = 4.$$

Solution: First we straighten out the variables in Eq. (2):

$$(1) \quad x_1 + 3x_2 + 5x_3 = 2,$$
$$(2) \quad 2x_1 - x_2 + 3x_3 = 1,$$
$$(3) \quad 3x_1 + 2x_2 + 8x_3 = 4.$$

Now subtract 2 times Eq. (1) from Eq. (2):

$$(1) \quad x_1 + 3x_2 + 5x_3 = 2,$$
$$(4) \quad -7x_2 - 7x_3 = -3,$$
$$(3) \quad 3x_1 + 2x_2 + 8x_3 = 4.$$

Subtract 3 times Eq. (1) from Eq. (3):

$$(1) \quad x_1 + 3x_2 + 5x_3 = 2,$$
$$(4) \quad -7x_2 - 7x_3 = -3,$$
$$(5) \quad -7x_2 - 7x_3 = -2.$$

Subtract Eq. (4) from Eq. (5):

$$(1) \quad x_1 + 3x_2 + 5x_3 = 2,$$
$$(2) \quad -7x_2 - 7x_3 = -3,$$
$$(6) \quad 0 = 1.$$

At this point we see that the solution set is empty; the given system is inconsistent. For the solution set for Eq. (6) is empty, and the intersection of Ø with any set is Ø.

Our next example illustrates the case of an infinite solution set.

EXAMPLE 5–20.   Solve:

$$(1) \quad x_1 + 3x_2 + 5x_3 = 2,$$
$$(2) \quad 2x_1 - x_2 + 3x_3 = 1,$$
$$(3) \quad 3x_1 + 2x_2 + 8x_3 = 3.$$

Solution: Subtract 2 times Eq. (1) from Eq. (2):

$$(1) \quad x_1 + 3x_2 + 5x_3 = 2,$$

$$(4) \quad \quad -7x_2 - 7x_3 = -3,$$

$$(3) \quad 3x_1 + 2x_2 + 8x_3 = 3.$$

Subtract 3 times Eq. (1) from Eq. (3):

$$(1) \quad x_1 + 3x_2 + 5x_3 = 2,$$

$$(4) \quad \quad -7x_2 - 7x_3 = -3,$$

$$(5) \quad \quad -7x_2 - 7x_3 = -3.$$

Subtract Eq. (4) from Eq. (5):

$$(1) \quad x_1 + 3x_2 + 5x_3 = 2,$$

$$(4) \quad \quad -7x_2 - 7x_3 = -3,$$

$$(6) \quad \quad \quad \quad 0 = 0.$$

At this point we see that the solution set for Eq. (6) is all of R^3. It does no harm to drop Eq. (6) from now on. For

$$[f_1;y_1] \cap [f_2;y_2] \cap R^3 = [f_1;y_1] \cap [f_2;y_2].$$

In other words, Eq. (6) imposes no restraint on the unknowns x_1, x_2, x_3, so we may as well drop it.

Now multiply Eq. (4) by $-\frac{1}{7}$:

$$(1) \quad x_1 + 3x_2 + 5x_3 = 2,$$

$$(7) \quad \quad x_2 + x_3 = \tfrac{3}{7}.$$

Subtract 3 times Eq. (7) from Eq. (1):

$$(8) \quad x_1 \quad \quad + 2x_3 = \tfrac{5}{7},$$

$$(7) \quad \quad x_2 + x_3 = \tfrac{3}{7}.$$

Here we must pause. There is no obvious way in which we can bring x_3 forward to "lead" an equation of its own without destroying what we have done for x_1 and x_2. We shall say that x_j is a *leading variable* in a system if it appears with coefficient 1 in some equation of the system and if the coefficients of all the preceding variables in that equation are 0. Thus x_1 and x_2 are leading variables in the system (8), (7) [also in the system (1), (7)], but x_3 is not. In fact, since two different variables cannot lead in the same equation, there can be no more than two leading variables in the system (8), (7).

The advantage in having x_j a leading variable is that we can use the equation in which it leads to produce $0 \cdot x_j$ in all the other equations of the system. This is done by subtracting an appropriate multiple of "its equation" from each of the other equations. This has the effect of making x_j appear exactly once in the entire system (after suppressing $0 \cdot x_j$ everywhere). Furthermore, this process does not change the coefficients of x_i for $i < j$.

Suppose this technique of producing leading variables and zero coefficients is pushed as far as possible. We may arrive at an inconsistency, as in Example 5–19; or at a unique solution, as in Example 5–18; or at a system [such as Eqs. (8), (7)] in which each equation has its own leading variable (all distinct, of course), but there still are some nonleading variables. In this last case we may assign arbitrary values to each of the nonleading variables and solve for the leading variables. This yields a complete solution, with the number of degrees of freedom equal to the number of nonleading variables.

To complete our solution of Example 5–20, we transpose the nonleading variable x_3 to obtain

$$(9) \quad x_1 \qquad = \tfrac{5}{7} - 2x_3,$$

$$(10) \qquad x_2 = \tfrac{3}{7} - x_3.$$

No matter what value is assigned to x_3 we can always complete the solution by giving x_1, x_2 the values indicated in Eqs. (9) and (10). Thus the solution set is

$$\left\{ \begin{pmatrix} \tfrac{5}{7} - 2x_3 \\ \tfrac{3}{7} - x_3 \\ x_3 \end{pmatrix} \middle| x_3 \in R \right\}.$$

It may also be written as follows:

$$\left\{ \begin{pmatrix} \tfrac{5}{7} \\ \tfrac{3}{7} \\ 0 \end{pmatrix} + t \begin{pmatrix} -2 \\ -1 \\ 1 \end{pmatrix} \middle| t \in R \right\}.$$

The particular choice $t = 0$ shows that

$$k = \begin{pmatrix} \tfrac{5}{7} \\ \tfrac{3}{7} \\ 0 \end{pmatrix}$$

is a solution. Every solution is of the form $k + tw$, where

$$w = \begin{pmatrix} -2 \\ -1 \\ 1 \end{pmatrix},$$

and for every $t \in R$, $k + tw$ is a solution.

In accordance with the results of Section 5–5, the difference between two solutions is an element of the null space $N(f)$, where f is the linear mapping defined by the original system:

$$\left. \begin{array}{l} f_1(x) = x_1 + 3x_2 + 5x_3 \\ f_2(x) = 2x_1 - x_2 + 3x_3 \\ f_3(x) = 3x_1 + 2x_2 + 8x_3 \end{array} \right\} \quad (x \in R^3).$$

Thus, $(k + tw) - k = tw \in N(f)$, for all $t \in R$. Conversely, suppose $u \in N(f)$. Then $k + u$ is a solution, so $k + u = k + tw$ for some $t \in R$, and $u = tw$. Therefore,

$$N(f) = \{tw \,|\, t \in R\}.$$

This could be verified directly, of course.

What about the range of f? We can already compute its dimension from

$$\dim R^3 = \dim \operatorname{rng} f + \dim N(f).$$

Since $\dim R^3 = 3$, $\dim N(f) = 1$, we find $\dim \operatorname{rng} f = 2$. Now there is another way to approach the range. The columns of the coefficient matrix A, which corresponds to f, may be regarded as vectors $v^{(1)}$, $v^{(2)}$, $v^{(3)}$ in the range. They are precisely the images of the unit vectors in the domain. Thus

$$v^{(1)} = \begin{pmatrix} 1 \\ 2 \\ 3 \end{pmatrix} = f\left(\begin{pmatrix} 1 \\ 0 \\ 0 \end{pmatrix}\right),$$

$$v^{(2)} = \begin{pmatrix} 3 \\ -1 \\ 2 \end{pmatrix} = f\left(\begin{pmatrix} 0 \\ 1 \\ 0 \end{pmatrix}\right),$$

$$v^{(3)} = \begin{pmatrix} 5 \\ 3 \\ 8 \end{pmatrix} = f\left(\begin{pmatrix} 0 \\ 0 \\ 1 \end{pmatrix}\right).$$

Since every vector in the domain is a linear combination $c_1e^{(1)} + c_2e^{(2)} + c_3e^{(3)}$ of the unit vectors, every vector in the range is a linear combination $c_1v^{(1)} + c_2v^{(2)} + c_3v^{(3)}$ of the columns of A. Conversely, every linear combination of the columns is in the range. Hence

$$\text{rng } f = \{c_1v^{(1)} + c_2v^{(2)} + c_3v^{(3)}|c_1, c_2, c_3 \in R\}.$$

It would appear that rng f has dimension 3, not 2! After all, $v^{(1)}$, $v^{(2)}$, $v^{(3)}$ constitute a generating set for rng f. The fallacy in this argument is that $v^{(1)}$, $v^{(2)}$, $v^{(3)}$ do not constitute a *minimal* generating set (a *basis*). It must be possible to express one of them as a linear combination of the others. In fact, it is easily verified that $v^{(3)} = 2v^{(1)} + v^{(2)}$. Hence, for all $c_1, c_2, c_3 \in R$,

$$c_1v^{(1)} + c_2v^{(2)} + c_3v^{(3)} = c_1v^{(1)} + c_2v^{(2)} + c_3(2v^{(1)} + v^{(2)})$$

$$= (c_1 + 2c_3)v^{(1)} + (c_2 + c_3)v^{(2)},$$

and rng f is generated by $\{v^{(1)}, v^{(2)}\}$. This must be a basis, because

$$\dim \text{ rng } f = 2.$$

The student should verify directly that neither of $v^{(1)}$, $v^{(2)}$ can be expressed as a linear combination (in this case, as a multiple) of the other.

EXAMPLE 5–21.   Solve:

$$(1) \quad x_1 + 2x_2 + 3x_3 + 4x_4 = b_1,$$

$$(2) \quad 3x_1 + 6x_2 + 10x_3 + 22x_4 = b_2.$$

(Here b_1, b_2 are regarded as constants.)
    Solution: Subtract 3 times Eq. (1) from Éq. (2):

$$(1) \quad x_1 + 2x_2 + 3x_3 + 4x_4 = b_1,$$

$$(3) \qquad\qquad\qquad x_3 + 10x_4 = -3b_1 + b_2.$$

Subtract 3 times Eq. (3) from Eq. (1):

$$(4) \quad x_1 + 2x_2 \qquad - 26x_4 = 10b_1 - 3b_2,$$

$$(3) \qquad\qquad\qquad x_3 + 10x_4 = -3b_1 + b_2.$$

The system is now in *reduced form:* We have produced as many leading variables as possible (x_1 and x_3), and they appear only once in the system. The complete solution is obtained by transposing the nonleading variables x_2, x_4:

(5) $x_1 = 10b_1 - 3b_2 - 2x_2 + 26x_4$,

(6) $x_3 = -3b_1 + b_2 - 10x_4$.

The solution set consists of all vectors of the form

$$\begin{pmatrix} 10b_1 - 3b_2 - 2x_2 + 26x_4 \\ x_2 \\ -3b_1 + b_2 - 10x_4 \\ x_4 \end{pmatrix}$$

$$= b_1 \begin{pmatrix} 10 \\ 0 \\ -3 \\ 0 \end{pmatrix} + b_2 \begin{pmatrix} -3 \\ 0 \\ 1 \\ 0 \end{pmatrix} + x_2 \begin{pmatrix} -2 \\ 1 \\ 0 \\ 0 \end{pmatrix} + x_4 \begin{pmatrix} 26 \\ 0 \\ -10 \\ 1 \end{pmatrix} \quad (x_2, x_4 \in R).$$

EXERCISES 5–11

1. For Example 5–21, determine the null space and range of the associated linear mapping of R^4 into R^2.

2. Compute the product

$$\begin{pmatrix} 1 & 2 & 3 & 4 \\ 3 & 6 & 10 & 22 \end{pmatrix} \begin{pmatrix} 10 & -3 & -2 & 26 \\ 0 & 0 & 1 & 0 \\ -3 & 1 & 0 & -10 \\ 0 & 0 & 0 & 1 \end{pmatrix}.$$

EXAMPLE 5–22. Solve:

(1) $2x_1 + 3x_2 = 1$,

(2) $3x_1 + 5x_2 = 0$.

Solution: We drop the variables and just carry the coefficients along:

$$\begin{array}{cc|c} 2 & 3 & 1 \\ 3 & 5 & 0 \end{array}.$$

Multiply row (1) by $\frac{1}{2}$:

$$\begin{array}{cc|c} 1 & \frac{3}{2} & \frac{1}{2} \\ 3 & 5 & 0 \end{array}.$$

Subtract 3 times row (1) from row (2) (the row numbers refer to the latest array):

$$\begin{array}{cc|c} 1 & \frac{3}{2} & \frac{1}{2} \\ 0 & \frac{1}{2} & -\frac{3}{2} \end{array}.$$

Multiply row (2) by 2:

$$\begin{array}{cc|c} 1 & \frac{3}{2} & \frac{1}{2} \\ 0 & 1 & -3 \end{array}.$$

Subtract $\frac{3}{2}$ times row (2) from row (1):

$$\begin{array}{cc|c} 1 & 0 & 5 \\ 0 & 1 & -3 \end{array}.$$

The solution is unique: $x_1 = 5$, $x_2 = -3$. To check, we form the product

$$\begin{pmatrix} 2 & 3 \\ 3 & 5 \end{pmatrix} \begin{pmatrix} 5 \\ -3 \end{pmatrix} = \begin{pmatrix} 1 \\ 0 \end{pmatrix}.$$

EXERCISES 5–12

1. Solve (and check) by the method of Example 5–22:

$$2x_1 + 3x_2 = 0,$$
$$3x_1 + 5x_2 = 1.$$

2. Find a matrix C satisfying

$$\begin{pmatrix} 2 & 3 \\ 3 & 5 \end{pmatrix} C = \begin{pmatrix} 1 & 0 \\ 0 & 1 \end{pmatrix}.$$

Now compute

$$C \begin{pmatrix} 2 & 3 \\ 3 & 5 \end{pmatrix}.$$

EXAMPLE 5–23.   Solve the systems

$$5x_1 + 3x_2 = 1, \qquad 5x_1' + 3x_2' = 0,$$
$$8x_1 + 5x_2 = 0, \qquad 8x_1' + 5x_2' = 1.$$

Solutions: We use the method of Example 5–22 on both systems simultaneously, since the coefficients on the left are the same.

$$\begin{array}{cc|cc} 5 & 3 & 1 & 0 \\ 8 & 5 & 0 & 1 \end{array}.$$

Multiply row (1) by $\frac{1}{5}$:

$$\begin{array}{cc|cc} 1 & \frac{3}{5} & \frac{1}{5} & 0 \\ 8 & 5 & 0 & 1 \end{array}.$$

Subtract 8 times row (1) from row (2):

$$\begin{array}{cc|cc} 1 & \frac{3}{5} & \frac{1}{5} & 0 \\ 0 & \frac{1}{5} & -\frac{8}{5} & 1 \end{array}.$$

Multiply row (2) by 5:

$$\begin{array}{cc|cc} 1 & \frac{3}{5} & \frac{1}{5} & 0 \\ 0 & 1 & -8 & 5 \end{array}.$$

Subtract $\frac{3}{5}$ times row (2) from row (1):

$$\begin{array}{cc|cc} 1 & 0 & 5 & -3 \\ 0 & 1 & -8 & 5 \end{array}.$$

The solutions are unique:

$$x = \begin{pmatrix} 5 \\ -8 \end{pmatrix}, \quad x' = \begin{pmatrix} -3 \\ 5 \end{pmatrix}.$$

Check:

$$\begin{pmatrix} 5 & 3 \\ 8 & 5 \end{pmatrix} \begin{pmatrix} 5 \\ -8 \end{pmatrix} = \begin{pmatrix} 1 \\ 0 \end{pmatrix},$$

$$\begin{pmatrix} 5 & 3 \\ 8 & 5 \end{pmatrix} \begin{pmatrix} -3 \\ 5 \end{pmatrix} = \begin{pmatrix} 0 \\ 1 \end{pmatrix}.$$

EXERCISE   5–13

Find a matrix B satisfying

$$\begin{pmatrix} 5 & 3 \\ 8 & 5 \end{pmatrix} B = I_2 \left[I_2 = \begin{pmatrix} 1 & 0 \\ 0 & 1 \end{pmatrix} \right].$$

Compute, for the same B,

$$B\begin{pmatrix} 5 & 3 \\ 8 & 5 \end{pmatrix}.$$

EXAMPLE 5–24.   For $A = \begin{pmatrix} 1 & -2 \\ 2 & -3 \end{pmatrix}$, find a matrix B such that $AB = I_2$.

Compute BA for the same B.

   Solution:

$$\begin{array}{cc|cc} 1 & -2 & 1 & 0 \\ 2 & -3 & 0 & 1 \end{array}.$$

Subtract 2 times row (1) from row (2):

$$\begin{array}{cc|cc} 1 & -2 & 1 & 0 \\ 0 & 1 & -2 & 1 \end{array}.$$

Add 2 times row (2) to row (1):

$$\begin{array}{cc|cc} 1 & 0 & -3 & 2 \\ 0 & 1 & -2 & 1 \end{array}.$$

Then

$$B = \begin{pmatrix} -3 & 2 \\ -2 & 1 \end{pmatrix}.$$

Check:

$$AB = \begin{pmatrix} 1 & -2 \\ 2 & -3 \end{pmatrix}\begin{pmatrix} -3 & 2 \\ -2 & 1 \end{pmatrix} = \begin{pmatrix} 1 & 0 \\ 0 & 1 \end{pmatrix}.$$

Now

$$BA = \begin{pmatrix} -3 & 2 \\ -2 & 1 \end{pmatrix}\begin{pmatrix} 1 & -2 \\ 2 & -3 \end{pmatrix} = \begin{pmatrix} 1 & 0 \\ 0 & 1 \end{pmatrix}.$$

EXAMPLE 5–25.   For $A = \begin{pmatrix} 1 & 2 \\ 2 & 4 \end{pmatrix}$, find a matrix B such that $AB = I_2$.

   Solution:

$$\begin{array}{cc|cc} 1 & 2 & 1 & 0 \\ 2 & 4 & 0 & 1 \end{array}.$$

Subtract 2 times row (1) from row (2):

$$\left(\begin{array}{cc|cc} 1 & 2 & 1 & 0 \\ 0 & 0 & -2 & 1 \end{array} \right).$$

The problem is impossible. We could have seen this in several ways.

(1) If the problem were solvable, then the unit vectors would both be in the range of the linear mapping f defined by

$$f(x) = Ax \qquad (x \in R^2).$$

Because the range of f is a vector space, all linear combinations of the unit vectors would be in the range, so $\operatorname{rng} f = R^2$. Thus f would be onto R^2, so f would be one-to-one (why?), and $N(f) = \{0_2\}$. But, by inspection, or directly, we find that

$$\begin{pmatrix} 1 & 2 \\ 2 & 4 \end{pmatrix} \begin{pmatrix} 2 \\ -1 \end{pmatrix} = \begin{pmatrix} 0 \\ 0 \end{pmatrix},$$

so $\begin{pmatrix} 2 \\ -1 \end{pmatrix} \in N(f)$, and $N(f) \neq \{0_2\}$. Contradiction.

(2) The range of f consists of all vectors of the form

$$x_1 \begin{pmatrix} 1 \\ 2 \end{pmatrix} + x_2 \begin{pmatrix} 2 \\ 4 \end{pmatrix} = (x_1 + 2x_2) \begin{pmatrix} 1 \\ 2 \end{pmatrix}.$$

Therefore $\operatorname{rng} f$ is one-dimensional, whereas $\operatorname{rng} f = R^2$ if the problem were solvable.

EXERCISES 5–14

1. Solve:

$$x_2 + x_3 = 1,$$
$$x_1 - x_2 - x_3 = 0,$$
$$2x_1 + x_2 + 2x_3 = 2.$$

2. Solve:

$$x_1 - x_2 + 3x_3 = 2,$$
$$2x_1 + x_2 - 5x_3 = 4.$$

3. Solve:

$$2x_1 + 6x_2 - 4x_3 = 0,$$
$$3x_1 + 9x_2 - 6x_3 = 4.$$

4. Solve:

$$2x_1 - 5x_2 + x_3 = 1,$$
$$x_1 - x_2 + 3x_3 = 0,$$
$$-x_1 + 4x_2 - x_3 = -2.$$

5. Solve:

$$x_1 - x_2 + 3x_3 + 5x_4 = 1,$$
$$-x_1 - 4x_2 + x_3 - x_4 = 5.$$

6. Solve by the method of Example 5–22:

$$2x_1 + 3x_2 = 2,$$
$$3x_1 - x_2 = 1.$$

7. Find a matrix A such that

$$A\begin{pmatrix} 1 & 4 \\ 2 & -3 \end{pmatrix} = I_2.$$

8. Find a matrix B such that

$$\begin{pmatrix} 2 & 4 \\ 1 & 2 \end{pmatrix} B = I_2.$$

9. Find a matrix A such that

$$\begin{pmatrix} 1 & 2 \\ 3 & 4 \end{pmatrix} A = \begin{pmatrix} 9 & 1 \\ 0 & 7 \end{pmatrix}.$$

10. Find the range and null space for f, where f is given by the matrix

$$\begin{pmatrix} 2 & 1 \\ 8 & 4 \end{pmatrix}.$$

11. Find a matrix B such that

$$B\begin{pmatrix} 1 & 0 & 2 \\ -1 & 1 & 0 \\ 3 & 1 & 0 \end{pmatrix} = \begin{pmatrix} 1 & 0 & 0 \\ 0 & 1 & 0 \\ 0 & 0 & 1 \end{pmatrix}.$$

*12. If A and B are $n \times n$ matrices such that $AB = I_n$, we say that B is the inverse of A, written A^{-1}. Not all $n \times n$ matrices have inverses. Find a necessary and sufficient condition that

$$A = \begin{pmatrix} a & b \\ c & d \end{pmatrix}$$

have an inverse.

13. Show that every matrix of the form

$$\begin{pmatrix} a & b \\ -b & a \end{pmatrix}$$

has an inverse, except for 0_2.

14. Let K be the set of all matrices of the form

$$\begin{pmatrix} a & b \\ -b & a \end{pmatrix}.$$

Prove:
    (a) K is closed under addition and multiplication by scalars.
    (b) K is closed under multiplication.
    (c) Multiplication in K is commutative.

15. (See Problem 14.) Write I for I_2. Show that the only elements $A \in K$ satisfying

$$A^2 = -I$$

are

$$J = \begin{pmatrix} 0 & 1 \\ -1 & 0 \end{pmatrix}$$

and

$$-J = \begin{pmatrix} 0 & -1 \\ 1 & 0 \end{pmatrix}.$$

16. (See Problems 14 and 15.) Writing elements of K in the form $aI + bJ$, derive a general formula for

$$(aI + bJ)(a'I + b'J).$$

Prove that $(aI + bJ)(aI - bJ)$ is always a scalar multiple of I. Use this to solve Problem 13 in a different way.

17. (See Problems 14, 15, and 16.) Find all solutions in K of the equation

$$A^3 = I.$$

Chapter 6

ANALYTIC GEOMETRY

6–1. THE FUNDAMENTAL CORRESPONDENCE

THERE SEEMS TO BE little doubt that the primary historical source of our number system is the counting process. If this were the only arithmetic operation needed, the natural numbers would be quite sufficient. Even when the measurement of line segments became necessary, it was still possible to get along quite well with the natural numbers. Thus, with a given segment AB as a unit, one could measure any segment CD which was an exact multiple of the unit, as in Figure 6–1. We could say, here, that the ratio of CD to AB is $4 : 1$, or that $CD = 4AB$. Suppose, however, that the length of CD, measured in AB units, were what we now call $1\frac{1}{2}$ (Figure 6–2). We could still extend CD by its own length to E and then say that $2CD = CE = 3AB$, or that $CD : AB = 3 : 2$. In general, to measure a segment CD in terms of the unit AB, one merely found an appropriate multiple n of CD which was exactly m units in length, and then had $nCD = mAB$, or $CD : AB = m : n$. Thus, by using pairs of natural numbers, measurement was still possible, apparently. This technique seemed to work quite well, and even when a chosen multiple of n of CD did not turn out to be an exact multiple of AB, it must have been thought that some higher multiple than n would so turn out.

We can well imagine the shock and consternation occasioned by the discovery that there were some segments CD for which no multiple would work. For example, if CD were the diagonal of a unit square, and if $CD : AB$ were equal to $m : n$ as above, then one could deduce from the Pythagorean theorem that $m^2 = 2n^2$. This is impossible, as we have seen.

It therefore became necessary to develop a more sophisticated system of numbers than that of the rationals m/n, which correspond to the ratios $m : n$. This development took a long time, and it is only within the past few hundred years that we have arrived at a real understanding of the number system (the reals) needed for measurement of all line segments.

254

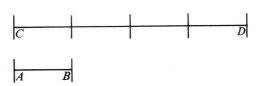

FIGURE 6–1

Rather than complain about the complexity of the system, we should be impressed by the simplicity of the axiom set (A,M,D,O) used to characterize the real number system R.

The *fundamental principle* that R is adequate to perform the measurement task required of it may be expressed as follows: *On any line L it is possible to set up a numerical scale.* More fully, this means that to each point of L we can assign a real number, and this assignment can be made in such a way that if x is assigned to C, y to D, then the length of CD (in terms of a given unit AB) is $y - x$ or $x - y$, whichever is nonnegative. Rather than speak of "assignment," we can be precise and say that we have set up a one-to-one correspondence f between L and R,

$$f : L \to R,$$

such that

$$\text{length of } CD = \left| f(D) - f(C) \right| \qquad (C, D \in L).$$

The symbol $|\;\;|$, which we have just used, is defined as follows:

Definition 6–1. $|z| = z$ if $z \geq 0$,
                      $= -z$, if $z < 0$.
(See Exercises 4–7.)

A further property of the correspondence f, which takes into account the role of AB as the unit, is that for every segment $A'B'$ (on L) with $A'B'$

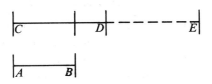

FIGURE 6–2

congruent to AB, we have

$$\text{length of } A'B' = |f(B') - f(A')| = 1.$$

It is appropriate to call a correspondence f of the type described above a *scale* (or coordinate system). When L is equipped with a scale we shall speak of it as a number line. Thus, our fundamental principle is that *every line can be made a number line in at least one way*. It is customary to indicate the scale by exhibiting the points to which 0 and 1 correspond:

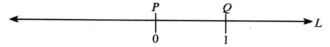

It can be proved that for any two distinct points P and Q on L, there is one and only one scale f such that $f(P) = 0$ and $f(Q) = 1$.

Another useful device is to label the point on L to which x corresponds as P_x:

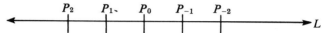

Notice that the scale just used is different from the one indicated a few lines above. In practice, we frequently drop the P from P_x and just use the numerical label x. In fact, we usually speak of "the point x" instead of "the point P_x" or "the point P such that $f(P) = x$." There is no great harm in this identification of a point with the number which corresponds to it, just so long as we bear in mind that there are many correspondences f—many scales—that will also work. "The point P" has meaning for us regardless of the scale used, but "the point x" is unambiguous only if the scale has been specified.

Given a scale f on L, we can prove that the correspondence (function, mapping) g from L to R given by

$$g(K) = 2f(K) + 1 \qquad (K \in L)$$

is also a scale. More generally, if $a, b \in R$ and $a \neq 0$, then the correspondence g from L to R defined by

$$g(K) = af(K) + b \qquad (K \in L)$$

is a scale on L. It is interesting (and not too difficult to prove) that every scale on L can be obtained in this way. Thus, though there are many possible scales on L, they are all related in a very simple manner.

The word "scale" is sometimes used in a broader sense as a one-to-one correspondence f between a subset of L and a subset of R, without even requiring the condition that the length of PQ should be given by

$|f(Q) - fP|$. Thus, if we needed to represent a wide range of data, say between .00001 and 100,000, we might use a "logarithmic scale":

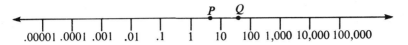

Here, if Q is one linear unit to the right of P, as in the diagram, then the corresponding scale values are related by

$$f(Q) = 10f(P).$$

Notice that there are no negative scale values. Although such "warped scales" have considerable utility, we shall not have occasion to use them here. To those who employ "scale" in the wider sense, ours would be a "linear scale."

Another common variant in terminology is to say that the same scale is being used on two lines L and L'. This means that the scale f on L and f' on L' are such that congruent segments on L and L' have the same length in both scales; the same unit applies to both. In terms of f and f', if $A'B'$ on L' is congruent to AB on L, then

$$|f'(B') - f'(A')| = |f(B) - f(A)|.$$

⟦What is the effect of the fundamental principle upon our state of knowledge? We may with some justice believe that the correspondence between points on a line and real numbers helps to clarify the real number system and make it more intuitive. We understand it better by matching it with something we "know," something as familiar as a straight line. In this sense, the correspondence is psychologically useful. But when we reflect that the real numbers were constructed to clarify the idea of linear measurement, we see that the shoe is on the other foot. The correspondence is logically useful to explain the deeper properties of the line in terms of a system for which the axioms have been explicitly stated. Indeed, for most of us the line belongs to the P-plane, and most students would be hard put to construct an adequate C-plane for it. To those of us who feel the need for such a construction, the fundamental principle provides an excellent answer. It tells us to take over the axioms for R with some slight modifications (mostly of terminology, such as reading "point of L" instead of "element of R") and to use them as defining axioms for the line. On the other hand, if one already had another axiomatic picture of the line, then the fundamental principle would have to be regarded as a theorem asserting the isomorphism of two given mathematical structures. Which of the above alternatives we choose will depend on our knowledge of or familiarity with the ideas of real number system and straight line. The choices are not exclusive; they can all be useful at one time or another, or even simultaneously.]

EXAMPLE 6–1. Construct a formula which connects the Fahrenheit and centigrade temperature scales.

Solution: For each temperature T, let $f(T)$ and $c(T)$ be the numerical values assigned to T in the two scales, respectively. By a remark made above, there exist constants a and b such that

(1) $$c(T) = af(T) + b \qquad \text{(all } T\text{)}.$$

Let T_1 be the temperature at which water freezes, T_2 that at which water boils. Then

$$f(T_1) = 32 \qquad c(T_1) = 0,$$
$$f(T_2) = 212 \qquad c(T_2) = 100.$$

Substituting T_1 and T_2 for T in Eq. (1), we get

(2) $$0 = 32a + b,$$
(3) $$100 = 212a + b.$$

Subtracting Eq. (2) from Eq. (3), we have

$$100 = 180a,$$
$$a = 5/9.$$

Putting this value for a in Eq. (2), we get

$$0 = 32\left(\frac{5}{9}\right) + b,$$
$$b = -\frac{160}{9}.$$

Thus, Eq. (1) becomes

$$c(T) = \frac{5}{9}f(T) - \frac{160}{9},$$

(4) $$c(T) = \frac{5}{9}(f(T) - 32) \qquad \text{(all } T\text{)}.$$

Equation (4) permits us to convert a Fahrenheit reading to centigrade. If we wished to convert centigrade to Fahrenheit, we would solve for $f(T)$ in terms of $c(T)$:

(5) $$f(T) = \frac{9}{5}c(T) + 32 \qquad \text{(all } T\text{)}.$$

[*Note:* Because of the existence of absolute zero, we do not have a complete one-to-one correspondence between physical temperatures and real numbers.]

EXERCISES 6-1

1. Do the Fahrenheit and centigrade scales ever yield the same reading? If so, where?

2. Construct a temperature scale g in which water freezes at $50°$ and boils at $250°$. Write down equations connecting $g(T)$ and $c(T)$, also $g(T)$ and $f(T)$. Does $g(T)$ ever coincide with $c(T)$? With $f(T)$?

Whenever we attempt to apply quantitative methods to particular fields of study, we meet with scaling problems similar to the one discussed above, of applying a scale to a straight line. In physical problems we meet categories of attributes like time, mass, speed, and so on. Measurement of these attributes involves prescribing carefully a sequence of operations, the ultimate goal of which is the assignment of a real number to a physical phenomenon. In other fields the problem becomes even more difficult. How do we set up scales to measure attitudes or values? What would be an appropriate unit of liking, or of trusting, or of color sensation? How would we measure richness of cultural background for an individual, and relate it to a measure of intelligence, or security, or aggressiveness? These are difficult questions, and it is by no means certain that they are properly framed, because they involve the assumption that the real numbers (or a subset of them) will yield an adequate description or means of measurement. Perhaps some other mathematical system than R (or, equivalently, a straight line) is more appropriate. A sphere, for example, has been proposed as a model for aspects of color vision. Higher-dimensional Euclidean spaces have been tried for the description of attitudes. It is quite conceivable that a Boolean algebra or a noncommutative group might serve us better as a pattern for some particular set of objects under consideration.

There is an obvious implication here for the student of psychology or sociology or economics, or any other field in which it is hoped that "quantitative" methods might be useful. If we broaden the realm of possible answers, we increase the likelihood of obtaining a satisfactory solution. We see, therefore, that measurement or scaling problems may broaden into the general problem of applying mathematics.

Just as our fundamental principle allows us to transform the line into a number line, so we can easily transform the plane into a number plane. Strictly speaking, we should say number-pair-plane, for the correspondence we set up will be between points in the plane and ordered pairs of real numbers—elements of $R^2 = R \times R$.

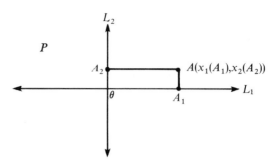

FIGURE 6-3

Let L_1 and L_2 be perpendicular lines in the plane P, intersecting at the point θ (Figure 6-3). On L_1 and L_2 we choose scales x_1 and x_2, respectively, so that $x_1(\theta) = 0$ and $x_2(\theta) = 0$. If A is any point in the plane, we construct the perpendiculars AA_1 and AA_2 to L_1 and L_2, passing through A and meeting L_1 and L_2 in A_1 and A_2, respectively. The scale value of A_1 is $x_1(A_1)$, and the scale value of A_2 is $x_2(A_2)$. To A we assign the number pair $(x_1(A_1), x_2(A_2))$. This assignment we denote by π. Thus we have the mapping of the plane P into $R \times R$,

$$\pi : P \to R \times R,$$

given by

(6) $$\pi(A) = (x_1(A_1), x_2(A_2)) \qquad (A \in P).$$

The correspondence π is one-to-one and onto $R \times R$, as we can see by constructing its inverse. Indeed, if $(a_1, a_2) \in R \times R$, there are unique points A_1 and A_2 on L_1 and L_2 whose scale values are a_1 and a_2:

$$x_1(A_1) = a_1,$$

$$x_2(A_2) = a_2.$$

The perpendiculars to L_1 and L_2 at A_1 and A_2 are then uniquely determined, and they intersect at the uniquely determined point A, which clearly satisfies Eq. (6). Therefore π^{-1} is a function defined on $R \times R$, and taking values in P:

$$\pi^{-1}((a_1, a_2)) = A.$$

Just as we agreed to label points on a line by their scale values, so we shall agree to label points in the plane by the number pairs which correspond to them by means of π. We shall even speak of "the point (a_1, a_2)" rather than "the point $\pi^{-1}((a_1, a_2))$" or "the point A whose image under

π is (a_1, a_2)." We shall call a_1 and a_2 the (rectangular) *coordinates* of A, the first one being the *abscissa* of A, the second the *ordinate* of A. For example, the coordinates of θ (the *origin*) are $(0,0)$, the coordinates of A_1 are $(x_1(A_1),0)$, and those of A_2 are $(0, x_2(A_2))$.

The correspondence π defined above may be called the *Cartesian correspondence*, after the great seventeenth-century French mathematician and philosopher Descartes.

In Figure 6–4 and Table 6–1 we give some examples of points in P together with their coordinates.

When two perpendicular lines L_1 and L_2 have been chosen in a plane P, together with scales x_1 and x_2, we say that we have set up a *coordinate system* in P. The correspondence π depends, of course, on our choice of coordinate system. In some cases it is desirable to have the same unit on L_1 and L_2. In many applications, however, it is convenient to choose different units on the two *axes* L_1 and L_2 (we call L_1 the x_1-*axis*, L_2 the x_2-*axis*). Later we shall see examples of both situations.

EXERCISES 6–2

1. Choose a coordinate system, drawing the axes and indicating the scale on each axis. Then put a dot at those points which correspond to $(1,5)$, $(-1,3)$, $(0,2)$, $(2,7)$, $(-4,-3)$, $(4,-4)$, $(3,5)$, $(1,1)$, $(-1,-1)$, $(\sqrt{2},5)$, $(2\pi, -\sqrt{3})$.

2. Set up a coordinate system in the plane with different units on the axes. Then choose seven points and make a table of their coordinates similar to Table 6–1.

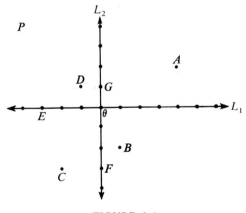

FIGURE 6–4

TABLE 6–1

X	$\pi(X)$	x_1, abscissa of X	x_2, ordinate of X
θ	$(0,0)$	0	0
A	$(4,2)$	4	2
B	$(1,-2)$	1	-2
C	$(-2,-3)$	-2	-3
D	$(-1,1)$	-1	1
E	$(-3,0)$	-3	0
F	$(0,-3)$	0	-3
G	$(0,1)$	0	1

3. In Figure 6–4, draw the lines BG and CA, then estimate the co-ordinates of the point of intersection.

4. Choose a coordinate system appropriate to represent the number pairs (0, 100,000), (1, 150,000), (2, 200,000), (3, 250,000), (4, 300,000). Mark the corresponding points in the plane.

5. In Figure 6–4 estimate by eye the length of the segment BG. Now measure it. Finally, compute it, using the Pythagorean theorem.

6. Discuss the relative advantages of using the same or different units on the two axes.

7. On a large sheet of paper draw two number lines L and M. The units need not be the same, nor the zero points. Let P_x and Q_x be the points on L and M corresponding to $x \in R$. Draw the lines $P_x Q_x$ for a number of values of x. These lines should in general shape out a smooth curve. (See Figure 6–5 for an example.) You may have to experiment with the positions of L and M and the scales to get the curve on your paper.

8. Let Q_a denote the intersection of the line through (5,0) and (0,a) with the line through (0,5) and ($-a$,0). Plot Q_a for a number of values of $a \in R$ and sketch a smooth curve. Can you guess what the locus $\{Q_a | a \in R\}$ is?

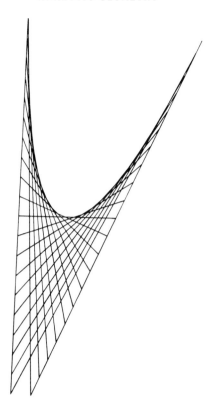

FIGURE 6–5

6–2. GRAPHS OF RELATIONS

Let us suppose that we have set up a coordinate system in the plane P, so that we have the correspondence $\pi : P \to R \times R$. To every subset of P there corresponds a subset of $R \times R$, and conversely. Now a subset of $R \times R$ is what we have called a relation between R and R. Thus, given a relation S, there is a subset $\pi^{-1}(S) = S'$ of P which corresponds to S. We call this subset the *graph of S*. For example, if

$$S = \{(x_1, x_2) \in R^2 | 0 \le x_1 \le 1\},$$

the graph of S is the shaded strip in Figure 6–6. Every pair in S corresponds to a point in S'; every point in S' corresponds to an element of S.

Conversely, if we start with the subset A of P in Figure 6–7, consisting of all the points on the line through θ and $(1,1)$, it is not difficult to see that

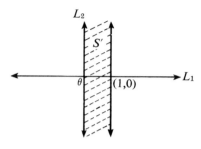

FIGURE 6–6

every point of A has its ordinate and abscissa equal, and that all points with this property lie in A. Therefore the subset of R^2 corresponding to A is

$$\pi(A) = \{(x_1, x_2) \in R^2 | x_2 = x_1\}.$$

The advantages of the one-to-one correspondence between subsets of the plane and relations in R^2 are of two complementary kinds. We can study subsets of P numerically or algebraically, by means uf the relations which are their images under π; we can study relations geometrically by means of their graphs.

To illustrate, suppose that S' and T' are the graphs of relations S and T. Then $S' \cap T'$ is the graph of $S \cap T$ and $S' \cup T'$ is the graph of $S \cup T$. Now if S and T have defining predicates (conditions, frequently equations) U and V,

$$S = \{(x_1, x_2) | U(x_1, x_2)\},$$

$$T = \{(x_1, x_2) | V(x_1, x_2)\},$$

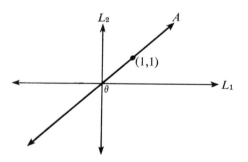

FIGURE 6–7

then

$$S \cap T = \{(x_1,x_2)|U(x_1,x_2) \wedge V(x_1,x_2)\},$$

$$S \cup T = \{(x_1,x_2)|U(x_1,x_2) \vee V(x_1,x_2)\}.$$

Therefore, corresponding to intersection of graphs we have conjunction of predicates, and to union of graphs we have disjunction of predicates (see Section 2–2).

We shall now show how to compute the distance between two points, given their coordinates in a system with the same unit on both axes. Suppose that $\pi(A) = (a_1,a_2)$, $\pi(B) = (b_1,b_2)$. Through A we draw the parallel to L_2, and through B we draw the parallel to L_1 (Figure 6–8). These intersect in C. Since AC is perpendicular to L_1, A and C have the same abscissa a_1. Similarly, B and C have the same ordinate b_2. Thus $\pi(C) = (a_1,b_2)$. The length of the segment BC is $|a_1 - b_1|$, and the length of CA is $|a_2 - b_2|$. Now the triangle ABC is a right triangle with AB as hypotenuse. By the Pythagorean theorem

$$AB^2 = BC^2 + CA^2.$$

Since

$$BC^2 = |a_1 - b_1|^2 = (\pm(a_1 - b_1))^2 = (a_1 - b_1)^2$$

and

$$CA^2 = |a_2 - b_2|^2 = (a_2 - b_2)^2,$$

we have

$$AB^2 = (a_1 - b_1)^2 + (a_2 - b_2)^2,$$

$$AB = \sqrt{(a_1 - b_1)^2 + (a_2 - b_2)^2}.$$

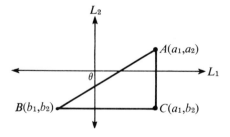

FIGURE 6–8

Either one of these formulas may be referred to as the *distance formula*. It is frequently more convenient to use the first, because of the absence of the square root.

EXAMPLE 6–2.   Compute the distance between $(1,3)$ and $(-2,-1)$.
   Solution:

$$d^2 = (1 - (-2))^2 + (3 - (-1))^2$$
$$= 3^2 + 4^2$$
$$= 25.$$

Therefore

$$d = \sqrt{25} = 5.$$

EXAMPLE 6–3.   Discuss the graph of the relation

$$S = \{(x_1,x_2) \in R^2 | (x_1 - 1)^2 + (x_2 - 3)^2 = 25\}.$$

Solution: If (x_1,x_2) is any point, the distance d from (x_1,x_2) to $(1,3)$ is given by

$$d^2 = (x_1 - 1)^2 + (x_2 - 3)^2.$$

Hence the defining condition for S is

$$d^2 = 25,$$

which is equivalent to

$$d = 5.$$

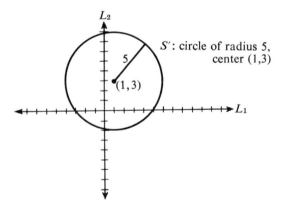

FIGURE 6–9

The graph of S will consist of all points at a distance 5 from $(1,3)$. Therefore it is a circle with center $(1,3)$ and radius 5 (Figure 6–9).

EXAMPLE 6–4.   Find a defining equation for the circle A with center $(-3,-2)$ and radius 4.

Solution: If (x_1,x_2) is any point, the distance d from (x_1,x_2) to $(-3,-2)$ is given by

$$d^2 = (x_1 + 3)^2 + (x_2 + 2)^2.$$

Hence

$$\pi(A) = \{(x_1,x_2) \in R^2 | (x_1 + 3)^2 + (x_2 + 2)^2 = 16\}.$$

EXAMPLE 6–5.   Find a defining equation for the set C of all points equidistant from a given point and a given line.

Solution: Choose a coordinate system in which the given line is the x_1-axis and the given point is on the x_2-axis, with coordinates $(0,a)$, where a is the distance from the given point to the given line (Figure 6–10). For the sake of variety, we let (x,y) be the coordinates of any point. The defining condition for C is $d_1 = d_2$. Since

$$d_1 = \sqrt{x^2 + (y - a)^2},$$
$$d_2 = |y|,$$

the condition is

$$|y| = \sqrt{x^2 + (y - a)^2}.$$

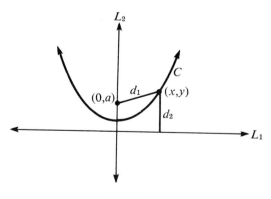

FIGURE 6–10

This is equivalent to

$$y^2 = x^2 + (y - a)^2,$$
$$= x^2 + y^2 - 2ay + a^2,$$

(1)
$$y = \frac{1}{2a}x^2 + \frac{a}{2}.$$

As a check, the pairs $(0, a/2)$, (a, a), and $(-a, a)$ should satisfy Eq. (1). The student should verify that they do. The curve C is a *parabola*.

EXAMPLE 6-6.   Find defining conditions for the line segment B between (1,1) and (2,2).

Solution: Referring to Figure 6-7, we see that B is a subset of the line A, since (1,1) and (2,2) are both on A. If (x_1, x_2) is a point of B, then $1 \leq x_1 \leq 2$. Thus

$$\pi(B) \subset \{(x_1, x_2) \in R^2 | x_1 = x_2 \wedge 1 \leq x_1 \leq 2\}.$$

Conversely, if $x_1 = x_2$ and $1 \leq x_1 \leq 2$, then (x_1, x_2) are the coordinates of a point of B. Thus

$$\pi(B) = \{(x_1, x_2) \in R^2 | x_1 = x_2 \wedge 1 \leq x_1 \leq 2\}.$$

EXERCISES 6-3

1. Find the distances between the following pairs of points:
   (a) (1,5) and (2,3).
   (b) (2,7) and (-1,0).
   (c) (1,4) and (-1,-4).
   (d) (0,-8) and (-3,7).
2. Find the midpoint of the line segment joining (1,3) and (5,5). Draw the diagram.
3. Show that the midpoint of the line segment joining (a_1, a_2) and (b_1, b_2) is

$$(\tfrac{1}{2}(a_1 + b_1), \tfrac{1}{2}(a_2 + b_2)).$$

Draw a diagram to illustrate.

4. Let $a \in R^2$, $b \in R^2$. Show that the point one-third of the way from a to b is $(\tfrac{1}{3}(2a_1 + b_1), \tfrac{1}{3}(2a_2 + b_2))$. Draw a diagram.

5. Let $a \in R^2$, $b \in R^2$. Discuss the graph of

$$\{(a_1 + s(b_1 - a_1), a_2 + s(b_2 - a_2)) | 0 \leq s \leq 1\}.$$

Draw a diagram.

6. Discuss the graph of

$$\{(t, 1 + 2t)|0 \leq t \leq 1\}.$$

Draw the diagram.

7. Discuss the graph of

$$A = \{(x,y)|x^2 + y^2 \leq 4\}.$$

Draw the diagram.

8. Discuss the graph of

$$B = \{(x,y)|1 \leq x^2 + y^2 \leq 4\}.$$

9. In the same diagram, sketch the graphs of the following relations:
   (a) $\{(x,y) \in R^2 | 1 \leq y \leq 2 \wedge x \in \{1,2,3,4,5\}\}$.
   (b) $\{(x,y) \in R^2 | (2 \leq x \leq 3 \vee 4 \leq x \leq 5) \wedge y = 1\}$.
   (c) $\{(x,y) \in R^2 | 2 \leq x \leq 3 \wedge y = 2\}$.

10. A subset C of the plane is called *convex* if the entire line segment between p and q is in C whenever both p and q are points of C.
   (a) Give two examples of convex sets.
   (b) Give two examples of nonconvex sets.
   (c) Show that the intersection of two convex sets is also convex.
   (d) Show that the union of two convex sets is not necessarily convex.

11. What is the smallest convex set containing two distinct points? (There is a smallest.)

12. What is the smallest convex set containing three distinct points? (Two cases.)

*13. Given a set B in the plane, show that there is a smallest convex set containing B. This means that there is a set C such that
   (a) $B \subset C$.
   (b) C is convex.
   (c) $(\forall D)(B \subset D \wedge D$ is convex $\rightarrow D \supset C)$.

14. In the same diagram, sketch the sets defined by
   (a) $x^2 + y^2 = 100$.
   (b) $(x - 5)^2 + y^2 \leq 4$.
   (c) $(x + 5)^2 + y^2 \leq 4$.
   (d) $y \geq 5 \wedge x^2 + y^2 \leq 100$.
   (e) $y = 5 \wedge -12 \leq x \leq 12$.
   (f) $x^2 + (y + 5)^2 \leq 1$.
   (g) $|x| \leq 3 \wedge -8 \leq y \leq -7$.

6–3. THE STRAIGHT LINE

Let P be a plane with a coordinate system L_1, L_2 and scales x_1, x_2. Let M be a line in P which is not parallel to L_2, that is, not vertical (Figure 6–11). We wish to describe the *direction* of M by a single number, called the *slope*

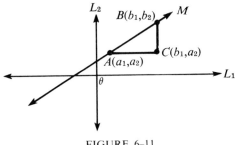

FIGURE 6-11

of M. For this purpose, choose two distinct points A and B on M, with coordinates (a_1, a_2) and (b_1, b_2), respectively. If we complete a right triangle with C as in Figure 6-11, we see that the coordinates of C are (b_1, a_2). By the *rise* from A to B we mean the number $b_2 - a_2$, which may be positive, negative, or zero. By the *run* from A to B we mean the number $b_1 - a_1$, which may be positive or negative, but not zero, since M is not vertical. We call the ratio

$$\frac{\text{rise from } A \text{ to } B}{\text{run from } A \text{ to } B}$$

the *slope* from A to B.

EXAMPLE 6-7.   The slope from $(1,3)$ to $(5,6)$ is

$$\frac{6 - 3}{5 - 1} = \frac{3}{4}.$$

The slope from $(5,6)$ to $(1,3)$ is

$$\frac{3 - 6}{1 - 5} = \frac{-3}{-4} = \frac{3}{4}.$$

Notice that the rise and run are not symmetrical in A and B, but

$$\text{rise from } B \text{ to } A = -(\text{rise from } A \text{ to } B),$$
$$\text{run from } B \text{ to } A = -(\text{run from } A \text{ to } B).$$

It follows that (as in Example 6-7) the slope from A to B *is* symmetrical in A and B, that is, it is equal to the slope from B to A.

Further, it is an important fact that the slope from A to B is independent of our choice of distinct points on M. In other words, if A' and B' are any other pair of distinct points on M, then the slope from A' to B' will be equal to the slope from A to B. To see this, we may suppose that A is to the left of B and that A' is to the left of B', since interchanging A and B will not change the slope, and a similar argument applies to A' and B'. Thus the two runs will be positive. If the rise from A to B is positive, then the rise from A' to B' will be positive, and conversely. If the rise from A to B is zero, then so is the rise from A' to B', and conversely. It follows that the two rises will be both positive, both zero, or both negative. If they are both zero, the slopes are also zero, and we are through. Otherwise, the triangles ABC and $A'B'C'$ are similar. From this it follows that

$$\frac{\text{rise from } A \text{ to } B}{\text{run from } A \text{ to } B} = \frac{\text{rise from } A' \text{ to } B'}{\text{run from } A' \text{ to } B'},$$

in case the rises are positive, and that

$$\frac{-(\text{rise from } A \text{ to } B)}{\text{run from } A \text{ to } B} = \frac{-(\text{rise from } A' \text{ to } B')}{\text{run from } A' \text{ to } B'},$$

in case the rises are negative. (It was necessary to make the case distinctions, because the Euclidean geometry we learned in high school did not deal with negative lengths.) In any case, therefore, the slopes are equal.

It follows that we may speak of the *slope of* M, meaning the slope from one point to another, without ambiguity. If M' is another line parallel to M, then M' will have the same slope as M, since the similarity argument still works. Thus, the slope of a line is really a function of its direction only, as we promised.

It remains to be seen that two distinct lines M and M' with the same slope are parallel. For if they were not, we could take for A and A' their point of intersection and for B and B' points one unit to the right of $A(= A')$ on the two lines as in Figure 6–12. Thus $1 =$ run from A to $B =$ run from A' to B', but rise from A to $B \neq$ rise from A' to B', since equality would imply that $B' = B$, hence $M' = M$, which is false. Therefore the slopes of M and M' are not equal, contradicting our hypothesis.

FIGURE 6–12

We have not assigned a slope to a vertical line, nor shall we do so. We say of L_2 or any line parallel to it simply that it has no slope. Every non-vertical line, of course, does have a slope.

EXERCISES 6–4

1. Find the slope of L_1.

2. Find the slope of the line through (3,4) and $(-4,2)$.

3. Show that a line of slope 0 is horizontal (parallel to L_1).

*4. If M and M' are perpendicular and if neither is vertical, show that (slope M) · (slope M') = -1.

5. What are the possible slopes for a line making an angle of 45° with either axis? 30°? 60°?

6. What is the range of the slope function? What is its domain? Is it one-to-one?

7. Describe what happens to the slope of AB as B moves around a circle, with center at A, in a counterclockwise direction (Figure 6–13). Start with B_0.

8. Describe in your own words the behavior of a line with a slope that is

(a) Numerically small.   (d) Negative.
(b) Numerically large.   (e) Nonexistent.
(c) Positive.

9. Show that the quadrilateral with vertices (1,1), $(\frac{3}{2},\frac{11}{4})$, (2,3), (3,2) is a trapezoid.

10. Test whether the points $(-1,-2)$, $(3,-1)$, and $6,-\frac{1}{2})$ lie on the same straight line.

11. For what values of x, if any, does $(x,1)$ lie on the line through $(-1,-2)$ and $(3,-1)$?

12. For what values of x and y does (x,y) lie on the line through (4,1) and (3,2)?

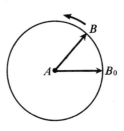

FIGURE 6–13

13. For what values of x and y does (x,y) lie on the line with slope $\frac{1}{8}$ passing through $(1,7)$?

14. Sketch the graph C of $\{(x,y)\in R^2|y = x^2\}$ and find the coordinates of those points on C with the abscissas 2, 1.5, 1.4, 1.3, 1.2, 1.1. Compute the slopes from these points to $(1,1)$.

15. Assuming that the graph of $\{(x,y)|y = 4x + 3\}$ is a straight line, find its slope.

16. What is the slope of the line through $(1,3)$ and $(1,5)$?

17. Compare "L has zero slope" and "L has no slope." What lines L satisfy the first? The second?

After our discussion of slope, it is not difficult to develop the general equation for a straight line. Let L be the line through (a,b) with slope m (there is one and only one such line). Let (x,y) be any point on L other than (a,b). Since the slope from (a,b) to (x,y) is also m, we must have

(1)
$$\frac{y - b}{x - a} = m,$$

(2)
$$y - b = m(x - a).$$

Observe that (a,b) also satisfies Eq. (2). Thus

$$\pi(L) \subset \{(x,y)\in R^2|y - b = m(x - a)\}.$$

Suppose now that (x,y) is a pair which satisfies Eq. (2). If $(x,y) = (a,b)$, then $(x,y)\in \pi(L)$. If $(x,y) \neq (a,b)$, then $x \neq a$, since that would imply [with Eq. (2)] that $y = b$, $(x,y) = (a,b)$. Hence in Eq. (2), we may divide by $x - a$ to get Eq. (1). This means that the slope from (a,b) to (x,y) is m, so that $(x,y)\in \pi(L)$.

Therefore,

$$\{(x,y)\in R^2|y - b = m(x - a)\} \subset \pi(L).$$

Finally,

$$\pi(L) = \{(x,y)\in R^2|y - b = m(x - a)\}.$$

EXAMPLE 6–8.   Find an equation for the line through $(2,5)$ with slope 3.

Solution: Here $(a,b) = (2,5)$, $m = 3$. The required equation is

$$y - 5 = 3(x - 2),$$
$$y = 3x - 1.$$

Equation (2) may put in the equivalent form

(3)
$$y = mx + c,$$

with $c = b - ma$. Every equation of the form (3) has a straight-line graph, for we can transform Eq. (3) into

(4) $y - c = m(x - 0)$,

which is a special case of Eq. (2). Thus, the graph of Eq. (3) is the straight line through $(0,c)$ with slope m.

EXAMPLE 6–9.   Show that the graph of

$$3y = 5x + 2$$

is a straight line.

   Solution: The given equation is equivalent to

$$y - \tfrac{2}{3} = \tfrac{5}{3}(x - 0).$$

Its graph is the line through $(0,\tfrac{2}{3})$ of slope $\tfrac{5}{3}$.

   The only lines not covered by our discussion are the ones which have no slope, namely, the vertical lines. If (a,b) is a point on a vertical line, then

(5) $x = a$

is a defining equation for the line:

$$\pi(L) = \{(x,y) \in R^2 | x = a\}.$$

Thus, every line has an equation of the form (3) or (5). Both of these are subsumed under the form

(6) $Ax + By = C$ $(A \neq 0 \text{ or } B \neq 0)$.

Conversely every equation of the form (6), with $A \neq 0$ or $B \neq 0$, has a straight-line graph. If $B \neq 0$, we can divide by B and transform Eq. (6) into

$$y = -\frac{A}{B}x + \frac{C}{B},$$

which is of the form (3) with $m = -A/B$. If $B = 0$, then $A \neq 0$, and we can transform Eq. (6) into

$$x = \frac{C}{A},$$

which is of the form (5), with $a = C/A$.

   If both A and B are 0 in Eq. (6), we get $0 = C$. The student may easily verify that the graph of $0 = C$ is either empty or the entire plane, according as $C \neq 0$ or $C = 0$.

EXAMPLE 6–10. Find an equation for the line through (2,3) and (5,7).

Solution 1: The slope $m = (7 - 3)/(5 - 2) = 4/3$. Using the "point-slope form," Eq. (2), with $(a,b) = (2,3)$, we have

$$y - 3 = \tfrac{4}{3}(x - 2),$$
$$3y - 9 = 4x - 8,$$
$$4x - 3y = -1.$$

Solution 2: We know that the line has an equation of the form (6):

$$Ax + By = C.$$

Since (2,3) is on the line, $x = 2$ and $y = 3$ must satisfy the equation, so

(7) $$2A + 3B = C.$$

Similarly, since (5,7) is on the line,

(8) $$5A + 7B = C.$$

Multiply Eq. (7) by 7, Eq. (8) by 3, and subtract:

$$-A = 4C,$$
$$A = -4C.$$

Similarly, by eliminating A from Eqs. (7) and (8) we get

$$B = 3C.$$

Taking $C = -1$ (for example), we find $A = 4$, $B = -3$, $C = -1$, and these values are easily seen to satisfy Eqs. (7) and (8). Inserting these values in Eq. (6), we get

$$4x - 3y = -1,$$

as in Solution 1.

EXAMPLE 6–11. Discuss and draw the graph of

$$3x + 2y = 4.$$

Solution: Solve for y:

$$y = -\tfrac{3}{2}x + 2.$$

The line has slope $-\tfrac{3}{2}$ and passes through the point (0,2) (Figure 6–14). For each increase of 2 in x, y decreases by 3. The line also contains $(2,-1)$.

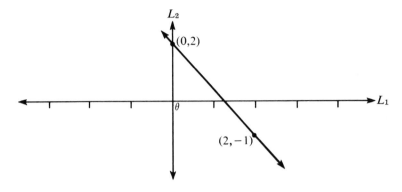

FIGURE 6–14

EXERCISES 6–5

1. What are the subsets of R^2 which correspond to:
   (a) The line through $(1,5)$ and $(-2,7)$.
   (b) The line through $(3,6)$ and $(3,2)$.
   (c) The line through $(1,1)$ and $(3,-7)$.
   (d) The line through $(\sqrt{3},\sqrt{2})$ with slope $\sqrt{2/3}$.

2. Find

$$\{(x,y) \in R^2 | 2x + y = 1 \wedge x + y = 4\}.$$

3. Find

$$\{(x,y) \in R^2 | 3x - y = 0\} \cap \{(x,y) \in R^2 | x - 2y = 5\}.$$

4. Draw the lines L and M determined by
   (a) $(2,2) \in L$, slope of $L = \frac{4}{5}$.
   (b) $\pi(M) = \{(x,y) \in R^2 | x + 2y = 1\}$.
   Find $L \cap M$.

5. Find the truth set in R^2 of

$$x_2 = 2x_1 + 1 \wedge 6x_1 = 3x_2 - 3a.$$

(The answer depends on a; discuss the dependence.)

6. Let L be the line through $(-2,0)$ with slope m. Let C be the graph of

$$\{(x,y) \in R^2 | x^2 + y^2 = 1\}.$$

Discuss the dependence of $L \cap C$ on m. Interpret geometrically the condition that $L \cap C$ is a singleton. For what values of m is this true?

7. Let C be the circle with center 0 and radius 2. Find the equations of the tangents from the point (2,4) to C (Figure 6–15).

8. Let C be the graph of $\{(x,y) \in R^2 | y = x^2\}$. Let L be the line through (1,1) with slope m. Determine m so that L is tangent to C. Do the same for L passing through (a,a^2) instead of (1,1).

9. Let $\pi(A) = (1,3)$, $\pi(B) = (2,5)$, $\pi(C) = (5,1)$. Prove that the line through the midpoints of segments AB and BC is parallel to AC.

10. What is the graph of

$$\{(2t,3t)|t \in R\}?$$

11. What is the graph of

$$\{(2t^2,3t^2)|t \in R\}?$$

12. What is the graph of

$$\{(x,y) \in R^2 | \exists t \in R, \ x = 2t + 1 \wedge y = 3t - 1\}?$$

13. Let A, B, C be the points of Problem 9. If AB and BC are adjacent sides of a parallelogram, find the coordinates of the fourth vertex D.

*14. Find the distance from (3,1) to the graph of $\{(x,y) \in R^2 | y = 2x\}$.

15. Describe the graph of

$$\{(x,y) \in R^2 | x + y = 7 \wedge x^2 + y^2 \leq 25\}.$$

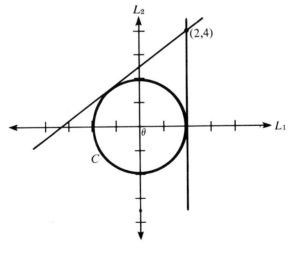

FIGURE 6–15

16. (a) Sketch the graph C of $\{(x,y) \in R^2 | y = x^3\}$.
  (b) Show that the point $(1 + h, (1 + h)^3)$ is on C, for all $h \in R$.
  (c) Compute the slope from $(1,1)$ to $(1 + h, (1 + h)^3)$, for $h \neq 0$.
  (d) Evaluate the slope in part (c) for $h = .1, .01, .001$.
  (e) Guess at the equation for the tangent to C at the point $(1,1)$.
17. In Problem 8 of Exercises 6–2, show that
  (a) The coordinates of Q_a are

$$x = 5a\left(\frac{a - 5}{a^2 + 25}\right) \quad \Bigg\} \quad (a \in R).$$
$$y = 5a\left(\frac{a + 5}{a^2 + 25}\right)$$

  (b) These coordinates satisfy

$$\left(x - \frac{5}{2}\right)^2 + \left(y - \frac{5}{2}\right)^2 = \frac{25}{2}$$

for all $a \in R$.
  (c) The locus $\{Q_a | a \in R\}$ is contained in a circle. Is it the entire circle?

6–4. GRAPHS OF FUNCTIONS

Among the relations in $R \times R$ that we are called upon to graph there are some specially important ones—the functions. They are characterized by the fact that for each $x \in R$, there is at most one $y \in R$ such that (x,y) belongs to the relation. This condition has a simple geometrical interpretation in terms of the graph of the relation: No vertical line intersects the graph in more than one point. Thus, in Figure 6–16, the circle K is not the graph of a function, since the dashed vertical meets it in two points, but the peculiar-shaped θABC is the graph of a function. The domain of this function is the set $\{x \in R | 0 \leq x \leq \text{abscissa of } C\}$, a proper subset of R.

Suppose that $f \subset R \times R$ is a function with domain D. Its graph is

$$G = \pi^{-1}(f)$$
$$= \pi^{-1}(\{(x,y) \in R^2 | y = f(x) \wedge x \in D\}).$$

Rather than use this somewhat cumbersome notation, we sometimes say that G is the graph of the equation

$$y = f(x) \qquad (x \in D).$$

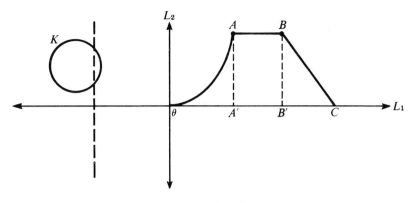

FIGURE 6–16

Just as we permitted an abuse of language by speaking of "the point (1,2)" instead of "the point π^{-1} ((1,2))," so also we could identify a function (or relation) and its graph. Thus, we could speak of the relation K given by

$$(x - a)^2 + (y - b)^2 = r^2,$$

or of the function θABC. No catastrophe would befall us, so long as we remember that the identification depends on our choice of coordinate system. The set θABC remains the same no matter what coordinate system we choose, since it is just a subset of the plane P. In the system of Figure 6–16 it is the graph of a function. If we chose another system, say by interchanging L_1 and L_2, it would not be the graph of a function.

The preceding remarks have the interesting consequence that we can sometimes simplify our study of a set in the plane by choosing a coordinate system adroitly. Thus, every parabola can be regarded as the graph of

$$y = ax^2 \qquad (x \in R)$$

for an appropriate $a > 0$. If we allowed different units on the two axes, we could even take $a = 1$. Of course, the conclusions reached by studying the parabola in simplified form would have to be stated in terms which are independent of the coordinate system used.

In graphing a function we are usually interested in the over-all shape of the graph rather than its minute details, although these may be of importance sometimes. We can give no hard-and-fast rules, but we can indicate some things to look for in the graph.

DOMAIN. If the domain of a function is given explicitly, there is no problem—except perhaps to keep it in mind. In many applications the

domain is not given, and it is up to us to determine it, with due consideration of the natural limitations of the problem. Thus, to study unit cost of
production as a function of number of items produced, the domain would
be a subset of the nonnegative integers, or of the nonnegative reals if we
wanted a smooth but slightly fictitious curve. If the expression

$$\frac{2x + 1}{(x - 1)(x - 2)}$$

arose naturally in the course of a problem, we might choose the domain of
the corresponding function as all of R with the exception of 1 and 2, to
avoid division by 0.

RANGE. This is usually more difficult to determine. It involves finding
maxima or minima of functions, for which our methods are quite meager at
the present point. They will improve later, however.

EXAMPLE 6–12.   Discuss the range of the function f given by

$$f(x) = x^2 - 2x \qquad (x \in R).$$

Solution:

$$x^2 - 2x = x^2 - 2x + 1 - 1$$

$$= (x - 1)^2 - 1.$$

$$\therefore \quad f(x) \geq -1 \qquad (x \in R),$$

$$f(1) = -1.$$

The minimum of f is attained at $x = 1$, and its value there is -1. For any
number $b \geq -1$, we can solve the equation

$$(x - 1)^2 - 1 = b,$$

$$(x - 1)^2 = 1 + b \geq 0,$$

$$x - 1 = \pm \sqrt{1 + b},$$

$$x = 1 \pm \sqrt{1 + b}.$$

Thus

$$\operatorname{rng} f = \{b \in R \mid b \geq -1\}.$$

We should bear in mind the possibility of internal gaps in the range.
For a wide class of functions (continuous functions defined on an interval,
for later reference) these do not occur.

LARGE VALUES. These are of two kinds: large values of x, the "independent variable," and large values of y, the "dependent variable."

EXAMPLE 6–13. Discuss the graph of

$$y = \frac{2x + 1}{(x - 1)(x - 2)} \qquad (x \in R, \; x \neq 1, 2),$$

with respect to large values.

Discussion: For large x, whether positive or negative, $2x + 1$ is approximately $2x$, and $(x - 1)(x - 2)$ is approximately x^2, so y is approximately $2/x$. If x is large and positive, y is close to 0 and positive; if x is large and negative, y is close to 0 and negative. The graph will look like Figure 6–17, the intermediate portions being omitted.

The values of x close to 1 and 2 will be "sensitive." They will be of four types:

(1) x close to 1 and less than 1. Here $2x + 1$ will be about 3, $x - 1$ will be small and negative, $x - 2$ will be about -1. Therefore y will be large and positive.

(2) x close to 1 and greater than 1. Here the situation will be the same as in (1), except that $x - 1$ is small and positive. Therefore y will be large and negative.

(3) x close to 2 and less than 2. Again y will be large and negative.

(4) x close to 2 and greater than 2. All factors are positive, so y will be large and positive.

Figure 6–18 shows what we have learned so far.

It does not take much more to complete the picture. The graph meets the L_1-axis wherever $y = 0$, in this case at $x = -\frac{1}{2}$. Figure 6–19 is a fair guess at the shape of the entire graph.

ZEROS. *A zero* of a function f is a number z in its domain for which $f(z) = 0$. If z is a zero, the point $(z,0)$ is on the graph. The curve may cross the L_1-axis, as in Figure 6–19 at $x = -\frac{1}{2}$, or it may not, as in the case of $y = x^2$ ($x \in R$) at $x = 0$. Usually an inspection of neighboring values of x will tell the tale.

FIGURE 6–17

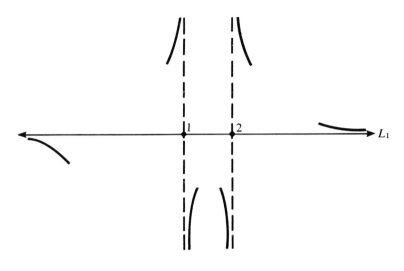

FIGURE 6–18

DIRECTION OF CHANGE. It is helpful to know intervals (in x) over which the functional values are increasing or decreasing. Again, the methods now available to us are too weak to deal with any but the simplest cases. Later, when we introduce the powerful tool of differentiation, we shall be able to discuss rate and direction of change.

SYMMETRY. This may sometimes cut our work in half. Thus, for

$$y = x^2 \qquad (x \in R),$$

whenever (x, y) is on the graph, so is $(-x, y)$. Two such points are situated symmetrically about the L_2-axis, so the graph to the right of L_2 will be reflected about L_2 as in a mirror (Figure 6–20).

In the case of

$$y = (x - 1)(x - 2) \qquad (x \in R),$$

we may change the form to exhibit symmetry about the line $x = \frac{3}{2}$:

$$y = x^2 - 3x + 2$$
$$= x^2 - 3x + (\tfrac{3}{2})^2 - (\tfrac{3}{2})^2 + 2$$
$$= (x - \tfrac{3}{2})^2 - \tfrac{1}{4}.$$

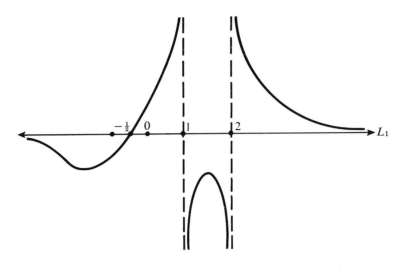

FIGURE 6–19

If the vertical axis were shifted to the line $x = \frac{3}{2}$, we would have a new scale x' on the L_1-axis given by $x' = x - \frac{3}{2}$, so our equation would be

$$y = x'^2 - \tfrac{1}{4}.$$

As in the previous example, if (x',y) is on the graph, so is $(-x',y)$. The student should draw a diagram showing both vertical axes, the horizontal

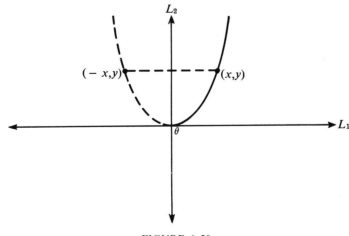

FIGURE 6–20

axis, and the curve. The minimum is also apparent from the new equation. The graph of

$$y = x^3 \qquad (x \in R)$$

shows a different kind of symmetry: if (x,y) is on the graph, then so is $(-x,-y)$. The graph is *symmetrical about the origin* (Figure 6–21).

PLOTTING POINTS. Occasionally it is helpful to make a small table of corresponding x and y values [number pairs $(x,y) \in f$] and to plot these points. This should be a last resort, however, since it is laborious and sometimes misleading.

Not all functions are given by means of a single formula. The curve θABC in Figure 6–16 is most easily described by dividing the domain into the three intervals

$$I_1 = \{x | 0 \le x \le \text{abscissa of } A\},$$

$$I_2 = \{x | \text{absc. } A \le x \le \text{absc. } B\},$$

$$I_3 = \{x | \text{absc. } B \le x \le \text{absc. } C\},$$

and then writing

$$y = rx^2 \qquad (x \in I_1)$$

$$= s \qquad (x \in I_2)$$

$$= mx + b \qquad (x \in I_3),$$

for appropriate constants r, s, m, b.

EXERCISES 6–6

Discuss and sketch the graph of:
1. $y = (x - 3)^2$.

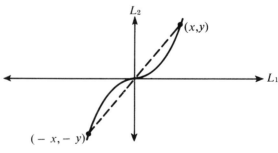

FIGURE 6–21

2. $y = 2 + (x - 1)^2$.
3. $y = x^2 + 2x$.
4. $y = (x + 1)x(x - 1)$.

5. $y = \dfrac{x + 2}{x + 1}$.

6. $y = x + \dfrac{1}{x}$.

7. $y = x - \dfrac{1}{x}$.

8. $y = \dfrac{1}{x^2 + 1}$.

9. $y = \dfrac{x - 1}{x^2 + 1}$.

10. $y = \dfrac{x^2 - 1}{x - 1}$.

11. $y = x + \dfrac{1}{x^2 + 1}$.

12. $y = (x - 1)^3$.
13. $y = (x - 1)^3 + 1$.
14. $y = |x|$.
15. $y = |x - 2|$.
16. $y = 3 + 2|x - 1|$.
17. $y = $ the greatest integer $\leq x$ $(x \in R)$.
18. $y = 1$ (x rational),
    $\quad = -1$ (x irrational).
19. $y = $ the distance from x to the nearest integer to x.

20. $y = \sqrt{1 - x^2}$.

21. $y = -\sqrt{x^2}$.

22. $(x - 2)^2 + (y - 3)^2 = 0$.

23. $y = \dfrac{1}{x^3 - x}$.

24. $y = (x^2 - 1)^2$.

Chapter 7

MEASURE, AREA, AND INTEGRATION

7-1. MEASURES

IN THIS CHAPTER we are concerned with the operation of measurement, which may take different forms depending on the type of object being measured. Thus, if we are measuring finite sets, we might use the *number of elements* in a set; if we are measuring regions in a plane, we might use the *area* of a region; if we are measuring regions in space, we might use the *volume* of region. Other examples are *area* of regions on a sphere, or on a cylinder; total *mass* of regions in space; *probability* of sets of outcomes of an experiment; total *assets* of sets of people; *number of honor students* in school classes; *number of primes* in finite sets of integers; *number of defectives* in samples of manufactured items.

In all these examples we can discern a few common properties. First, that which is measured is a *set* of a certain type, that is, one belonging to a certain *class* of sets. Next, to each set of the class we assign a nonnegative real number, the measure of the set. Thus, we have a function defined on the class and taking values in the nonnegative reals. Finally, "The whole is equal to the sum of its parts." By this we mean that a set S composed of two disjoint subsets S_1 and S_2 has a measure equal to the sum of the measures of S_1 and S_2. For this to make sense, we must of course assume that if S_1 and S_2 belong to the class of sets being measured (the domain of the measure function), then their union $S_1 \cup S_2$ also belongs to the class. For later purposes it is convenient to assume also that the difference of two sets in the class is again in the class. We are therefore led to the following definitions.

Definition 7–1. A *ring of sets* is a nonempty collection **R** of sets satisfying
  (a) *If* $S, T \in \mathbf{R}$, *then* $S \cup T \in \mathbf{R}$.
  (b) *If* $S, T \in \mathbf{R}$, *then* $S - T \in \mathbf{R}$.

286

Briefly, a ring of sets is closed under union and difference. We remark that it must then be closed under intersection, for

$$S \cap T = S - (S - T).$$

In our application to measure, we shall always assume that the ring **R** is a collection of subsets of a given set V.

Definition 7–2.   A *measure in* V is a real-valued function m defined on a ring **R** of subsets of V and satisfying
(a) For all $S \in \mathbf{R}, m(S) \geq 0$.
(b) For all $S, T \in \mathbf{R}$, if $S \cap T = \emptyset$, then $m(S \cup T) = m(S) + m(T)$.
We sometimes write mS instead of $m(S)$. It may happen that $m(S \cup T) = m(S) + m(T)$ even if S and T are not disjoint.

EXAMPLE 7–1. $V = Z$ (the set of integers). **R** is the class of finite subsets of V. For $S \in \mathbf{R}$, mS is the number of elements in S.

EXAMPLE 7–2. $V = \{1,2,3,4,5,6\}$. **R** is the class of all subsets of V. For $S \in \mathbf{R}$, $mS = \frac{1}{6}$ of the number of elements in S. In this case, m may be interpreted as the probability of getting an element of S in the throw of a single fair die. Thus, the probability of getting an even number is

$$m(\{2,4,6\}) = \tfrac{1}{6}(3) = \tfrac{1}{2}.$$

EXAMPLE 7–3. V and **R** as in Example 7–1. For $S \in \mathbf{R}$, define $mS =$ the square of the number of elements in S. Then m is *not* a measure, since it violates condition (b) of Definition 7–2. For example, if $S = \{3\}$, $T = \{4,5\}$, then $mS = 1$, $mT = 4$, but $m(S \cup T) = 9 \neq mS + mT$.

Because we have so many examples of measures, it is worth our while to prove a few simple theorems which apply to all of them.

Theorem 7–1. $\emptyset \in \mathbf{R}$, and $m(\emptyset) = 0$.
Proof: **R** is nonempty, so there is an $S \in \mathbf{R}$. By (b) of Definition 7–1, $S - S = \emptyset \in \mathbf{R}$. By (b) of Definition 7–2,

$$m(\emptyset) = m(\emptyset \cup \emptyset) = m(\emptyset) + m(\emptyset).$$
$$\therefore \quad 0 = m(\emptyset).$$

Theorem 7–2.   If $S, T \in \mathbf{R}$ and $S \subset T$, then

$$m(T - S) = mT - mS.$$

Proof: Since $S \cap (T - S) = \emptyset$ and $S \cup (T - S) = T$,
$$mT = m(S \cup (T - S)) = mS + m(T - S).$$

Theorem 7–3. If $S, T \in \mathbf{R}$ and $S \subset T$, then $mS \leq mT$.
Proof: By Theorem 7–2,

$$mT - mS = m(T - S) \geq 0,$$

from (a) of Definition 7–2.

Theorem 7–4. If $S, T \in \mathbf{R}$, then $m(S \cup T) = mS + mT - m(S \cap T)$ (Figure 7–1).
Proof: $S \cup T = S \cup (T - S)$ and $S \cap (T - S) = \varnothing$, so by (b) of Definition 7–2,

(1) $$m(S \cup T) = mS + m(T - S).$$

Also, $T - S = T - (S \cap T)$, and $S \cap T \subset T$, so by Theorem 7–2,

(2) $$m(T - S) = mT - m(S \cap T).$$

Combining Eqs. (1) and (2), we get the desired result.

EXAMPLE 7–4.   How many integers from 1 to 60 inclusive are divisible by 2 or 3?
Solution: Let S be the subset of $\{1, \ldots, 60\}$ consisting of those integers divisible by 2, T the corresponding set for 3. Then $S \cap T$ is the corresponding set for 6. Hence, if m is the measure of Example 7–1,

$$m(S \cup T) = mS + mT - m(S \cap T)$$

$$= 30 + 20 - 10$$

$$= 40.$$

EXERCISE 7–1

How many integers from 1 to 60 inclusive are divisible by 4 or 6?

Theorem 7–5. If $S, T \in \mathbf{R}$, then $m(S \cup T) \leq mS + mT$.
Proof: Left to the student.

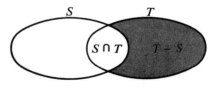

FIGURE 7–1

Definition 7-3.   If S_i, $i = 1, 2, \ldots, n$, are sets, then

$$\bigcup_{i=1}^{n} S_i = \{x \mid \exists i, 1 \leq i \leq n, x \in S_i\},$$

$$\bigcap_{i=1}^{n} S_i = \{x \mid \forall i, 1 \leq i \leq n, x \in S_i\}.$$

We sometimes write

$$\bigcup_{i=1}^{n} S_i = S_1 \cup S_2 \cup \cdots \cup S_n,$$

$$\bigcap_{i=1}^{n} S_i = S_1 \cap S_2 \cap \cdots \cap S_n.$$

Theorem 7-6.   If $S_i \in R(1 \leq i \leq n)$ and $S_i \cap S_j = \emptyset(1 \leq i < j \leq n)$, then

$$m(\bigcup_{i=1}^{n} S_i) = \sum_{i=1}^{n} mS_i.$$

Proof: Use induction on n and (b) of Definition 7-2.

Theorem 7-7.   If $S_i \in R(1 \leq i \leq n)$, then

$$m(\bigcup_{i=1}^{n} S_i) \leq \sum_{i=1}^{n} mS_i.$$

Proof: Use induction on n and Theorem 7-5.

The property of m expressed in Theorem 7-6 is referred to as *finite additivity*. If we had an infinite sequence (S_i) and the corresponding result held (with suitable interpretations for the union and sum), we would have *countable additivity*. In more advanced treatments it is useful to impose this as a stronger condition, especially in the theory of probability. At the present time we do not need it. Also, it is sometimes convenient to drop condition (a) of Definition 7-2, thus allowing measures with positive and negative values. These are called *signed measures*.

EXERCISES 7-2

1. If $S_1, S_2, S_3 \in R$, show that

$$m(S_1 \cup S_2 \cup S_3) = mS_1 + mS_2 + mS_3$$
$$- m(S_1 \cap S_2) - m(S_2 \cap S_3) - m(S_1 \cap S_3)$$
$$+ m(S_1 \cap S_2 \cap S_3).$$

2. How many integers from 1 to 6,000 are divisible by 2 or 3 or 5?

3. Let m be a measure defined for all subsets of a finite set V. Show that m is completely determined by its values on the singletons in V.

4. Carry out the proofs of Theorems 7–5, 7–6, and 7–7.

5. Let m be a measure, c a positive number. Show that cm is also a measure. What about $c + m$?

6. Let m_1, m_2 be measures defined on the same ring $\mathbf{R}$. Show that $m_1 + m_2$ is a measure on $\mathbf{R}$. Can $m_1 - m_2$ ever be a measure on $\mathbf{R}$?

7. If $\mathbf{R}$ is a ring of subsets of V, is it necessarily true that $V \in \mathbf{R}$?

8. Let m be a measure defined on a ring $\mathbf{R}$ of subsets of V, and suppose that $V \in \mathbf{R}$ and $m(V) = 1$. If $S,T \in \mathbf{R}$ are such that $m(S \cap T) = m(S)m(T)$, prove that $m(S' \cap T') = m(S')m(T')$. ($S' = V - S$.) What about $m(S \cap T')$?

9. Let m be a measure defined on a ring $\mathbf{R}$ of subsets of V, and let A be a fixed element of $\mathbf{R}$. Define $m_1(S) = m(S \cap A)$ for all $S \in \mathbf{R}$. Show that m_1 is also a measure. What about m_2, defined by $m_2(S) = m(S - A)$ for all $S \in \mathbf{R}$?

10. Let p be a fixed element of V. For all $S \subset V$, define m by

$$m(S) = \begin{cases} 1, \text{ if } p \in S \\ 0, \text{ if } p \notin S. \end{cases}$$

Is m a measure? What is the domain of m?

11. Let $p,q \in V$, $p \neq q$. For all $S \subset V$, define m by

$$m(S) = \begin{cases} 1, \text{ if } \{p,q\} \subset S, \\ 0, \text{ if } \{p,q\} \not\subset S. \end{cases}$$

Is m a measure? What is the domain of m?

12. Let $\mathbf{R}$ be the ring of all finite subsets of V, and let f be function from V into the reals. For all $S \in \mathbf{R}$, define

$$m(S) = \sum_{x \in S} f(x),$$

($m(\emptyset) = 0$). Under what condition on f is m a measure?

13. Show that every finite ring of sets is a Boolean algebra. Is this true of every ring of sets?

14. If possible, give examples of rings of sets with two elements; four elements; five elements; eight elements.

15. A market researcher reported that out of a sample of 100, there were 70 who liked Squishies, 40 who liked Gooeys, 20 who liked both, and 20 who liked neither. His employer fired him. Why?

16. Comment on the following data: An appraiser values lots A and B together at $1,000, lots B and C together at $1,000, and lots A and C together at $4,000.

7–2. AREA

There are many possible measures in the plane, but very few that fit our familiar intuitive conception of area. One essential requirement is that congruent figures should have equal areas. In the physical plane, congruence of two figures involves the idea of superposing one upon the other to fit exactly. We can make the idea precise in the conceptual plane by the following definition:

Definition 7–4.   Two subsets S and T of the plane are *congruent*, $S \cong T$, if there is a one-to-one correspondence f between S and T such that the distance between any two points of S is equal to the distance between the corresponding points in T:

$$\forall p,q \in S,\ d(p,q) = d(f(p), f(q)).$$

Our definition agrees with the ordinary notion of congruence in the case of segments, triangles, circles, and so on.

Our requirement that area be invariant under congruence can now be stated as follows:

(1) $\forall S, T \in \mathbf{R},\ (S \cong T) \to (mS = mT)$.

The next demand that we make of our area function is hardly a restriction at all. It is merely a matter of fixing the unit of area.

(2) If K is a square of side 1, plus its interior, then $mK = 1$.

There remains only one question: What is to be the ring $\mathbf{R}$ of subsets of the plane on which area is defined? Naturally, we want $\mathbf{R}$ to be as large as possible, to include all "reasonable" sets such as triangles, polygons, circles, ellipses (all with their interiors), as well as unions and differences of such sets. We do not insist on very large sets, such as the entire plane, or a half-plane, or an angle plus its interior. To clarify the meaning of "very large," we shall say that a set S is *bounded* if there is some circle which contains S in its interior. Then a "very large" set is one that is not bounded. It should be clear to the student that the union and difference of two bounded sets are also bounded sets. That is, the collection of all bounded sets in the plane is a ring $\mathbf{R}$. Is it possible that there is an area function with $\mathbf{R}$ as its domain?

At this point, higher mathematics comes to our assistance. It was proved about 50 years ago that *there exists at least one measure m in the plane, defined on the ring $\mathbf{R}$ of all bounded sets, and satisfying conditions (1) and (2) above.* We should be quite pleased to accept as an area function any measure of this kind.

Let us be very clear about the situation. Most of us have a good intuitive grasp of the concept of area as a measure of size or extent, derived from the physical plane. What we have done is to set down a few conditions, in the conceptual plane, that we would like to demand of an area function. Reasonable as these conditions may seem, there is no guarantee in advance that they are consistent. This is precisely the content of the theorem stated in the preceding paragraph.

We shall digress for a moment to convince the student that the theorem is far from trivial. Consider the analogous question of volume in three-space R^3. Does there exist a measure m defined for all bounded sets in R^3, invariant under congruence, which assigns to the unit cube the value 1? The answer is *no*! To see this, we assemble the following facts:

(1) If there were such a measure m, it could be proved that two spheres of different radii have different measures. Actually, the familiar volume formula $mS = \frac{4}{3}\pi r^3$ would hold, but we do not need it.

(2) Given any two (solid) spheres S and T of different radii, there is a positive integer n (depending on S and T), and two collections of subsets of S and T, say, $\{S_1, S_2, \ldots, S_n\}$ and $\{T_1, T_2, \ldots, T_n\}$, such that

(a) $S = S_1 \cup S_2 \cup \cdots \cup S_n$.
(b) $T = T_1 \cup T_2 \cup \cdots \cup T_n$.
(c) S_i and S_j are disjoint, for all $i \neq j$.
(d) T_i and T_j are disjoint, for all $i \neq j$.
(e) $S_1 \cong T_1, S_2 \cong T_2, \ldots, S_n \cong T_n$.

In other words, we can break up S into a finite number of disjoint sets, then reassemble these sets (or congruent copies of them) to make up T.

From (a) and (c) we derive

$$mS = mS_1 + mS_2 + \cdots + mS_n.$$

Similarly, from (b) and (d),

$$mT = mT_1 + mT_2 + \cdots + mT_n.$$

From (e) and the fact that m is invariant under congruence, we have

$$mS_1 = mT_1, mS_2 = mT_2, \ldots, mS_n = mT_n.$$

Therefore $mS = mT$. This contradiction of (1) proves our assertion.

The key to the argument is the almost unbelievable statement (2). It is known as the *Banach-Tarski* paradox. If we analyze our incredulity, we see that we argue roughly as we did above: The corresponding pieces cannot be congruent, for they would have the same volume, and then the spheres would have the same volume. The flaw in this argument is the hidden assumption that the pieces have volume, that is, that they all belong to the domain of m. It is just asking too much of a volume function that it be defined for *all* bounded sets, including the "wild" sets S_i and T_i. We must settle for a smaller ring of sets on which to define volume.

In the light of our discussion of volume, the existence of an area function defined for all bounded sets in the plane does not appear at all obvious. In fact, the proof (due to Banach) is quite deep.

Actually there are many different "area functions." This lack of uniqueness would be a source of embarrassment to us were it not for the fact that all area functions agree on a very wide subclass of **R**, so wide that it includes all the "reasonable" sets mentioned above. It is worthwhile for us to investigate this subclass, so that we may speak about the area of one of its elements without ambiguity. Our plan is therefore to assume simply that we have an area function m and to prove under this assumption a few theorems about mS for certain sets S. Naturally, these theorems hold for any area function whatsoever.

We begin with an "obvious" theorem. Before proceeding to the proof, we ask the student to put aside the text and prove it for himself.

Theorem 7–8. If p is a point, then $m\{p\} = 0$.

Proof: By condition (1) above (invariance of m under congruence), any two one-point sets must have the same area c. Let n be an arbitrary positive integer. Inside K, a unit square, we can find n distinct points $p_1, p_2, \ldots, p_n$. Let $A = \{p_1, p_2, \ldots, p_n\}$. Then by Theorem 7–6,

$$mA = \sum_{i=1}^{n} m\{p_i\} = \sum_{i=1}^{n} c = nc.$$

By Theorem 7–3, $mA \leq mK$, because $A \subset K$. By condition (2), $mK = 1$. Combining our results, we see that $nc \leq 1$. Thus, c is a nonnegative number satisfying

$$c \leq \frac{1}{n} \qquad (n \in N).$$

It follows that $c = 0$ (see Chapter 4).

Theorem 7–9. If pq is a line segment, then $m(pq) = 0$.

Proof: There is a natural number k such that the length of pq is less than k. Therefore pq is contained in the union of k congruent line segments of length less than 1. By Theorem 7–7,

$$m(pq) \leq km(p_1q_1),$$

where p_1q_1 is one of the segments. Thus, it is sufficient to show that a line segment p_1q_1 of length less than 1 has zero area. But, just as in the proof of Theorem 7–8, we can find an arbitrarily large number of disjoint line segments congruent to p_1q_1 inside a unit square. The area of each one must therefore be zero.

Theorem 7–10. If S is any finite union of line segments, then $mS = 0$.
Proof: This follows directly from Theorems 7–7 and 7–9.

By a triangular region we mean the set consisting of a triangle plus its interior. A polygonal region is a finite (possibly empty) union of triangular regions. The boundary of a polygonal region S is the set of points of S which are not completely surrounded by points of S. For an example, see Figure 7–2. The shaded set, plus the line segments rs, st, su, and so on, forms the polygonal region S. The point p is not on the boundary of S; the point q is. The boundary of S is

$$yz \cup zr \cup rs \cup su \cup uv \cup vx \cup xy \cup yw \cup wv \cup vs \cup st \cup ty.$$

By Theorem 7–10, the boundary of a polygonal region has zero area, being a finite union of line segments. When two polygonal regions are united, another one is formed. If the two regions do not overlap, that is, intersect only in points of the boundaries, then the area of the union is equal to the sum of the areas. For the intersection is a subset of a set of area zero, namely, the union of the boundaries. In Figure 7–3,

$$m(S \cup T) = mS + mT - m(pq)$$

$$= mS + mT.$$

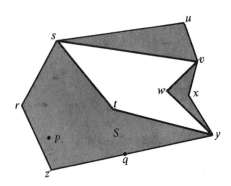

FIGURE 7–2

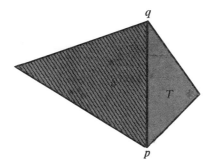

FIGURE 7–3

It should be clear that the boundaries of polygonal regions may be ignored as far as area computations are concerned. We may omit part or all of the boundary without changing the area.

It is common practice to use the term "triangle" ambiguously to refer to a triangular region or its boundary; similarly for other geometrical figures. When there is no danger of confusion we shall follow this practice.

Theorem 7–11.   If S is a square of side $1/n$ ($n \in N$), then $mS = 1/n^2$.

Proof: By drawing lines parallel to the sides of a unit square K we can subdivide it into n^2 copies of S which intersect only on their boundaries. Therefore

$$1 = mK = n^2 \cdot mS.$$

Theorem 7–12.   If T is a rectangle with sides of rational lengths a and b, then $mT = ab$.

Proof: We may suppose that $a = p/n$, $b = q/n$; p, q, n are positive integers. We can subdivide T into pq squares of side $1/n$. Therefore

$$mT = pq\left(\frac{1}{n^2}\right) = \left(\frac{p}{n}\right)\left(\frac{q}{n}\right) = ab.$$

Theorem 7–13.   If T is a rectangle with sides of lengths a and b, then $mT = ab$ (Figure 7–4).

MODERN MATHEMATICS

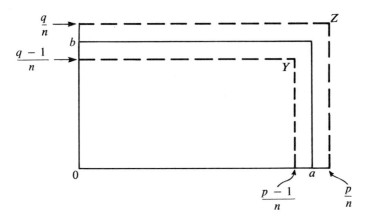

FIGURE 7-4

Proof: Choose an arbitrary positive integer n. For some positive integer k, we have $na \le k$. Let p be the smallest of such k's. Then

$$p - 1 < na \le p,$$

$$\frac{p - 1}{n} < a \le \frac{p}{n}.$$

Similarly, there exists a positive integer q such that

$$\frac{q - 1}{n} < b \le \frac{q}{n}.$$

Constructing the auxiliary dashed lines as in the figure, we find that the given rectangle T is enclosed between the rectangles Y and Z. Using the area formula of Theorem 7–12, we get

(1) $$\frac{(p - 1)}{n} \cdot \frac{(q - 1)}{n} \le mT \le \frac{p}{n} \cdot \frac{q}{n}.$$

Now, from the conditions determining p and q, we have

$$\frac{(p - 1)}{n} \cdot \frac{(q - 1)}{n} \le ab \le \frac{p}{n} \cdot \frac{q}{n}.$$

The numbers mT and ab both lie in the interval

$$\left[\frac{(p - 1)(q - 1)}{n^2}, \frac{pq}{n^2} \right],$$

so the absolute value of their difference is at most equal to the length of the interval:

$$\left| m(T) - ab \right| \leq \frac{pq}{n^2} - \frac{(p-1)(q-1)}{n^2} = \frac{p+q-1}{n^2}.$$

Since p/n^2 is approximately a/n and q/n^2 is approximately b/n, the right side is not much larger than $(1/n)(a+b)$, which is very small if n is large. To make this argument precise, observe that

$$p < na + 1,$$

$$q < nb + 1,$$

so

$$p + q - 1 < n(a + b) + 1 \leq n(a + b + 1),$$

$$\frac{p+q-1}{n^2} < \frac{a+b+1}{n}.$$

Therefore

$$\left| mT - ab \right| < \frac{a+b+1}{n} \qquad (n \in N).$$

Now the greatest lower bound of

$$\left\{ \frac{a+b+1}{n} \,\middle|\, n \in N \right\}$$

is 0, so

$$0 \leq \left| mT - ab \right| \leq 0,$$

$$mT = ab.$$

The method used in the preceding proof is of considerable interest. By enclosing the given region between two regions of known area, we were able to squeeze its area mT between two known numbers. We were able to find a number, ab, which was also squeezed between the same two numbers. This enabled us to estimate the difference between mT and ab. Because the length of the enclosing interval could be made arbitrarily small, by choosing n large, the constant difference $\left| mT - ab \right|$ was also shown to be arbitrarily small, therefore equal to 0.

An alternate approach is possible. Starting with the inequalities (1), we could deduce that

$$\text{l.u.b.}\left\{\frac{(p - 1)(q - 1)}{n^2} \,\Big|\, n \in N \right\} \le m(T),$$

$$m(T) \le \text{g.l.b.}\left\{\frac{pq}{n^2} \,\Big|\, n \in N \right\}.$$

Now if it could be proved that the l.u.b. and g.l.b. are equal, say to A, then we would know that $mT = A$. If also we could show that $A = ab$, the theorem would be proved.

This process of squeezing an unknown area between a g.l.b. and an l.u.b. is the basis for the classical calculation of the area of a circle. Indeed, as we shall see, there are many other areas which can be computed in the same way. The method is of fundamental importance in the integral calculus.

The next two theorems are quite standard. Their proofs are left to the student.

Theorem 7–14.   If S is a parallelogram with base and altitude of lengths b and h, then $mS = bh$ (Figure 7–5).

Theorem 7–15.   If T is a triangle with base and altitude of lengths b and h, then $mT = \frac{1}{2} bh$ (Figure 7–6).

Because every polygonal region can be subdivided into a finite number of "almost" disjoint triangles, its area can be calculated unambiguously, no matter what are a function is used. This provides us with a wide class of "decent" sets, but not quite wide enough. To make it wider, we recall the "squeezing process." Let S be a set for which there are sequences of polygonal regions P_n and Q_n satisfying

(1) $$P_n \subset S \subset Q_n$$

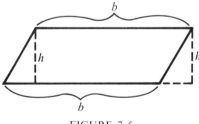

FIGURE 7-5

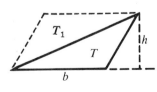

FIGURE 7-6

and

(2) $$\text{l.u.b.}\{mP_n | n \in N\} = \text{g.l.b.}\{mQ_n | n \in N\}.$$

Then it must be true that mS is equal to this common value, which does not depend on the area function being used. Therefore S will be a "decent" set. It can be shown that the collection $\mathbf{R}_0$ of sets of this type (they are called *Jordan sets*) is a ring. All area functions must agree on $\mathbf{R}_0$. We could, if we wished, restrict our attention to the Jordan sets, and then area would be defined uniquely.

Let us recapitulate the inclusion relations which hold between the various classes of sets under discussion. We denote by $\mathbf{P}$ the class of polygonal regions and by $\mathbf{U}$ the class of all bounded sets for which all area functions agree—the sets of uniqueness. Then we have

$$\mathbf{P} \subset \mathbf{R}_0 \subset \mathbf{U} \subset \mathbf{R}.$$

All three inclusions are proper. For example, a circle (plus interior) is a Jordan set (element of $\mathbf{R}_0$), which is not a polygonal region (element of $\mathbf{P}$).

The defining property (2) for Jordan sets may be paraphrased as follows. S is a Jordan set if it can be squeezed between two polygonal regions P and Q such that $m(Q - P)$ is arbitrarily small (Figure 7–7). In terms of the sequences (P_n) and (Q_n) above, this means that

(3) $$\text{g.l.b.}\{m(Q_i - P_j) | i,j \in N\} = 0.$$

EXERCISES 7–3

1. Carry out in detail the proofs of Theorems 7–10, 7–14, and 7–15.

2. What happens to the area of a rectangle if you double each of its sides? What about a parallelogram, keeping the angles fixed? The same for a triangle?

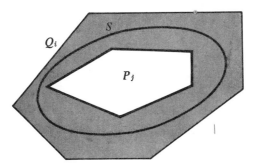

FIGURE 7–7

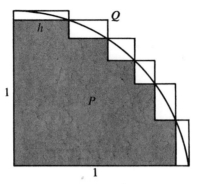

FIGURE 7–8

3. In Figure 7–8 S is the quarter-circle, P (shaded) is a polygonal region contained in S, Q is one containing S. If h is the length of the longest base of all the rectangles, show that $m(Q - P) \leq h$. Hence, prove that S is a Jordan set.

4. Show that the region S bounded by the curve $y = x^2$, the segment (0,0) to (1,0), and the segment (1,0) to (1,1) is a Jordan set (Figure 7–9).

5. In Problem 4 estimate the area of S by constructing appropriate polygonal regions P and Q such that $P \subset S \subset Q$.

6. Carry out the instructions of Problems 4 and 5 for the region T in Figure 7–10.

7. If A is the area of a circle of radius r, prove (without using the known formula for A) that $2r^2 < A < 4r^2$. Try to improve these estimates.

8. Let T be a right triangle. Show that the area of T can be approximated very closely by using unions of rectangles with sides parallel to the legs of T (Figure 7–11).

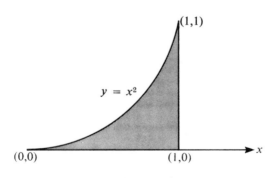

FIGURE 7–9

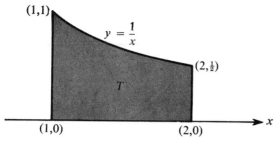

FIGURE 7–10

*9. Let f be a positive, increasing function on the interval $[a,b]$. That is, if $x,x' \in [a,b]$ and $x < x'$, then $f(x) < f(x')$. Let S be the set of points (x,y) such that $a \leq x \leq b$ and $0 \leq y \leq f(x)$. Show that S is a Jordan set (Figure 7–12).

*10. Prove that the union of two Jordan sets is also a Jordan set.

11. Discuss the advantages and disadvantages of restricting the area function to $\mathbf{P}$; to $\mathbf{R}_0$; to $\mathbf{U}$.

7–3. THE INTEGRAL

Let f be a real-valued function defined on the interval $[a,b]$. For the moment we shall assume that f is bounded and nonnegative. An important problem is to determine the area of the region T under the curve $y = f(x)$, above the x-axis, and between the verticals $x = a$ and $x = b$ (Figure 7–13).

We shall attempt to approximate mT above and below by the areas of polygonal regions of a special type, namely, finite unions of rectangles with bases on the x-axis. These regions will be of two kinds: those contained in T and those containing T.

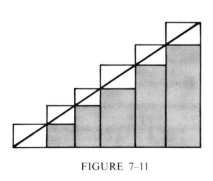

FIGURE 7–11

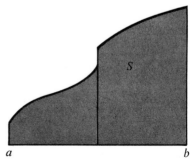

FIGURE 7–12

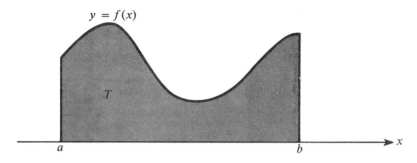

$y = f(x)$

FIGURE 7–13

Let s be the area of any one of the special regions contained in T. Then s will be called a *lower sum* (Figure 7–14). Similarly, if a special region contains T, its area S will be called an *upper sum* (Figure 7–15). Let L denote the set of all lower sums, U the set of all upper sums. It is clear that

$$s \leq mT \leq S \qquad (s \in L, S \in U).$$

Now if T is a bounded set, as we have assumed, then mT exists and is simultaneously an upper bound of L and a lower bound of U. Therefore L has a least upper bound $\underline{B}$, U has a greatest lower bound $\bar{B}$, and

$$\underline{B} \leq mT \leq \bar{B}.$$

Definition 7–5. If $\underline{B} = \bar{B}$, we say that f is *integrable* over $[a,b]$, and we define

$$\int_a^b f(x)\,dx = \underline{B} = \bar{B}.$$

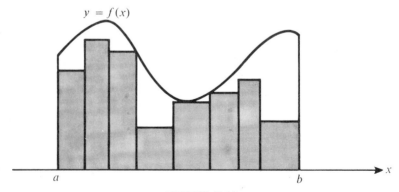

$y = f(x)$

FIGURE 7–14

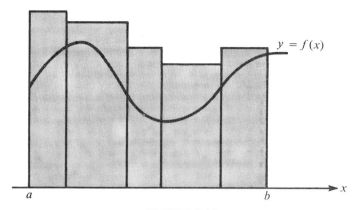

FIGURE 7–15

If f is integrable, then

$$mT = \int_a^b f(x)\,dx.$$

Furthermore, T is a Jordan set, in accordance with our discussion in Section 7–2. The converse is also true: If T is a Jordan set, then f is integrable over $[a,b]$. This is not too difficult to prove, but we shall not do so since we have no need for the result here.

Let us turn our attention to the formation of the upper and lower sums. Suppose that $[c,d]$ is a subinterval of $[a,b]$ which serves as a base for one of the rectangles in a special region contained in T. If h is the height of the rectangle, then for each $x \in [c,d]$, $h \leq f(x)$. Hence

$$h \leq \text{g.l.b.}\{f(x)|x \in [c,d]\}.$$

Now if h were actually less than this g.l.b., as in the case of the fourth rectangle in Figure 7–14, we could increase the height of that rectangle and get a larger lower sum, and therefore a better approximation to mT. Thus, there is no real loss if we assume always that

$$h = \text{g.l.b.}\{f(x)|x \in [c,d]\}.$$

If we do make this assumption, then the lower sum depends only on the set of bases of our rectangles, or on the set of their endpoints. Let

$$a = x_0 < x_1 < x_2 < \cdots < x_n = b$$

be these endpoints, and let

$$y_1 = \text{g.l.b.}\{f(x)|x_0 \le x \le x_1\},$$
$$y_2 = \text{g.l.b.}\{f(x)|x_1 \le x \le x_2\},$$

.

.

.

$$y_n = \text{g.l.b.}\{f(x)|x_{n-1} \le x \le x_n\}.$$

Then the corresponding lower sum is

$$s = y_1(x_1 - x_0) + y_2(x_2 - x_1) + \cdots + y_n(x_n - x_{n-1})$$
$$= \sum_{i=1}^{n} y_i(x_i - x_{i-1}).$$

Similarly, if we assume that a special region containing T satisfies the condition that the height of each rectangle is as small as possible, we get an upper sum of the form

$$S = \sum_{i=1}^{n} Y_i(x_i - x_{i-1}),$$

where

$$Y_i = \text{l.u.b.}\{f(x)|x_{i-1} \le x \le x_i\} \qquad (i = 1, \ldots, n).$$

These remarks have an important consequence. Suppose that f is *nondecreasing* on $[a,b]$; that is,

$$\forall x,y \in [a,b], x \le y \to f(x) \le f(y).$$

Let $\{x_0,x_1,x_2,\ldots,x_n\}$ be the points of subdivision of $[a,b]$ leading to an upper sum S and a lower sum s of the particular type just described (Figure 7–16). The g.l.b. of f on each interval $[x_{i-1},x_i]$ is easily seen to be the value of f at x_{i-1}; in fact, this is the minimum value of f in the interval. Thus

$$y_1 = f(x_0),$$
$$y_2 = f(x_1),$$

.

.

.

$$y_n = f(x_{n-1}),$$

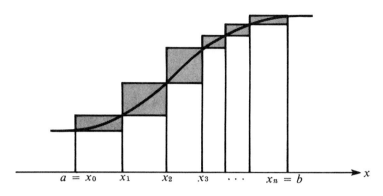

FIGURE 7-16

SO

$$s = f(x_0)(x_1 - x_0) + f(x_1)(x_2 - x_1) + \cdots + f(x_{n-1})(x_n - x_{n-1}).$$

Similarly,

$$Y_1 = f(x_1),$$
$$Y_2 = f(x_2),$$

.
.
.

$$Y_n = f(x_n),$$

and

$$S = f(x_1)(x_1 - x_0) + f(x_2)(x_2 - x_1) + \cdots + f(x_n)(x_n - x_{n-1}).$$

Now the difference between these sums is

$$S - s = (f(x_1) - f(x_0))(x_1 - x_0) + (f(x_2) - f(x_1))(x_2 - x_1)$$
$$+ \cdots + (f(x_n) - f(x_{n-1}))(x_n - x_{n-1})$$
$$= \sum_{i=1}^{n} (f(x_i) - f(x_{i-1}))(x_i - x_{i-1}).$$

Geometrically, this difference is the sum of the areas of the shaded rectangles in Figure 7-16. Let δ be the largest of the differences $x_i - x_{i-1}$. Since $f(x_i) - f(x_{i-1}) \geq 0$, we have

$$(f(x_i) - f(x_{i-1}))(x_i - x_{i-1}) \leq (f(x_i) - f(x_{i-1}))\delta,$$

for all $i = 1, 2, \ldots, n$. Adding up all these inequalities, we get

$$S - s \leq \sum_{i=1}^{n} (f(x_i) - f(x_{i-1}))\delta$$

$$= \delta\{(f(x_1) - f(x_0)) + (f(x_2) - f(x_1)) + \cdots + (f(x_n) - f(x_{n-1}))\}$$

$$= \delta(f(x_n) - f(x_0))$$

(1) $$S - s \leq \delta(f(b) - f(a)).$$

Since $\delta > 0$ is completely at our disposal, we can make the right side smaller than any given positive number. This means that

$$\text{g.l.b.}\{S - s\} = 0.$$

In other words, there are upper and lower sums arbitrarily near to each other. As we have seen, this is equivalent to $\underline{B} = \bar{B}$, the integrability of f over $[a,b]$. Thus we have proved an important result:

Theorem 7–16. If f is nondecreasing over $[a,b]$, then it is integrable over $[a,b]$.

A similar argument shows that we can replace "nondecreasing" by "nonincreasing"; that is,

$$\forall x,y \in [a,b], x \leq y \rightarrow f(x) \geq f(y).$$

If f is either nondecreasing or nonincreasing over $[a,b]$, we say that it is *monotonic* on $[a,b]$. Thus:

Theorem 7–17. If f is monotonic on $[a,b]$, it is integrable over $[a,b]$.

Since many of the functions we meet are monotonic, at least over some intervals, Theorem 7–17 is very useful. Furthermore, the inequality (1) gives us valuable practical information. A generalization of (1) which is valid for both cases of monotonicity is

(2) $$S - s \leq \delta|f(b) - f(a)|.$$

Since $\int_a^b f(x)\, dx$ lies in the interval $[s,S]$, any number in that interval will supply us with an approximation to the integral, with an error at most equal to $S - s$, and inequality (2) gives us an upper estimate for the error.

EXAMPLE 7–5.   Estimate $\int_0^1 x^2\, dx$ with an error no greater than $\frac{1}{10}$.
Solution: Choose $x_0 = 0$, $x_1 = .2$, $x_2 = .4$, $x_3 = .6$, $x_4 = .8$, $x_5 = 1$.

The corresponding lower sum is

$$s = 0^2(.2) + (.2)^2(.2) + (.4)^2(.2) + (.6)^2(.2) + (.8)^2(.2)$$

$$= (.2)(.1)^2(2^2 + 4^2 + 6^2 + 8^2)$$

$$= (.002) \cdot 2^2(1^2 + 2^2 + 3^2 + 4^2)$$

$$= (.008)(30) = .24.$$

The corresponding upper sum is

$$S = (.2)^2(.2) + (.4)^2(.2) + (.6)^2(.2) + (.8)^2(.2) + (1)^2(.2)$$

$$= (.2)(.1)^2(2^2 + 4^2 + 6^2 + 8^2 + 10^2)$$

$$= (.002) \cdot 2^2(1^2 + 2^2 + 3^2 + 4^2 + 5^2)$$

$$= (.008)(55) = .44.$$

As predicted by inequality (2), the difference $S - s$ is no greater than $\delta|f(b) - f(a)| = .2(1^2 - 0^2) = .2$. If we choose as our approximation the midpoint of the interval $[s,S] = [.24, .44]$, we get

$$\int_0^1 x^2 \, dx \doteq .34,$$

with an error certainly no greater than $\frac{1}{2}(S - s) = .1$. Actually, the error is much smaller.

An interesting special case arises when we choose all the subintervals to be of equal length. Since their total length is $b - a$, this common length is

$$\delta = \frac{b - a}{n}.$$

Thus, for a nondecreasing function,

$$S = \delta(f(x_1) + f(x_2) + \cdots + f(x_n))$$

$$= \frac{b - a}{n}(f(x_1) + f(x_2) + \cdots + f(x_n)).$$

Since the integral is approximated by S, we see that

$$\frac{1}{b - a}\int_a^b f(x) \, dx \doteq \frac{1}{n}\sum_{i=1}^n f(x_i).$$

This means that the number on the left may be interpreted as an *average* of the function f. In fact, we *define* the average of any function f over

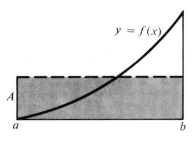

$$y = f(x)$$

$$A$$

$$a \qquad\qquad\qquad b$$

FIGURE 7–17

$[a,b]$ as the height of that constant function which yields the same area as f over $[a,b]$, we find

$$(b - a)A = \int_a^b f(x)\,dx,$$

$$A = \frac{1}{b - a}\int_a^b f(x)\,dx.$$

In Figure 7–17 the shaded rectangle has an area equal to the area under the curve.

EXERCISE 7–4

Suppose that f is monotonic on $[a,b]$, and that we form the upper and lower sums S and s by choosing n equal subintervals. Prove that

$$S - s = \frac{b - a}{n}|f(b) - f(a)|.$$

So far we have restricted ourselves to nonnegative functions. To remove the restriction, we shall temporarily abandon the area interpretation of the integral, but retain Definition 7–5, with an appropriate meaning for the upper and lower sums. Suppose that f is a bounded function defined on $[a,b]$; that is, there is a positive number k such that

$$-k \leq f(x) \leq k \qquad (x \in [a,b]).$$

For every subdivision

$$a = x_0 < x_1 < x_2 < \cdots < x_n = b$$

we define, as before,

$$\left.\begin{matrix} y_i \\ Y_i \end{matrix}\right\} = \left.\begin{matrix} \text{g.l.b.} \\ \text{l.u.b.} \end{matrix}\right\} \{f(x)|x_{i-1} \leq x \leq x_i\} \qquad (i = 1, \ldots, n).$$

These exist, because f is bounded. Again, we define the lower and upper sums,

$$s = \sum_{i=1}^{n} y_i(x_i - x_{i-1}),$$

$$S = \sum_{i=1}^{n} Y_i(x_i - x_{i-1}).$$

It will still be true (though not quite obvious) that *every* lower sum is less than or equal to *every* upper sum, whether they come from the same subdivision or not. It follows that

$$\underline{B} = \text{l.u.b.}\{s\}, \bar{B} = \text{g.l.b.}\{S\}$$

both exist, and that $\underline{B} \leq \bar{B}$. Now we can take over Definition 7–5 word for word as the general definition of integrability and integral. If $f \geq 0$ on $[a,b]$, the two definitions coincide, and the integral may be interpreted as an ordinary area.

Now suppose that $f \leq 0$ on $[a,b]$. Define

$$g(x) = -f(x) \geq 0 \qquad (a \leq x \leq b).$$

Choose an arbitrary subdivision as above, and let y_i', Y_i' be the g.l.b.'s and l.u.b.'s associated with g and the intervals of this subdivision. It should be fairly clear that $Y_i' = -y_i$ and $y_i' = -Y_i$. Hence, if s is any lower sum for f, $-s$ will be an upper sum for g, and conversely. Similarly, if S is an upper sum for f, then $-S$ will be a lower sum for g, and conversely. It follows from these statements that

(3) $$\int_a^b f(x)\,dx = -\int_a^b g(x)\,dx.$$

The situation is illustrated in Figure 7–18. Now $g \geq 0$, so $\int_a^b g(x)\,dx = mT'$ $= mT$, since $T \cong T'$. Therefore

(4) $$\int_a^b f(x)\,dx = -mT.$$

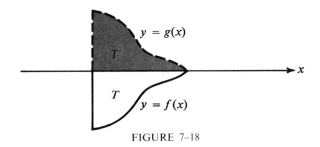

FIGURE 7–18

The upshot of our discussion is this: If the region between the curve $y = f(x)$ and the x-axis lies below the axis, the integral represents the area taken with the negative sign.

Actually, the proof of Eq. (3) did not involve the hypothesis that $f \leq 0$. Therefore, in general,

$$(5) \qquad \int_a^b (-f(x))\, dx = -\int_a^b f(x)\, dx.$$

We now state, without proof, two important properties of the integral.

Theorem 7–18. If $a < c < b$ and if f is integrable over $[a,b]$, then f is integrable over $[a,c]$ and $[c,b]$, and

$$(6) \qquad \int_a^b f(x)\, dx = \int_a^c f(x)\, dx + \int_c^b f(x)\, dx.$$

Conversely, if f is integrable over $[a,c]$ and $[c,b]$, then it is integrable over $[a,b]$.

Theorem 7–19. If f and g are integrable over $[a,b]$, then $f + g$ is integrable over $[a,b]$, and

$$(7) \qquad \int_a^b (f(x) + g(x))\, dx = \int_a^b f(x)\, dx + \int_a^b g(x)\, dx.$$

As an application of Theorem 7–18, consider a function of the kind illustrated in Figure 7–19, taking positive and negative values over various subintervals. Using Theorem 7–18 and Eq. (4), we have

$$\int_a^b f(x)\, dx = \int_a^r f(x)\, dx + \int_r^s f(x)\, dx + \int_s^t f(x)\, dx + \int_t^u f(x)\, dx + \int_u^b f(x)\, dx$$

$$= mT_1 - mT_2 + mT_3 - mT_4 + mT_5.$$

Thus, the integral may be interpreted as the *signed area* of the region T between the curve and the x-axis.

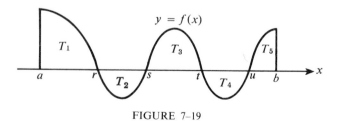

FIGURE 7–19

It is convenient to introduce the following definition:

Definition 7–6. If $a < b$ and f is integrable over $[a,b]$, then

$$\int_b^a f(x)\,dx =_{\text{df}} - \int_a^b f(x)\,dx.$$

Also, for any f,

$$\int_a^a f(x)\,dx = 0.$$

It follows that Eq. (6) is satisfied no matter what the relative order of a, b, c; indeed, this was the motivation behind Definition 7–6. The student should verify a few of the cases as an exercise. Of course, it is assumed that f is integrable over all the intervals mentioned.

With our new definitions of the integral, Theorem 7–17 is still valid. Using it together with Theorem 7–18, we see that if f is monotonic over each of the intervals $[a_1,a_2]$, $[a_2,a_3],\dots$, $[a_{k-1},a_k]$, then it is integrable over $[a_1,a_k]$. This gives us a very wide class of integrable functions. Most of the functions of elementary analysis are of this type, called *piecewise monotonic*.

Suppose that f is integrable over $[a,b]$. Define $g(x) = cf(x)$ $(x \in [a,b])$, where c is a positive constant. Let s, S denote lower and upper sums for f, and let s', S' be lower and upper sums for g. It should be clear that every s' is cs for some s, every S' is cS for some S; conversely, every cs is an s', every cS is an S'. From this it follows that

$$\int_a^b g(x)\,dx = c \int_a^b f(x)\,dx,$$

or, substituting for g,

$$\int_a^b (cf(x))\,dx = c \int_a^b f(x)\,dx.$$

Combining this result with Eq. (5), we have

Theorem 7–20. If f is integrable over $[a,b]$, and if c is a real number, then cf is integrable over $[a,b]$ and

(8) $$\int_a^b cf(x)\,dx = c \int_a^b f(x)\,dx.$$

This holds even if $b \leq a$, by Definition 7–6.

Theorems 7–19 and 7–20 together provide us with an interesting example of a vector space (see Chapter 5). Let W be the set of all functions integrable over $[a,b]$. Then W is a vector space: It is closed under addition and multiplication by scalars, and the other properties are easily checked. Let J be the function from W to R defined by

$$J(f) = \int_a^b f(x)\,dx \qquad (f \in W).$$

Then Eqs. (7) and (8) tell us that J is a *linear mapping* from W to R. W is an infinite-dimensional vector space.

A simple but useful property of the integral allows us to make estimates: If $f \le g$, that is, $f(x) \le g(x)$ $(x \in [a,b])$, and if f, $g \in W$, then $J(f) \le J(g)$. For

$$J(g) - J(f) = J(g - f) = \int_a^b (g(x) - f(x))\,dx \ge 0,$$

since the integral of a nonnegative function is nonnegative.

EXERCISE 7–5

If f and $|f|$ are in W, show that

$$\int_a^b f(x)\,dx \le \int_a^b |f(x)|\,dx,$$

$$\int_a^b f(x)\,dx \ge - \int_a^b |f(x)|\,dx,$$

$$\left| \int_a^b f(x)\,dx \right| \le \int_a^b |f(x)|\,dx.$$

Theorem 7–20 may be thought of in the following way: If the region T is stretched by a factor c in the vertical direction, then the signed area of T is multiplied by c (Figure 7–20).

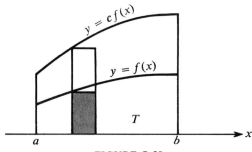

FIGURE 7–20

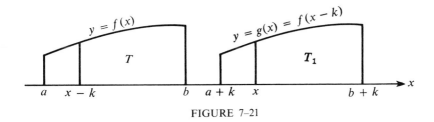

FIGURE 7–21

There are other simple changes we can make in T with predictable results. For example, we can shift T horizontally by k units, and the area will not be changed (Figure 7–21). Of course the function will be a new one, say g, defined on the interval $[a + k, b + k]$. If $x \in [a + k, b + k]$, the value of g at x will be the same as the value of f at $x - k$. Thus

$$g(x) = f(x - k) \qquad (x \in [a + k, b + k]).$$

Since $T_1 \cong T$, the integrals will be equal. We have therefore proved:

Theorem 7–21. If f is integrable over $[a,b]$, then

(9)
$$\int_{a+k}^{b+k} f(x - k)\, dx = \int_{a}^{b} f(x)\, dx$$

for every real k.

Another change that we can make is to stretch T by a factor $c > 0$ in the horizontal direction. The interval $[a,b]$ is changed into $[ca,cb]$ (Figure 7–22). If g is the new function, then

$$g(x) = f(x/c) \qquad (x \in [ca,cb]).$$

For every union of rectangles approximating T there is a corresponding union of rectangles, stretched horizontally by a factor c, which will

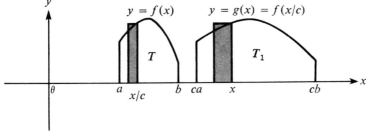

FIGURE 7–22

approximate T_1. Corresponding heights will be the same. Therefore the signed area of T_1 is c times that of T, and

$$\int_{ca}^{cb} g(x)\,dx = c \int_{a}^{b} f(x)\,dx,$$

that is,

$$\int_{ca}^{cb} f(x/c)\,dx = c \int_{a}^{b} f(x)\,dx \qquad (c > 0).$$

An alternate form is obtained by writing the equation in terms of g. Because

$$f(x) = g(cx) \qquad (x \in [a,b]),$$

$$\int_{ca}^{cb} g(x)\,dx = c \int_{a}^{b} g(cx)\,dx \qquad (c > 0).$$

In this form, the equation still holds for $c = 0$. We leave it to the student as an exercise to show that it also holds for $c = -1$, hence for all real c.

Theorem 7–22.   If g is integrable over $[ca,cb]$, then

(10) $$\int_{ca}^{cb} g(x)\,dx = c \int_{a}^{b} g(cx)\,dx,$$

for all real c.

For $c > 0$, Eq. (10) may be transformed into

$$\frac{1}{cb - ca}\int_{ca}^{cb} g(x)\,dx = \frac{1}{b - a}\int_{a}^{b} g(cx)\,dx.$$

This has the very reasonable interpretation that the *averages* of the two functions over their respective domains are equal. Loosely speaking, each function spends the same *proportion* of its time near any given value.

Several remarks about the symbols used in integration are in order. The integral sign is merely an elongated S, standing for summation. Its use arose from the intuitive idea that the area of T may be obtained by summing many little pieces or elements of area, as in Figure 7–23. Each element of area consists of a rectangle of height $f(x)$ and base Δx. Thus we obtain

$$mT = \mathop{S}_{x=a}^{x=b} f(x)\Delta x.$$

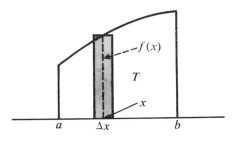

FIGURE 7–23

As we have seen, it is indeed possible to approximate the area by means of lower sums like

$$\sum y_i(x_i - x_{i-1}) = \sum y_i\Delta x_i,$$

where we have put $\Delta x_i = x_i - x_{i-1}$. The upper sums may be written as

$$\sum Y_i\Delta x_i,$$

and they also approximate the area. Since

$$y_i \leq f(x) \leq Y_i \qquad (x_{i-1} \leq x \leq x_i),$$

an arbitrary choice of x in each interval, say x_i', will lead to a sum

$$\sum_{i=1}^{n} f(x_i')\Delta x_i$$

which lies in $[s,S]$. This will also be a good approximation to the area.
   The variable "x" in

$$\int_a^b f(x)\,dx$$

acts like a summation index. It may be replaced by any other not already in use. Thus

$$\int_a^b f(x)\,dx = \int_a^b f(t)\,dt = \int_a^b f(u)\,du.$$

EXERCISES 7–6

1. By subdividing $[0,1]$ into five equal parts, estimate

$$\int_0^1 x^3\,dx.$$

Estimate the error.

2. By subdividing [1,2] into five equal parts, estimate

$$\int_1^2 \frac{1}{x}\,dx.$$

Estimate the error.

3. By subdividing [3,6] into five equal parts, estimate

$$\int_3^6 \frac{1}{x}\,dx.$$

4. By subdividing [0,1] into five equal parts, estimate

$$\int_0^1 \frac{1}{x+1}\,dx.$$

5. Prove, for integrable f, that

$$\int_0^1 f(1-x)\,dx = \int_0^1 f(x)\,dx.$$

6. Prove

$$\int_0^1 (1-x)^2\,dx = 1 - 2\int_0^1 x\,dx + \int_0^1 x^2\,dx.$$

Using Problem 5, in the form

$$\int_0^1 (1-x)^2\,dx = \int_0^1 x^2\,dx, \text{ evaluate } \int_0^1 x\,dx.$$

7. Using Theorem 7–22, prove that for all $c \in R$,

(a) $\displaystyle\int_0^c x\,dx = c^2 \int_0^1 x\,dx.$

(b) $\displaystyle\int_0^c x^2\,dx = c^3 \int_0^1 x^2\,dx.$

(c) $\displaystyle\int_0^c x^3\,dx = c^4 \int_0^1 x^3\,dx.$

8. Prove

$$\int_1^2 \frac{2\,dx}{1+4x^2} = \int_2^4 \frac{dt}{1+t^2}.$$

9. Suppose that $f(-x) = f(x)$ $(x \in R)$. Prove

$$\int_{-3}^{3} f(x)\,dx = 2 \int_{0}^{3} f(x)\,dx.$$

(Of course, assume integrability.)

10. Suppose that $f(-x) = -f(x)(x \in R)$. Prove

$$\int_{a}^{a} f(x)\,dx = 0.$$

(Assume integrability.)

11. A particle moves with decreasing speed in a straight line. Following are observed speeds at various times:

t, sec	0	.1	.2	.25	.3	.5
v, cm/sec	15	13	10	9	8	6

Estimate the distance traveled in the time interval $[0, .5]$. Give an upper bound for the error.

12. At each time t between t_0 and t_1, the speed of a particle moving in a straight line is $v(t) > 0$. Let d be the distance between the positions at t_0 and t_1. If s is a lower sum for v over $[t_0,t_1]$, S an upper sum, show that $s \le d \le S$. Give an interpretation for $\int_{t_0}^{t_1} v(t)\,dt$, if v is integrable over $[t_0,t_1]$.

13. Write down an integral for the mass of a rod of variable linear density (mass per unit length) $d(x)$, Figure 7–24.

14. Write down an integral for the volume of a solid of variable cross-sectional area $A(x)$, Figure 7–25.

15. Let $u(t)$ be the rate of decay of a radioactive substance at time t. Interpret

$$\int_{t_0}^{t_1} u(t)\,dt.$$

*16. Prove

$$\int_{0}^{1} x^2\,dx + \int_{0}^{1} \sqrt{x}\,dx = 1.$$

$y = d(x)$

0   L x

FIGURE 7–24

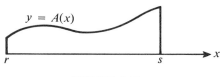

FIGURE 7–25

7–4. THE INTEGRAL OF x^n

In this section we shall evaluate the integral

$$\int_a^b x^n \, dx \qquad (n = 0,1,2,\ldots)$$

explicitly.

First of all, we observe that

$$\int_a^b x^n \, dx = \int_0^b x^n \, dx - \int_0^a x^n \, dx,$$

so it is sufficient to evaluate

$$F(c) = \int_0^c x^n \, dx \qquad (c \in R).$$

Next, let us apply Theorem 7–22, with $g(x) = x^n$ $(x \in R)$, and the special values $a = 0$ and $b = 1$. We get

$$\int_0^c x^n \, dx = c \int_0^1 (cx)^n \, dx = c^{n+1} \int_0^1 x^n \, dx.$$

Therefore

$$F(c) = A_n c^{n+1} \qquad (c \in R),$$

where A_n depends on n but not on c:

$$A_n = \int_0^1 x^n \, dx.$$

Thus

(1) $$\int_a^b x^n \, dx = F(b) - F(a) = A_n(b^{n+1} - a^{n+1}).$$

It remains to determine the constant A_n. The technique that we use is quite simple, in principle, although it requires some attention to detail to make it work. Let us first sketch the method. In Figure 7–26 we propose to look at the area of the shaded region in two different ways. On the one hand, it is given by the integral

$$\int_1^b x^n \, dx = A_n(b^{n+1} - 1),$$

from Eq. (1) above. On the other hand, we can estimate the area by means of the rectangles contained in and containing the region. The smaller rectangle has base $b - 1$ and altitude 1, so its area is $b - 1$. The larger rectangle has base $b - 1$ and altitude b^n, so its area is $(b - 1)b^n$. Therefore

$$b - 1 \leq A_n(b^{n+1} - 1) \leq (b - 1)b^n \qquad (b > 1).$$

Dividing through by $b - 1$, we have

$$1 \leq A_n\left(\frac{b^{n+1} - 1}{b - 1}\right) \leq b^n \qquad (b > 1).$$

Now it is well known and easy to prove that

$$\frac{b^{n+1} - 1}{b - 1} = b^n + b^{n-1} + \cdots + b + 1,$$

so

(2) $$1 \leq A_n(b^n + b^{n-1} + \cdots + b + 1) \leq b^n \qquad (b > 1).$$

At this point, an incorrect step would be to put $b = 1$ in inequalities (2) and get

$$1 \leq A_n(n + 1) \leq 1.$$

$$\therefore \quad A_n = \frac{1}{n + 1}.$$

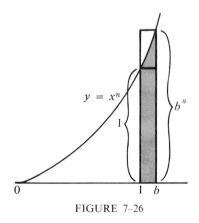

$$y = x^n$$

$$b^n$$

$$1$$

FIGURE 7–26

It is incorrect because (2) was derived only for $b > 1$. Nevertheless, the idea is a good one.

To make the argument precise, we take greatest lower bounds in (2):

$$(3) \qquad 1 \le A_n \, \text{g.l.b.}\{b^n + \cdots + 1 | b > 1\} \le \text{g.l.b.}\{b^n | b > 1\} = 1,$$

so

$$(4) \qquad A_n \, \text{g.l.b.}\{b^n + \cdots + 1 | b > 1\} = 1.$$

Now $b^n + \cdots + 1$ is a sum of $n + 1$ terms, each between 1 and b^n. Therefore,

$$n + 1 \le b^n + \cdots + 1 \le (n + 1)b^n,$$

$$n + 1 \le \text{g.l.b.}\{b^n + \cdots + 1 | b > 1\} \le (n + 1) \, \text{g.l.b.}\{b^n | b > 1\} = n + 1,$$

so

$$\text{g.l.b.}\{b^n + \cdots + 1 | b > 1\} = n + 1.$$

Substituting in Eq. (4), we get

$$A_n = \frac{1}{n + 1},$$

as desired. This, together with Eq. (1), proves the important result

$$(5) \qquad \int_a^b x^n \, dx = \frac{1}{n + 1}(b^{n+1} - a^{n+1}) \qquad (a, b \in R, n \ge 0).$$

In the course of the proof we have used the following facts, which we ask the student to prove as exercises.

EXERCISES 7–7

1. Prove: If $f(b) \le g(b)$ for all $b > 1$, then

$$\text{g.l.b.}\{f(b) | b > 1\} \le \text{g.l.b.}\{g(b) | b > 1\}.$$

2. Prove:

$$\text{g.l.b.}\{b^n | b > 1\} = 1 \qquad (n = 0, 1, 2, \ldots).$$

[*Hint:* Put $b = 1 + h$, $0 < h \le 1$, and show by induction on n (or otherwise) that

$$(1 + h)^n \le 1 + (2^n - 1)h \qquad (n = 0, 1, \ldots).$$

Thus, to make $(1 + h)^n < 1 + p$, say, choose $h < p/(2^n - 1)$.]

By using formula (5) above and Theorems 7–19 and 7–20, we can evaluate the integral of any polynomial function

$$p(x) = c_0 + c_1x + c_2x^2 + \cdots + c_nx^n \qquad (x \in R).$$

EXAMPLE 7–6.   Find the area under the curve

$$y = 2 + 4x + 3x^2$$

between $x = 2$ and $x = 3$.

Solution: $A = \int_2^3 (2 + 4x + 3x^2)\,dx$

$$= \int_2^3 2\,dx + 4 \int_2^3 x\,dx + 3 \int_2^3 x^2\,dx$$

$$= 2 + 4\left(\frac{3^2 - 2^2}{2}\right) + 3\left(\frac{3^3 - 2^3}{3}\right)$$

$$= 31.$$

EXERCISES 7–8

1. Evaluate the following integrals:

(a) $\int_3^4 (3x^2 + 2x^3)\,dx.$

(b) $\int_0^1 (1 + x + x^2 + x^3 + x^4)\,dx.$

(c) $\int_{-2}^2 (5 + 2x + 3x^3 + 17x^5)\,dx.$

(d) $\int_0^c \dfrac{1 - x^4}{1 + x}\,dx \qquad (c > 0).$

2. For $c > 0$, show that

$$0 < \int_0^c \frac{x^4}{1 + x}\,dx \le \frac{c^5}{5}.$$

3. Suppose that $a, b, c > 0$. Prove that

$$\int_{ca}^{cb} \frac{dx}{x} = \int_a^b \frac{dx}{x}.$$

4. Suppose that a, b, $c > 0$. Prove that

$$\int_{ca}^{cb} \frac{dx}{x^2} = \frac{1}{c} \int_{a}^{b} \frac{dx}{x^2}.$$

5. Prove that

$$\int_{0}^{1} (1 + x)^{100}\, dx = \frac{2^{101} - 1}{101}.$$

6. Evaluate

(a) $\int_{0}^{1} (4 + 4x)^{12}\, dx.$

(b) $\int_{2}^{5} (6 + 2x)^{10}\, dx.$

(c) $\int_{-1}^{3} (1 + 5x)^{7}\, dx.$

7. Prove by induction on $n \geq 1$ that

$$(1 + h)^n \geq 1 + nh \qquad (h \geq -1).$$

8. Solve for T (v_0 and g are constants):

$$\int_{0}^{T} (v_0 - gt)\, dt = 0.$$

9. The linear density of a rod of length L at every point is proportional to the distance from that point to one end. Prove that the mass of the rod is proportional to L^2.

10. Find three functions f such that

$$\int_{0}^{1} f(u)\, du = 0.$$

11. For $h > 0$, show that

$$9 < \frac{1}{h} \int_{3}^{3+h} x^2\, dx < 9 + 6h + h^2.$$

12. Let E be a function from R into R, taking only positive values, and satisfying

$$E(x) = 1 + \int_{0}^{x} E(t)\, dt \qquad (x \in R).$$

Prove:

(a) $E(x) - E(y) = \int_y^x E(t)\,dt \qquad (x, y \in R).$

(b) $x \geq y \to E(x) \geq E(y) \qquad (x, y \in R).$

(c) $x \geq 0 \to E(x) \geq 1 \qquad (x \in R).$

(d) $E(x) \geq 1 + \int_0^x dt = 1 + x \qquad (x \geq 0).$

(e) $E(x) \geq 1 + \int_0^x (1 + t)\,dt = 1 + x + \dfrac{x^2}{2} \qquad (x \geq 0).$

(f) $E(x) \geq 1 + x + \dfrac{x^2}{2} + \dfrac{x^3}{2 \cdot 3} \qquad (x \geq 0).$

(g) $E(x) \geq 1 + \dfrac{x}{1!} + \dfrac{x^2}{2!} + \cdots + \dfrac{x^n}{n!} \qquad (n \geq 0, x \geq 0).$

Let $E(1) = e$. Prove:

(h) $E(x) \leq 1 + \int_0^x e\,dt = 1 + ex \qquad (0 \leq x \leq 1).$

(i) $E(x) \leq 1 + \int_0^x (1 + et)\,dt = 1 + x + e\dfrac{x^2}{2} \qquad (0 \leq x \leq 1).$

(j) $E(x) \leq 1 + x + \dfrac{x^2}{2} + e\dfrac{x^3}{2 \cdot 3} \qquad (0 \leq x \leq 1).$

(k) $E(x) \leq 1 + \dfrac{x}{1!} + \dfrac{x^2}{2!} + \cdots + \dfrac{x^n}{n!} + e\dfrac{x^{n+1}}{(n+1)!} \qquad (n \geq 0, 0 \leq x \leq 1).$

(l) Put $x = 1$ in (j) to obtain $e \leq 3$.

(m) Using (g) and (k), estimate $E(.1)$ with an error $< .0001$.

13. Starting with Eq. (1), p. 318, show that

(a) $\int_0^1 (1 + x)\,dx = 1 + A_1.$

(b) $\int_0^1 (1 + x)\,dx = \int_1^2 x\,dx = A_1(2^2 - 1^2).$

(c) $A_1 = \tfrac{1}{2}.$

14. Starting with Eq. (1) and Problem 13, show that

(a) $\int_0^1 (1 + x)^2 \, dx = 1 + 2A_1 + A_2$.

(b) $\int_0^1 (1 + x)^2 \, dx = \int_1^2 x^2 \, dx = A_2(2^3 - 1^3)$.

(c) $A_2 = \frac{1}{3}$.

15. Use the method and results of Problems 13 and 14 to show that

(a) $A_3 = \frac{1}{4}$.
(b) $A_4 = \frac{1}{5}$.

7–5. THE LOGARITHM AND THE EXPONENTIAL

One of the most important functions of analysis for theoretical and practical purposes is the exponential

$$f(x) = e^x \qquad (x \in R).$$

Here e is a certain constant, approximately equal to 2.71828. The importance of the exponential function stems from the fact that it satisfies the equation

(1) $$e^{x+y} = e^x \cdot e^y \qquad (x, y \in R),$$

or, in functional notation,

(2) $$f(x + y) = f(x)f(y) \qquad (x, y \in R).$$

For positive integers n, the values of the exponential are familiar to us:

$$e^1 = e, \;\; e^2 = e \cdot e, \;\; e^3 = e^2 \cdot e^1 = e \cdot e \cdot e,$$

and so on. Also $e^0 = 1$, and

$$e^{-1} = \frac{1}{e}, \;\; e^{-2} = \frac{1}{e^2}, \;\; e^{-3} = \frac{1}{e^3},$$

and so on. Putting $x = y = \frac{1}{2}$ in Eq. (1), we get $e = e^{1/2} \cdot e^{1/2}$, so that $e^{1/2} = \sqrt{e}$. Similarly, $e^{1/n}$ is the nth root of e. Because $e^{m/n} = e^{1/n + \cdots + 1/n} = (e^{1/n})^m$, the meaning of e^x is clear for all rational values of x. But what about irrational values? For example, what is the meaning of $e^{\sqrt{2}}$, or e^π?

Before attempting to answer these questions, we remark that a much more fundamental question has been bypassed. Does there really exist an exponential function? More precisely, does there exist a monotonic increasing function f such that $f(1) = e$ and such that the functional Eq. (2) holds? We have implicitly assumed an affirmative answer. Under these assumptions we can show how to evaluate $f(x)$ for every real number x. Thus f is uniquely determined by the conditions stated above. Furthermore, we can prove that f is a one-to-one correspondence between R and the positive reals R^+. The inverse of f is therefore also a function, with domain R^+; it is called the logarithm. Thus, for all $x \in R^+$ and $y \in R$,

$$y = \log x$$

is equivalent to

$$x = e^y.$$

From this definition we can prove the characteristic property of the logarithm:

(3) $$\log (ab) = \log a + \log b \qquad (a,b \in R^+).$$

We have just sketched rapidly a possible way to develop the elementary theory of the exponential and logarithmic functions. It is not the path that we shall take, however. Instead, we shall first give an independent definition of the logarithmic function, then prove that it satisfies Eq. (3) and that it is a one-to-one correspondence between R^+ and R. Next we shall define the exponential as the inverse of the logarithm, and finally we shall prove that the exponential has all the properties required above. In this way we shall have proved the fundamental assertion about the existence of the exponential function by actually constructing it. In the course of our admittedly unhistorical development of the theory, we shall show how two important concepts are surprisingly and beautifully related. The first—the exponential function—we have already discussed. The second is the area under the hyperbola $y = 1/x$ between two abscissas a and b.

EXERCISES 7–9

1. Prove Eq. (3) on the basis of what has been stated before it.
2. Assuming Eq. (3), prove that

$$\log a^n = n \log a \qquad (a \in R^+, n \in N).$$

3. Assuming Eq. (3), prove that

$$\log \frac{1}{a} = - \log a \qquad (a \in R^+).$$

7–6. THE INTEGRAL OF $1/x$

The graph of $y = 1/x$ ($x \neq 0$) is shown in Figure 7–27. Since the function is not defined at 0 and "blows up" badly for x near 0, we do not attempt to integrate over an interval containing 0. If the endpoints are negative, the fact that the two shaded regions in Figure 7–27 are congruent shows that

$$\int_{-b}^{-a} \frac{dx}{x} = -\int_{a}^{b} \frac{dx}{x}.$$

Therefore we may confine our attention to integrating over intervals $[a,b]$ with $a,b > 0$. It is convenient to pin down one of the endpoints, say at 1, and to define the logarithmic function as follows (see Figure 7–28):

Definition 7–7. $\log c = \displaystyle\int_{1}^{c} \frac{dx}{x}$ $(c > 0)$.

Then for $a,b > 0$,

$$\int_{a}^{b} \frac{dx}{x} = \int_{1}^{b} \frac{dx}{x} - \int_{1}^{a} \frac{dx}{x} = \log b - \log a.$$

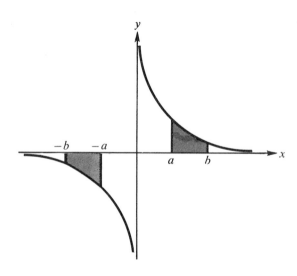

FIGURE 7–27

If $c > 1$, log c is just the area of the shaded region in Figure 7–28 and is therefore positive. If $0 < c < 1$,

$$\log c = \int_1^c \frac{dx}{x} = - \int_c^1 \frac{dx}{x},$$

and log c is negative. Clearly log $1 = 0$, in accordance with our convention. If $0 < a < b$, then

$$\log b - \log a = \int_a^b \frac{dx}{x} > 0,$$

so log $a <$ log b. Therefore log is a strictly increasing function.

We shall now derive an important property of log from Theorem 7–22. Taking $g(x) = 1/x$ $(x > 0)$, with a, b, $c > 0$, we get

(1)
$$\int_{ca}^{cb} \frac{dx}{x} = c \int_a^b \frac{dx}{cx} = \int_a^b \frac{dx}{x}.$$

From this we see that the area of the region between two points a and b depends only on the ratio b/a. For example, taking $a = 2$, $b = 3$, and various values of c, we get

$$\int_2^3 \frac{dx}{x} = \int_4^6 \frac{dx}{x} = \int_6^9 \frac{dx}{x} = \int_1^{3/2} \frac{dx}{x} = \int_{1/2}^{3/4} \frac{dx}{x}.$$

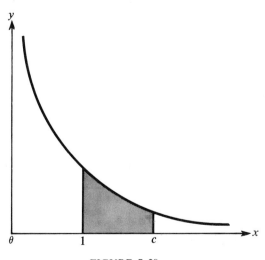

FIGURE 7–28

In all cases, the ratio of the endpoints is $\frac{3}{2}$. Now, in Eq. (1), take the special case $a = 1$. Then

$$\int_c^{cb} \frac{dx}{x} = \int_1^b \frac{dx}{x},$$

$$\log cb - \log c = \log b,$$

(2) $$\log cb = \log c + \log b \qquad (c,b > 0).$$

Thus, if $\log c = 7$, $\log b = 3$, then $\log cb = 10$. Given $\log c$ and $\log b$ we can calculate $\log$ of the product cb by adding $\log c$ and $\log b$. If we were to make a table of the log function, it would look like this:

x	$\ldots$	c	$\ldots$	b	$\ldots$	cb	$\ldots$
$\log x$	$\ldots$	c'	$\ldots$	b'	$\ldots$	$c' + b'$	$\ldots$

⟦Our previous remarks may be interpreted as follows: The set of positive numbers, equipped with the operation of *multiplication*, forms a group R^+. The set of real numbers, equipped with the operation of *addition*, forms a group R. The function log is a mapping from R^+ into R,

$$\log: R^+ \to R,$$

and it carries the group operation ($\cdot$) in R^+ over into the group operation ($+$) in R. Since log is one-to-one ($a > b$ implies $\log a > \log b$), log is an *isomorphism* of R^+ into R. We shall see later that log is *onto* R, so the two groups have precisely the same structure.⟧

Let us consider some consequences of Eq. (2). Taking $b = 1/c$, we get

$$\log 1 = \log c + \log \frac{1}{c} \qquad (c > 0).$$

Since $\log 1 = 0$,

(3) $$\log \frac{1}{c} = -\log c \qquad (c > 0).$$

If $0 < c \le 1$, then $1/c \ge 1$, so we may concentrate on the numbers ≥ 1. If $a,b > 0$, then

$$\log \frac{a}{b} = \log \left(a \cdot \frac{1}{b} \right) = \log a + \log \frac{1}{b},$$

(4) $$\log \frac{a}{b} = \log a - \log b \qquad (a,b > 0).$$

Thus, division in R^+ corresponds to subtraction in R.
Next, in Eq. (2), take $b = c$:

$$\log c^2 = 2 \log c \qquad (c > 0).$$

In Eq. (2) take $b = c^2$:

$$\log c^3 = \log c + \log c^2 = 3 \log c \qquad (c > 0).$$

By induction on $n \geq 1$,

(5) $$\log c^n = n \log c \qquad (n \geq 1, c > 0).$$

Also

$$\log c^{-n} = \log \frac{1}{c^n} = -\log c^n = -n \log c.$$

Therefore Eq. (5) holds for positive and negative integers. For $n = 0$, $\log c^0 = \log 1 = 0$, so this case is also included.

By choosing $c > 1$ (so that $\log c > 0$) and n large and positive in Eq. (5), we can find numbers c^n such that $\log c^n$ is arbitrarily large and positive. Similarly, by choosing $c < 1$ and n large and positive, we see that $\log c^n$ is arbitrarily large and negative. Thus the range of log is unbounded above and below.

What about small and positive values of log? Let h be a positive number. Then in the interval $[1, 1 + h]$, $1/x \leq 1$, so

$$0 < \log (1 + h) = \int_1^{1+h} \frac{dx}{x} \leq \int_1^{1+h} dx = h.$$

That is, there are arbitrarily small positive values of log.

Now we are prepared to prove that *every real number k is assumed as a value of log.* By our remarks above, there are values of log both less than and greater than k. Therefore the set

$$A = \{x > 0 | \log x \leq k\}$$

is nonempty and bounded above. Let

$$a = \text{l.u.b. } A.$$

We assert that $\log a = k$, and we prove it by showing that the possibilities $\log a < k$ and $\log a > k$ lead to contradictions. Suppose that $\log a < k$.

Put $h = k - \log a > 0$. Then $a(1 + h) > a$, so $a(1 + h) \notin A$ and $\log(a(1 + h)) > k$. But

$$\log (a(1 + h)) = \log a + \;\log (1 + h)$$

$$\leq \log a + h$$

$$= \log a + k - \log a$$

$$= k.$$

This is a contradiction. Now suppose that $\log a > k$. Put $h = \log a - k > 0$. Then $a/(1 + h) < a$. But

$$\log \left(\frac{a}{1 + h} \right) = \log a - \log (1 + h)$$

$$\geq \log a - h$$

$$= k.$$

If $x \in A$,

$$\log x \leq k \leq \log \left(\frac{a}{1 + h} \right),$$

$$x \leq \frac{a}{1 + h}.$$

Therefore $a/(1 + h)$ is an upper bound of A which is less than the least upper bound a. This is a contradiction. Therefore $\log a = k$. It is clear that no other number a' satisfies this equation. For if $a' > a$, $\log a' > \log a = k$; if $a' < a$, then $\log a' < \log a = k$.

This result has an important consequence. Given $c > 0$ and an integer $n \geq 1$, we are accustomed to speaking of the nth root of c, written $c^{1/n}$, as the positive number b such that $b^n = c$. But we have never shown that such a number exists. Now we can do so. In fact, define b as the positive number which satisfies $\log b = (1/n) \log c$. Then

$$\log c = n \log b = \log b^n,$$

$$c = b^n.$$

In exactly the same way, we can define c^r, for an arbitrary real r, as that positive b such that $\log b = r \log c$. This definition is a proper generalization of c^n, c^{-n}, $c^{1/n}$, $c^{m/n}$, and so on; it coincides with the previously established definitions.

Let e be the number satisfying $\log e = 1$. Then $\log e^2 = 2 \log e = 2$, $\log e^3 = 3$, and in general $\log e^n = n$. In fact, using the definition above, e^r is that positive number such that $\log e^r = r \log e = r$. The function *exp* defined by $\exp x = e^x \, (x \in R)$ is the *exponential* function. It is of such tremendous importance in mathematics and its applications that its definition merits emphasis.

Definition 7–8. For all $x \in R$, $\exp x = e^x$ is the unique positive number satisfying

$$\log e^x = x.$$

Another form of the definition is

(6) $$y = e^x \Leftrightarrow \log y = x \qquad (x \in R, \, y > 0).$$

In this form it is clear that exp is the inverse of log; it is the mapping from R to R^+ which carries addition in R over into multiplication in R^+. For suppose that $x, x' \in R$, $y = \exp x$, $y' = \exp x'$. Then by Eq. (6), $\log y = x$, $\log y' = x'$, and

$$\log yy' = \log y + \log y' = x + x'.$$

Using Eq. (6) again, we get

$$yy' = \exp(x + x').$$

Putting in the values of y and y', we have

$$\exp x \cdot \exp x' = \exp(x + x').$$

Theorem 7–23. For all $a, b \in R$, $\exp(a + b) = \exp a \cdot \exp b$. In words, to multiply exponentials we add the exponents.

EXERCISE 7–10

Prove that $\exp(\log x) = x \, (x > 0)$. [*Hint:* Put $\exp(\log x) = y$, apply Eq. (6), and use the one-to-one property of log.]

The logarithmic function just defined and discussed is sometimes called the *natural logarithm*, to emphasize that the "natural" base e is being used, rather than the "common" base 10.

EXERCISES 7–11

1. Plot the curve $y = 1/x \, (1 \leq x \leq 2)$ carefully on graph paper with a fine grid. By counting squares, estimate the area under the curve, that is,

$$\int_1^2 \frac{dx}{x} = \log 2.$$

2. Given that log 2 = .6931, log 3 = 1.0986, log 5 = 1.6094 (to four decimals), compute log x for x = 4, 6, 8, 9, 10, 1.2, $\frac{3}{4}$, $\frac{2}{5}$, .01.

3. (See Problem 2.) By using $7^4 = 2,401 \doteq 2,400 = 2^5 \cdot 3 \cdot 5^2$, estimate log 7.

*4. Let Q denote the set of rationals. For $c \in R$, let

$$k = \text{l.u.b.}\{e^r | r \in Q, r < c\}.$$

Prove that $k = e^c$. [*Hint:* Define b by $k = e^b$. Then $b \le c$ (why?). Next, assume that $b < c$. There is an $r \in Q$ such that $b < r < c$ (why?). Then $k = e^b < e^r$. But by definition of k, $e^r \le k$. This contradiction proves that $b = c$, as desired.]

*5. For $c \in R$, let

$$t = \text{g.l.b.}\{e^r | r \in Q, r > c\}.$$

Prove that $t = e^c$.

*6. Let f be any function from R to R^+ such that

$$f(1) = e.$$
$$a > b \rightarrow f(a) > f(b) \qquad (a,b \in R).$$
$$f(a + b) = f(a)f(b) \qquad (a,b \in R).$$

Prove:
  (a) For all $r \in Q$, $f(r) = e^r$.
  (b) l.u.b. $\{f(r) | r \in Q, r < c\} \le f(c)$ $(c \in R)$.
  (c) g.l.b. $\{f(r) | r \in Q, r > c\} \ge f(c)$ $(c \in R)$.
  (d) $f(c) = e^c$ $(c \in R)$.

7–7. APPROXIMATION OF LOGARITHMS AND EXPONENTIALS

By this time we know a great deal about the logarithmic function. We can even calculate it as accurately as we please, by computing upper and lower sums for the integral

$$\int_1^x \frac{dt}{t}.$$

If we use n equal subintervals, an upper bound for the error is

$$S - s = \frac{(b - a)|f(b) - f(a)|}{n}$$

$$= \frac{(x-1)\left(1 - \dfrac{1}{x}\right)}{n}$$

$$= \frac{(x-1)^2}{nx} \qquad (x > 1).$$

Equality holds here, because the integrand is monotonic.

In point of fact, however, this method of calculating the logarithm is quite slow and impractical. Consider, for example, the problem of computing log 1.1 correct to three decimals. For this we need an error $< .0005$. Putting $x = 1.1$, we get

$$S - s = \frac{(1.1 - 1)^2}{1.1n} \doteq \frac{.009}{n} < .0005,$$

from which we see that we need $n > 18$. Even if we halve the error by using the approximation $(s + S)/2$ for log 1.1, we still need $n > 9$. Of course the approximation might be much better than we think, but our analysis so far has not guaranteed this. The difficulty is that the error is proportional to $1/n$, which is much too large for the effort expended.

The method we propose to use is a fairly general one. We first approximate the integrand (the function being integrated) by a polynomial and then integrate the polynomial. It is important to carry along an estimate of the errors involved.

Suppose that $x = 1 + h, 0 < h < 1$. Then

$$\log x = \log (1 + h) = \int_1^{1+h} \frac{dt}{t}$$

$$= \int_0^h \frac{dt}{1 + t}.$$

We approximate the integrand $1/(1 + t)$ as follows. Let n be a positive integer. Then

$$(1 + t)(1 - t + t^2 - t^3 + \cdots + (-1)^{n-1}t^{n-1})$$

$$= 1 - t + t^2 - t^3 + \cdots + (-1)^{n-1}t^{n-1}$$

$$\quad + t - t^2 + t^3 - \cdots - (-1)^{n-1}t^{n-1} + (-1)^{n-1}t^n$$

$$= 1 - (-1)^n t^n.$$

Therefore

$$\frac{1}{1+t} = \frac{1 - (-1)^n t^n}{1+t} + \frac{(-1)^n t^n}{1+t},$$

(1) $$\frac{1}{1+t} = (1 - t + t^2 - \cdots + (-1)^{n-1} t^{n-1}) + (-1)^n \frac{t^n}{1+t}.$$

The first term on the right of Eq. (1) is the approximating polynomial; the second is the error. If we integrate both sides of Eq. (1) between 0 and h, we get

$$\log(1 + h) = \int_0^h (1 - t + t^2 - \cdots + (-1)^{n-1} t^{n-1}) \, dt + (-1)^n \int_0^h \frac{t^n}{1+t} \, dt$$

$$= h - \frac{h^2}{2} + \frac{h^3}{3} - \cdots + (-1)^{n-1} \frac{h^n}{n} + (-1)^n R_n,$$

where

$$R_n = \int_0^h \frac{t^n}{1+t}.$$

Now, for $0 \le t \le h$,

(2) $$\frac{1}{2} t^n \le \frac{t^n}{1+t} \le t^n,$$

because $0 < h < 1$. Integrating (2), we obtain

$$\frac{1}{2} \int_0^h t^n \, dt \le R_n \le \int_0^h t^n \, dt,$$

$$\frac{1}{2} \frac{h^{n+1}}{n+1} \le R_n \le \frac{h^{n+1}}{n+1}.$$

Therefore, for some number θ between $\frac{1}{2}$ and 1 (depending on h and n, but we don't care)

(3) $$R_n = \theta \frac{h^{n+1}}{n+1} \qquad (\tfrac{1}{2} \le \theta \le 1).$$

Hence, for $0 < h < 1$, $n \ge 1$,

(4) $$\log(1 + h) = h - \frac{h^2}{2} + \cdots + (-1)^{n-1} \frac{h^n}{n} + (-1)^n \theta \frac{h^{n+1}}{n+1}.$$

In the example discussed earlier, $h = .1$. If we choose $n = 2$, we get

$$0 < R_2 \leq \frac{h^3}{3} = \frac{.001}{3} = .0003^+ < .0004.$$

Thus, for some positive $E < .0004$,

$$\log(1.1) = .1 - \frac{(.1)^2}{2} + E$$

$$= .095 + E$$

$$= .0952 \pm .0002.$$

If we choose $n = 3$,

$$0 < R_3 \leq \frac{h^4}{4} = \frac{.0001}{4} = .000025 < .00003.$$

$$\log(1.1) = .1 - \frac{(.1)^2}{2} + \frac{(.1)^3}{3} - E$$

$$= .09533^+ - E,$$

where $0 < E < .00003$. Thus, being generous,

$$\log(1.1) = .09532 \pm .00002.$$

The formula (4) gives such excellent results, at least for small values of h, that electronic computers do not need to store tables of logarithms. They can calculate them, using a standard subroutine, almost as rapidly as it would take to search for them.

The graph of $y = \log x$ $(x > 0)$ is shown in Figure 7-29.

If it is necessary to use logarithms to some other base, say 10, the transition can be made quite readily. We would define

$$y = \log_{10} x \Leftrightarrow x = 10^y \qquad (y \in R, x > 0).$$

Taking natural logarithms on the right, we have

$$\log x = \log(10^y) = y \log 10,$$

$$y = \frac{\log x}{\log 10},$$

$$\log_{10} x = \frac{\log x}{\log 10}.$$

The value of $\log 10$, to four decimals, is 2.3026.

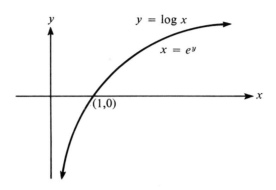

FIGURE 7–29

The exponential function will be discussed in more detail later. It is worthwhile, however, to get some idea about its size. Suppose that $0 \leq x \leq 1$. For $n \geq 1$, the inequalities

$$\frac{x/n}{1 + (x/n)} \leq \int_1^{1 + (x/n)} \frac{dt}{t} \leq \frac{x}{n}$$

follow by integration from

$$\frac{1}{1 + (x/n)} \leq \frac{1}{t} \leq 1 \qquad \left(1 \leq t \leq 1 + \frac{x}{n}\right).$$

Hence

$$\frac{x/n}{1 + (x/n)} \leq \log\left(1 + \frac{x}{n}\right) \leq \frac{x}{n},$$

$$\frac{x}{n + x} \leq \log\left(1 + \frac{x}{n}\right) \leq \frac{x}{n}.$$

Because $x \leq 1$, $n + x \leq n + 1$, so

$$\frac{x}{n + 1} \leq \frac{x}{n + x}.$$

Therefore

$$\frac{x}{n + 1} \leq \log\left(1 + \frac{x}{n}\right) \leq \frac{x}{n}.$$

From the inequality on the left,

$$x \le (n + 1)\log\left(1 + \frac{x}{n}\right) = \log\left[\left(1 + \frac{x}{n}\right)^{n+1}\right],$$

$$e^x \le \left(1 + \frac{x}{n}\right)^{n+1}.$$

From the inequality on the right,

$$\log\left[\left(1 + \frac{x}{n}\right)^{n}\right] = n\log\left(1 + \frac{x}{n}\right) \le x,$$

$$\left(1 + \frac{x}{n}\right)^{n} \le e^x.$$

Hence

(5) $$\left(1 + \frac{x}{n}\right)^{n} \le e^x \le \left(1 + \frac{x}{n}\right)^{n+1} \qquad (0 \le x \le 1, n \ge 1).$$

The difference E between these two bounds is small if n is large, because

$$E = \left(1 + \frac{x}{n}\right)^{n+1} - \left(1 + \frac{x}{n}\right)^{n} = \left(1 + \frac{x}{n}\right)^{n}\left(1 + \frac{x}{n} - 1\right)$$

$$= \left(1 + \frac{x}{n}\right)^{n}\left(\frac{x}{n}\right)$$

$$\le \frac{xe^x}{n} \le \frac{e}{n}.$$

Putting $x = 1$ in Eq. (5), $n = 1$, we get $e \le 2^2 = 4$. Hence

$$E \le \frac{4}{n}.$$

It follows that

(6) $$e^x \doteq \left(1 + \frac{x}{n}\right)^{n} \qquad (0 \le x \le 1)$$

for large n. Actually, this is true for all $x \in R$. The particular range $[0,1]$ was chosen for simplicity. There are much better approximation formulas for e^x, as we shall see later.

EXERCISES 7-12

1. Compute a four-place table of log x for $x = 1.0,\ 1.1,\ 1.2, \ldots, 1.9$. Then check your results against a standard table.

2. If the annual interest rate is r, and if interest is compounded n times a year, the amount at the end of a year would be

$$A_n = P\left(1 + \frac{r}{n}\right)^n,$$

where P is the initial amount. Prove that if n is very large,

$$\log A_n \doteq r + \log P.$$

3. How many equal subintervals would one need to calculate log 1.2 to five decimals, using the lower sum as an approximation?

4. Prove that $(e^x)^y = e^{xy}$ $(x, y \in R)$.

5. Explain how you would use a table of logarithms to calculate square roots.

6. Prove that the exponential function takes on all positive values [rng exp $= \{a | a > 0\}$].

7. Make a rough sketch of the graph of the exponential function.

8. Prove that $h - (h^2/2) \le \log(1 + h) \le h$ $(0 \le h \le 1)$.

9. Show that if $(\log x)/x < k$, then $(\log x^2)/x^2 < 2k/x$. What can you conclude about the relative sizes of log x and x when x is large? About x and e^x?

*10. Show that if $1 < x < y$, then

$$\frac{\log x}{x - 1} > \frac{\log y}{y - 1}.$$

[Hint: $\dfrac{1}{x - 1}\displaystyle\int_1^x \frac{dt}{t} =$ average of $\dfrac{1}{t}$ in $[1, x]$.]

11. For $h > 0$, show that

$$\log(1 + h) < \frac{h(1 + (h/4))}{1 + (h/2)}.$$

(Use an upper sum with $n = 2$ and simplify.)

12. For $0 < h < 1$, show that

$$h < \log\left(\frac{1}{1 - h}\right) < \frac{h}{1 - h}.$$

13. Prove that $5^{\log 3} = 3^{\log 5}$.

14. Show that if h is small and positive, then e^h is close to 1. What about h small and negative?

15. If you used Eq. (4) to calculate $\log 1.01$ correct to 10 decimals, how large would you have to choose n?

16. Calculate to four decimals:

(a) $\displaystyle\int_{100}^{102} \frac{dx}{x}$.

(b) $\displaystyle\int_{50}^{51} \frac{dx}{x}$.

(c) $\displaystyle\int_{49}^{50} \frac{dx}{x+1}$.

Chapter 8

LIMITS, CONTINUITY, AND
DIFFERENTIATION

8–1. LIMITS OF SEQUENCES

WE BEGIN THIS CHAPTER by studying the "long-run" behavior of sequences of real numbers. The simplest type of behavior that we may reasonably expect is *convergence* or ultimate approach to a fixed value. Before giving a precise definition of this concept, we shall illustrate it by a few examples.

EXAMPLE 8–1. (a) The sequence $(1,\frac{1}{2},\frac{1}{3},\ldots)$, the typical term of which is $1/n$, converges to 0.

(b) In our discussion of the decimal representation of the real numbers we saw that if

$$r = .d_1 d_2 d_3 \cdots ,$$

then r is the unique number common to all the intervals $[a_n, a_n + 10^{-n}]$, where

$$a_n = .d_1 d_2 d_3 \cdots d_n.$$

That is, for every $n \in N$,

$$a_n \leq r \leq a_n + 10^{-n}.$$

The sequence (a_n), $n \in N$, converges to r.

(c) The sequence $(-1,\frac{1}{2},-\frac{1}{3},\frac{1}{4},\ldots)$, the typical term of which is $(-1)^n/n$, converges to 0.

(d) The sequence $(1,0,\frac{1}{3},0,\frac{1}{5},0,\ldots)$ converges to 0.

(e) If f is a monotonically increasing function defined on $[0,1]$, then the sequence

$$S_n = \frac{1}{n}\left[f\left(\frac{1}{n}\right) + f\left(\frac{2}{n}\right) + f\left(\frac{3}{n}\right) + \cdots + f\left(\frac{n}{n}\right)\right] \qquad (n \in N)$$

340

converges to $\int_0^1 f(x)\,dx$. Here S_n is the upper sum corresponding to the partition of $[0,1]$ into n equal parts. As we have seen, it differs from the integral by at most

$$\frac{1}{n}(f(1) - f(0)).$$

(f) The sequence $(1,\frac{1}{2},1,\frac{1}{3},1,\frac{1}{4},\ldots)$ does *not* converge to any real number. One part of the sequence converges to 1 and another part converges to 0.

(g) The sequence $(1,2,3,4,\ldots)$ does *not* converge to any real number, nor does any part of it.

In (a) through (e) above, with the sequence (a_n), $n \in N$, there is associated a real number r, called the *limit* of the sequence. The nth term a_n *and all succeeding terms* are eventually excellent approximations to the limit r. The excellence of the approximation may be specified in advance, and no matter how close the desired approximation, it can be achieved by choosing n large enough.

Consider Example 8–1(a), for instance. Suppose we want approximation to within $h = .01$. Then we may choose $n = 101$, and we see that each of the terms

$$\frac{1}{101}, \frac{1}{102}, \frac{1}{103}, \ldots$$

differs from the limit 0 by at most h. Suppose we change our h to .001. Then we may choose $n = 1{,}001$, and we see that each of the terms

$$\frac{1}{1{,}001}, \frac{1}{1{,}002}, \frac{1}{1{,}003}, \ldots$$

differs from 0 by at most h. No matter what $h > 0$ we may select as a test, the challenge can always be met. For we know that there is $n \in N$ such that $n > 1/h$, from which it follows that

$$0 < \frac{1}{n} < h, \qquad 0 < \frac{1}{n+1} < h, \qquad 0 < \frac{1}{n+2} < h, \ldots,$$

so that all the terms from the nth one on deviate from 0 by an amount less than h.

Notice that the sequence in Example 8–1(f) does not fulfill our requirements. If 0 is suggested as the limit, then it is true that there are terms of the sequence which are within $h = .01$, say, of 0, but always beyond such terms there are others which are far away from 0. Thus we cannot assure that all succeeding terms to the nth are excellent approximations. If any other number r is suggested as a limit, it also will fail the test.

We should now be ready for the formal definition.

Definition 8–1.   Suppose that $(a_n), n \in N$ is a sequence of real numbers, and that r is a real number. We say that a_n *converges to r*, or $\lim_{n \to \infty} a_n = r$, or $a_n \to r$, iff for every $h > 0$, there exists an $n \in N$ such that

$$|a_k - r| < h \qquad (k = n, n + 1, n + 2, \ldots).$$

Written out symbolically, the condition is

(1)
$$\forall h > 0,\ \exists n \in N\ \textit{such that}$$
$$|a_k - r| < h \qquad (k \geq n).$$

The symbol "$\lim_{n \to \infty} a_n = r$" is read "the limit of a_n is r, as n tends to infinity," or "the limit of a_n is r, as n increases without bound," or simply "the limit of a_n is r."

There is an unfortunate but unavoidable conflict between two standard uses of the arrow, one for implication and one for convergence. For this reason, from now on the broad arrow ($\Rightarrow$) will be used for implication.

We emphasize that to establish convergence we must meet the challenge posed by *every* positive number h. The n that we use to meet the challenge will depend on h in general, and if one n works for a given h, so will all larger n's. We need not choose the very first one.

EXAMPLE 8–2.   Show that $\lim_{n \to \infty} \dfrac{2n + 1}{n + 1} = 2$.

Solution: Consider, for $k \in N$,

$$|a_k - r| = \left| \frac{2k + 1}{k + 1} - 2 \right| = \left| \frac{(2k + 1) - 2(k + 1)}{k + 1} \right|$$

$$= \left| \frac{-1}{k + 1} \right| = \frac{1}{k + 1}.$$

Given an $h > 0$, we will have

$$\frac{1}{k + 1} < h$$

whenever

$$\frac{1}{h} < k + 1.$$

Now we know that there is an $n \in N$ such that $1/h < n$. For such an n, $k \geq n$ implies

$$k + 1 > n > \frac{1}{h},$$

$$k + 1 > \frac{1}{h},$$

$$\frac{1}{k + 1} < h.$$

Therefore, for one such n,

$$|a_k - r| < h \qquad (k \geq n),$$

as desired. If $h = .001$, for instance, $1/h = 1,000$, and an acceptable n is 2,354. Thus

$$|a_k - 2| < .001 \qquad (k \geq 2,354).$$

⟦To understand more fully the meaning of "$a_n \to r$," consider the inequality $|a_k - r| < h$ in the defining condition (1). It is equivalent to

$$-h < a_k - r < h,$$

or to

$$r - h < a_k < r + h.$$

From this we see that a_k falls inside the open interval $(r - h, r + h)$. That this happens for all $k \geq n$ is equivalent to

$$\{a_n, a_{n+1}, a_{n+2}, \ldots\} \subset (r - h, r + h).$$

Let us define a *tail* of the sequence (a_n) as any *set* of the form

$$T_n = \{a_n, a_{n+1}, \ldots\} = \{a_k | k \geq n\}.$$

Each $n \in N$ determines such a tail. Then

$$\lim_{n \to \infty} a_n = r$$

is equivalent to

(2) $\qquad \forall h > 0, \exists n \in N$ such that $T_n \subset (r - h, r + h).$

In words, *every open interval about r contains some tail of the sequence* (a_n).

EXAMPLE 8–3.   If $a_n \to 2$ and $b_n \to 3$, show that $a_n + b_n \to 5$.

Solution: Let S_n, T_n, V_n be the nth tails of the sequences (a_n), (b_n), $(a_n + b_n)$, respectively. Given $h > 0$, we must find an n such that

(3) $$V_n \subset (5 - h, 5 + h).$$

By hypothesis, there exist n_1 and n_2 such that

$$S_{n_1} \subset \left(2 - \frac{h}{2}, 2 + \frac{h}{2}\right),$$

$$T_{n_2} \subset \left(3 - \frac{h}{2}, 3 + \frac{h}{2}\right).$$

Let n be the larger of n_1 and n_2. If $k \geq n$, then

$$2 - \frac{h}{2} < a_k < 2 + \frac{h}{2},$$

$$3 - \frac{h}{2} < b_k < 3 + \frac{h}{2}.$$

Therefore

$$5 - h < a_k + b_k < 5 + h \qquad (k \geq n).$$

This is equivalent to statement (3). ▌

It is clear from the definition of convergence that $a_n \to r$ is equivalent to $a_n - r \to 0$. Thus, if we could recognize when an arbitrary sequence converges to 0, we could handle any convergent sequence. Let us call a sequence that converges to 0 a *null sequence*. If $a_n \to r$, then $(a_n - r) = (b_n)$ is a null sequence, and conversely. Thus every convergent sequence is of the form $(r + b_n)$, where (b_n) is a null sequence.

We shall now give some theorems which are useful for theoretical and practical purposes.

Theorem 8–1.   Every null sequence is bounded.

Proof: Let $a_n \to 0$. Choose $h = 1$. Then $\exists n_1$ such that

$$|a_n| < 1 \qquad (n \geq n_1).$$

Let B be the largest of the numbers

$$1, |a_1|, |a_2|, \ldots, |a_{n_1}|.$$

Then

$$|a_n| \leq B \qquad (n \geq 1).$$

Corollary.   Every convergent sequence is bounded.
Proof: Left to the student.

Theorem 8–2.   The sum of two null sequences is a null sequence.
Proof: Let $(a_n), (b_n)$ be null sequences. Given $h > 0$, $\exists n_1$ such that

$$|a_n| < \frac{h}{2} \qquad (n \geq n_1).$$

Similarly, $\exists n_2$ such that

$$|b_n| < \frac{h}{2} \qquad (n \geq n_2).$$

If $n_0 = \max(n_1, n_2)$, then $n \geq n_0$ implies that

$$|a_n + b_n| \leq |a_n| + |b_n| < \frac{h}{2} + \frac{h}{2} = h.$$

Therefore $(a_n + b_n)$ is a null sequence.

Theorem 8–3.   If (a_n) is a null sequence and (b_n) is a bounded sequence, then $(a_n b_n)$ is a null sequence.
Proof: Suppose that $|b_n| \leq B \, (n \geq 1)$. Given $h > 0$, $\exists n_0$ such that

$$|a_n| < \frac{h}{B + 1} \qquad (n \geq n_0).$$

Then for $n \geq n_0$,

$$|a_n b_n| = |a_n| \cdot |b_n| \leq \frac{h}{B + 1} \cdot B < h.$$

Corollary 1.   If (a_n) is a null sequence and (b_n) is a convergent sequence, then $(a_n b_n)$ is a null sequence.

Corollary 2.   If (a_n) is a null sequence and b is real, then (ba_n) is a null sequence.

Theorem 8–4.   If (a_n) is a null sequence, then $(|a_n|)$ is a null sequence, and conversely.
Proof: Left to the student.

Theorem 8–5.   If (a_n) is a null sequence and $|b_n| \leq |a_n|$ for all $n \in N$, then (b_n) is a null sequence.
Proof: Left to the student.

Theorem 8–6. If $a_n \to a, b_n \to b$, then $a_n + b_n \to a + b$.

Proof: By assumption, $(a_n - a)$ and $(b_n - b)$ are null sequences. By Theorem 8–2, so is

$$(a_n - a + b_n - b) = ((a_n + b_n) - (a + b)).$$

Therefore $a_n + b_n \to a + b$.

Theorem 8–7. If $a_n \to a, b_n \to b$, then $a_n b_n \to ab$.

Proof: For all $n \in N$, $a_n = a + h_n$, $b_n = b + k_n$, where (h_n), (k_n) are null sequences. Hence

$$a_n b_n = (a + h_n)(b + k_n)$$

$$= ab + ak_n + bh_n + h_n k_n.$$

By Corollary 2 of Theorem 8–3, (ak_n) and (bh_n) are null sequences, and by Corollary 1, so is $(h_n k_n)$. Hence, by Theorem 8–2, applied twice,

$$(ak_n + bh_n + h_n k_n)$$

is a null sequence.

Corollary 1. If b is real and $a_n \to a$, then $ba_n \to ba$.

Corollary 2. Let $P(x) = c_0 + c_1 x + c_2 x^2 + \cdots + c_k x^k$ $(x \in R)$ be a polynomial function. If $a_n \to a$, then $P(a_n) \to P(a)$.

Proof: This follows by repeated application of Theorem 8–6 and 8–7 and Corollary 1 to Theorem 8–7.

EXERCISES 8–1

1. Give all the proofs above which were left to the student.

2. If $a_n \to a, a_n \to b$, prove that $a = b$. (This justifies our speaking of *the* limit of a_n.)

3. If $a_n \to a, b_n \to a$, and $a_n \le c_n \le b_n$ for all $n \in N$, show that $c_n \to a$.

4. If $a_n \to a$ and $a_n \le k$ $(n \in N)$, show that $a \le k$. [*Hint:* Assume that $a > k$, then apply Definition 8–1 with $h = \frac{1}{2}(a - k)$.]

5. Evaluate the following limits, if they exist:

(a) $\lim \dfrac{n + 2}{n + 7}$.

(b) $\lim (3 + 2^{-n})$.

(c) $\lim (1 - (-1)^n)$.

(d) $\lim \log \left(1 + \dfrac{1}{n}\right)$.

(e) $\lim \left[\log(2n + 7) - \log n\right]$.

(f) $\lim \left[\sqrt{n + 100} - \sqrt{n}\right]$.

(g) $\lim \dfrac{(3 + (1/n))^2 - 3^2}{1/n}$.

(h) $\lim c^n \quad (0 \leq c \leq 2)$.

(i) $\lim \sqrt{9 + \dfrac{1}{n}}$.

6. If $a_n \to a$, show that $a_{n+5} \to a$.

7. If $a_n \to a$ and $k \in N$, show that $\displaystyle\lim_{n \to \infty} a_{n+k} = a$.

So far we have not considered quotients of convergent sequences. The problem is complicated by the fact that the quotient a_n/b_n does not exist if $b_n = 0$. Even if $b_n \neq 0 \, (n \in N)$, it may happen that $b_n \to 0$. In this case anything can happen. Indeed, if (c_n) is an arbitrary sequence, we can find convergent sequences (a_n) and (b_n) such that

$$\frac{a_n}{b_n} = c_n \qquad (n \in N).$$

All we need do is take

$$a_n = \frac{c_n}{n(1 + |c_n|)} \qquad (n \in N),$$

$$b_n = \frac{1}{n(1 + |c_n|)} \qquad (n \in N).$$

The student should verify that b_n is never 0 and that $a_n \to 0$, $b_n \to 0$. The situation is simpler when $\lim b_n \neq 0$.

Theorem 8–8. If $b_n \to b \neq 0, b_n \neq 0 \, (n \in N)$, then $1/b_n \to 1/b$.

Proof: We may assume that $b > 0$. Applying Definition 8–1 to (b_n) with $h = b/2$, we see that there exists $n_0 \in N$ such that

$$|b_n - b| < \frac{b}{2} \qquad (n \geq n_0).$$

That is,

$$-\frac{b}{2} < b_n - b < \frac{b}{2} \qquad (n \geq n_0).$$

From the first inequality,

$$b_n > \frac{b}{2} \qquad (n \geq n_0),$$

$$\frac{1}{b_n} < \frac{2}{b} \qquad (n \geq n_0).$$

Thus the sequence $(1/b_n)$ is bounded. For $n \in N$,

$$\frac{1}{b_n} - \frac{1}{b} = \frac{b - b_n}{bb_n} = \frac{1}{bb_n}(b - b_n).$$

Since $(1/bb_n)$ is bounded and $(b - b_n)$ is a null sequence, $((1/b_n) - (1/b))$ is also a null sequence, by Theorem 8–3.

Theorem 8–9. If $a_n \to a, b_n \to b \neq 0, b_n \neq 0 \,(n \in N)$, then $a_n/b_n \to a/b$.
Proof: Follows from Theorems 8–8 and 8–7.

There are many occasions when it is convenient to speak of a sequence *increasing without bound*, or *tending to infinity*.

Definition 8–2. Let (a_n) be a sequence. If for every real H, there exists an $n_0 \in N$ such that $a_n > H$ for every $n \geq n_0$, we say that (a_n) *increases without bound*, or $\lim\limits_{n \to \infty} a_n = +\infty$, or $a_n \to +\infty$.

There is a similar definition for $\lim\limits_{n \to \infty} a_n = -\infty$ or $a_n \to -\infty$, replacing "$a_n > H$" by "$a_n < H$."

Theorem 8–10. If $a_n \to 0, a_n > 0 \,(n \in N)$, then $1/a_n \to +\infty$.
Proof: Left to the student.

Notice that we do *not* say that (a_n) converges if Definition 8–2 is satisfied, in spite of the symbols used. The only convergent sequences are those that satisfy Definition 8–1. All others are *divergent*. Among the divergent sequences are those that diverge to infinity, as in Definition 8–2, but other modes of divergence are possible.

There is an important class of sequences for which only the two possibilities exist: convergence, or divergence to infinity. They are the *monotone* sequences. We say that (a_n) is *nondecreasing* if

$$a_1 \leq a_2 \leq a_3 \leq \cdots$$

and that it is *nonincreasing* if

$$a_1 \geq a_2 \geq a_3 \geq \cdots .$$

If one or the other holds, then (a_n) is *monotone*.

It is obvious that a nondecreasing sequence is bounded below. It may or may not be bounded above. We shall show that in the first case, it converges, and in the second it diverges to $+\infty$.

Theorem 8–11. If a nondecreasing sequence (a_n) has no upper bound, then $a_n \to +\infty$.

Proof: Given a real number H, we know that H is not an upper bound of $\{a_n | n \in N\}$. Hence $\exists n_0 \in N$ such that $a_{n_0} > H$. If $n \geq n_0$, then $a_n \geq a_{n_0} > H$. Thus Definition 8–2 is satisfied and $a_n \to +\infty$.

Theorem 8–12. If a nondecreasing sequence (a_n) has an upper bound, then

$$\lim_{n \to \infty} a_n = \text{l.u.b.} \{a_n | n \in N\}.$$

Proof: Let $a = \text{l.u.b.} \{a_n | n \in N\}$. Given $h > 0$, $a - h$ is not an upper bound, so $\exists n_0$ such that $a - h < a_{n_0}$. For all $n \geq n_0$,

$$a - h < a_n,$$

since (a_n) is nondecreasing. Because a is an upper bound,

$$a_n \leq a \qquad (n \in N).$$

Therefore

$$a - h < a_n \leq a \qquad (n \geq n_0),$$

so

$$|a_n - a| < h \qquad (n \geq n_0).$$

Thus $a_n \to a$, as required.

Of course, there are theorems similar to Theorems 8–11 and 8–12, obtained by changing "nondecreasing" to "nonincreasing," "$a_n \to +\infty$" to "$a_n \to -\infty$," "upper bound" to "lower bound," and "l.u.b.$\{a_n | n \in N\}$" to "g.l.b.$\{a_n | n \in N\}$." We leave these to the student.

EXAMPLE 8–4. Consider the sequence (a_n) given by $a_1 = 0$, $a_2 = \sqrt{2}$, $a_3 = \sqrt{2 + \sqrt{2}}$, $a_4 = \sqrt{2 + \sqrt{2 + \sqrt{2}}}$, and in general, $a_{n+1} = \sqrt{2 + a_n}$ $(n \geq 1)$. Prove that (a_n) converges and find the limit.

Solution: We begin by showing that (a_n) is nondecreasing. First, $a_2 > a_1$. If we have already proved that $a_{n+1} > a_n$ for some n, then

$$2 + a_{n+1} > 2 + a_n,$$

$$\sqrt{2 + a_{n+1}} > \sqrt{2 + a_n},$$

$$a_{n+2} > a_{n+1}.$$

Therefore, by induction,

$$a_1 < a_2 < a_3 < \cdots.$$

Next, $a_1 < 2$. If we have already proved that $a_n < 2$ for some n, then

$$a_{n+1} = \sqrt{2 + a_n} < \sqrt{2 + 2} = 2.$$

Therefore, by induction,

$$a_n < 2 \qquad (n \in N).$$

By Theorem 8–12, $a_n \to a$, say. Since

$$a_{n+1}^2 = 2 + a_n \qquad (n \in N),$$

$$a^2 = \lim_{n \to \infty} a_{n+1}^2 = 2 + \lim_{n \to \infty} a_n = 2 + a,$$

$$a^2 - a - 2 = 0,$$

$$(a - 2)(a + 1) = 0.$$

Thus $a = 2$ or $a = -1$. Because $a_n \geq 0$ $(n \in N)$, $a \geq 0$. Hence $a = 2$.

EXERCISES 8–2

1. Prove Theorem 8–10.
2. Prove: If $a_n \to a \neq 0$, $b_n \to 0$, $b_n \neq 0$ $(n \in N)$, then $|a_n/b_n| \to +\infty$.
3. Prove that $a_n \to a$ implies $a_{2n} \to a$. Is the converse true?
4. For the sequence $[(3n + 7)/(3n + 1)]$, find a tail contained in the interval $(1 - \tfrac{1}{10}, 1 + \tfrac{1}{10})$.
5. Define the sequence (s_n) by

$$s_1 = 1,$$

$$s_2 = 1 - \tfrac{1}{2},$$

$$s_3 = 1 - \tfrac{1}{2} + \tfrac{1}{3},$$

$$s_4 = 1 - \tfrac{1}{2} + \tfrac{1}{3} - \tfrac{1}{4},$$

and so on. Prove

 (a) $s_1 > s_3 > s_5 > \cdots$.
 (b) $s_1 > 0, s_3 > 0, s_5 > 0, \ldots$.
 (c) $\lim\limits_{n \to \infty} s_{2n-1}$ exists, $= s$, say.
 (d) $\lim\limits_{n \to \infty} s_{2n} = s$.
 (e) $\lim\limits_{n \to \infty} s_n = s$.

 6. Prove Example 8-1.
*7. Show that

$$\lim_{n \to \infty} \left(\frac{1}{n+1} + \frac{1}{n+2} + \cdots + \frac{1}{2n} \right) = \log 2.$$

[*Hint:* $\dfrac{1}{n+k} = \dfrac{1}{n}\left(\dfrac{1}{1+(k/n)}\right)$. Compare the sum with $\displaystyle\int_0^1 \dfrac{dx}{1+x}$.]

*8. Evaluate

$$\lim_{n \to \infty} \left(\frac{1}{n+1} + \frac{1}{n+2} + \cdots + \frac{1}{3n} \right).$$

 9. Prove

$$a_n^2 \to 3,\ a_n > 0\ (n \in N)\ \text{imply}\ a_n \to \sqrt{3}.$$

10. Define $a_1 = 2$, $a_2 = \frac{1}{2}(2 + \frac{3}{2})$, $a_3 = \frac{1}{2}\left(a_2 + \dfrac{3}{a_2}\right)$, and in general, $a_{n+1} = \frac{1}{2}\left(a_n + \dfrac{3}{a_n}\right)$ $(n \geq 1)$. Let $c_n = a_n^2 - 3$, so that $c_1 = 1, c_2 = \frac{1}{16}$. Prove:

 (a) $c_{n+1} = \dfrac{1}{4}\left(\dfrac{c_n^2}{3 + c_n}\right)$ $(n \geq 1)$.
 (b) $\forall n \in N\ (c_n > 0 \Rightarrow c_{n+1} > 0)$.
 (c) $\forall n \in N,\ c_n > 0$.
 (d) $\forall n \in N,\ c_{n+1} < \frac{1}{12}c_n^2 < \frac{1}{10}c_n^2$.
 (e) $c_2 < 10^{-1}; c_3 < 10^{-3}; c_4 < 10^{-7}; c_5 < 10^{-15}$.
 (f) $c_n \to 0$.
 (g) $a_n \to \sqrt{3}$.

*11. Evaluate

$$\lim_{n \to \infty} \left(\frac{1}{1 \cdot 2} + \frac{1}{2 \cdot 3} + \frac{1}{3 \cdot 4} + \cdots + \frac{1}{n(n+1)} \right).$$

*12. Evaluate

$$\lim_{n \to \infty} \frac{1}{\sqrt{n+1}} \left(\frac{1}{\sqrt{2}+\sqrt{1}} \quad \frac{1}{\sqrt{3}+\sqrt{2}} \quad \frac{1}{\sqrt{n+1}+\sqrt{n}} \right).$$

13. (See Chapter 7.) Prove $[1 + (1/n)]^n \to e$.

14. Evaluate

$$\lim_{n \to \infty} \frac{f[x + (1/n)] - f(x)}{1/n}$$

for

  (a) $f(x) = x^2$.
  (b) $f(x) = x^3$.
  (c) $f(x) = x^4$.
  (d) $f(x) = x^3 + x^4$.
  (e) $f(x) = 3x^4 - 2x^2 + x$.

(The domain of each of these functions is R.)

15. A particle moves along the x-axis in such a way that its position at time t is

$$x(t) = t^2 + t^3 \qquad (t \in R).$$

Let V_n be its average speed over the interval $[2, 2 + 1/n]$, for each $n \in N$. Thus

$$V_1 = \frac{x(3) - x(2)}{3 - 2} = \frac{36 - 12}{1} = 24,$$

$$V_2 = \frac{x(2 + \tfrac{1}{2}) - x(2)}{(2 + \tfrac{1}{2}) - 2} = 19\tfrac{3}{4}.$$

Evaluate $\lim_{n \to \infty} V_n$.

16. Show that $\lim_{n \to \infty} n(\log(n+1) - \log n) = 1$.

17. Evaluate $\lim_{n \to \infty} \dfrac{1}{h_n} \displaystyle\int_{2}^{2+h_n} x^2 \, dx$, if $h_n \to 0$ through positive values.

18. Suppose that $\lim_{n \to \infty} a_n = r$ and that $a_n < b$ $(n \in N)$. Show by an example that the conclusion $r < b$ does not necessarily follow.

19. Suppose that $\lim_{n \to \infty} a_n = r$. Prove that $\lim_{n \to \infty} |a_n| = |r|$.

8-2. LIMITS OF FUNCTIONS

In the preceding section we considered the "long-run" behavior of sequences (a_n), $n \in N$. An infinite sequence may properly be regarded as a function with domain N. Speaking fancifully, we have been studying the behavior of such functions for values of $n \in N$ "near the point at infinity." For that purpose it was not necessary for the function to be defined at that "point."

In the same way we can discuss the behavior of a function f, defined on a domain $D \subset R$, near a point $c \in R$. *We shall require that there be a sequence (x_n) in $D - \{c\}$ converging to c.* This merely ensures that there are points of D arbitrarily close to c without being equal to it, so that we may speak nontrivially about the behavior of f near c. The condition will be violated if and only if there is an open interval containing c but no points of D other than (perhaps) c. We do not demand that $c \in D$. For brevity, if c satisfies the requirement stated above with respect to D, we shall write $c \in D^*$. If $c \in D^*$, then the sequences (x_n) in $D - \{c\}$ converging to c will be called *acceptable*. It is the behavior of the sequence $(f(x_n))$ for all such sequences (x_n) that interests us here.

Definition 8-3. Suppose that $c \in (\operatorname{dom} f)^*$. If there is a number L such that

$$\lim_{n \to \infty} f(x_n) = L$$

for every acceptable sequence (x_n), then we say that

$$\lim_{x \to c} f(x) = L.$$

Note that $\lim f(x_n)$ is required by the definition to be the same for all acceptable sequences. Actually it is enough that $\lim f(x_n)$ *exist* for every acceptable sequence; it can then be proved that the limit is independent of the sequence.

EXAMPLE 8-5. $f(x) = x^2$ $(0 < x < 1)$. Here $D = (0,1)$, $D^* = [0,1]$. Take $c = 0$, so that $c \notin D^*$ but $c \notin D$. Therefore $D - \{c\} = D = (0,1)$, and the acceptable sequences satisfy $x_n \to 0$, $0 < x_n < 1$ $(n \in N)$. For every such (x_n), $f(x_n) = x_n^2 \to 0$. Hence $\lim_{x \to 0} f(x) = 0$.

EXAMPLE 8-6. $f(x) = x^2$ $(0 < x < 1)$, $f(0) = 7$. Here $D = [0,1)$, $D^* = [0,1]$. Take $c = 0$, so that $c \in D^*$. $D - \{c\} = (0,1)$. The acceptable sequences are the same as those of Example 8–5, and again $\lim\limits_{x\to 0} f(x) = 0$. Notice that the value of f at c is completely irrelevant to the existence or value of $\lim\limits_{x\to c} f(x)$.

EXAMPLE 8–7. $f(x) = x^2 + 7$ $(x < 2)$, $f(x) = 5x + 1$ $(x > 2)$, $c = 2$. Here $D = R - \{2\}$, $D^* = R$, and $D - \{c\} = D = R - \{2\}$. The acceptable sequences satisfy $x_n \to 2$, $x_n \neq 2$ $(n \in N)$. We may write $x_n = 2 + h_n$ $(n \in N)$, where (h_n) is a null sequence, $h_n \neq 0$ $(n \in N)$. If $h_n < 0$,

$$f(x_n) = f(2 + h_n) = (2 + h_n)^2 + 7$$

$$= 11 + 4h_n + h_n^2.$$

If $h_n > 0$,

$$f(x_n) = f(2 + h_n) = 5(2 + h_n) + 1$$

$$= 11 + 5h_n.$$

Thus, whether h_n is positive or negative,

$$|f(x_n) - 11| \leq 5|h_n| + h_n^2 \to 0.$$

It follows that $\lim\limits_{x\to 2} f(x) = 11$. The student should sketch the graph of f.

EXAMPLE 8–8. $f(x) = 4$ $(x < 0)$, $f(0) = 3$, $f(x) = 5$ $(x > 0)$, $c = 0$. Here $D = D^* = R$, $D - \{c\} = R - \{0\}$. The sequence $(1/n)$ is acceptable, and

$$\lim_{n\to\infty} f(1/n) = \lim_{n\to\infty} 5 = 5.$$

The sequence $(-1/n)$ is also acceptable, and

$$\lim_{n\to\infty} f(-1/n) = \lim_{n\to\infty} 4 = 4.$$

Therefore $\lim\limits_{x\to 0} f(x)$ does not exist. We can construct an acceptable sequence (x_n) for which $\lim f(x_n)$ does not exist. Indeed, take

$$x_n = \frac{1}{n} \qquad (n = 1,3,5,7,\ldots),$$

$$x_n = -\frac{1}{n} \qquad (n = 2,4,6,8,\ldots).$$

Then the sequence $(f(x_n))$ is

$$(5,4,5,4,5,4,\ldots),$$

clearly not convergent.

EXAMPLE 8–9. $g(h) = \dfrac{(x + h)^3 - x^3}{h}$ $(h \neq 0)$, $c = 0$. Here x is fixed.

$D = R - \{0\}$, $D^* = R$, $D - \{c\} = R - \{0\}$. If $h_n \to 0$, $h_n \neq 0$ $(n \in N)$, then

$$g(h_n) = \frac{1}{h_n}[x^3 + 3x^2 h_n + 3xh_n^2 + h_n^3 - x^3]$$

$$= 3x^2 + 3xh_n + h_n^2 \qquad (n \in N),$$

so

$$\lim g(h_n) = 3x^2, \text{ and } \lim_{h \to 0} g(h) = 3x^2.$$

We may also define $\lim_{x \to +\infty} f(x)$, under suitable conditions.

Definition 8–4. Suppose that dom f is not bounded above. If $f(x_n) \to L$ for every sequence (x_n) such that $x_n \to +\infty$ and $x_n \in D$ $(n \in N)$, then we say that

$$\lim_{x \to +\infty} f(x) = L.$$

EXERCISES 8–3

1. Frame appropriate definitions for
   (a) $\lim_{x \to c} f(x) = +\infty$.
   (a') $\lim_{x \to c} f(x) = -\infty$.
   (b) $\lim_{x \to +\infty} f(x) = +\infty$.
   (b') $\lim_{x \to +\infty} f(x) = -\infty$.
2. Evaluate the following, if the "limits" exist:
   (a) $\lim_{x \to +\infty} \dfrac{x^2 + 1}{x + 1}$.

   (b) $\lim_{x \to -\infty} \dfrac{x^2 - 2}{x + 3}$.

   (c) $\lim_{x \to +\infty} \dfrac{x^2 + 2x + 7}{x^2 - 3x + 4}$.

   (d) $\lim_{x \to 5} (3x^2 - 5x + 2)$.

   (e) $\lim_{h \to 0} \dfrac{(2 + h)^4 - 2^4}{h}$.

   (f) $\lim_{x \to 0} \dfrac{1}{x}$.

(g) $\lim\limits_{x \to 0} \left| \dfrac{1}{x} \right|$.

(h) $\lim\limits_{y \to 1} \dfrac{y^2 - 2y + 1}{y^2 - 1}$.

3. Prove that $\lim\limits_{x \to +\infty} \dfrac{\log x}{x} = 0$. [*Hint:* First show that $\log u < u$ for all

$u > 0$. Then observe that $\dfrac{\log x}{x} = \dfrac{2}{\sqrt{x}} \cdot \dfrac{\log\sqrt{x}}{\sqrt{x}}$.]

4. Prove that $\lim\limits_{x \to +\infty} \dfrac{\log x}{x^{1/50}} = 0$.

5. If P is a polynomial function, show that for every $c \in R$, $\lim\limits_{x \to c} P(x) = P(c)$.

6. If $|x| < 1$, show that

$$\lim_{n \to \infty}(1 + x + x^2 + \cdots + x^n) = \dfrac{1}{1 - x}.$$

7. A particle moves in a straight line. Its position at each time t is $f(t)$. Give a physical interpretation to

(a) $\dfrac{f(5) - f(3)}{2}$.

(b) $\dfrac{f(t_2) - f(t_1)}{t_2 - t_1}$ $(t_2 \neq t_1)$.

(c) $\lim\limits_{h \to 0} \dfrac{f(t + h) - f(t)}{h}$, if it exists $(t \in R)$.

8. (See Problem 7.) A body dropped from rest falls a distance (in feet) $S = \frac{1}{2}gt^2$ in t seconds. Find its speed at 10 seconds.

9. A body falls a distance (in feet) $s = 6t + \frac{1}{2}gt^2$ in t seconds. Find its initial speed.

10. In the following diagram, $m(x)$ is the mass (in pounds) of the segment $[0,x]$ of a linear rod (x in feet):

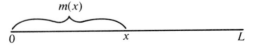

$m(x)$

0 x L

Give a physical interpretation to

(a) $\dfrac{m(x_2) - m(x_1)}{x_2 - x_1}$ $(x_1 \neq x_2; x_1, x_2 \in [0,L])$.

(b) $\displaystyle\lim_{h\to 0}\frac{m(x+h)-m(x)}{h}$, if it exists $(0 \le x \le L)$.

11. A function f is defined on the half-open interval $[0,1)$ and is non-decreasing: If $x \le y$, then $f(x) \le f(y)$. Discuss $\displaystyle\lim_{x\to 1} f(x)$ under each of two hypotheses:

   (a) f is bounded.
   (b) f is unbounded.

12. Given that f is bounded and integrable on $[a,b]$, evaluate

$$\lim_{x\to c}\int_a^x f(t)\,dt \qquad (a \le c \le b).$$

*13. C is a nonempty subset of the positive reals such that g.l.b. $C \notin C$. Show that there is sequence (c_n) in C such that

   (a) $c_1 > c_2 > c_3 > \cdots$.
   (b) $c_n \to$ g.l.b. C.

14. Suppose that $a \in D$ but $a \notin D^*$, where $D \subset R$. Show that a sequence (x_n) in D which converges to a must be constant from some point on: $\exists n_0 \in N$ such that $(\forall n)\, n > n_0 \Rightarrow x_n = a$.

*15. Let $c \in (\operatorname{dom} f)^*$. Show that $\displaystyle\lim_{x\to c} f(x) = L$ is equivalent to $\forall h > 0$, $\exists k > 0$ such that

$$\forall x \in \operatorname{dom} f - \{c\},\ |x - c| < k \Rightarrow |f(x) - L| < h.$$

16. Let f be a nondecreasing function on R. If $\displaystyle\lim_{\substack{n\to\infty \\ n\in N}} f(n) = L$, show that

$\displaystyle\lim_{x\to\infty} f(x) = L$.

17. Assuming that $\displaystyle\lim_{h\to 0}\frac{e^h - 1}{h} = 1$, evaluate

$$\lim_{h\to 0}\frac{e^{x+h} - e^x}{h}.$$

8–3. CONTINUITY OF FUNCTIONS

We have seen that $\displaystyle\lim_{x\to c} f(x)$ and $f(c)$ have nothing to do with each other, *in general*. One or the other, both or neither may exist, and even if they both exist they may not be equal. There is an important class of functions, all of which are well-behaved in this respect. They can be described by saying that for a given $c \in \operatorname{dom} f$, if $x \in \operatorname{dom} f$ is close to c, then $f(x)$ is close to $f(c)$.

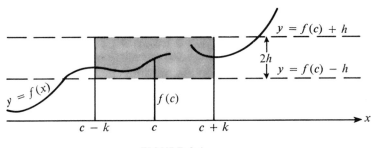

FIGURE 8–1

Definition 8–5. Let $c \in \mathrm{dom}\, f$. Then f is *continuous at* c iff for every $h > 0$ there exists a $k > 0$ such that

(1) $\qquad |x - c| < k \Rightarrow |f(x) - f(c)| < h \qquad (x \in \mathrm{dom}\, f)$.

Figure 8–1 illustrates the definition. Given an $h > 0$, we form the horizontal strip between the dashed lines $y = f(c) - h$ and $y = f(c) + h$. Then there is an interval $(c - k, c + k)$ containing c such that the graph of $y = f(x)$ does not break out of the strip so long as x stays within the interval. The gap in the graph indicates the possibility that some points of the interval may not belong to dom f. The situation illustrated must hold for *every* $h > 0$, of course.

In Figure 8–2, f is not continuous at c. There is a choice of $h > 0$ such that no interval $(c - k, c + k)$ has the required property. The graph breaks out of the strip in *every* interval.

We can obtain a very useful equivalent to continuity by translating into the language of limits.

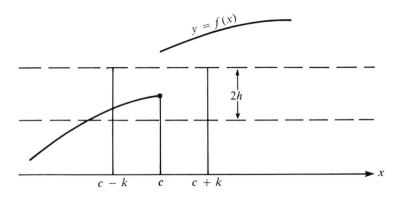

FIGURE 8–2

Theorem 8–13. Let $c \in \mathrm{dom}\, f$. Then f is continuous at c if and only if

(2)   For every sequence (x_n) in $\mathrm{dom}\, f$, $x_n \to c \Rightarrow f(x_n) \to f(c)$.

Proof: First, suppose that f is continuous at c and that (x_n) is a sequence in $\mathrm{dom}\, f$ such that $x_n \to c$. We shall prove that $f(x_n) \to f(c)$. For if $h > 0$, Definition 8–5 guarantees a $k > 0$ such that the implication (1) holds. Because $x_n \to c$, eventually x_n gets to be inside $(c - k, c + k)$. That is, $\exists n_0 \in N$ such that

$$|x_n - c| < k \qquad (n > n_0).$$

It follows from (1) that

$$|f(x_n) - f(c)| < h \qquad (n > n_0).$$

This means that $f(x_n) \to f(c)$.

To prove the converse, suppose that statement (2) holds but f is not continuous at c. Then there exists an $h > 0$ such that no $k > 0$ makes (1) true. In particular, $k = 1/n \,(n \in N)$ does not work, so in each interval $(c - (1/n), c + (1/n))$ there is a point $x_n \in \mathrm{dom}\, f$ such that $|f(x_n) - f(c)| \geq h$. Clearly $x_n \to c$. Because (2) holds, $f(x_n) - f(c) \to 0$, and

$$0 = \lim_{n \to \infty} |f(x_n) - f(c)| \geq h > 0.$$

This contradiction completes the proof.

It is almost true that (2) is equivalent to

(3) $\lim_{x \to c} f(x) = f(c)$.

The difficulty is merely that we may have $c \notin (\mathrm{dom}\, f)^*$, so that $\lim_{x \to c} f(x)$ does not exist. The situation is clarified by the following theorem:

*Theorem 8–14.** Let $c \in \mathrm{dom}\, f$. If $c \notin (\mathrm{dom}\, f)^*$, then f is continuous at c. If $c \in (\mathrm{dom}\, f)^*$, then f is continuous at c if and only if $\lim_{x \to c} f(x)$ exists and is equal to $f(c)$.

Proof: Suppose that $c \notin (\mathrm{dom}\, f)^*$. We assert that there is an interval $(c - (1/n), c + (1/n))$, for some $n \in N$, such that the only point of $\mathrm{dom}\, f$ in the interval is c. For if not, in each such interval there would be a point $x_n \in \mathrm{dom}\, f$, $x_n \neq c$. The sequence (x_n) converges to c, so it is acceptable. This contradicts $c \notin (\mathrm{dom}\, f)^*$. Given $h > 0$, we can take $k = 1/n$. Then $|x - c| < 1/n$, $x \in \mathrm{dom}\, f$ imply that $x = c$; therefore $|f(x) - f(c)| = 0 < h$. Thus f is continuous at c.

[*Note:* A point c of the type just discussed is "far away" from the rest of dom f; it is called an *isolated point* of dom f. From the standpoint of continuity, such points are rather trivial and uninteresting. A function is continuous at each isolated point of its domain. Most of the functions we discuss here will have domains without any isolated points.]

Now suppose that $c \in (\text{dom } f)^*$. If f is continuous at c, and if (x_n) is an acceptable sequence, then $x_n \to c$, $f(x_n) \to f(c)$, and $\lim_{x \to c} f(x)$ exists and is equal to $f(c)$. Conversely, if $\lim_{x \to c} f(x)$ exists and is equal to $f(c)$, we can prove that f is continuous at c. For consider any sequence (x_n) converging to c. Let y_r be the rth element of (x_n) such that $y_r \neq c$. If there are finitely many y_r, then $x_n = c$ for $n > n_0$, so $f(x_n) \to f(c)$. If there are infinitely many y_r, the sequence (y_r) is acceptable, and $f(y_r) \to f(c)$. The other elements of (x_n) are all equal to c. Thus $f(x_n) \to f(c)$. Therefore f is continuous at c.

EXERCISES 8–4

1. Prove that every polynomial function is continuous at every $c \in R$.

2. Suppose that dom $f = $ dom g and that f and g are both continuous at c. Prove that $f + g$ and fg are also continuous at c.

3. Let $A = \{1/n \mid n \in N\}$. Define

$$f(x) = x \qquad (x \in A),$$
$$f(x) = 0 \qquad (x \in R - A).$$

Find the set of points at which f is continuous.

4. Let $A = \{1/n \mid n \in N\}$. Define

$$f(x) = 1 \qquad (x \in A),$$
$$f(x) = 0 \qquad (x \in R - A).$$

Find the set of points at which f is continuous.

5. Suppose that f is continuous at c. Prove that $|f|$ is continuous at c. Is the converse true?

There are several important theorems that hold for functions defined only on a closed interval as domain and continuous at every point of the interval. Actually, even if the function has a larger domain, we may wish to ignore the rest of it. This permits a slight weakening of the hypothesis and makes the theorems applicable to a wider class of functions. This motivates the following definitions:

Definition 8–6. Let $D \subset \mathrm{dom}\, f$. The restriction of f to D, written $f|D$, is the function with domain D defined by

$$(f|D)(x) = f(x) \qquad (x \in D).$$

(See Section 2–4.)

Definition 8–7. Let $D \subset \mathrm{dom}\, f$. If $f|D$ is continuous at each $c \in D$, we say that f is continuous on D. If f is continuous at every point of its domain, we say that f is continuous.

Observe that the continuity of f on D is equivalent to the continuity of $f|D$.

EXERCISE 8–5

(a) Show that if f is continuous at $c \in D$, then $f|D$ is continuous at c.

(b) Show that if f is continuous at each point of D, then f is continuous on D.

It may happen that $f|D$ is continuous at c even though f is not. For example, consider the function f defined by

$$f(x) = 0 \qquad (x < 1),$$

$$f(x) = 3 \qquad (1 \le x \le 2),$$

$$f(x) = 7 \qquad (x > 2).$$

Let $D = [1,2]$. Then f is not continuous at the points 1 and 2, but $f|D$ is continuous at each point of D. Thus f is continuous on D.

Suppose that f is continuous on the closed interval $[a,b]$. One of the strongest intuitions we have about continuity is that the values of f, as we move from a to b, must pass through all values between $f(a)$ and $f(b)$. In Figure 8–3, we would expect that somewhere between a and b there is a point c such that $f(c) = v$. Indeed, if this were not so, we would change our definition of continuity. This property of continuous functions, which we shall prove, is called the *Darboux property*. Unfortunately there are "wild" functions which have the Darboux property, so we cannot take it as our definition of continuity. The definition that we have adopted (Definition 8–5) is the culmination of a long series of trials and errors by the mathematical community. It serves us quite well, as we shall see.

The conclusion we seek in the next theorem is slightly stronger than the Darboux property. It tells us not only that the graph of $y = f(x)$ meets the boundary of the region $y < v$, but also that it meets it at a point c to

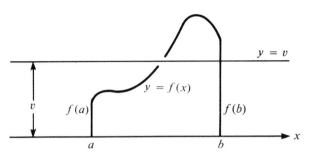

FIGURE 8–3

the left of which the graph stays in the region. That is, c is the first point where the graph breaks out of the region. We shall therefore refer to the following theorem as "the breakout theorem."

Theorem 8–15. Let f be continuous on $[a,b]$, $f(a) \le v \le f(b)$. Then there is a point $c \in [a,b]$ such that
(a) $f(c) = v$,
(b) $(\forall x) a \le x < c \Rightarrow f(x) < v$.

Proof: Let $A = \{x \in [a,b] \mid f(x) \ge v\}$. A is nonempty, for it contains b. It is obviously bounded below. Let $c = $ g.l.b. A. If $a \le x < c$, then $x \notin A$, because c is a lower bound of A. Therefore $f(x) < v$. Thus (b) holds. Next, there is a sequence (x_n) in A which converges to g.l.b. $A = c$. (See Problem 2 of Exercise 8–6 below.) For each $n \in N$, $f(x_n) \ge v$, so

(1) $$f(c) = \lim_{n \to \infty} f(x_n) \ge v.$$

If $c = a$, then $v \le f(c) = f(a) \le v$, so (a) holds. If $a < c$, there exists a sequence (x'_n) in (a,c) which converges to c. By (b), $f(x'_n) < v$ for each $n \in N$, so

(2) $$f(c) = \lim_{n \to \infty} f(x'_n) \le v.$$

Combining the inequalities (1) and (2), we get $f(c) = v$, which is (a). This completes the proof.

EXERCISES 8–6

1. State and prove the analogue of Theorem 8–15 for the case $f(a) \ge v \ge f(b)$.

2. Let A be a set with g.l.b. $A = c$. Show that there is a sequence (a_n) such that $a_n \in A$ $(n \in N)$ and $a_n \to c$.

The following corollary to Theorem 8–15 will be used heavily in our next theorem.

Corollary. Let f be continuous on $[a,b]$, and let

$$0 \le v \le |f(b) - f(a)|.$$

Then there is a point $c \in [a,b]$ such that
(a) $|f(c) - f(a)| = v$,
(b) $(\forall x)\, a \le x < c \Rightarrow |f(x) - f(a)| < v$.

Proof: We need only observe that the function g defined by

$$g(x) = |f(x) - f(a)| \qquad (a \le x \le b)$$

is continuous on $[a,b]$, and then apply Theorem 8–15 to g.

This corollary assures us that the graph of $y = f(x)$ "breaks out" of the open strip

$$f(a) - v < y < f(a) + v$$

at a first "breakout point" c (Figure 8–4).

We are already familiar with a wide class of functions which are integrable over an interval $[a,b]$, namely, the monotonic functions. Another useful class of integrable functions consists of those which are continuous on $[a,b]$.

Theorem 8–16.   If f is continuous on $[a,b]$, then it is integrable over $[a,b]$.
Proof (see Figure 8–5): There is no loss of generality in assuming that $b - a < \frac{1}{2}$, for we can split up the original interval into a finite number of intervals each of length less than $\frac{1}{2}$. If f is integrable over each one then it is integrable over their union $[a,b]$.

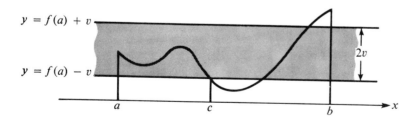

FIGURE 8–4

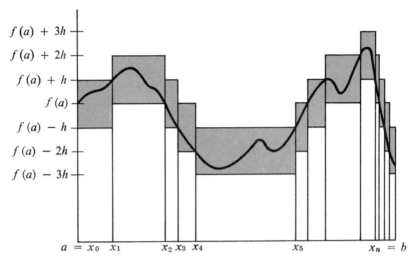

FIGURE 8-5

Our plan is to construct upper and lower sums for f which are arbitrarily close to each other. Thus, if $h > 0$ is given, we shall find a finite sequence

$$a = x_0 < x_1 < x_2 < \cdots < x_n = b$$

partitioning $[a,b]$, such that the corresponding upper and lower sums S and s satisfy

$$S - s < h.$$

We begin by defining $x_0 = a$. If $|f(x) - f(x_0)| \le h$ for all $x \in [a,b]$, we define $x_1 = b$ and stop the construction, with $n = 1$. If $h < |f(\bar{x}) - f(x_0)|$ for some $\bar{x} \in [x_0,b]$, we apply the corollary to Theorem 8–15 to the interval $[a,\bar{x}]$, with $v = h$. Let x_1 be the "breakout point," so that

(1) $$|f(x_1) - f(x_0)| = h,$$

(2) $$|f(x) - f(x_0)| \le h \qquad (x_0 \le x \le x_1).$$

Next, if $|f(x) - f(x_1)| \le h$ for all $x \in [x_1,b]$, we define $x_2 = b$ and stop the construction, with $n = 2$. If $h < |f(\bar{x}) - f(x_1)|$ for some $\bar{x} \in [x_1,b]$, we apply the same corollary to the interval $[x_1,\bar{x}]$, with $v = h$. Let x_2 be the breakout point:

(3) $$|f(x_2) - f(x_1)| = h,$$

(4) $$|f(x) - f(x_1)| \le h \qquad (x_1 \le x \le x_2).$$

Continuing in this way, we obtain a sequence (x_n), with $x_0 < x_1 < x_2 < \cdots$, which may be finite or infinite, a priori. We prove now that it cannot be infinite. For then (x_n) is an increasing sequence which is bounded above (by b), so it converges to some $c \in [a,b]$ (Theorem 8–12). From the method of construction—Eqs. (1), (3), and so on—

$$|f(x_n) - f(x_{n-1})| = h \qquad (n \in N).$$

By continuity, $f(x_n) \to f(c)$, $f(x_{n-1}) \to f(c)$, so

$$h = \lim_{n \to \infty} |f(x_n) - f(x_{n-1})|$$

$$= \left| \lim_{n \to \infty} (f(x_n) - f(x_{n-1})) \right|$$

$$= \left| \lim_{n \to \infty} f(x_n) - \lim_{n \to \infty} f(x_{n-1}) \right|$$

$$= 0.$$

This contradiction of $h > 0$ shows that our assumption that (x_n) is an infinite sequence must have been false. Hence the sequence is finite. The only way that the construction can stop, however, is that for some $n \geq 1$,

(5) $$|f(x) - f(x_{n-1})| \leq h \qquad (x_{n-1} \leq x \leq b),$$

and then we take $x_n = b$. Thus we have

$$a = x_0 < x_1 < x_2 < \cdots < x_n = b.$$

The inequalities (2), (4), and so on, together with (5), yield

$$|f(x) - f(x_0)| \leq h \qquad (x_0 \leq x \leq x_1),$$

$$|f(x) - f(x_1)| \leq h \qquad (x_1 \leq x \leq x_2),$$

(6)
$$\vdots \qquad\qquad \vdots$$

$$|f(x) - f(x_{n-2})| \leq h \qquad (x_{n-2} \leq x \leq x_{n-1}),$$

$$|f(x) - f(x_{n-1})| \leq h \qquad (x_{n-1} \leq x \leq x_n).$$

These inequalities assure us that in each of the subintervals $[x_{i-1}, x_i]$ ($i = 1, 2, \ldots, n$), the function varies by no more than $2h$. If we form the upper and lower sums S and s corresponding to this partition, we see that each interval $[x_{i-1}, x_i]$ contributes to $S - s$ an amount no greater than $2h(x_i - x_{i-1})$, the area of the shaded rectangle lying above $[x_{i-1}, x_i]$. The sum of all these areas is exactly $2h(b - a)$, since their heights are the same ($= 2h$) and their bases add up to $(b - a)$. Therefore

$$S - s \leq 2h(b - a) < h.$$

(Recall that we have assumed $b - a < \frac{1}{2}$.) Since h was arbitrary, f is integrable on $[a,b]$. This completes our proof.

From Figure 8–5, or from the preceding proof, we see that any two points of $[a,b]$ which belong to the same or adjacent subintervals have functional values close to each other. Indeed, if x and x' are such points, then $|f(x') - f(x)| \leq 3h$. Now suppose that d is the smallest of the lengths $x_i - x_{i-1}$ $(i = 1, \ldots, n)$. If the distance between two points is less than d, they must lie in the same or adjacent subintervals; otherwise they would bracket between them a full subinterval $[x_{i-1}, x_i]$ and their distance would exceed $x_i - x_{i-1} \geq d$. Thus, given h, we have found a d such that

$$\forall x, x' \in [a,b], |x - x'| < d \Rightarrow |f(x) - f(x')| \leq 3h.$$

Now h was a completely arbitrary positive number. Hence, given any $h' > 0$, we can first choose an $h > 0$ such that $3h < h'$. Dependent on this h alone, d is determined by our construction and works for every x and x'. We have therefore proved the following interesting theorem (in the statement we drop the prime on the h; this is harmless).

Theorem 8–17. Let f be continuous on $[a,b]$. Then for every $h > 0$, there exists a $d > 0$ such that

$$|x' - x| < d \Rightarrow |f(x') - f(x)| < h \qquad (x, x' \in [a,b]).$$

This looks something like Definition 8–5. The difference is that in the definition, one of the points whose functional values are to be compared is given (namely, c). For this point, if we are challenged to make $f(x)$ closer to $f(c)$ than h, we can meet the challenge by requiring that x be closer to c than k. The number k that we use will depend on c in general, as well as on h. Change c and we may well have to change k. Contrast this with Theorem 8–17. We are challenged to make $f(x)$ closer to $f(x')$ than h without being told in advance which x' is to be used as a test. The challenge is met by producing a d which works simultaneously or *uniformly* for all $x' \in [a,b]$. For this reason, the property stated in the conclusion of Theorem 8–17 is called *uniform continuity* (with respect to $[a,b]$). The theorem asserts, therefore, that every function which is continuous on $[a,b]$ is uniformly continuous on $[a,b]$. The fact that $[a,b]$ is closed and bounded is crucial, as the following examples show.

EXAMPLE 8–10. Let $f(x) = x^2$ ($x \in R$). Then f is continuous, but the challenge with $h = 1$ cannot be met uniformly on R. Given any $d > 0$, we can find points $x, x' \in R$ closer together than d but with $|f(x') - f(x)| \geq 1$. Indeed, take $x' = (1/d) + (d/2)$, $x = 1/d$. Then

$$|f(x') - f(x)| = |x'^2 - x^2| = \left|\left(\frac{1}{d} + \frac{d}{2}\right)^2 - \left(\frac{1}{d}\right)^2\right|$$

$$= 1 + \frac{d^2}{4} > 1.$$

The trouble here is that R is not bounded.

EXAMPLE 8–11. Let $f(x) = 1/x$ ($0 < x \leq 1$). Then f is continuous but not uniformly continuous on $(0,1]$. Given any $d > 0$, we can find points x, $x' \in \text{dom } f$ closer together than d but with $|f(x') - f(x)| \geq 1$. If $d \geq 1$, simply take $x = \frac{1}{2}$, $x' = \frac{1}{4}$. If $d < 1$, take $x = d$, $x' = d/2$. Then

$$|f(x') - f(x)| = \left|\frac{1}{x'} - \frac{1}{x}\right| = \left|\frac{2}{d} - \frac{1}{d}\right| = \frac{1}{d} > 1.$$

The trouble here is that $(0,1]$ is not closed.

EXAMPLE 8–12. Let $f(x) = x^2$ ($0 \leq x^2 \leq 9$). For all $x, x' \in [0,9]$,

$$|f(x') - f(x)| = |x'^2 - x^2|$$

$$= |x' + x| \cdot |x' - x|$$

$$\leq 18|x' - x|.$$

If we are challenged to make the difference less than $h = 10^{-7}$, say, we need only require that

$$|x' - x| < d = \tfrac{1}{18}10^{-7}.$$

For an arbitrary $h > 0$, we would choose $d = h/18$. Hence f is uniformly continuous on $[0,9]$.

EXERCISE 8–7

How close together must the radii of two concentric circles be taken to make the area of the region between them less than .01 square inches? Can you give a numerical answer? What if you are told that the radii do not exceed 20 inches?

Another consequence of our proof of Theorem 8–16 is the following:

Theorem 8–18. If f is continuous on $[a,b]$, then it is bounded on $[a,b]$. *Proof:* Left to the student.

Theorem 8–19. Suppose that f is continuous on D and that $f(x) \neq 0$ $(x \in D)$. Then $1/f$ is continuous on D.

Proof: We apply the criterion of Theorem 8–13. Let $c \in D$ and let (x_n) be a sequence in D such that $x_n \to c$. Then $f(x_n) \to f(c)$, so $1/f(x_n) \to 1/f(c)$, by Theorem 8–8. Therefore $1/f$ is continuous at c. Since c was arbitrary in D, $1/f$ is continuous on D.

To appreciate the next theorem, which is very important, consider the following example:

$$f(x) = x + 2 \qquad (0 < x < 1).$$

Clearly f is continuous and bounded on $(0,1)$, and

$$\text{g.l.b.}\{f(x) | 0 < x < 1\} = 2,$$

$$\text{l.u.b.}\{f(x) | 0 < x < 1\} = 3.$$

But there are no points in $(0,1)$ at which these bounds are actually assumed as functional values. In other words, f does not assume a maximum or a minimum on its domain. This situation cannot arise when f is continuous on a closed and bounded interval $[a,b]$.

Theorem 8–20. If f is continuous on the closed, bounded interval $[a,b]$, then f assumes a maximum and minimum on $[a,b]$. That is, there exist $c,d \in [a,b]$ such that

$$f(c) \leq f(x) \leq f(d) \qquad (a \leq x \leq b).$$

Proof: By Theorem 8–18, f is bounded on $[a,b]$, so it has a least upper bound

$$M = \text{l.u.b.}\{f(x) | a \leq x \leq b\}.$$

We must show that $\exists d \in [a,b]$ such that $f(d) = M$. Assume that there is no such point d. Then the function g defined by

$$g(x) = M - f(x) \qquad (x \in [a,b])$$

is continuous and never zero on the interval $[a,b]$. By Theorem 8–19, $1/g$ is also continuous on $[a,b]$. By Theorem 8–18, $1/g$ is bounded on $[a,b]$; there exists a positive number k such that

$$\frac{1}{g(x)} \leq k \qquad (x \in [a,b]).$$

That is,

$$\frac{1}{M - f(x)} \leq k,$$

$$M - f(x) \geq \frac{1}{k},$$

$$f(x) \leq M - \frac{1}{k} \qquad (x \in [a,b]).$$

This means that $M - (1/k)$ is an upper bound of f smaller than the least upper bound M. This contradiction proves that there is a $d \in [a,b]$ such that $f(d) = M$. There is a similar proof showing that f assumes a minimum value on $[a,b]$.

The following result is sometimes called the *mean value theorem* for integrals (actually there are several mean value theorems):

Theorem 8–21. Let f be continuous on $[a,b]$. Then there exists $c \in [a,b]$ such that

(1)
$$\frac{1}{b - a} \int_a^b f(x)\,dx = f(c).$$

The intuitive interpretation of the left side of Eq. (1) is the average or *mean* of f in $[a,b]$. The theorem asserts that the mean of f is actually assumed as a value of f. The continuity condition is critical, as the following example shows. Let

$$f(x) = 0 \qquad (0 \leq x < \tfrac{1}{2}),$$
$$f(x) = 10 \qquad (\tfrac{1}{2} \leq x \leq 1).$$

The mean of f is 5, but there is no $c \in [0,1]$ for which $f(c) = 5$.

Proof of Theorem 8–21: Let M and m be the l.u.b. and g.l.b. of f in $[a,b]$. Then by Theorem 8–20, there exist $x_1, x_2 \in [a,b]$ such that

$$f(x_1) = m, \qquad f(x_2) = M.$$

Since

$$(b - a)m \leq \int_a^b f(x)\,dx \leq (b - a)M,$$

the number

$$v = \frac{1}{b-a} \int_a^b f(x)\, dx$$

lies between $f(x_1)$ and $f(x_2)$. Applying the Darboux property (Theorem 8-15) to f on $[x_1, x_2]$ or $[x_2, x_1]$, we get a point $c \in [a,b]$ such that $f(c) = v$.

EXERCISES 8-8

1. A *zero* of a function f is a number $c \in \text{dom } f$ such that $f(c) = 0$; that is, c is a root of the equation $f(x) = 0$. Prove that the third-degree polynomial function P given by

$$P(x) = x^3 + 100x + 7 \qquad (x \in R)$$

has a (real) zero. [*Hint:* Show that 0 lies between $P(-1{,}000)$ and $P(1{,}000)$.]

2. Show that every odd-degree polynomial function (with real coefficients) has a real zero.

3. Let f be a continuous function with domain a closed interval. Prove that the range of f is also a closed interval.

4. A point starts at the origin and moves in the (x,y)-plane so that at each time $t \geq 0$ its coordinates are

$$x = f(t),$$

$$y = g(t),$$

where f and g are continuous functions, at least one of which is unbounded. Prove that for each $r > 0$, there is a first time at which the point meets the circle $x^2 + y^2 = r^2$.

5. Let f be bounded and integrable on $[a,b]$, and let

$$F(x) = \int_a^x f(t)\, dt \qquad (x \in [a,b]).$$

Prove that F is continuous on $[a,b]$. [*Hint:* Estimate $F(x + h) - F(x)$ for x fixed, h small.]

*6. Define f by

$$f(x) = x^2 \qquad\qquad (0 \leq x \leq 1),$$

$$f(x) = 1 - (x - 1)^3 \quad (1 \leq x \leq 2).$$

Show that a square (based on the x-axis) can be inscribed in Figure 8-6. [*Hint:* For each $x \in [0,1]$, let s and t be the sides of the inscribed rectangle with one vertex at $(x,0)$. Define $d(x) = s(x) - t(x)$. Then $d(0) = 2$, $d(1) = -1$.]

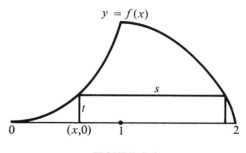

$$y = f(x)$$

FIGURE 8–6

7. For each $m \in R$, define the function f_m by

$$f_m(x) = \frac{\log (1 + x)}{x} \qquad (x > 0),$$

$$f_m(0) = m.$$

Show that there is exactly one $m \in R$ such that f_m is continuous.

8. Let $f(x) = 1/x$ $(3 \le x \le 4)$. Show that for all $x, x' \in [3,4]$,

$$\left| f(x') - f(x) \right| \le \tfrac{1}{9}\left| x' - x \right|.$$

9. Let $f(x) = \sqrt{x}$ $(x \ge 9)$. Show that for all $x, x' \in \operatorname{dom} f$,

$$\left| f(x') - f(x) \right| \le \tfrac{1}{6}\left| x' - x \right|.$$

[*Hint:* Use the identity

$$\sqrt{x'} - \sqrt{x} = \frac{x' - x}{\sqrt{x'} + \sqrt{x}}.\bigg]$$

10. Prove that $\lim\limits_{x \to +\infty} \left(\sqrt{x + 7} - \sqrt{x} \right) = 0$.

*11. For $u \in R$, let $N(u)$ denote the number of distinct real solutions of

$$ux^2 - x + 1 = 0.$$

For what values of u is N continuous?

8–4. THE DERIVATIVE

Let f be a function defined on an open interval $I = (c - k, c + k)$. An important problem is to determine the approximate behavior of f on I from a knowledge of its behavior at c. In general the problem is insoluble, of course, because we can define a function arbitrarily at points other than c, and knowledge of $f(c)$ is no help at all. But if we suppose that f is continuous at c, we know that $f(a)$ is close to $f(c)$ if a is close to c. For example, we know that $\sqrt{100.4}$ is close to $\sqrt{100} = 10$. Another way of expressing continuity at c is

$$f(c + h) - f(c) \to 0 \qquad (h \to 0).$$

Thus, if we define

$$e(h) = f(c + h) - f(c) \qquad (|h| < k),$$

then

$$\lim_{h \to 0} e(h) = 0.$$

We shall have considerable use for error functions of the type e just mentioned. Accordingly, we make the following definition.

Definition 8–8. Let e be a function such that $0 \in (\text{dom } e)^*$. If $\lim\limits_{h \to 0} e(h) = 0$, we call e a *null function*. We shall denote by $\mathbf{N}$ the class of null functions.

In the older literature, such a function e would be called an infinitesimal. The term has fallen into some disrepute because of occasional inexact or sloppy usage, but the concept is a perfectly good one.

In our terminology, a function f is continuous at c if $\exists e \in \mathbf{N}$ such that

$$f(c + h) = f(c) + e(h) \qquad (|h| < k).$$

Let us return to the problem of approximating $\sqrt{100.4}$. Of course we could "calculate" it by applying the algorithm we all learned in grade school, but really, what is that algorithm? It is merely a method for computing better and better rational approximations, so we are led back to our original problem. Perhaps there is a better method than grinding out one decimal at a time.

We replace the error .4 by h, $|h| < 1$, in order to treat the problem more generally. Thus, with $f(x) = \sqrt{x}$ $(x \geq 0)$, and $c = 100$, we have

$$f(c) = \sqrt{100} = 10,$$

$$f(c + h) = \sqrt{100 + h} \qquad (|h| < 1).$$

Then

$$e(h) = \sqrt{100 + h} - 10$$

$$= \frac{\left(\sqrt{100 + h} - 10\right)\left(\sqrt{100 + h} + 10\right)}{\sqrt{100 + h} + 10}$$

$$= \frac{(100 + h) - 100}{\sqrt{100 + h} + 10},$$

so

(1) $$e(h) = \frac{h}{\sqrt{100 + h} + 10} \qquad (|h| < 1).$$

Now, estimating roughly, for $|h| < 1$,

$$\sqrt{100 + h} + 10 > \sqrt{99} + 10$$

$$> \sqrt{81} + 10$$

$$= 19,$$

so

(2) $$|e(h)| \le \frac{|h|}{19},$$

and $e \in \mathbf{N}$.

Can we do better than the estimate (2)? The denominator in Eq. (1) is

$$10 + \sqrt{100 + h} = 10 + (10 + e(h))$$

$$= 20 + e(h),$$

so (1) becomes

(3) $$e(h) = \frac{h}{20 + e(h)} \doteq \frac{h}{20}.$$

To see how good the approximation is, look at the new error

$$e(h) - \frac{h}{20} = \frac{h}{20 + e(h)} - \frac{h}{20}$$

$$= -\frac{h e(h)}{20(20 + e(h))}$$

$$= -\frac{h^2}{20(20 + e(h))^2}$$

$$= h e_1(h),$$

say, where

(4) $$e_1(h) = -\frac{h}{20(20 + e(h))^2}.$$

Thus e_1 is also a null function, and

$$e(h) = \frac{h}{20} + he_1(h),$$

(5) $$\sqrt{100 + h} = 10 + \frac{h}{20} + he_1(h).$$

As before, we can bound the error:

(6) $$|he_1(h)| = \frac{h^2}{20(20 + e(h))^2} \le \frac{h^2}{20 \cdot 19^2}.$$

This is far better than the error estimate (2).

For $h = .4$, our first approximation was

$$\sqrt{100.4} \doteq 10,$$

with an error bound about

$$\frac{.4}{20} = .02.$$

Now, Eq. (5) yields the approximation

$$\sqrt{100.4} \doteq 10.02000$$

with an error bound about

$$\frac{(.4)^2}{20^3} = .00002.$$

We could carry our approximation farther by splitting $e_1(h)$ into the principal term $-h/20^3$ and a new error, which could also be bounded, and feeding this into Eq. (5) to get

(7) $$\sqrt{100 + h} = 10 + \frac{h}{20} - \frac{h^2}{20^3} + \text{error}.$$

This would yield, for $h = .4$,

$$\sqrt{100.4} \doteq 10.01998000,$$

with an error bound about two units in the last place.

The method used here may seem rather special, but actually it is widely applicable. We aim to improve the formula

$$f(c + h) = f(c) + e(h)$$

by writing $e(h)$ as a constant multiple of h plus an error of the form $he_1(h)$, where e_1 is also a null function. This will yield a formula similar to (5):

$$f(c + h) = f(c) + mh + he_1(h),$$

where $e_1 \in \mathbf{N}$. If this can be done, there is only one constant m that will work. For, with $h \neq 0$, we can solve for $m + e_1(h)$:

$$m + e_1(h) = \frac{f(c + h) - f(c)}{h}.$$

The left side tends to m as $h \to 0$, so the right side must tend to m, and we get

$$m = \lim_{h \to 0} \frac{f(c + h) - f(c)}{h}.$$

This determines m.

Definition 8–9. Let f be defined on an open interval $(c - k, c + k)$. If there exist a number m and a null function e_1 such that

(8) $$f(c + h) = f(c) + mh + he_1(h) \qquad (|h| < k),$$

then f is said to be *differentiable at* c, and the number m is called the *derivative of f at c*, written $f'(c)$.

We have seen that a necessary condition for f to be differentiable at c is the existence of

$$m = \lim_{h \to 0} \frac{f(c + h) - f(c)}{h}.$$

This condition is also sufficient, for if it holds, there exists a null function e_1 such that

$$\frac{f(c + h) - f(c)}{h} = m + e_1(h) \qquad (0 < |h| < k),$$

so

$$f(c + h) - f(c) = mh + he_1(h) \qquad (0 < |h| < k).$$

Since this equation holds for $h = 0$, we obtain Eq. (8). We have therefore proved the following theorem:

Theorem 8–22. Let f be defined on $(c - k, c + k)$. Then f is differentiable at c, with derivative m, if and only if

$$\lim_{h \to 0} \frac{f(c + h) - f(c)}{h}$$

exists and is equal to m.

EXERCISE 8–9

Prove that differentiability at c implies continuity at c. Is the converse true?

It is interesting to compare geometrically the approximations to f near c which are yielded by continuity and differentiability. In the first case we approximate by the constant function g_1 given by

$$g_1(c + h) = f(c) \qquad (h \in R).$$

Its graph is the horizontal line at height $f(c)$ above the h-axis (Figure 8–7). In the second case, we approximate by the linear function g_2 given by

$$g_2(c + h) = f(c) + mh \qquad (h \in R).$$

Its graph is the line through $(0, f(c))$ with slope m (Figure 8–8).

Notice that we have drawn the approximating line in Figure 8–8 tangent to the given curve. We could prove that this is the case were it not for the fact that we have never defined the tangent to a curve. A reasonable definition might be as follows. Let P be a point on the curve C, Q any

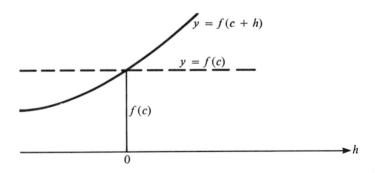

FIGURE 8–7

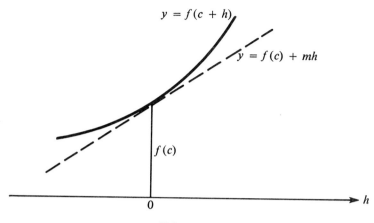

FIGURE 8–8

other point on C, and $s(P,Q)$ the slope of the secant line through P and Q. If $\lim\limits_{Q \to P} s(P,Q)$ exists, then the line through P with this limiting slope is called the tangent to C at P. This definition should satisfy our intuition fairly well, except possibly for the case when the "limit secant" is vertical. Leaving aside this case, we see that

$$\lim_{Q \to P} s(P,Q) = \lim_{h \to 0} \frac{f(c + h) - f(c)}{h},$$

where c is the abscissa of P, $c + h$ is the abscissa of Q, and C is the graph of $y = f(x)$ (Figure 8–9).

Let us consider some examples of differentiation.

EXAMPLE 8–13. $f(x) = x^3$ $(x \in R)$, $c \in R$. Then for every $h \in R$,

$$\begin{aligned}
f(c + h) - f(c) &= (c + h)^3 - c^3 \\
&= 3c^2h + 3ch^2 + h^3 \\
&= 3c^2h + h(3ch + h^2) \\
&= 3c^2h + he_1(h).
\end{aligned}$$

Here $e_1(h) = 3ch + h^2 \to 0$ as $h \to 0$, so $e_1 \in N$. Hence f is differentiable at c, and $f'(c) = 3c^2$.

EXAMPLE 8–14. $f(x) = 1/x$ $(x \neq 0)$, $c \neq 0$. Then for $|h| < |c|$, so that $c + h \neq 0$,

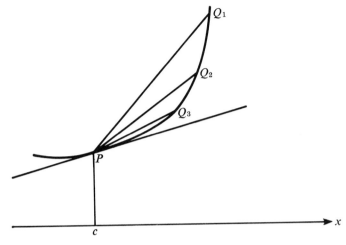

FIGURE 8–9

$$f(c + h) - f(c) = \frac{1}{c + h} - \frac{1}{c}$$

$$= -\frac{h}{c(c + h)}$$

$$= \frac{h}{c}\left[-\frac{1}{c + h} + \frac{1}{c}\right] - \frac{h}{c^2}$$

$$= -\frac{h}{c^2} + \frac{h}{c}\left[\frac{h}{c(c + h)}\right]$$

$$= -\frac{1}{c^2}h + he_1(h).$$

Here

$$e_1(h) = \frac{h}{c^2(c + h)} \to 0$$

as $h \to 0$, so $e_1 \in \mathbf{N}$. Hence f is differentiable at c, and $f'(c) = -1/c^2$.
Alternate solution: For $0 < |h| < |c|$,

$$\frac{f(c + h) - f(c)}{h} = -\frac{1}{c(c + h)} \to -\frac{1}{c^2}$$

as $h \to 0$. Then apply Theorem 8–22.

EXAMPLE 8–15. $f(x) = \log x$ $(x > 0)$, $c > 0$. For $|h| < c$,

$$\frac{f(c + h) - f(c)}{h} = \frac{1}{h} \int_c^{c+h} \frac{1}{t}\, dt.$$

For $h > 0$, apply the mean value theorem (Theorem 8–21) to the interval $[c, c + h]$, with the function $1/j$. (Recall that j is the identity function: $j(x) = x$ $(x \in R)$.) Then there exists a number q in the interval such that

$$\frac{f(c + h) - f(c)}{h} = \frac{1}{q}.$$

For each h, choose one such q. This defines a function q such that

$$c \le q(h) \le c + h \qquad (0 < h < c),$$

$$\frac{f(c + h) - f(c)}{h} = \frac{1}{q(h)} \qquad (0 < h < c).$$

As $h \to 0+$ (through positive values), $q(h) \to c$. Hence

$$\lim_{h \to 0+} \frac{f(c + h) - f(c)}{h} = \frac{1}{c}.$$

We leave to the student the case $h < 0$. The final result is that

(9) $$\log'(c) = \frac{1}{c} \qquad (c > 0).$$

EXAMPLE 8–16. Let g be differentiable at c, with $g(c) = a$, $g'(c) = m$. Define

$$f(x) = xg(x) \qquad (x \in \operatorname{dom} g).$$

Then there is an $e_1 \in N$ such that

$$g(c + h) = a + mh + he_1(h).$$

Hence

$$f(c + h) = (c + h)g(c + h)$$
$$= (c + h)(a + mh) + he_1(h)(c + h)$$
$$= ca + h(a + cm) + h[mh + e_1(h)(c + h)].$$

Putting

$$e_2(h) = mh + e_1(h)(c + h),$$

we see that $e_2 \in \mathbf{N}$. Hence

$$f(c + h) = cg(c) + h(g(c) + cg'(c)) + he_2(h)$$
$$= f(c) + (g(c) + cg'(c))h + he_2(h).$$

By Definition 8–9, f is differentiable at c, and

(10) $$f'(c) = g(c) + cg'(c).$$

EXAMPLE 8–17.   Let $f(x) = |x|$ $(x \in R)$, $c = 0$. Then

$$f(c + h) - f(c) = |h| = h \qquad (h > 0)$$
$$= -h \qquad (h < 0),$$

so

$$\lim_{h \to 0+} \frac{f(c + h) - f(c)}{h} = 1,$$

$$\lim_{h \to 0-} \frac{f(c + h) - f(c)}{h} = -1.$$

Therefore f is not differentiable at 0. No linear approximation is good enough near 0.

EXAMPLE 8–18.   Let g be differentiable at c^2, $c \in R$. Define $f(x) = g(x^2)$ $(x^2 \in \text{dom } g)$. Is f differentiable at c?

Solution: $f(c + h) = g((c + h)^2) = g(c^2 + k)$, where

$$k = 2ch + h^2.$$

Observe that $k \to 0$ as $h \to 0$. From the differentiability of g at c^2,

$$g(c^2 + k) = g(c^2) + g'(c^2)k + ke_1(k),$$

where $e_1 \in \mathbf{N}$. Thus

$$f(c + h) = f(c) + g'(c^2)(2ch + h^2) + ke_1(k)$$
$$= f(c) + 2cg'(c^2)h + h^2g'(c^2) + ke_1(k).$$

Now

$$h^2g'(c^2) + ke_1(k) = h^2g'(c^2) + (2ch + h^2)e_1(k)$$
$$= h[hg'(c^2) + (2c + h)e_1(k)]$$
$$= he_2(h),$$

where $e_2 \in \mathbf{N}$. Hence

$$f(c + h) = f(c) + 2cg'(c^2)h + he_2(h),$$

and f is differentiable at c, with

$$f'(c) = 2cg'(c^2).$$

EXAMPLE 8–19. $f(x) = \displaystyle\int_0^x (1 + t^3)^{10}\, dt \qquad (x \in R).$

Put $g(t) = (1 + t^3)^{10}$, for brevity. We could of course expand g in full, integrate term by term, and then attempt to differentiate f at c. A better scheme is the following:

$$\frac{1}{h}(f(c + h) - f(c)) = \frac{1}{h}\int_c^{c+h} g(t)\, dt \qquad (h \neq 0).$$

Now by the mean value theorem,

$$\frac{1}{h}\int_c^{c+h} g(t)\, dt = g(b(h)),$$

where $b(h)$ lies between c and $c + h$. Since g is continuous, $g(b(h)) \to g(c)$ as $h \to 0$. Hence

$$\lim_{h \to 0} \frac{f(c + h) - f(c)}{h} = g(c),$$

and

$$f'(c) = g(c) = (1 + c^3)^{10}.$$

It should be apparent from the preceding examples that it is possible to differentiate many functions. Although the methods we used may appear to be rather special, most of them are actually of fairly general applicability. It will be useful for us to derive a number of rules, which we state as theorems.

Theorem 8–23. If f and g have a common domain and are both differentiable at c, and if $r, s \in R$, then $rf + sg$ is differentiable at c and

$$(rf + sg)'(c) = rf'(c) + sg'(c).$$

Proof: By assumption, for h small,

$$f(c + h) = f(c) + hf'(c) + he_1(h),$$

$$g(c + h) = g(c) + hg'(c) + he_2(h),$$

where $e_1, e_2 \in \mathbf{N}$. Hence

$$rf(c + h) + sg(c + h) = rf(c) + sg(c)$$

$$+ h[rf'(c) + sg'(c)] + h[re_1(h) + se_2(h)].$$

Since

$$re_1(h) + se_2(h) \to 0 \qquad (h \to 0),$$

the result follows from Definition 8–9.

Theorem 8–24. If f and g have a common domain and are both differentiable at c, then their product is also and

$$(fg)'(c) = f'(c)g(c) + f(c)g'(c).$$

Proof: Let $f(c) = a_1$, $f'(c) = b_1$, $g(c) = a_2$, $g'(c) = b_2$. Then for h small,

$$f(c + h) = a_1 + b_1h + he_1(h),$$

$$g(c + h) = a_2 + b_2h + he_2(h),$$

where $e_1, e_2 \in \mathbf{N}$. Then

$$f(c + h)g(c + h) = a_1a_2 + (a_1b_2 + a_2b_1)h + he_3(h),$$

where

$$e_3(h) = b_1b_2h + (a_1 + b_1h)e_2(h) + (a_2 + b_2h)e_1(h).$$

Clearly $e_3 \in \mathbf{N}$ and the result follows from Definition 8–9.

Theorem 8–25. Let $j(x) = x \ (x \in R)$. Then for all $n \in N$, $c \in R$,

(11) $$(j^n)'(c) = nc^{n-1}.$$

Proof: For $n = 1$ the result is trivial, for

$$\lim_{h \to 0} \frac{j(c + h) - j(c)}{h} = \lim_{h \to 0} 1 = 1.$$

We proceed by induction on n. Suppose the result holds for a given $n \in N$.

Then by Theorem 8–24,

$$(j^{n+1})'(c) = (j \cdot j^n)'(c) = j'(c)j^n(c) + j(c)(j^n)'(c)$$
$$= 1 \cdot c^n + c \cdot nc^{n-1} = c^n + nc^n$$
$$= (n+1)c^n.$$

Therefore the result holds for $n + 1$. By the induction principle it holds for all $n \in N$.

Observe that the derivative of a constant function is 0, so that Eq. (11) holds also for $n = 0$. In Example 8–14 we proved that

$$(j^{-1})'(c) = (-1)c^{-2} \qquad (c \neq 0),$$

so that Eq. (11) holds for $n = -1$. Is it possible that it holds whenever n is an integer?

Theorem 8–26.   If n is a negative integer, then

$$(j^n)'(c) = nc^{n-1} \qquad (c \neq 0).$$

Proof: Put $n = -m$, $m \in N$. We shall prove the result in the form

$$(j^{-m})'(c) = -mc^{-m-1} \qquad (c \neq 0),$$

for all $m \in N$. As we saw, it holds for $m = 1$. Assuming that it holds for a given $m \in N$, we find

$$(j^{-m-1})'(c) = (j^{-1}j^{-m})'(c)$$
$$= (j^{-1})'(c)j^{-m}(c) + j^{-1}(c)(j^{-m})'(c)$$
$$= (-c^{-2})c^{-m} + c^{-1}(-mc^{-m-1})$$
$$= -c^{-m-2} - mc^{-m-2}$$
$$= -(m+1)c^{-(m+1)-1}.$$

Hence the result holds for $m + 1$. By the induction principle, it holds for all $m \in N$.

There are many cases in which a function f is differentiable at every point in its domain. When this is so, we get a new function f', defined by

$$f'(x) = \lim_{h \to 0} \frac{f(x+h) - f(x)}{h} \qquad (x \in \operatorname{dom} f).$$

Even when f is not differentiable everywhere in its domain, the derivative function f' can be defined wherever it exists. In this sense, we can rewrite the rules obtained above as follows:

(A) $$(rf + sg)' = rf' + sg',$$

(B) $$(fg)' = f'g + fg',$$

(C) $$(j^n)' = nj^{n-1} \qquad (n \text{ an integer}).$$

It follows from (A) and (C) that for any sequence of coefficients (a_n) and for any integers p, q with $p \le q$,

(D) $$\left(\sum_{n=p}^{q} a_n j^n \right)' = \sum_{n=p}^{q} n a_n j^{n-1}.$$

It frequently happens that we must differentiate a power of a function f which is known to be differentiable. For example, consider $g = f^5$. By assumption, if $c \in \operatorname{dom} f'$, $|h|$ small, then

$$f(c + h) = f(c) + e(h),$$

where $e \in \mathbf{N}$,

$$e(h) = f'(c)h + he_1(h),$$

and $e_1 \in \mathbf{N}$. Now

$$g(c + h) = f^5(c + h) = (f(c) + e(h))^5.$$

Put $b = f(c)$, $k = e(h)$. Then since j^5 is differentiable at b and k is small,

$$(b + k)^5 = b^5 + 5b^4 k + ke_2(k),$$

where $e_2 \in \mathbf{N}$. Now

$$5b^4 k + ke_2(k) = 5b^4(f'(c)h + he_1(h))$$
$$+ h(f'(c) + e_1(h))e_2(e(h))$$
$$= 5b^4 f'(c)h + he_3(h),$$

where

$$e_3(h) = 5b^4 e_1(h) + (f'(c) + e_1(h))e_2(e(h)) \to 0 \text{ as } h \to 0.$$

Collecting all our results, we get

$$g(c + h) = g(c) + 5f^4(c)f'(c)h + he_3(h).$$

Hence

$$g'(c) = (f^5)'(c) = 5f^4(c)f'(c).$$

Since this holds for all $c \in \operatorname{dom}(f')$,

$$(f^5)' = 5f^4 f'.$$

What we appear to have done is differentiate the power function j^5, substitute f, then correct by multiplying by f'. Now substitution of f for the variable in u yields the composition of u and f, namely $u \circ f$. Thus, with $u = j^5$, the results can be written in the form

$$(u \circ f)' = (u' \circ f) \cdot f'.$$

This somewhat mysterious result can be made reasonable as follows. Write $w = u \circ f$. Make a triple table of corresponding values of x, f, and w:

$$
\begin{array}{c|c|c}
x & f & w \\
\hline
c & f(c) & u(f(c))
\end{array}
$$

Now a change Δx in x sets off a "chain reaction." It produces a change Δf in f, which in turn produces a change Δw in w. Comparing the final change with the initial one, we look at

$$\frac{\Delta w}{\Delta x} = \frac{\Delta w}{\Delta f} \cdot \frac{\Delta f}{\Delta x}.$$

The ratio of the increment in a function to the increment in the variable converges to the derivative at the initial value of the variable. Thus

$$\frac{\Delta f}{\Delta x} \to f'(c),$$

$$\frac{\Delta w}{\Delta f} \to u'(f(c)),$$

so

$$w'(c) = \lim_{\Delta x \to 0} \frac{\Delta w}{\Delta x} = u'(f(c))f'(c).$$

From this way of looking at the problem, it is natural to call this result the "chain rule." There is a notation for the derivative which is in common use which makes the chain rule look like a triviality. One writes

$$f'(x) = \lim_{\Delta x \to 0} \frac{\Delta f}{\Delta x} = \frac{df}{dx}.$$

Then the chain rule appears as

$$\frac{dw}{dx} = \frac{dw}{df} \cdot \frac{df}{dx}.$$

Of course, if these were ordinary fractions, we could cancel the df's and have an identity. But df/dx is not defined as a fraction, but as a limit. It is an inseparable symbol; the df and dx have no independent existence (at least here).

Actually, the intuitive "incremental ratio" argument given above is almost correct. It breaks down only because the Δf by which we divide and multiply might be 0 even though Δx is not 0, and this can happen for very many arbitrarily small values of Δx. The argument can be rescued by considering separately the evil values of Δx, but we prefer to give a proof based on Definition 8–9 like the one for f^5 above.

Theorem 8–27. If f is differentiable at c and if u is differentiable at $f(c)$, then $u \circ f$ is differentiable at c, and

$$(u \circ f)'(c) = u'(f(c)) \cdot f'(c).$$

In other words,

(E) $$(u \circ f)' = (u' \circ f) \cdot f'.$$

Proof: For small $|h|$,

$$f(c + h) = f(c) + e(h),$$

$$e(h) = f'(c)h + he_1(h),$$

where $e, e_1 \in \mathbf{N}$. Also, for small $|k|$,

$$u(f(c) + k) = u(f(c)) + u'(f(c))k + ke_2(k), \quad e_2 \in \mathbf{N}.$$

Put $k = e(h)$, so that $|k|$ is small if $|h|$ is small. Then

$$(u \circ f)(c + h) = u(f(c) + e(h))$$

$$= u(f(c)) + u'(f(c))e(h) + e(h)e_2(e(h))$$

$$= (u \circ f)(c) + (u' \circ f)(c) \cdot f'(c)h + he_3(h),$$

where

$$e_3(h) = u'(f(c))e_1(h) + (f'(c) + e_1(h))e_2(e(h)) \to 0.$$

By Definition 8–9, the result follows.

EXERCISES 8–10

1. Prove

(F)
$$\left(\frac{1}{g}\right)' = -\frac{1}{g^2} \cdot g'.$$

2. Combine rules (B) and (F) to get

(G)
$$\left(\frac{f}{g}\right)' = \frac{gf' - fg'}{g^2}.$$

3. Prove

(H)
$$(\log \circ f)' = \frac{f'}{f}.$$

4. Differentiate:
   (a) $j^2 + 9j^7$.
   (b) $(j + 5)^{100}$.
   (c) $\log \circ (1 + j^2)$.
   (d) $(1 + j^2)^2 - (1 - j^2)^2 - 4j^2$.
   (e) $\dfrac{1}{j + 1}$.
   (f) $1 + \dfrac{j}{1!} + \dfrac{j^2}{2!} + \dfrac{j^3}{3!} + \cdots + \dfrac{j^{20}}{20!}$.
   (g) $j \log \circ j$.

5. Assume that the exponential function exp is differentiable. By differentiating both sides of the identity

$$\log \circ \exp = j,$$

prove that $\exp' = \exp$. That is, the exponential function satisfies the *differential equation* $y' = y$.

Theorem 8–28

(I) $\exp' = \exp.$

Proof: First we show that the exponential function is continuous at 0. From our discussion in Section 7–7, inequality (5), with $n = 1$, yields

$$1 + h \le e^h \le (1 + h)^2 \qquad (0 \le h \le 1).$$

Letting $h \to 0$ through positive values, we see that

$$\lim_{h \to 0+} e^h = 1$$

Therefore,

$$1 = \lim_{h \to 0+} \frac{1}{e^h} = \lim_{h \to 0+} e^{-h} = \lim_{h \to 0-} e^h,$$

and

$$\lim_{h \to 0} e^h = 1 = e^0.$$

Thus, for h small,

$$k(h) = e^h - 1$$

is also small (i.e., $k \in \mathbf{N}$). Now the logarithm has derivative 1 at the point 1, so for small k,

$$\log(1 + k) = k + ke_1(k).$$

In particular,

$$h = \log e^h = \log(1 + k(h))$$
$$= k(h)(1 + e_1(k(h))),$$

so

$$\frac{e^h - 1}{h} = \frac{k(h)}{h} = \frac{1}{1 + e_1(k(h))}.$$

Letting $h \to 0$, we get

(12)
$$\lim_{h \to 0} \frac{e^h - 1}{h} = 1.$$

Finally, if $c \in R$,

$$\frac{e^{c+h} - e^c}{h} = \frac{e^c(e^h - 1)}{h} \to e^c,$$

so the derivative of exp at c exists:

$$\exp' c = \exp c.$$

Since c was arbitrary, the theorem is proved.

EXERCISES 8–11

1. Find the derivative at $c \in R$ of the function whose value at each x in R is

(a) xe^x.

(b) $\exp(x^2 + 1)$.

(c) $1/e^x$.

(d) $\log(\exp 3x)$.

2. Define the (hyperbolic) functions cosh, sinh by

$$\cosh x = \tfrac{1}{2}(e^x + e^{-x}),$$

$$\sinh x = \tfrac{1}{2}(e^x - e^{-x}) \qquad (x \in R).$$

Prove:

(a) $\cosh^2 x - \sinh^2 x = 1 \qquad (x \in R)$.

(b) $\cosh' = \sinh$.

(c) $\sinh' = \cosh$.

3. Write an equation for the tangent to (the graph of) $y = e^x$ at the point where $x = 1$; $x = c$; $x = \log 5$.

4. Let f and g be differentiable at c, with $g'(c) \neq 0$. Prove that if $f(c) = g(c) = 0$, then

(J)
$$\lim_{x \to c} \frac{f(x)}{g(x)} = \frac{f'(c)}{g'(c)}.$$

5. For fixed $a \in R$, we have defined the power function j^a by

$$j^a(x) = x^a = \exp(a \log x) \qquad (x > 0).$$

Prove that $(j^a)' = aj^{a-1}$. Hence show that for $c > 0$, h small,

$$(c + h)^a \doteq c^a + ac^{a-1}h.$$

Use this to estimate $\sqrt[3]{1001}$.

6. Define f by

$$f(x) = 0 \qquad (x \neq 1/n, n \geq 1),$$

$$f(x) = x \qquad (x = 1/n, n \geq 1).$$

Show that f is continuous at 0 but not differentiable at 0.

7. Define g by

$$g(x) = 0 \qquad (x \neq 1/n, n \geq 1),$$

$$g(x) = x^2 \qquad (x = 1/n, n \geq 1).$$

Show that g is differentiable at 0.

8. Suppose that f is strictly increasing on $(c - k, c + k)$, $k > 0$, and that f is differentiable at c. Prove that $f'(c) \geq 0$. Is it necessarily true that $f'(c) > 0$?

9. Suppose that dom $f = R$ and that $f'(2)$ exists and is different from 0. Show that every interval $(2 - k, 2 + k)$, $k > 0$, contains points x, y such that $f(x) > f(2)$ and $f(y) < f(2)$.

*10. Sketch the graph of $y = xe^x$ and show that the curve attains a minimum at the point $(-1, -1/e)$.

8–5. THE FUNDAMENTAL THEOREM

In this section we develop a remarkable connection between the integral and the derivative. Up to now we have calculated integrals by various devices, more or less special. The *fundamental theorem* will provide us with a powerful method for computing many integrals. But first we prove several theorems which are of considerable importance in themselves.

Theorem 8–29   (*Rolle's Theorem*).   Let f be continuous on the closed interval $[a,b]$ and differentiable on the open interval (a,b). Suppose that $f(a) = f(b) = 0$. Then there is a point c in (a,b) such that $f'(c) = 0$.

The conclusion has the geometrical interpretation that somewhere inside (a,b) the tangent is horizontal (Figure 8–10).

Proof: By Theorem 8–20, f assumes both the maximum M and the minimum m on $[a,b]$. Clearly $m \le 0 \le M$. If $m = 0 = M$, then f is constant on $[a,b]$ and $f'(c) = 0$ for all $c \in (a,b)$. If not, then $m < 0$ or $M > 0$, say the latter. Let c be a point in $[a,b]$ such that $f(c) = M$. Then $c \ne a$, $c \ne b$, since $f(a) = f(b) = 0$. Hence $c \in (a,b)$. Let (x_n) be a sequence in (c,b) that converges to c. Then

$$\frac{f(x_n) - f(c)}{x_n - c} \le 0 \qquad (n \in N),$$

because $f(x_n) \le M = f(c)$ and $x_n - c > 0$. Hence

$$f'(c) = \lim_{n \to \infty} \frac{f(x_n) - f(c)}{x_n - c} \le 0.$$

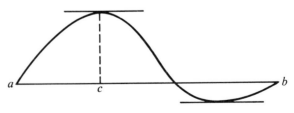

FIGURE 8–10

Now let (u_n) be a sequence in (a,c) converging to c. Then

$$\frac{f(u_n) - f(c)}{u_n - c} \geq 0 \qquad (n \in N),$$

because $f(u_n) \leq M = f(c)$ and $u_n - c < 0$. Hence

$$f'(c) = \lim_{n \to \infty} \frac{f(u_n) - f(c)}{u_n - c} \geq 0.$$

Therefore $f'(c) = 0$ and the theorem is proved. A similar argument works if $f(c) = m < 0$.

In the course of the proof we showed that the derivative at a point c where the maximum (or minimum) is assumed must be zero, provided that c is an interior point. We cannot dispense with this condition, as the example

$$f(x) = x \qquad (0 \leq x \leq 1)$$

shows. To make the proof work, there had to be sequences (x_n) and (u_n) in (a,b) converging to c from both sides.

However, the condition that f takes its absolute maximum or minimum at c can be relaxed. Let us say that f has a *relative* (or *local*) *maximum* at c if there is some open interval (a',b') containing c such that

$$f(x) \leq f(c) \qquad (x \in \operatorname{dom} f, a' < x < b').$$

A similar definition holds for *relative minimum*. Then, if $(a',b') \subset \operatorname{dom} f$, the sequences (x_n) and (u_n) can be found in (a',b') and the conclusion $f'(c) = 0$ can be reached. In particular, if $\operatorname{dom} f = [a,b]$ and $f(c)$ is a relative maximum or minimum, then $c = a$ or $c = b$ or $f'(c) = 0$. To find all relative maxima and minima, we need only check a, b, and $\{c \mid f'(c) = 0\}$. Of course, some of these points may not work, as the following example will show.

EXAMPLE 8–20.   Given $f(x) = 3x^5 - 5x^3 (-\sqrt{5/3} \leq x \leq 2)$. Find all local maxima and minima.

Solution (see Figure 8–11):

$$f(x) = x^3(3x^2 - 5) = 3x^3(x - \sqrt{5/3})(x + \sqrt{5/3}),$$

so $f(-\sqrt{5/3}) = 0$. Also $f(2) = 56$. For $-\sqrt{5/3} < x < 2$,

$$f'(x) = 15x^4 - 15x^2 = 15x^2(x^2 - 1)$$
$$= 15x^2(x - 1)(x + 1).$$

Thus $f'(x) = 0 \Leftrightarrow x = 0, 1, -1$. Now $f(-1) = 2$, $f(0) = 0$, $f(1) = -2$.

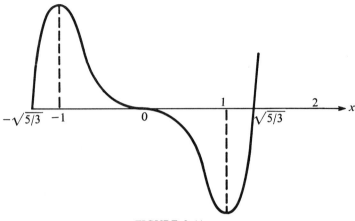

FIGURE 8–11

Comparing the values at $-\sqrt{5/3}$, -1, 0, 1, 2, we see that f has an absolute maximum at $x = 2$ and an absolute minimum at $x = 1$. If x is slightly larger than $-\sqrt{5/3}$, then $3x^3 < 0$, $x - \sqrt{5/3} < 0$, $x + \sqrt{5/3} > 0$, so $f(x) > 0 = f(-\sqrt{5/3})$. Therefore f has a local minimum at $-\sqrt{5/3}$. Next, if x is slightly less than -1, then $15x^2 > 0$, $x - 1 < 0$, $x + 1 < 0$, so $f'(x) > 0$. This means that f is increasing as x approaches -1 from the left. If x is slightly greater than -1, then $15x^2 > 0$, $x - 1 < 0$, $x + 1 > 0$, so $f'(x) < 0$. This means that f is decreasing as x moves away from -1 to the right. Therefore f has a local maximum at $x = -1$. [We could also have argued from symmetry, since $f(-x) = -f(x)$ near $x = -1$, and f has a minimum at $x = 1$.] Finally, if x is slightly less than 0, then $x^3 < 0$, $3x^2 - 5 < 0$, so $f(x) > 0$; if x is slightly greater than 0, then $x^3 > 0$, $3x^2 - 5 < 0$, so $f(x) < 0$. Therefore the curve crosses the x-axis at $x = 0$, and that point provides neither a local maximum nor minimum.

Theorem 8–29 tells us that (for the right sort of curve) we can find a tangent parallel to a given chord, provided that the chord is horizontal. It seems reasonable that the last proviso is superfluous, for chords and tangents know nothing of the coordinate system that we impose on the plane.

Theorem 8–30 (*Mean Value Theorem for Derivatives*). Let f be continuous on the closed interval $[a,b]$ and differentiable on the open interval (a,b). Then there is a point $c \in (a,b)$ such that

$$f'(c) = \frac{f(b) - f(a)}{b - a}.$$

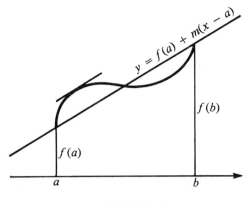

FIGURE 8–12

Proof (see Figure 8–12): We consider, instead of f, the vertical deviation of the curve from the chord. The chord passes through $(a, f(a))$ and has slope

$$m = \frac{f(b) - f(a)}{b - a}.$$

The height at each $x \in [a,b]$ is

$$f(a) + m(x - a),$$

so the deviation at x is

$$D(x) = f(x) - f(a) - m(x - a).$$

Now D is continuous on $[a,b]$, differentiable on (a,b), and $D(a) = D(b) = 0$. By Rolle's theorem there is a $c \in (a,b)$ such that $D'(c) = 0$:

$$0 = D'(c) = f'(c) - m.$$

Therefore

$$f'(c) = m = \frac{f(b) - f(a)}{b - a}.$$

EXERCISES 8–12

1. Let f, g be continuous on $[a,b]$ and differentiable on (a,b), with $g'(c) \neq 0$ ($c \in (a,b)$). Show that $g(b) \neq g(a)$ and that there is a $c \in (a,b)$ such that

$$\frac{f(b) - f(a)}{g(b) - g(a)} = \frac{f'(c)}{g'(c)}.$$

[*Hint:* Apply Rolle's theorem to

$$D(x) = f(x) - f(a) - \left(\frac{f(b) - f(a)}{g(b) - g(a)}\right)(g(x) - g(a)).]$$

2. Apply Exercise 8–12(1) to obtain

$$\frac{e^x - 1 - x}{x^2} = \frac{e^c - 1}{2c} \qquad (0 < c < x).$$

Now, $\lim\limits_{c \to 0} (e^c - 1)/c = 1$. Hence, if x is small,

$$\frac{e^x - 1 - x}{x^2} \doteq \frac{1}{2},$$

$$e^x \doteq 1 + x + \frac{x^2}{2}.$$

By considering now

$$\frac{e^x - (1 + x + (x^2/2))}{x^3},$$

show that

$$e^x \doteq 1 + x + \frac{x^2}{2} + \frac{x^3}{6}.$$

Use this to calculate exp (.1) and check with a four-place exponential table.

Theorem 8–31.   If $f'(x) = 0$ for all $x \in (a,b)$, then f is constant on (a,b).
   Proof: Let $u, v \in (a,b)$, $u < v$. Then f is continuous on $[u,v]$ and differentiable on (u,v). By Theorem 8–30, $\exists x \in (u,v)$ such that

$$\frac{f(v) - f(u)}{v - u} = f'(x) = 0.$$

Therefore $f(v) = f(u)$. Since u and v were arbitrary, f is constant.

By a *primitive* (or *antiderivative*) of f on (a,b) we mean any F such that

$$F'(x) = f(x) \qquad (x \in (a,b)).$$

Any two primitives F, G of f on (a,b) can differ by at most a constant on (a,b), for

$$(F - G)'(x) = F'(x) - G'(x) = f(x) - f(x) = 0 \qquad (x \in (a,b)).$$

Theorem 8–32   (*The Fundamental Theorem*). Let f be continuous on $[a,b]$. Then f has primitives on (a,b), and if F is any primitive,

(K) $$\int_r^s f(t)\,dt = F(s) - F(r)$$

for all r, s such that $a < r < s < b$. Furthermore, every F can be extended to be continuous on $[a,b]$, and then (K) holds for all $r, s \in [a,b]$.

Proof: Consider the function G defined by

$$G(x) = \int_a^x f(t)\,dt \qquad (a \le x \le b).$$

If $x, x + h \in [a,b]$, $h \ne 0$, then

$$\frac{G(x + h) - G(x)}{h} = \frac{1}{h}\int_x^{x+h} f(t)\,dt = f(c)$$

for some c between x and $x + h$, by the mean value theorem for integrals (Theorem 8–21). By the continuity of f, $f(c) \to f(x)$ as $h \to 0$. Therefore

$$G'(x) = f(x) \qquad (x \in (a,b)).$$

Thus G is a primitive of f on (a,b). Also G is continuous on $[a,b]$, and for all $r, s \in [a,b]$,

$$G(s) - G(r) = \int_a^s f(t)\,dt - \int_a^r f(t)\,dt$$

$$= \int_r^s f(t)\,dt.$$

If F is any primitive of f on (a,b), then there is a number C such that

$$F(x) = G(x) + C \qquad (a < x < b).$$

We extend F to the endpoints by

$$F(a) = G(a) + C = C,$$
$$F(b) = G(b) + C.$$

Then

$$F(x) = G(x) + C \qquad (a \le x \le b),$$

so F is also continuous on $[a,b]$. Finally, $F(s) - F(r) = G(s) - G(r)$, and (K) holds for all $r, s \in [a,b]$.

EXAMPLE 8–21.   Let $F(x) = e^x \ (x \in R)$.   Then $F'(x) = f(x) = e^x \ (x \in R)$.
Therefore

$$\int_a^b e^t \, dt = e^b - e^a \qquad (a,b \in R).$$

EXAMPLE 8–22.   Evaluate

$$\int_0^1 t e^t \, dt.$$

Solution: We look for a primitive of the integrand in the form

$$F(t) = Ae^t + Bte^t \qquad (t \in R).$$

Then we must have

$$F'(t) = Ae^t + Be^t + Bte^t$$
$$= (A + B)e^t + Bte^t.$$

Choose $B = 1, A + B = 0$, so $A = -1$. Thus

$$F(t) = te^t - e^t,$$

and

$$\int_0^1 te^t \, dt = F(1) - F(0) = 0 - (-1) = 1.$$

EXAMPLE 8–23.   Evaluate

$$\int_0^{10^6} xe^{-x^2} \, dx.$$

Solution: Let $F(x) = e^{-x^2} \ (x \in R)$. Then $f(x) = F'(x) = -2xe^{-x^2}$,

$$\int_0^{10^6} xe^{-x^2} \, dx = -\tfrac{1}{2} \int_0^{10^6} (-2xe^{-x^2}) \, dx$$
$$= -\tfrac{1}{2}(F(10^6) - F(0))$$
$$= \tfrac{1}{2} - \tfrac{1}{2}e^{-10^{12}}.$$

This is reasonably close to $\tfrac{1}{2}$.

EXAMPLE 8–24.   Under suitable assumptions on g, find another expression
for

$$\int_a^b g(x^3)x^2 \, dx \qquad (0 \le a \le b).$$

Solution: If $a \leq x \leq b$, then $a^3 \leq x^3 \leq b^3$. Assume that g is continuous on $[a^3, b^3]$. Then g has a primitive G on $[a^3, b^3]$. Define

$$H(x) = G(x^3) \qquad (x \in [a,b]).$$

By the chain rule,

$$H'(x) = G'(x^3) \cdot 3x^2 \qquad (x \in (a,b)),$$

so the given integral is

$$\int_a^b \tfrac{1}{3} H'(x)\, dx = \tfrac{1}{3}(H(b) - H(a))$$

$$= \tfrac{1}{3}(G(b^3) - G(a^3)) = \tfrac{1}{3} \int_{a^3}^{b^3} g(x)\, dx.$$

EXAMPLE 8–25. Evaluate

$$\int_0^{\log 2} \frac{e^x - e^{-x}}{e^x + e^{-x}}\, dx.$$

Solution: Let $f(x) = e^x + e^{-x}$ $(x \in R)$, $g(t) = 1/t$ $(t > 0)$, $G(t) = \log t$ $(t > 0)$. Then

$$(G \circ f)'(x) = G'(f(x))f'(x)$$

$$= g(f(x))f'(x)$$

$$= \frac{f'(x)}{f(x)}$$

$$= \frac{e^x - e^{-x}}{e^x + e^{-x}}.$$

Hence the integral is

$$(G \circ f)(\log 2) - (G \circ f)(0)$$

$$= \log(e^{\log 2} + e^{-\log 2}) - \log(e^0 + e^{-0})$$

$$= \log(2 + \tfrac{1}{2}) - \log 2$$

$$= \log \tfrac{5}{4}.$$

EXERCISES 8–13

1. Let f be a differentiable function whose derivative is continuous on $[a,t]$ for all t. Prove:

(a) $\int_a^t f'(x)\, dx = f(t) - f(a)$.

(b) $\int_a^t f^2(x)f'(x)\,dx = \frac{1}{3}(f^3(t) - f^3(a))$.

2. Let f and g have continuous derivatives in $[a,b]$. Prove that

$$\int_a^b f(x)g'(x)\,dx + \int_a^b f'(x)g(x)\,dx = f(b)g(b) - f(a)g(a).$$

Use this to evaluate

(a) $\int_1^2 \log x\,dx \qquad [f(x) = \log x, g(x) = x]$.

(b) $\int_0^3 xe^x\,dx \qquad [f(x) = e^x, g(x) = x]$.

(c) $\int_5^{10} x^7 \log x\,dx$.

This technique is called *integration by parts*.

3. Differentiate:

(a) $\int_0^x e^{t^2}\,dt \qquad (x \in R)$.

(b) $\int_x^0 t^3 e^{2t}\,dt \qquad (x \in R)$.

(c) $\int_{x+1}^{x+2} \sqrt{1 + t^2}\,dt \qquad (x \in R)$.

(d) $\int_0^{x^4} e^{-t^2}\,dt \qquad (x \in R)$.

4. Let (x,x^2) be a point on the curve $y = x^2$. Find an equation for the line tangent to the curve at (x,x^2).

5. Find the maxima and minima of the following functions:
(a) $f(x) = x^2 + 1 \qquad (-1 \le x \le 3)$.
(b) $f(x) = x^3 - 3x^2 - 9x \qquad (-2 \le x \le 5)$.
(c) $f(x) = xe^{-x} \qquad (x \ge 0)$.

6. If u is a function of time t, we call u' the (instantaneous) rate of change of u. Radioactive substances decay at a rate proportional to the amount of u remaining. That is, $u' = -cu$, where c is a positive constant. Show that one function which satisfies this *differential equation* is $y(t) = e^{-ct}$. Let u be *any* solution, and consider

$$f(t) = u(t)e^{ct}.$$

Find f'. What do you conclude about u?

7. For the differential equation

$$u'(t) - u(t) = e^{2t},$$

show that

$$y(t) = e^{2t} + ce^{t}$$

is a solution, for every $c \in R$. [It can be proved that every solution is of this form. Try it, by putting $u(t) = v(t)e^{t}$, computing $u'(t) - u(t)$ and equating to e^{2t}.]

8. In error analysis one attempts to estimate errors in outputs caused by given (small) input errors. If y is one of the inputs or outputs, its error is denoted by Δy. Thus, if $u = x^2$, then $\Delta u \doteq 2x\,\Delta x$. Given that $u = f(x)$, estimate Δu, for $f(x) = x^3, f(x) = e^x, f(x) = \sqrt[3]{x}$.

9. The *relative error* in y is defined as $\Delta y/y$. If $u = xy$, show that

$$\frac{\Delta u}{u} \doteq \frac{\Delta x}{x} + \frac{\Delta y}{y}.$$

Find the relative error for $u = x^a$.

10. A particle moves in a straight line so that its position at each time t is $s = f(t)$. Its velocity is defined as $v = ds/dt = f'(t)$, and its acceleration is $a = dv/dt$. Find v and a for the following laws of motion:
(a) $s = v_0 t + \frac{1}{2}gt^2$ (v_0, g constant).
(b) $s = ce^{3t}$ (c constant).
Find the most general law for the case of zero acceleration.

11. A merchant can sell $100 - x$ items at a price x per unit ($0 \le x \le 100$). How does he maximize his revenue?

12. A manufacturer has fixed costs of \$500. In addition it costs him \$11 to make each unit. If he produces x units, he can sell them all at a price of $20 - (x/100)^2$ dollars per unit. What is his maximum profit?

13. A closed cylindrical can is supposed to contain a given volume of fluid. Show that the height must equal the diameter in order to minimize the total material used (i.e., the surface area). What if the can is open at the top?

14. Give an example of a continuous function f on $[0,1]$ with $f(0) = 0 = f(1)$, but with no horizontal tangent. Does this contradict Rolle's theorem?

15. For each price p, the amount of a commodity that can be sold at that price is called the demand $u(p)$. This defines the demand schedule (or function) u. Usually (not always!), u is a nonincreasing function:

$$p_2 \ge p_1 \Rightarrow u(p_2) \le u(p_1).$$

Assuming that u is differentiable, show that this implies $u' \leq 0$. Is the converse true?

16. (See Problem 15.) Elasticity of demand is defined by

$$k = -\frac{p}{u}u'.$$

(The minus sign is used to make k nonnegative.) In general, elasticity changes as we move along a given demand curve. Find all demand curves for which k is constant. [*Hint:* Write the equation in the form $(k \log p)'$ + $(\log u)' = 0$.]

17. Sketch the graph of $y = x^2(x - 1)$. Find all maxima and minima.

18. Sketch the graph of $y = x/(x^2 + 1)$. Find all maxima and minima.

19. Prove

$$-\frac{1}{\sqrt{2e}} \leq xe^{-x^2} \leq \frac{1}{\sqrt{2e}} \qquad (x \in R).$$

20. The *second derivative* f'' is defined as $(f')'$. Show that $y = Ae^x + Be^{-x}$ is a solution of the differential equation

$$y'' - y = 0$$

for any constants A, B.

*21. Let f be a (real) solution of the differential equation

$$f''(x) + f(x) = 0 \qquad (x \in R).$$

Prove: (a) There is a constant C such that

$$f'^2(x) + f^2(x) = C \qquad (x \in R).$$

(b) f is bounded.

Chapter 9

PROBABILITY

9–1. INTRODUCTION

THE THEORY OF PROBABILITY originated in the study of games of chance. Since then it has proved to be of tremendous value in the physical and social sciences, in commerce and industry. Our purpose in this chapter is to give a brief indication of the mathematical theory, suitably restricted for the sake of simplicity.

In the distant past, when man was confronted with uncertainty, he would appeal to superstition or sheer guesswork. Later, in some special cases, he began to discern a long-term regularity which could usually be relied upon. Thus, if a coin is tossed once, it is impossible to predict whether it will fall head or tail. If it is tossed a hundred times, it is still impossible to predict the precise number of heads, but we can say with some degree of assurance that approximately one-half of the trials will result in heads. If we increase the number of trials, the ratio of the number of heads to the number of trials seems to settle down (converge) to the value $\frac{1}{2}$.

What is important in the example above is not the particular value $\frac{1}{2}$, but the apparent tendency of a ratio to settle down to a fixed value. We would not be too surprised if this value turned out to be .52 instead of .50. The deviation could easily be ascribed to a slight imbalance of the coin. But we would be very surprised, almost incredulous, if after a thousand tosses with a ratio close to $\frac{1}{2}$, this ratio began to drift down to $\frac{1}{4}$ or to oscillate between $\frac{1}{4}$ and $\frac{3}{4}$. Things just don't happen that way with coins— they do sometimes with people and animals.

The empirical observations just made are not confined to the tossing of coins. We find again and again that when many trials of a given experiment are made, the outcomes seem to distribute themselves according to a pattern which becomes more and more stable. To be specific, suppose that there are n trials and that we are interested in the number s of occurrences of a certain event E. Each occurrence of E we shall call a *success*. The ratio

s/n we call the *relative frequency* of E. What we seem to observe is that s/n tends to a fixed number P as n increases. Of course, if we change the event E we would expect to get a different value of P. To indicate the dependence on E, we write $P(E)$.

To illustrate, suppose that our experiment is the roll of a single die, with the set of possible outcomes $\{1,2,3,4,5,6\}$. The event E might be that the outcome is even. If $n = 1,000$ and $s = 522$, then the relative frequency $s/n = .522$. We might guess that $P(E) = \frac{1}{2}$ or very close to it. The limiting ratio $\frac{1}{2}$ is attractive a priori, since the number of outcomes contributing to E is 3 while the total number is 6. Underlying this type of reasoning is the assumption that all outcomes are "equally likely," i.e., that they have the same long-run relative frequency. Whether the assumption is justified in the light of the experimental results is a question to be answered by the theory of statistical inference. Experience, however, convinces us that $P(E)$, whatever its value, does exist as a limiting relative frequency. It is customary to call $P(E)$ the *probability* of E, or the *statistical probability* of E.

There is another way to construe the term "the probability of E." If we were asked to bet on the occurrence of an event E, we might be willing to accept either side of the bet if the odds were set at \$2 on E versus \$3 on non-E. In this case we would be setting the value of the *subjective probability* of E at

$$\frac{2}{5} = \frac{2}{2 + 3}.$$

If we would accept "even money," then our value for $P(E)$ would be $\frac{1}{2}$.

There are serious objections to either of the "definitions" of probability proposed above. For example, we cannot be certain that the limiting frequency exists, or we might run into the difficulty of nonrepeatable experiments. On the other hand, subjective probability varies from one person to the next or from one time to the next.

Fortunately, as students of the mathematical theory of probability, we do not have to decide the issue, interesting as it may be. We need only say how probability acts, not what it is, nor how we determine it. Almost all scientists and mathematicians are agreed on the few simple properties to be ascribed to probability. Thus we leave the thorny problems of the physical plane of probability to epistemologists, philosophers, and others who are interested. In the same way, we can state the laws that govern the flow of heat without having to discuss what heat "really is." The conceptual system that we construct can be studied quite independently. Whether we regard heat as molecular energy, as a mysterious fluid called "phlogiston," or as the manifestation of the will of a supernatural enemy of Smokey the Bear, the answers that we obtain in that system are the same, provided that the basic laws or assumptions are the same.

9–2. PROBABILITY SPACES

Our goal in this section is to set down the basic properties (axioms) of probability. There is no logical necessity to justify our axioms or terminology. Nevertheless we shall try to make them seem reasonable by referring to the physical plane as the psychological and historical source of our axiom system.

As we have seen in the examples of Section 9–1, to each experiment we can assign the set of all possible outcomes. In the case of the toss of a coin, this set is {head,tail} or, to abbreviate, $\{H,T\}$. For the roll of a die, the set of all possible outcomes is $\{1,2,3,4,5,6\}$. In general, this set is called the *sample space*. Abstractly, we postulate a nonempty set V as sample space. Its elements are called *outcomes* or *elementary events*.

Next, if we are interested in an event E, we must be able to say when it has occurred. That is, for each outcome we must decide whether E has occurred or not. It does not matter how we describe the event; all we care about really is the set of outcomes that correspond to its occurrence. Thus there is nothing lost if we identify E with this set. An *event* then is simply a certain collection of outcomes or subset of the sample space. As we shall see later, however, not all subsets will be regarded as events.

To each event E we assign a number $P(E)$, called the *probability of E*. Therefore P is a function defined on the class of events. Since relative frequencies are nonnegative, we shall require the same of the values of P:

(1) $$\forall E, P(E) \geq 0.$$

If we take $E = V$, we achieve success on every trial, so for n trials, $s = n$. The relative frequency is always 1, so

(2) $$P(V) = 1.$$

From the standpoint of subjective probability this is reasonable. We simply assign the value 1 to the complete certainty that some outcome will occur. We do not insist on the converse: It is perfectly possible to have $P(E) = 1$ with $E \neq V$. Similarly, we could demand that $P(\emptyset) = 0$. Because we can derive this from later axioms, we omit it now.

Two events E and F are called *mutually exclusive* if the occurrence of one implies the nonoccurrence of the other; that is, if $E \cap F = \emptyset$. In this case, the number of occurrences of $E \cup F$ is given by

$$s(E \cup F) = s(E) + s(F).$$

Therefore the relative frequencies add up in the same way, and so do the probabilities:

$$P(E \cup F) = P(E) + P(F), \quad if \quad E \cap F = \emptyset.$$

This is the fundamental additivity property shared by all measures (see Chapter 7). For important technical reasons, we shall demand somewhat more, namely, *countable additivity*. This means that if we have a sequence of events (E_i), $i \in N$, which are pairwise mutually exclusive $[i \neq j \Rightarrow E_i \cap E_j = \emptyset]$, then the union of all the E_i has a probability equal to the "sum" of the $P(E_i)$, defined by

$$\sum_{i=1}^{\infty} P(E_i) = \lim_{n \to \infty} \sum_{i=1}^{n} P(E_i).$$

Thus, our countable additivity axiom is

(3) $$P\left(\bigcup_{i=1}^{\infty} E_i \right) = \sum_{i=1}^{\infty} P(E_i), \quad if \quad E_i \cap E_j = \emptyset \quad (i \neq j).$$

Just as in the case of measures, we must specify the domain of P. This will be the collection $\mathbf{E}$ of events. We shall require that $\mathbf{E}$ be closed under the operations of forming differences and countable unions $\bigcup_{i=1}^{\infty} E_i$ and, because of Eq. (2), that V be an element of $\mathbf{E}$. It may seem strange to the student that we do not simply define P for *all* subsets of V. In some cases this is possible, but in others an attempt to define P universally leads to a contradiction similar to the Banach-Tarski paradox (see Chapter 7). Therefore we must content ourselves by requiring that the domain of P be a *σ-algebra*, according to the following definition.

Definition 9–1. A σ-algebra in V is a collection $\mathbf{E}$ of subsets of V such that

(a) $V \in \mathbf{E}$.
(b) If $E, F \in \mathbf{E}$, then $E - F \in \mathbf{E}$.
(c) If (E_i), $i = 1, 2, \ldots$, is a sequence of sets in $\mathbf{E}$, then $\bigcup_{i=1}^{\infty} E_i \in \mathbf{E}$.

We remark that a σ-algebra is also closed under complementation and countable intersection, for if E is in **E**, then so is $E' = V - E$; if $E_i \in$ **E** ($i = 1, 2, \ldots$), then so are E'_i, hence

$$\bigcup_{i=1}^{\infty} E'_i = \left(\bigcap_{i=1}^{\infty} E_i \right)',$$

and finally

$$\bigcap_{i=1}^{\infty} E_i = V - \left(\bigcap_{i=1}^{\infty} E_i \right)'.$$

(We recall that

$$\bigcup_{i=1}^{\infty} E_i = \{v \in V \mid \exists i \in N, v \in E_i\},$$

$$\bigcap_{i=1}^{\infty} E_i = \{v \in V \mid \forall i \in N, v \in E_i\}.)$$

In particular, **E** is a Boolean algebra of subsets of V.

We can now summarize our requirements.

Definition 9–2.   A *probability space* consists of a triple $(V, \mathbf{E}, P)$, where V is a nonempty set, **E** is a σ-algebra of subsets of V, and P is a function on **E** satisfying
(1) $\forall E \in$ **E**, $P(E) \geq 0$.
(2) $P(V) = 1$.
(3) If $E_i \in$ **E**, $i = 1, 2, \ldots$, and $E_i \cap E_j = \emptyset$ for $i \neq j$, then

$$P\left(\bigcup_{i=1}^{\infty} E_i \right) = \sum_{i=1}^{\infty} P(E_i).$$

The set V is called the *sample space;* its elements are called *outcomes* or *elementary events*. The elements E of **E** are called *events*. The countably additive measure P is called *probability* (probability function, probability distribution).

In the following examples we exhibit some probability spaces in common use. It should be clearly understood that in each case an assumption is being made about the underlying probability space. In our solutions we shall be very explicit about these assumptions. Many problems become quite easy when this is done.

The term "at random" is sometimes used to indicate a particular probability space, as in Examples 9–5 to 9–8. At other times it merely indicates the presence of *some* probability space.

From now on we shall use the notation $|E|$ for the number of elements in E.

EXAMPLE 9–1. $V = \{1, \ldots, n\}$. **E** is the collection of all subsets of V. For $E \in \mathbf{E}$,

$$P(E) = \frac{|E|}{n}.$$

Because all outcomes have the same probability $1/n$, this is called the case of equally likely outcomes. When we say "choose a number at random from 1 to n," we are referring to this case. Computations of probability reduce to counting.

EXAMPLE 9–2.   Two fair coins are tossed independently. The outcomes are the pairs (H,H), (H,T), (T,H), (T,T), where the first entry refers to the first coin, the second entry to the second coin. Thus

$$V = \{H,T\} \times \{H,T\}.$$

E is the collection of all subsets of V. Since V has four elements, **E** has $16 = 2^4$ elements. For $E \in \mathbf{E}$,

$$P(E) = \frac{|E|}{4}.$$

Thus, the probability of getting at least one head is $\frac{3}{4}$, since here

$$E = \{(H,H), (H,T), (T,H)\}.$$

EXAMPLE 9–3.   A fair coin is tossed 10 times in a row. The outcomes are the 10-tuples $(x_1, x_2, \ldots, x_{10})$, where each x_i is H or T, according as the ith toss comes up heads or tails. Thus

$$V = \{H,T\}^{10} = \{H,T\} \times \cdots \times \{H,T\} \qquad \text{(10 factors)}.$$

The number of outcomes is $1{,}024 = 2^{10}$. **E** is the collection of all subsets of V. The number of events (subsets of V) is $2^{1{,}024}$. For each event E,

$$P(E) = \frac{|E|}{1{,}024}.$$

EXAMPLE 9–4.   A fair coin is tossed and independently a fair die is rolled. The sample space V consists of all pairs (x_1, x_2), where x_1 is H or T and x_2 is 1, 2, 3, 4, 5, or 6. Thus

$$V = \{H, T\} \times \{1, 2, 3, 4, 5, 6\}.$$

The number of outcomes is $2 \cdot 6 = 12$. **E** is the collection of all subsets of V. The number of events (subsets of V) is 2^{12}. For each event E,

$$P(E) = \frac{|E|}{12}.$$

EXAMPLE 9–5.   A point is chosen "at random" in the unit interval $V = [0,1]$. The elementary events are the points of V. **E** is a certain collection of subsets of V (not all!); it is the smallest σ-algebra in V which contains all the intervals in V. An event $E \in \mathbf{E}$ is called a Borel set. P is an extension to **E** of the length function on intervals. For some events E we can compute $P(E)$ by integration. Thus, if we define $f(x) = 1 \, (x \in E)$, $= 0 \, (x \notin E)$, and if f is integrable on $[0,1]$, then

$$P(E) = \int_0^1 f(x)\, dx.$$

For instance, if $E = [\frac{1}{4}, \frac{1}{2}] \cup [\frac{3}{4}, 1]$, then $P(E) = \frac{1}{2}$. This probability distribution on $[0,1]$ assigns to every interval its length. We call it the *uniform distribution* on $[0,1]$.

EXAMPLE 9–6.   What is the probability that a number chosen at random in $[0,1]$ is of the form $1/n, n \in N$?

Solution: We assume the uniform distribution on $[0,1]$. If $a \in V$, then

$$V = [0,a) \cup \{a\} \cup (a,1].$$

$$\therefore \quad 1 = P(V) = P([0,a)) + P(\{a\}) + P((a,1]),$$

$$1 = a + P(\{a\}) + 1 - a,$$

$$0 = P(\{a\}).$$

Hence

$$P(E) = P\left(\bigcup_{n=1}^{\infty} \{1/n\} \right) = \sum_{n=1}^{\infty} P(\{1/n\})$$

$$= \lim_{k \to \infty} \sum_{n=1}^{k} P(\{1/n\})$$

$$= \lim_{k \to \infty} 0 = 0.$$

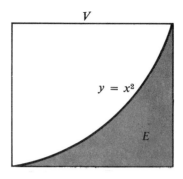

FIGURE 9-1

EXAMPLE 9–7.   Two numbers are chosen at random in [0,1], independently. What is the probability that the second is no greater than the square of the first?

Solution: The outcomes are pairs (x,y), with $x,y \in [0,1]$. Thus $V = [0,1] \times [0,1]$, the unit square. **E** is a certain collection of subsets of V (not all!); it is the smallest σ-algebra in V which contains all the rectangles in V. An event $E \in$ **E** is called a Borel set (in V). P is an extension to **E** of the area function on rectangles. Our event $E = \{(x,y) \in V | y \leq x^2\}$ (Figure 9–1). Therefore $P(E) = $ area $(E) = \int_0^1 x^2 \, dx = \frac{1}{3}$.

EXAMPLE 9–8.   Two members are chosen at random in [0,1], independently. What is the probability that the sum of their squares is no greater than 1?

Solution: The probability space is the same as that of Example 9–7. The event E is $\{(x,y) \in V | x^2 + y^2 \leq 1\}$ (Figure 9–2). Therefore $P(E) = \text{area}(E) = \pi/4$.

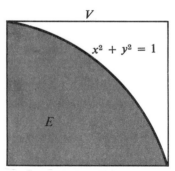

FIGURE 9-2

EXAMPLE 9–9. A natural number is chosen at random. What is the probability that it is even?

Solution: The sample space $V = N$. $\mathbf{E}$ is the collection of all subsets of V. Write

$$P_n = P(\{n\}) \qquad (n \in V).$$

Then for any $E \in \mathbf{E}$,

$$P(E) = \sum_{n \in E} p_n.$$

In particular, if E is the set of even numbers $\{2,4,6,8,\ldots\}$,

$$P(E) = p_2 + p_4 + p_6 + \cdots.$$

This is all that we can say without knowing what distribution is meant by "at random." In this case it is not possible to assign equal probability to each element of V. For if $p_n = 0$ $(n \in V)$, then

$$1 = P(V) = \sum_{n=1}^{\infty} p_n = 0,$$

and if $p_n = a > 0$ $(n \in V)$, then

$$P(V) = \sum_{n=1}^{\infty} p_n = \sum_{n=1}^{\infty} a,$$

and the series does not converge. There is no natural way of interpreting the term "at random" here.

EXAMPLE 9–10. A nonnegative integer n is chosen at random, with $p_n = P(\{n\})$ proportional to $h^n/n!$ $(n \geq 0)$. Here h is a fixed positive number. What is the probability that n is even?

Solution: First we determine the constant of proportionality c in

$$p_n = c\frac{h^n}{n!} \qquad (n \geq 0).$$

Here $V = \{0,1,2,\ldots\}$, so

$$1 = P(V) = \sum_{n=0}^{\infty} p_n = c \sum_{n=0}^{\infty} \frac{h^n}{n!}.$$

It can be shown that

$$\sum_{n=0}^{\infty} \frac{x^n}{n!} = e^x \qquad (x \in R).$$

Hence $1 = ce^h$, $c = e^{-h}$, and

$$p_n = e^{-h} \frac{h^n}{n!} \qquad (n \in V).$$

If $E = \{0, 2, 4, \ldots\}$, then

$$P(E) = \sum_{n=2m} p_n = \sum_{m=0}^{\infty} e^{-h} \frac{h^{2m}}{(2m)!}$$

$$= e^{-h} \sum_{m=0}^{\infty} \frac{h^{2m}}{(2m)!}.$$

Now

$$e^h = 1 + \frac{h}{1!} + \frac{h^2}{2!} + \frac{h^3}{3!} + \frac{h^4}{4!} + \cdots,$$

$$e^{-h} = 1 - \frac{h}{1!} + \frac{h^2}{2!} - \frac{h^3}{3!} + \frac{h^4}{4!} - \cdots.$$

Adding and dividing by 2, we get

$$\frac{1}{2}(e^h + e^{-h}) = 1 + \frac{h^2}{2!} + \frac{h^4}{4!} + \cdots$$

$$= \sum_{m=0}^{\infty} \frac{h^{2m}}{(2m)!}.$$

Hence

$$P(E) = e^{-h} \cdot \tfrac{1}{2}(e^h + e^{-h}),$$

$$= \tfrac{1}{2}(1 + e^{-2h}).$$

The distribution of Example 9–10 is called the *Poisson distribution* with parameter h. It occurs frequently in applications. For example, let X be the number of calls coming into a switchboard in a time interval of t minutes. Then the probability that $X = n\,(n \geq 0)$ is given by

$$p_n = e^{-h} \frac{h^n}{n!},$$

where $h = kt$, k being a number independent of t. (Actually k is the expected number of calls per minute.)

The preceding are typical straightforward problems arising in the theory and application of probability. *Given* a probability space, we are asked to

compute the probability of a certain event. We do not ask—at this stage—
how we know that this particular distribution holds, rather than some
other. The problem of determining which probability space applies best in
a given physical situation is generally of a higher order of sophistication
than the straightforward ones mentioned above. In Example 9–3 above,
it is easy enough to see that the probability of getting exactly 7 heads out
of 10 tosses is $120/1,024 = .12$ approximately. But is such an outcome in
an actual experiment sufficient to convince us that the coin is not fair?
The proper formulation and answering of such questions belong to the
realm of statistical inference rather than pure probability. We refrain from
such questions here.

Up to now we have been dealing with probability spaces in the greatest
generality. As some of our examples have shown, we can run into difficult
technical problems of a measure-theoretic nature when the sample space
is too large. In such cases we may find it necessary to restrict the class of
events **E**. Rather than fuss with the question whether a certain subset of V
is in **E** or not, *we shall henceforth restrict our attention to sample spaces
which are finite*. Furthermore, *every subset of V will be allowed as an event*:
E is the Boolean algebra of all subsets of V. The slight loss in generality
caused by these restrictions is more than compensated for by the simplicity
of stating and proving our results. The essential ideas will still be there.

Since **E** is now determined by V, we may omit it from our notation, and
write (V,P) instead of (V,E,P) for the probability space. Given (V,P) we
shall write p_v for $P(\{v\})$, $v \in V$. *The probability function P is completely determined as soon as we know p_v for all $v \in V$*. Indeed, for every event E,

$$P(E) = \sum_{v \in E} p_v.$$

Given V, what values of p_v are permitted? The only requirements are

(a) $p_v \geq 0 \qquad (v \in V)$.

(b) $\sum_{v \in V} p_v = 1$.

Both of these are clearly necessary, and it is not difficult to see that they
are sufficient. Notice that we permit some probabilities p_v to be 0. This is
convenient, since we can put in or leave out the corresponding points of
the sample space without changing any of the probabilities.

EXERCISES 9-1

Wherever appropriate, state explicitly what V, **E**, and P are to be.
1. Let $V = R$, **E** the collection of all subsets of R, and P the function on

E defined by

$$P(E) = \begin{cases} 1, & \text{if} \quad 5 \in E, \\ 0, & \text{if} \quad 5 \notin E. \end{cases}$$

Is (V,E,P) a probability space?

2. If we choose a number at random from 1 to 15 (see Example 9–1), what is the probability of getting an even number?

3. A fair coin is tossed four times in a row. What is the probability of getting exactly two heads? At least two heads?

4. A point is chosen "at random" in the unit interval $[0,1]$. What is the probability of getting a number of the form $.7\dots$? What is the probability of getting a number x such that $x^2 - x + \frac{3}{16} \geq 0$?

*5. What is the probability that a number chosen at random in $[0,1]$ is rational?

6. Two numbers are chosen at random in $[0,1]$, independently. What is the probability that they differ by more than $\frac{1}{2}$?

7. A nonnegative integer n is chosen at random from a Poisson distribution with parameter 3. What is the probability that n is positive?

8. A point is chosen at random in the unit square $[0,1] \times [0,1]$. What is the probability that the sum of its coordinates is greater than $3/2$?

9. A point (x,y) is chosen at random in the circle $x^2 + y^2 \leq 1$ (i.e., probability is proportional to area). What is the probability that the point falls outside the circle of center $(0,0)$, radius $\frac{1}{2}$?

10. Examine the following argument. "If a point is chosen at random in $V = [0,1]$, then $P(\{v\}) = 0$ for all $v \in V$. Therefore

$$P(V) = \sum_{v \in V} P(\{v\}) = \sum_{v \in V} 0 = 0.$$

This contradicts $P(V) = 1$."

11. Find all possible σ-algebras in $V = \{H,T\}$.

12. A fair die is rolled 100 times. What is the probability that it comes up even every time? [*Hint:* $E = \{2,4,6\}^{100}$. What is $|E|$?]

13. Let $V = \{1,2,3,4\}$, **E** = the collection of all subsets of V. Define two different probability functions P for which $P(\{2\}) = P(\{3\})$.

14. What is the probability that the first digit in the decimal expansion of $\pi/10$ is 7? The second digit? The 864th digit?

15. I have a coin in my pocket. What is the probability that it comes up heads at least once if I toss it three times?

16. Try to assign a sensible meaning to the question "Doctor, what are my chances of surviving this operation?" (What is a reasonable probability space?)

17. Consider the following statement: "The probability of an accident in the kitchen is greater than the probability of an accident in the street." What is a reasonable probability space?

9–3. RANDOM VARIABLE, EXPECTATION, VARIANCE

To introduce the concept of random variable, we consider an experiment in which we choose one person at random out of a given population V. Thus the sample space is V, and the probability function assigns equal chances to each element of V. Having chosen $v \in V$, we may wish to inquire about the age or height or weight, or some other numerical attribute of v. Each of these, of course, depends on v; that is, it is a function on V. It is customary to call such a function a random variable, although the name is not quite suitable. (It has been remarked, aptly, that it is neither random nor a variable.)

Definition 9–3. Given a probability space (V,P) and a real-valued function f on V, the pair (f,P) is called a (real) *random variable relative to P*, or *on* (V,P).

Observe that a random variable is not merely a function on a set V. It is important that there be a given probability distribution P on V. If P is changed to Q we get a different random variable, even though we use the same function on V.

EXAMPLE 9–11. Let $V = \{H,T\}$. Define the probability functions P and Q by

$$P(\{H\}) = \tfrac{1}{2}, \qquad Q(\{H\}) = \tfrac{1}{4},$$
$$P(\{T\}) = \tfrac{1}{2}, \qquad Q(\{T\}) = \tfrac{3}{4}.$$

Let f be the function on V given by

$$f(H) = 3, \qquad f(T) = 7.$$

Then f on (V,P) is a different random variable from f on (V,Q).

In applications, the associated probability function is frequently pushed into the background, and the random variable (f,P) is denoted simply by f. Often the letters x, y, z, and so on, are used for random variables, rather than the usual function letters f, g, and so on.

Given a random variable x on (V,P), we can form a new probability space as follows. The sample space W is the range of x, that is, $W = x(V) \subset R$. If $A \subset W$, we define

$$Q(A) = P(\{v \in V \mid x(v) \in A\}).$$

We may abbreviate by writing

$$Q(A) = P(x \in A),$$

read, "the probability that x is in A." If $A = \{a\}$, we write $P(x = a)$ for $P(x \in A)$. It is fairly easy to see that (W,Q) is a probability space. The effect of this transfer of probability from V to W is to highlight the distribution of values of x, while collapsing any variation that has no relevance to x.

EXAMPLE 9–12.   Let $V = \{1,2,\ldots,100\}$, $P(\{i\}) = 1/100$ for $1 \le i \le 100$. Define the random variable x on (V,P) by

$$x(i) = 0 \qquad (i \text{ even}),$$
$$x(i) = 1 \qquad (i \text{ odd}).$$

Then $W = \{0,1\}$, and

$$Q(\{0\}) = P(x = 0) = \frac{50}{100} = \frac{1}{2},$$

$$Q(\{1\}) = P(x = 1) = \tfrac{1}{2}.$$

EXAMPLE 9–13.   Let $V = \{1,\ldots,6\} \times \{1,\ldots,6\}$, $P(\{(i,j)\}) = 1/36$ for $i,j = 1,\ldots,6$. Define the random variable x on (V,P) by

$$x(i,j) = i + j \qquad (1 \le i, j \le 6).$$

Then $W = \{2,3,\ldots,12\}$, and the distribution of x is given by the following;

s	2	3	4	5	6	7	8	9	10	11	12
$Q(\{s\})$	$\dfrac{1}{36}$	$\dfrac{2}{36}$	$\dfrac{3}{36}$	$\dfrac{4}{36}$	$\dfrac{5}{36}$	$\dfrac{6}{36}$	$\dfrac{5}{36}$	$\dfrac{4}{36}$	$\dfrac{3}{36}$	$\dfrac{2}{36}$	$\dfrac{1}{36}$

For instance,

$$P(x = 6) = P(i + j = 6)$$

$$= P(\{(1,5), (2,4), (3,3), (4,2), (5,1)\})$$

$$= \frac{5}{36}.$$

Our table gives the distribution of the total count in the roll of a pair of dice (assumed fair and independent of each other).

To know a random variable x completely we need to know the probability space (W,Q). This means that we must know all the values of the function x and the associated probabilities. To get a quick though incomplete picture, we may form the *expected value* of x, obtained by weighting each value of x with its probability and summing. If $W = \{w_1,\ldots,w_n\}$ and $Q(\{w_i\}) = 1/n \, (i = 1,\ldots,n)$, we get

$$\frac{1}{n}(w_1 + w_2 + \cdots + w_n),$$

the ordinary arithmetic mean of the w's. In general we cannot expect so simple a result.

Definition 9–4. If x is a random variable on (V,P) with associated probability space (W,Q), the *expected value* or *expectation* of x is given by

(1) $$E(x) = \sum_w wQ(\{w\}).$$

Another term used is the mean value of x. $E(x)$ can also be expressed in terms of (V,P):

(2) $$E(x) = \sum_{v\in V} x(v)p_v.$$

To see this, for each $w \in W$ collect all the terms in the sum for which $x(v) = w$. The coefficient of w will be

$$\sum_{x(v)=w} p_v = P(x = w) = Q(\{w\}).$$

Summing over all the w's, we get the right side of Eq. (1).

EXERCISE 9–2

Compute the expectations of the random variables in Examples 9–11, 9–12, 9–13, using both formulas (1) and (2).

Theorem 9–1. If x and y are random variables on (V,P), then

$$E(x + y) = E(x) + E(y).$$

Proof: This is not so clear from formula (1), but is seen easily from (2):

$$E(x + y) = \sum_v (x(v) + y(v))p_v$$

$$= \sum_v x(v)p_v + \sum y(v)p_v$$

$$= E(x) + E(y).$$

Prove: (a) If x is a random variable and $c \in R$, then $E(cx) = cE(x)$.
(b) If c is a constant, then $E(c) = c$.

The mean $E(x)$ is a "measure of central tendency" for the random variable x. It is not the only one possible, but is most commonly used. Knowing $m = E(x)$, we still have no indication as to how closely the values of x tend to cluster around m. We could, of course, compute the deviations $x - m$ and average them. Unfortunately $E(x - m) = E(x) - E(m) = m - m = 0$, so we get no new information. Somewhat better would be to compute the absolute deviations $|x - m|$ and form the average $E(|x - m|)$. This is sometimes done, but the resulting measure of deviation is not easy to work with analytically. The most common measure is the *variance of* x:

Definition 9–5. $\sigma^2(x) = E((x - m)^2)$.

Theorem 9–2. If x is a random variable with mean m, variance σ^2, then

(3) $$\sigma^2 = E(x^2) - m^2.$$

Proof:

$$\begin{aligned}
\sigma^2(x) &= E((x - m)^2) \\
&= E(x^2 - 2mx + m^2) \\
&= E(x^2) - 2mE(x) + E(m^2) \\
&= E(x^2) - 2m^2 + m^2 \\
&= E(x^2) - m^2.
\end{aligned}$$

EXERCISES 9–4

1. If $m = E(x)$ and $a \in R$, show that

$$E((x - a)^2) = \sigma^2(x) + (a - m)^2.$$

2. If x is a random variable with mean m, variance σ^2, show that $y = ax + b$ has mean $am + b$, variance $a^2\sigma^2$.

3. Suppose that x is a random variable with mean m, variance $\sigma^2 \neq 0$. Prove that

$$y = \frac{x - m}{\sigma}$$

has mean 0, variance 1.

4. If $x_1, x_2, \ldots, x_n$ are random variables on (V,P), with $E(x_i) = m_i$ $(i = 1, \ldots, n)$, show that

$$E\left(\frac{1}{n} \sum_{i=1}^{n} x_i\right) = \frac{1}{n} \sum_{i=1}^{n} m_i.$$

In particular, if $m_1 = m_2 = \cdots m_n$,

$$E\left(\frac{1}{n} \sum_{i=1}^{n} x_i\right) = m_1.$$

Although the variance of x is easy to work with, it is of the wrong dimension with respect to x. If we multiply x by a, we multiply the variance by a^2 (see Problem 2 of Exercises 9–4). Accordingly, we define the *standard deviation* of x, $\sigma(x)$, as the positive square root of the variance. This definition has already been anticipated by our notation:

Definition 9–6. $\sigma(x) = \sqrt{\sigma^2(x)}$.

EXERCISE 9–5

Prove: $\sigma(ax + b) = |a|\sigma(x)$.

It is customary to measure deviations from the mean in units of the standard deviation. We shall now prove a theorem which says, roughly, that large deviations from the mean are unlikely.

Theorem 9–3 (*The Tchebycheff Inequality*). Let x be a random variable on (V,P) with mean m, standard deviation $\sigma \neq 0$. Then if $k > 0$,

$$P(|x - m| \geq k\sigma) \leq \frac{1}{k^2}.$$

Proof:
$$\sigma^2 = \sum_{v} (x(v) - m)^2 p_v$$
$$= \Sigma_1 + \Sigma_2,$$

say, where in Σ_1 we sum over all v such that $|x(v) - m| \geq k\sigma$, and in Σ_2, all others. Because $\Sigma_2 \geq 0$, we have

$$\sigma^2 \geq \Sigma_1 |x(v) - m|^2 p_v$$
$$\geq k^2\sigma^2 \Sigma_1 p_v$$
$$= k^2\sigma^2 P(|x - m| \geq k\sigma).$$

Dividing by $k^2\sigma^2$, we get the required result.

As an example, if x has mean 0, standard deviation .1, the probability that x deviates from 0 by more than .5 is no greater than $1/5^2 = .04$.

9–4. CONDITIONAL PROBABILITY, INDEPENDENCE

Let (V,P) be a probability space, representing, so to speak our best knowledge of the probable outcome of an experiment. Suppose that B is an event with $P(B) > 0$, and that somehow we learn that B must occur. We must now readjust our probability assignments in the light of this knowledge. For example, we would assign to B the probability 1, since B is now certain. If C is disjoint from B, then C is now impossible, so we would assign to it the probability 0. The new probability function is called the *conditional probability, given B.* For an event $E \subset V$, we write

$$P(E|B)$$

for the conditional probability of E, given B.

It seems reasonable to assign to any event E a new probability proportional to the old probability of the part of E that belongs to B, that is, of $E \cap B$. This suggests that for some constant k, we define

$$P(E|B) = kP(E \cap B) \qquad (E \subset V).$$

To determine k, take the special case $E = B$. Then we get

$$1 = P(B|B) = kP(B \cap B) = kP(B).$$

Therefore, $k = 1/P(B)$, and

$$P(E|B) = \frac{P(E \cap B)}{P(B)} \qquad (E \subset V).$$

To support our proposed definition, we appeal to the long-run frequency interpetation of probability. Consider a long sequence of n trials, and suppose that $S(B)$ is the number of occurrences of B, and that among these, $S(E \cap B)$ is the number of occurrences of $E \cap B$. We have agreed to limit our attention to those cases in which B occurs. *Among these,* the ratio of successes (occurrences of E) to trials is

$$\frac{S(E \cap B)}{S(B)} = \frac{[S(E \cap B)/n]}{[S(B)/n]}$$

$$= \frac{P(E \cap B)}{P(B)},$$

approximately.

Definition 9–7. Let (V,P) be a probability space, $B \subset V$, $P(B) > 0$. Then

$$P(E|B) = \frac{P(E \cap B)}{P(B)} \qquad (E \subset V)$$

is called the *conditional probability of E, given B.*

EXERCISE 9–6

Prove that conditional probability satisfies the definition of probability (nonnegative, countably additive, etc.).

EXAMPLE 9–14. What is the probability that a fair die comes up even, given that it comes up greater than 3?
Solution: $A = \{2,4,6\}$, $B = \{4,5,6\}$, $A \cap B = \{4,6\}$. Thus

$$P(A|B) = \frac{P(\{4,6\})}{P(\{4,5,6\})} = \frac{2}{3}.$$

EXERCISES 9–7

1. There are four cards in a box: the ace of spades, the ace of hearts, a king, and a queen. A hand of two cards is drawn from the box at random (all hands equally likely). What is the probability that the hand is a pair of aces? What is the conditional probability of this event, given that one of the cards drawn is an ace? The same, given that one of the cards is the ace of spades?

2. Let $B_1, \ldots, B_n$ be mutually exclusive events such that $\bigcup_{i=1}^{n} B_i = V$, with $P(B_i) > 0$ $(1 \leq i \leq n)$. Prove:

$$P(A) = \sum_{i=1}^{n} P(B_i)P(A|B_i) \qquad (A \subset V).$$

3. Under the hypotheses of Problem 2, with $P(A) \neq 0$, show that

$$P(B_j|A) = \frac{P(B_j)P(A|B_j)}{\sum_{i=1}^{n} P(B_i)P(A|B_i)} \qquad (j = 1, \ldots, n).$$

This is known as Bayes' theorem.

Definition 9–8. Events A and B are called *independent* iff

$$P(A \cap B) = P(A)P(B).$$

This definition is motivated by the following intuitive considerations. Suppose that we have two experiments, the outcomes of which can have no possible influence on each other (e.g., two coins are tossed a mile apart). Then the conditional probability of the event A for the first experiment, given that B occurs for the second, will be equal to the (unconditioned) probability of A. That is,

$$P(A|B) = P(A).$$

But

$$P(A|B) = \frac{P(A \cap B)}{P(B)},$$

so

$$P(A \cap B) = P(A)P(B).$$

The student should attempt to give a long-run frequency interpretation of independence of two events.

Notice that the definition does not require that $P(A)$ or $P(B)$ be positive. In fact, if either $P(A) = 0$ or $P(B) = 0$, then A and B are independent.

EXERCISE 9-8

Given that A and B are independent events, show that A and B' are independent; also A' and B, A' and B'.

Definition 9-9. Events $A_1, A_2, \ldots, A_n$ are called *independent* iff $P(C_1 \cap C_2 \cap \cdots \cap C_n) = P(C_1)P(C_2) \cdots P(C_n)$, where $C_1 = A_1$ or A'_1, $C_2 = A_2$ or $A'_2, \ldots, C_n = A_n$ or A'_n.

Observe that this is consistent with Definition 9–8, because of Exercise 9–8. We may interpret independence of $A_1, \ldots, A_n$ as meaning that knowledge of the occurrence of nonoccurrence of any subcollection of the A's yields no new information about those A's not in the subcollection.

These conditions may appear to be difficult to achieve. Actually they are not. Let us consider n trials (of the same or different experiments) that "have nothing to do with each other." We may regard the n-tuple of outcomes as one single outcome of a joint experiment. Thus our sample space is $V = V_1 \times V_2 \times \cdots \times V_n$. On V we define a probability P as follows: For $v = (v_1, v_2, \ldots, v_n) \in V$, we set

(1) $$P(\{v\}) = P_1(\{v_1\})P_2(\{v_2\}) \cdots P_n(\{v_n\}).$$

It is easily verified that (V,P) is a probability space, called the *product* of the spaces (V_i, P_i), $i = 1, \ldots, n$. We have already used this technique in some of our examples.

Now suppose that $B_1 \subset V_1, \ldots, B_n \subset V_n$. Each B_i is an event depending on the outcome of the ith trial. It corresponds to an event A_i in the product space, given by

(2) $\qquad A_i = V_1 \times \cdots \times V_{i-1} \times B_i \times V_{i+1} \times \cdots \times V_n.$

That is, $v = (v_1, \ldots, v_n) \in A_i$ if and only if $v_i \in B_i$. From Eqs. (1) and (2) it follows readily that

(3) $\qquad P(A_i) = P_i(B_i) \qquad (i = 1, \ldots, n).$

Also,

(4) $\qquad A_1 \cap A_2 \cap \cdots \cap A_n = B_1 \times B_2 \times \cdots \times B_n,$

so

(5) $\qquad P(A_1 \cap A_2 \cap \cdots \cap A_n) = P(B_1 \times B_2 \times \cdots \times B_n).$

By writing $B_1 \times B_2 \times \cdots \times B_n$ as a union of singletons $\{v\}$ and using Eq. (1), we get

$$
\begin{aligned}
(6) \quad P(B_1 \times B_2 \times \cdots \times B_n) &= \sum_{v_1 \in B_1} \cdots \sum_{v_n \in B_n} P_1(\{v_1\}) \cdots P_n(\{v_n\}) \\
&= \sum_{v_1 \in B_1} P_1(\{v_1\}) \cdot \sum_{v_2 \in B_2} P_2(\{v_2\}) \cdots \sum_{v_n \in B_n} P_n(\{v_n\}) \\
&= P_1(B_1) P_2(B_2) \cdots P_n(B_n). \\
&= P(A_1) P(A_2) \cdots P(A_n)
\end{aligned}
$$

by Eq. (3). Finally, Eqs. (5) and (6) yield

(7) $\qquad P(A_1 \cap A_2 \cap \cdots \cap A_n) = P(A_1) P(A_2) \cdots P(A_n).$

Because the B_i were arbitrary events in V_i, we could replace any of them by their complements. Since B_i' corresponds to A_i' by Eq. (2), we could put primes on any or all of the A_i in Eq. (7). The upshot of our discussion is that *the sets $A_1, \ldots, A_n$ are independent.*

We are now ready to discuss independent random variables.

Definition 9–10. Random variables $x_1, \ldots, x_n$ on (V,P) are called *independent* iff for every collection $D_1, \ldots, D_n$ of subsets of R, the sets

$$A_i = \{v \in V \mid x_i(v) \in D_i\} \qquad (i = 1, \ldots, n)$$

are independent.

Theorem 9–4. $x_1, \ldots, x_n$ are independent random variables on (V,P) if and only if for every n-tuple of reals $(w_1, \ldots, w_n)$,

$$P(x_1 = w_1 \wedge x_2 = w_2 \wedge \cdots \wedge x_n = w_n) = P(x_1 = w_1)P(x_2 = w_2) \cdots$$

$$P(x_n = w_n).$$

We omit the proof, which is quite straightforward. The student should carry it out in detail for $n = 2$ and $n = 3$.

*EXERCISE 9–9

Let $x_1, \ldots, x_n$ be independent random variables on (V,P), and let $f_1, \ldots, f_n$ be any functions from R to R. Then $f_1(x_1), f_2(x_2), \ldots, f_n(x_n)$ are independent random variables on (V,P). [$f_i(v)$ is the functional value of $f_i(x_i)$ at v; we could also have written $f_i \circ x_i$.]

An important property of independent random variables is that the expected value of their product is equal to the product of their expected values.

Theorem 9–5. Let $x_1, \ldots, x_n$ be independent random variables with $E(x_i) = m_i$. Then

$$E(x_1 x_2 \cdots x_n) = m_1 m_2 \cdots m_n.$$

Proof: If $w_1, \ldots, w_n$ run separately over all the values of $x_1, \ldots, x_n$, respectively, their product $w_1 \cdots w_n$ runs over all values of $x_1 \cdots x_n$. Hence

$$E(x_1 \cdots x_n) = \sum_{w_1} \sum_{w_2} \cdots \sum_{w_n} w_1 \cdots w_n P(x_1 = w_1 \wedge \cdots \wedge x_n = w_n)$$

$$= \sum_{w_1} \sum_{w_2} \cdots \sum_{w_n} w_1 \cdots w_n P(x_1 = w_1)P(x_2 = w_2) \cdots P(x_n = w_n)$$

$$= \sum_{w_1} w_1 P(x_1 = w_1) \cdot \sum_{w_2} w_2 P(x_2 = w_2) \cdots \sum_{w_n} w_n P(x_n = w_n)$$

$$= E(x_1)E(x_2) \cdots E(x_n).$$

The student should take careful note that not every pair of random variables x and y satisfies

$$E(xy) = E(x)E(y).$$

If this equation is satisfied, we say that x and y are *uncorrelated*. Thus, independent random variables are uncorrelated. The converse is false: x and y may be uncorrelated without being independent.

EXAMPLE 9–15.   Let $V = \{H,T\}$, $P(\{H\}) = P(\{T\}) = \frac{1}{2}$. Define x and y by

$$x(H) = 1, \quad y(H) = 2,$$
$$x(T) = 3, \quad y(T) = 4.$$

Then

$$xy(H) = 2, \quad xy(T) = 12.$$

Hence $E(x) = 2$, $E(y) = 3$, but $E(xy) = 7$.

EXAMPLE 9–16.   Let $V = \{a,b,c\}$, $P(\{a\}) = P(\{b\}) = P(\{c\}) = \frac{1}{3}$. Define x and y by

$$x(a) = -1, \quad y(a) = 1,$$
$$x(b) = 0, \quad y(b) = 0,$$
$$x(c) = 1, \quad y(c) = 1.$$

Then x and y are not independent, for

$$P(y = 0 | x = 0) = 1,$$

but $P(y = 0) = \frac{1}{3}$. On the other hand,

$$E(x)E(y) = 0 = E(xy).$$

EXAMPLE 9–17.   If a fair coin is tossed n times, we let y be the number of 2-runs, a 2-run being an occurrence of a head followed by a head or a tail by a tail. Thus, if we get $HHHTTT$, there are four 2-runs and $y = 4$. What is the expected number of 2-runs?

  Solution: Let $x_i = 1$ if the ith toss is a head, $x_i = -1$ if it is a tail $(i = 1,\ldots,n)$. The x_i are independent random variables, and $E(x_i) = 0$. The random variable

$$\tfrac{1}{2}(1 + x_i x_{i+1}) = \begin{cases} 1, & \text{if } x_{i+1} = x_i, \\ 0, & \text{if } x_{i+1} \neq x_i. \end{cases}$$

Therefore

$$y = \sum_{i=1}^{n-1} \tfrac{1}{2}(1 + x_i x_{i+1}),$$

$$E(y) = \sum_{i=1}^{n-1} \tfrac{1}{2}(1 + E(x_i x_{i+1}))$$

$$= \sum_{i=1}^{n-1} \tfrac{1}{2}(1 + E(x_i)E(x_{i+1}))$$

$$= \sum_{i=1}^{n-1} \tfrac{1}{2}$$

$$= \frac{n-1}{2}.$$

A similar technique can be used to find the expected number of 3-runs, 4-runs, etc.

Theorem 9–6. Let $x_i, \ldots, x_n$ be independent random variables with means $m_1, \ldots, m_n$, variances $\sigma_1^2, \ldots, \sigma_n^2$. Let $a_1, \ldots, a_n \in R$. Then

$$\sigma^2(a_1x_1 + a_2x_2 + \cdots + a_nx_n) = a_1^2\sigma_1^2 + a_2^2\sigma_2^2 + \cdots + a_n^2\sigma_n^2.$$

Proof: Let $y_i = x_i - m_i$. Then $E(y_i) = 0, \sigma^2(y_i) = \sigma^2(x_i) = \sigma_i^2(i = 1, \ldots, n)$. Also, if $i \neq j$, $E(y_iy_j) = E(y_i)E(y_j) = 0$.
Hence

$$\sigma^2\left(\sum_{i=1}^{n} a_ix_i\right) = \sigma^2\left(\sum a_iy_i + \sum a_im_i\right)$$

$$= \sigma^2\left(\sum a_iy_i\right) = E\left(\left(\sum a_iy_i\right)^2\right) - E^2\left(\sum a_iy_i\right)$$

$$= E\left(\left(\sum a_iy_i\right)^2\right) = E\left(\sum a_i^2y_i^2 + \sum a_ia_jy_iy_j\right)$$

$$= \sum a_i^2 E(y_i^2) + \sum_{i \neq j} a_ia_jE(y_iy_j)$$

$$= \sum_{i=1}^{n} a_i^2\sigma_i^2.$$

[*Note:* The conclusion and the proof of Theorem 9–6 are unchanged if we replace "independent" by "pairwise uncorrelated."]

Corollary. Let $x_1, \ldots, x_n$ be independent random variables with the same standard deviation σ. Then the *sample mean*

$$\bar{X}_n = \frac{1}{n} \sum_{i=1}^{n} x_i$$

has the standard deviation $\sigma/\sqrt{n}$.

Proof: $\sigma^2(\bar{X}_n) = \dfrac{1}{n^2} \sum_{i=1}^{n} \sigma^2 = \dfrac{\sigma^2}{n}$. Take square roots.

EXAMPLE 9–18.   If x and y are independent random variables, then

$$E(x + y) = E(x) + E(y),$$

$$E(x - y) = E(x) - E(y),$$

$$\sigma^2(x + y) = \sigma^2(x) + \sigma^2(y),$$

$$\sigma^2(x - y) = \sigma^2(x) + \sigma^2(y).$$

EXERCISES 9–10

1. An experiment has two possible outcomes, success and failure. The probability of success is p, that of failure is q. Let y be the number of successes in n independent trials of the experiment. Prove:

    (a) $E(y) = np$.

    (b) $\sigma(y) = \sqrt{npq}$.

2. Let y be the number of heads appearing in 100 independent tosses of a fair coin. Use the Tchebycheff inequality to estimate the probability that y deviates from 50 by at least 15.

3. Let y be the number of heads appearing in 10,000 independent tosses of a fair coin. Use the Tchebycheff inequality to estimate the probability that y deviates from 5,000 by at least 1,500.

4. Would you place more trust in the average of 100 measurements of a length than in the average of 25? Explain.

5. What is the effect of a change of scale $x' = ax + b$ on the mean? The variance? The standard deviation?

6. A random variable x has the following distribution:

x	-3	1	9
$P(\{x\})$	$\frac{1}{4}$	$\frac{1}{2}$	$\frac{1}{4}$

Find the mean, variance, and standard deviation of x. Find a change of scale $y = ax + b$ such that $E(y) = 0$, $\sigma(y) = 1$.

7. Let x be the number of heads in four independent tosses of a fair coin. Compute the distribution of x, as well as $E(x)$, $\sigma^2(x)$, and $E(|x - 2|)$.

8. If a fair coin is tossed n times independently, what is the expected number of 3-runs? [Hint: In the notation of Example 9–17, consider the random variable $\frac{1}{2}(1 + x_i x_{i+1}) \cdot \frac{1}{2}(1 + x_{i+1} x_{i+2})$.]

9. A fair coin is tossed 100 times. What is the probability of head on the 100th toss, given that head appears on tosses 1 through 99?

9-5.   LONG-RUN BEHAVIOR OF SAMPLE MEANS

Let us consider an experiment with associated probability space (V_1,P_1). A numerical observation may be regarded as a random variable x_1 on (V_1,P_1). If we make n independent observations of the same phenomenon, we have n random variables x_i on (V_i,P_i) $(i = 1,...,n)$, where the sample spaces and probability functions are copies of (V_1,P_1). As we have seen, we may regard the x_i as independent random variables on the product space

$$(V,P) = (V_1,P_1) \times (V_2,P_2) \times \cdots \times (V_n,P_n).$$

All the x_i have the same distribution; in particular they have the same mean m and standard deviation σ. (We assume that $\sigma \neq 0$, to avoid triviality.)

The *sample mean* is the random variable

(1)
$$X = \bar{X}_n = \frac{1}{n} \sum_{i=1}^{n} x_i.$$

We already know that

(2)
$$E(X) = m,$$

(3)
$$\sigma(X) = \frac{\sigma}{\sqrt{n}}.$$

Equation (3) tells us that the total probability mass for X concentrates itself around the mean m, more and more as $n \to \infty$. To get a numerical estimate of this concentration, we can use the Tchebycheff inequality. For every $k > 0$,

(4)
$$P\left(|X - m| \geq k \frac{\sigma}{\sqrt{n}}\right) \leq \frac{1}{k^2}.$$

In this form we can see that there is not much probability that X will fall outside the shrinking interval

$$\left(m - k\frac{\sigma}{\sqrt{n}}, m + k\frac{\sigma}{\sqrt{n}}\right).$$

Since k is arbitrary, however, we can transform this into a statement about any fixed interval $(m - h, m + h)$. Put

$$k = \frac{h\sqrt{n}}{\sigma}$$

in inequality (4). Then we get

(5) $$P(|X - m| \geq h) \leq \frac{\sigma^2}{nh^2}.$$

The right side tends to 0, σ and h being fixed. Thus we have proved the following theorem, which goes by the name *the (weak) law of large numbers.*

Theorem 9–7. *If* x_1, x_2,... *are independent random variables with common mean* m *and standard deviation* $\sigma \neq 0$, *then for each* $h > 0$,

$$\lim_{n \to \infty} P(|\bar{X}_n - m| \geq h) = 0.$$

It is possible to prove much stronger statements. One of these is the celebrated *central limit theorem.* It tells us that if all the x_i have the same distribution, as in our discussion above, then the random variable $\bar{X}_n - m$, measured according to its natural scale, has a distribution which gets closer and closer to a certain fixed (continuous) distribution, the so-called *normal distribution.* This convergence takes place no matter what the original distribution was.

Theorem 9–8 (*Central Limit Theorem*). If x_1, x_2,... are independent random variables with the same distribution, mean m, and standard deviation $\sigma \neq 0$, then for all $s \leq t$,

$$\lim_{n \to \infty} P\left\{ s \leq \frac{\bar{X}_n - m}{\sigma/\sqrt{n}} \leq t \right\} = \frac{1}{\sqrt{2\pi}} \int_s^t e^{-x^2/2} \, dx.$$

The quantity on the right is the area under the "bell-shaped" curve $y = (1/\sqrt{2\pi}) \exp(-x^2/2)$, between the abscissas s and t. This area function has been tabulated quite accurately.

EXERCISES 9–11

1. Using an exponential table, make a careful graph of the curve

$$y = \frac{1}{\sqrt{2\pi}} e^{-x^2/2}.$$

2. Let y be the number of successes in n independent trials of the same experiment, with probability of success p, failure q. Using the central limit theorem, estimate

$$P\{|y - np| \leq 3\sqrt{npq}\}$$

for large n. Look up the value in a table of areas of the normal probability curve.

BIBLIOGRAPHY

Andree, Richard V., *Selections from Modern Abstract Algebra*, Holt, New York, 1958.

Arrow, Kenneth J., *Social Choice and Individual Values*, Wiley, New York, 1951.

Ball, W. W. R., *Mathematical Recreations and Essays* (rev. by H. S. M. Coxeter, Macmillan, New York, 1956.

Beckenbach, Edwin, and Bellman, Richard, *An Introduction to Inequalities*, Random House, New Mathematical Library, New York, 1961.

Begle, E. G., *Introductory Calculus with Analytic Geometry*, Holt, New York, 1954.

Bell, E. T., *Men of Mathematics*, Simon and Schuster, New York, 1937.

Birkhoff, G., and MacLane, S., *A Survey of Modern Algebra*, Macmillan, New York, 1965.

Bridgman, P. W., *Logic of Modern Physics*, Macmillan, New York, 1927.

Bush, Robert R., and Mosteller, Frederick, *Stochastic Models for Learning*, Wiley, New York, 1955.

Cantor, Georg, *Contributions to the Founding of the Theory of Transfinite Numbers* (translated), Dover, New York, ca. 1955[n.d.].

Carroll, Lewis, *The Complete Works of Lewis Carroll*, Random House, The Modern Library, New York, 1936.

Churchman, C. W., Ackoff, R. L., and Arnoff, E. L., *Introduction to Operations Research*, Wiley, New York, 1957.

Courant, Richard, *Differential and Integral Calculus*, Interscience, New York, 1936.

Courant, Richard, and Robbins, Herbert, *What is Mathematics?*, Oxford University Press, New York, 1941.

Dantzig, Tobias, *Number, the Language of Science*, Macmillan, New York, 1954.

Davis, Philip J., *The Lore of Large Numbers*, Random House, New York, 1961.

Dresden, Arnold, *An Invitation of Mathematics*, Holt, New York, 1936.

Eves, Howard, *An Introduction to the History of Mathematics*, Holt, New York, 1953.

Feller, William, *An Introduction to Probability Theory and its Applications* (2nd ed.), Wiley, New York, 1957.

Frank, Philipp, *Modern Science and its Philosophy*, Braziller, New York, 1955.

Frank, Philipp, *Philosophy of Science*, Prentice-Hall, Englewood Cliffs, N.J., 1962.

Ghiselin, B., ed., *The Creative Process*, New American Library, New York, 1955.

Hadamard, J., *The Psychology of Invention in the Mathematical Field*, Princeton University Press, Princeton, N.J., 1949.

Hadley, G., *Linear Algebra*, Addison-Wesley, Reading, Mass., 1961.

Hardy, G. H., *Mathematician's Apology*, Cambridge University Press, Cambridge, 1940.

Kasner, E., and Newman, J., *Mathematics and the Imagination*, Simon and Schuster, New York, 1940.

Kline, Morris, *Mathematics and the Physical World*, Crowell, New York, 1959.

Kline, Morris, *Mathematics in Western Culture*, Oxford University Press, New York, 1953.

Larsen, Harold D., *Rinehart Mathematical Tables*, Holt, New York, 1948.

Lieber, Lillian R., *The Education of T. C. Mits*, Norton, New York, 1944.

Lieber, Lillian R., and Hugh G., *Non-Euclidean Geometry*, Science Press, Lancaster, Pa., 1931.

Luce, R. Duncan, ed., *Developments in Mathematical Psychology*, Free Press, New York, 1960.

Luce, R. Duncan, and Raiffa, Howard, *Games and Decisions*, Wiley, New York, 1957.

Meserve, Bruce E., and Sobel, Max A., *Mathematics for Secondary School Teachers*, Prentice-Hall, Englewood Cliffs, N.J., 1962.

Newman, J. R., *Science and Sensibility*, 2 vols., Simon and Schuster, New York, 1961.

Newman, J. R., ed., *The World of Mathematics*, 4 vols., Simon and Schuster, New York, 1956.

Neyman, J., *First Course in Probability and Statistics*, Holt, New York, 1950.

Niven, Ivan, *Numbers: Rational and Irrational*, Random House, New York, 1961.

Phillips, Hubert ("Caliban"), *My Best Puzzles in Logic and Reasoning*, Dover, New York, 1961.

Poincaré, Henri, *Science and Method* (translated), Dover, New York, 1952.

Polya, G., *How to Solve It*, Princeton University Press, Princeton, N.J., 1945.

Polya, G., *Mathematics and Plausible Reasoning*, 2 vols., Princeton University Press, Princeton, N.J., 1954.

Rademacher, H., and Toeplitz, O., *The Enjoyment of Mathematics*, translated by H. Zuckerman, Princeton University Press, Princeton, N.J., 1957.

Rosenbloom, Paul, *The Elements of Mathematical Logic*, Dover, New York, 1950.

Sawyer, W. W., *What is Calculus About?*, Random House, New York, 1961.

Stabler, E. R., *An Introduction to Mathematical Thought*, Addison-Wesley, Reading, Mass., 1953.

Stoll, Robert R., *Sets, Logic, and Axiomatic Theories*, Freeman, San Francisco, 1961.

Struik, Dirk J., *A Concise History of Mathematics*, Dover, New York, 1948.

Suppes, Patrick, *Introduction to Logic*, Van Nostrand, Princeton, N.J., 1957.

Weyl, Hermann, "Emmy Noether," *Scripta Mathematica*, Vol. 3., 1935, pp. 201–220.

Weyl, Hermann, "A Half Century of Mathematics," *American Mathematical Monthly*, Vol. 58, 1951, pp. 523–553.

Weyl, Hermann, "Mathematics and Logic," *American Mathematical Monthly*, Vol. 53, 1946, pp. 2–13.

Whitehead, A. N., *An Introduction to Mathematics*, Oxford University Press, New York, 1948.

Whitehead, A. N., *Science and the Modern World*, New American Library, New York, 1948.

Wiener, Norbert, *I Am a Mathematician*, Doubleday, New York, 1956.

Wilder, R. L., *Introduction to the Foundations of Mathematics*, Wiley, New York, 1952.

Wilks, S. S., *Elementary Statistical Analysis*, Princeton University Press, Princeton, N.J., 1948.

Williams, J. D., *The Compleat Strategyst*, McGraw-Hill, New York, 1954.

Zippin, Leo, *Uses of Infinity*, Random House, New York, 1962.

SELECTED ANSWERS

CHAPTER 1

Exercises 1–1

1. (a) True. (b) True. (c) True. (d) False.
4. (a) The captain is sometimes sober.
   (b) Everybody loves Saturday night.
   (c) The square of an integer minus the integer is always even.
   (d) The cube of an integer minus the integer is always divisible by 3.
   (e) There is a number whose product by 0 is not equal to 1.
6. (a) Every number has a negative.
   (b) There is a number which is the negative of all numbers.
8. (Loosely) There's a sucker born every minute.
10. (a) Ambiguous. Either $(\exists x)(\forall t)\, xFt$ or $(\forall t)(\exists x)\, xFt$.
    (b) Ambiguous, but probably $(\exists t)(\forall x)\, xFt$ is meant.
12. (a) $(\exists x)(\exists y)(\exists z)\, xMy$ and xMz and $y \neq z$.
    (b) $(\forall x)(\forall y)(\forall z)$ If xMy and xMz then $y = z$.
14. (a) x: Nonnegative reals, y: reals. True. *or* x: Reals, y: reals. False.
    (b) x,y,z: Reals. False.
    (c) x,y,z: Reals. True.
17. $(10 + 3)(10 - 3) = 100 - 3^2; (10 + 36)(10 - 36) = 100 - 36^2$.
19. $3^2 - 3 + 41$ is a prime. $10^2 - 10 + 41$ is a prime. $41^2 - 41 + 41$ is a prime. No, but $n^2 - n + 41$ is a prime for $n = 0,1,2,\ldots,40$.
20. $\forall n > 0, 1 + 2 + \cdots + n = n(n + 1)/2$.
23. (a) Jim. (b) Joe. (c) Joe. (d) Yes. (e) Yes. (f) Yes. The "$+$" has nothing to do with ordinary addition.

Exercises 1–2

1. No. 3. No. 5. Yes.
7. If "he" refers to a specific person, this is a proposition; otherwise not.
9. Yes. 11. Yes. 13. Yes.

Exercises 1–3

1. John is not young.
3. John is not both young and wealthy.
5. Some professors are not absent-minded.
7. Some professors are absent-minded.
9. Sometimes it rains but doesn't pour.

Exercises 1–4

1. (a) $\sim p \to r$. (b) $q \wedge s \to p$. (e) $(\sim q \to \sim r) \wedge (\sim r \to \sim q)$ or $\sim r \leftrightarrow \sim q$.
   (g) $\sim q \leftrightarrow \sim r$. (i) $\sim r \to p$.

Truth tables

(a)

p	r	$\sim p \to r$
T	T	T
T	F	T
F	T	T
F	F	F

(b)

q	s	p	$q \wedge s$	$q \wedge s \to p$
T	T	T	T	T
T	T	F	T	F
T	F	T	F	T
T	F	F	F	T
F	T	T	F	T
F	T	F	F	T
F	F	T	F	T
F	F	F	F	T

(e)

q	r	$\sim q \to \sim r$	$\sim r \to \sim q$	$(\sim q \to \sim r) \wedge (\sim r \to \sim q)$
T	T	T	T	T
T	F	T	F	F
F	T	F	T	F
F	F	T	T	T

(g)

q	r	$\sim q \leftrightarrow \sim r$
T	T	T
T	F	F
F	T	F
F	F	T

Compare with Problem 1(e).

(i)

r	p	$\sim r \to p$
T	T	T
T	F	T
F	T	T
F	F	F

Compare with Problems 1(a) and 1(c).

2. (a)

P	Q	$\sim Q$	$P \to Q$
T	T	F	T
T	F	T	F
F	T	F	T
F	F	T	T

The only row in which both premises are true is the fourth, so P is false, $\sim P$ is true.

(c)

P	Q	$P \to Q$	$\sim Q \to \sim P$
T	T	T	T
T	F	F	F
F	T	T	T
F	F	T	T

The premise $P \to Q$ is true in rows 1, 3, and 4, and so is the conclusion $\sim Q \to \sim P$.

4. (a)

p	q	$p \vee q$	$q \vee p$	$p \vee q \leftrightarrow q \vee p$
T	T	T	T	T
T	F	T	T	T
F	T	T	T	T
F	F	F	F	T

(b)

p	q	r	$p \wedge (q \vee r)$	$(p \wedge q) \vee (p \wedge r)$	$p \wedge (q \vee r) \leftrightarrow (p \wedge q) \vee (p \wedge r)$
T	T	T	T	T	T
T	T	F	T	T	T
T	F	T	T	T	T
T	F	F	F	F	T
F	T	T	F	F	T
F	T	F	F	F	T
F	F	T	F	F	T
F	F	F	F	F	T

(c)

p	q	$q \wedge \sim q$	$p \vee (q \wedge \sim q)$	$p \vee (q \wedge \sim q) \leftrightarrow p$
T	T	F	T	T
T	F	F	T	T
F	T	F	F	T
F	F	F	F	T

(d)

p	$p \vee \sim q$
T	T
F	T

(f)

p	q	a $p \leftrightarrow q$	$p \wedge q$	$\sim p \wedge \sim q$	b $(p \wedge q) \vee (\sim p \wedge q)$	$a \leftrightarrow b$
T	T	T	T	F	T	T
T	F	F	F	F	F	T
F	T	F	F	F	F	T
F	F	T	F	T	T	T

5. (a)

p	q	$\sim p \wedge \sim q$
T	T	F
T	F	F
F	T	F
F	F	T

p	q	$\sim p$	$\sim q$	$\sim \sim p$	$\sim \sim q$	$\sim \sim p \wedge \sim \sim q$
T	T	F	F	T	T	T
T	F	F	T	T	F	F
F	T	T	F	F	T	F
F	F	T	T	F	F	F

(e)

p	q	r	$p \wedge q$	$(p \wedge q) \wedge r$
T	T	T	T	T
T	T	F	T	F
T	F	T	F	F
T	F	F	F	F
F	T	T	F	F
F	T	F	F	F
F	F	T	F	F
F	F	F	F	F

(g)

p	q	r	$p \vee q$	$(p \vee q) \vee r$	$q \vee r$	$p \vee (q \vee r)$	$(p \vee q) \vee r \leftrightarrow p \vee (q \vee r)$
T	T	T	T	T	T	T	T
T	T	F	T	T	T	T	T
T	F	T	T	T	T	T	T
T	F	F	T	T	F	T	T
F	T	T	T	T	T	T	T
F	T	F	T	T	T	T	T
F	F	T	F	T	T	T	T
F	F	F	F	F	F	F	T

(i)

p	q	$p \vee q$	$\sim(p \vee q)$	$\sim p \wedge \sim q$	$\sim(p \vee q) \leftrightarrow \sim p \wedge \sim q$
T	T	T	F	F	T
T	F	T	F	F	T
F	T	T	F	F	T
F	F	F	T	T	T

(k)

p	q	$p \rightarrow q$	$q \rightarrow p$	$(p \rightarrow q) \wedge (q \rightarrow p)$
T	T	T	T	T
T	F	F	T	F
F	T	T	F	F
F	F	T	T	T

(m)

p	q	$p \rightarrow q$	$q \rightarrow p$	$(p \rightarrow q) \rightarrow (q \rightarrow p)$
T	T	T	T	T
T	F	F	T	T
F	T	T	F	F
F	F	T	T	T

(o)

p	q	$p \rightarrow q$	$\sim q \rightarrow \sim p$	$(p \rightarrow q) \leftrightarrow (\sim q \rightarrow \sim p)$
T	T	T	T	T
T	F	F	F	T
F	T	T	T	T
F	F	T	T	T

(q)

p	q	$p \vee \sim p$	$q \vee \sim q$	$p \vee \sim p \leftrightarrow q \vee \sim q$
T	T	T	T	T
T	F	T	T	T
F	T	T	T	T
F	F	T	T	T

(s)

p	q	$p \rightarrow q$	$q \rightarrow p$	$(p \rightarrow q) \wedge (q \rightarrow p)$	$p \leftrightarrow q$	$(p \rightarrow q) \wedge (q \rightarrow p) \leftrightarrow (p \leftrightarrow q)$
T	T	T	T	T	T	T
T	F	F	T	F	F	T
F	T	T	F	F	F	T
F	F	T	T	T	T	T

(u)

p	q	$p \rightarrow q$	$\sim(p \rightarrow q)$	$\sim(p \rightarrow q) \rightarrow p$
T	T	T	F	T
T	F	F	T	T
F	T	T	F	T
F	F	T	F	T

(w)

p	$\sim p \rightarrow p$	$(\sim p \rightarrow p) \rightarrow p$
T	T	T
F	F	T

(y)

p	q	r	$p \rightarrow q$	$q \rightarrow r$	$(q \rightarrow r) \rightarrow (p \rightarrow q)$	$(p \rightarrow q) \rightarrow ((q \rightarrow r) \rightarrow (p \rightarrow q))$
T	T	T	T	T	T	T
T	T	F	T	F	T	T
T	F	T	F	T	F	T
T	F	F	F	T	F	T
F	T	T	T	T	T	T
F	T	F	T	F	T	T
F	F	T	T	T	T	T
F	F	F	T	T	T	T

Exercises 1–5

1. (a) Show that $p \wedge \sim q$ has the same truth table as $p \wedge \sim q$.
   (b) Every proposition has the same truth value as itself, as any fool can plainly see.
   (c) Use Rule 2, Substitution, substituting $p \wedge \sim q$ for p throughout $p \leftrightarrow p$.
3. (a) No. (b) No. (c) Yes.
4. (a) Since P and Q are always true, so is $P \wedge Q$.
   (b) Since P is always true, $\sim P$ is always false; since $\sim P \vee Q$ is always true and $\sim P$ is always false, Q is always true.
   (c) If Q were sometimes true, then $P \wedge Q$ would be sometimes true (since P is always true), and $\sim(P \wedge Q)$ would be sometimes false.

This contradicts $\models \sim(P \wedge Q)$. Therefore Q is never true, so $\sim Q$ is always true. Or else, look at the truth table

P	Q	$\sim(P \wedge Q)$
T	T	F
T	F	T

The second row is the only one that applies.

(d)

P	Q	$P \vee Q$
F	T	T
F	F	F

The first row is the only one that applies.

(e)

P	Q	$Q \rightarrow \sim P$
T	T	F
T	F	T

The second row is the only one that applies.

7.

p	q	$p \mid q$
T	T	F
T	F	T
F	T	T
F	F	T

(a) From above,

$\sim p$	$p \mid p$
T	T
F	F

Or, use substitution, substituting p for q in the definition: $p \mid q \equiv \sim(p \wedge q)$. This yields $p \mid p \equiv \sim(p \wedge p) \equiv \sim p$.

(b)

p	q	$p \mid p$	$q \mid q$	$(p \mid p) \mid (q \mid q)$	$p \vee q$
T	T	F	F	T	T
T	F	F	T	T	T
F	T	T	F	T	T
F	F	T	T	F	F

Or, use replacement and substitution:

$$(p|p)|(q|q) \equiv \sim p | \sim q \equiv \sim(\sim p \wedge \sim q) \equiv \sim \sim p \vee \sim \sim q \equiv p \vee q.$$

(c)

p	q	$p|q$	$(p|q)|(p|q)$	$p \wedge q$
T	T	F	T	T
T	F	T	F	F
F	T	T	F	F
F	F	T	F	F

Or, use substitution in (a) and the definition

$$(p|q)|(p|q) \equiv \sim(p|q) \equiv \sim \sim(p \wedge q) \equiv p \wedge q.$$

(d)

p	q	$q|q$	$p|(q|q)$	$p \rightarrow q$
T	T	F	T	T
T	F	T	F	F
F	T	F	T	T
F	F	T	T	T

Or, use substitution in (a) and the definition

$$p|(q|q) \equiv p | \sim q \equiv \sim(p \wedge \sim q) \equiv p \rightarrow q.$$

(e) There are several equivalent forms for $p \leftrightarrow q$; probably the simplest is $p \leftrightarrow q \equiv [(p|(q|q))|(q|(p|p))] | [(p|(q|q)) | (q|(p|p))]$.

9. (a)

p	$1 - p$
1	0
0	1

(b) See text.

(c)

p	q	$p + q$	$p + q - pq$
1	1	2	1
1	0	1	1
0	1	1	1
0	0	0	0

(d)

p	q	$1 - p + pq$
1	1	1
1	0	0
0	1	1
0	0	1

(e)

p	q	$1 - p - q + 2pq$
1	1	1
1	0	0
0	1	0
0	0	1

Your discussion should contain a comparison of the tables for these functions with those for the five connectives. Thus $1 - p$ corresponds to $\sim p$, pq to $p \wedge q$, $p + q - pq$ to $p \vee q$, $1 - p + pq$ to $p \rightarrow q$, and $1 - p - q + 2pq$ to $p \leftrightarrow q$.

11. *First proof:* Construct a table for $P \wedge Q$, $Q \vee R$, $P \wedge R$.

	P	Q	R	$P \wedge Q$	$Q \wedge R$	$P \wedge R$
1.	T	T	T	T	T	T
2.	T	T	F	T	F	F
3.	T	F	T	F	F	T
4.	T	F	F	F	F	F
5.	F	T	T	F	T	F
6.	F	T	F	F	F	F
7.	F	F	T	F	F	F
8.	F	F	F	F	F	F

But since by hypothesis $P \wedge Q \equiv Q$, lines 5 and 6 of the table do not apply; since $Q \wedge R \equiv R$, lines 3 and 7 do not apply. This leaves lines 1, 2, 4, and 8, and in these remaining lines $P \wedge R \equiv R$.

Second proof:

(a) $Q \wedge R \equiv R$. Given.

(b) $(P \wedge Q) \wedge R \equiv R$. Replacement of Q by $P \wedge Q$ (given) in (a).

(c) $(P \wedge Q) \wedge R \equiv P \wedge (Q \wedge R)$. Substitution in $(p \wedge q) \wedge r \leftrightarrow p \wedge (q \wedge r)$.

(d) $P \wedge (Q \wedge R) \equiv R$. Symmetry and transitivity of "$\equiv$," (c) and (b).

(e) $P \wedge Q(\wedge R) \equiv P \wedge R$. Replacement of $Q \wedge R$ by R in (a).

(f) $P \wedge R \equiv R$. Symmetry and transitivity of "$\equiv$," (d) and (e). Briefly:
$P \wedge R \equiv P \wedge (Q \wedge R) \equiv (P \wedge Q) \wedge R \equiv Q \wedge R \equiv R$.

Exercises 1–6

2. (c) There are men over 6 feet tall and there are men less than 5 feet tall, but there is not any man who is both.

4. (b) It is true that "All animals speak Greek $\leftrightarrow$ all animals have wings," but "For all animals, speaking Greek is equivalent to possessing wings" is false.

5. (c) The arrow cannot be reversed. Let $P(x,y)$ stand for $x = y$.

6. (d) $\sim(\exists x)(\forall y)\, P(x,y) \equiv (\forall x)(\exists y)\, \sim P(x,y).$
7. (b) $(\forall x)\, \sim(P(x) \wedge Q(x)) \equiv (\forall x)\, (\sim P(x) \vee \sim Q(x)).$
   (d) $(\forall x)\, \sim(P(x) \vee Q(x)) \equiv (\forall x)\, (\sim P(x) \wedge \sim Q(x)).$
8. (c) For all x, there is a y and a z such that $x + y \neq z$. [or: $(\forall x)(\exists y)(\exists z)$ $x + y \neq z$.]
   (e) There is a positive number h such that for all positive numbers k there is an x such that $-k < x - 2 < k$ and either $-h \geq x^2 - 4$ or $x^2 - 4 \geq h$.
9. For the purposes of this problem, regard "proud" as the negation of "humble," "weak" as the negation of "powerful." Then the negations are:
   (a) All men are either proud or weak.
   (c) All powerful men are proud or All men are either weak or proud or All humble men are weak.
   (e) Some men are either proud or weak.
   (g) Some powerful men are proud or Some men are powerful and proud or Some proud men are powerful.
10. From the tautology we can infer

$$[(\forall x)\, W(x) \rightarrow (\forall x)\, H(x)] \vee [(\forall x)\, H(x) \rightarrow (\forall x)\, W(x)]$$

and $(\forall x)\, [(W(x) \rightarrow H(x)) \vee (H(x) \rightarrow W(x))]$, but not

$$[(\forall x)\, (W(x) \rightarrow H(x))] \vee [(\forall x)\, (H(x) \rightarrow W(x))].$$

Exercises 1–7

In each case consider the questions of existence and uniqueness. In 1, 4, 5, and 6, give examples.

1. For each real x, there is one and only one integer n such that $n \leq x$ and $(\forall m)\, m \leq x \rightarrow m \leq n$. The definition is satisfactory.
2. There are two real numbers x such that $x^2 = 5$. The definition is not satisfactory. Modify it to "the positive real number ...."
5. The two domains of definition overlap. When this happens we must check to see that our definitions agree on the overlap. In this case, $|0| = 0$ according to the upper line and $|0| = 0$ according to the lower, and $0 = -0$, so the definition is satisfactory.
7. Does this agree with the usual meaning of "$+$" when a/b and c/d are integers? Does the definition yield the same answer if the representation "$(ka)/(kb)$" is used instead of "a/b"? The symbol "$+$" on the left is being defined in terms of "$+$" on the right. Why is this not a circular definition?
9. This interesting operation has been named "addiply." Thus, "1 addiply 2 equals 5." It may be worthwhile to discuss the properties of "$*$." For

example, does $a*b = b*a$? What is $a*(b*c)$? $(a*b)*c$? Does $a*(b*c) = (a*b)*c$? What is $a*0$? $a*(-1)$? Can we always solve for x the equation $a*x = b$? Compare addiplication with addition; multiplication. See Problem 8 of Exercises 3–9.

10. Is there such a real number x? If so, then $2 = 1 + 1 = 0 \cdot x + 0 \cdot x = (0 + 0)x = 0 \cdot x = 1$.

12. Is the definition unambiguous? Suppose we use two different circles, with different radii; do we get the same meaning for "π"? Do we need a prior definition of the length of the circumference?

13. No comment.

CHAPTER 2

Exercises 2–1

1. (a) $\{1,2,3,4,5,6,7,8,9\}$.
    (c) $\{\ \}$ or $\emptyset$.
    (e) $\{3 \text{ heads, 2 heads and 1 tail, 1 head and 2 tails, 3 tails}\}$.
    (g) $\{(0,0),(0,1),(1,0),(1,1)\}$.

2. (a) n is even $\wedge 2 \le n \le 10$.
    (c) n is a nonzero square ≤ 25.
    (e) n is a (positive) divisor of 30.

3. (a) Yes. (c) Yes. (e) No.

4. (a) $7 \in \{1,3,5,7,9\}$.
    (c) $(\forall x)(x \in A \rightarrow x \in B)$.
    (e) $(\forall x) \sim (x \in A \wedge x \in B) \text{ or } (\forall x)(x \notin A \vee x \notin B) \text{ or } \sim (\exists x)(x \in A \wedge x \in B)$.
    (g) $(\exists x)(\exists y)(x \ne y \wedge A = \{x,y\})$.

6. $\{a,b\} = \{a',b'\}$ is equivalent to

$$[a \in \{a',b'\} \wedge b \in \{a',b'\}] \wedge [a' \in \{a,b\} \wedge b' \in \{a,b\}],$$

which is equivalent to

$$[(p \vee q) \wedge (r \vee s)] \wedge [(p \vee r) \wedge (q \vee s)].$$

Using Problem 5, we get the required result.

7. (a) True. (c) True. (e) True. (g) True. (i) True. (k) False.

8. (a) 0, 1, 2. (c) (0,0), (1,1), (4,2). (f) 1, 2. (h) 0.

10. (a) A, B, E, F, and H have one element each, D has 3, and C and G have no elements.
    (b) $A = H, B = F, C = G$.

12. $\{a,b\} = \{b,c\} \wedge \{b,c\} = \{c,d\}$
    $\leftrightarrow (a = c) \wedge (b = d)$ [by Eq. (3)]
    $\leftrightarrow (a,b) = (c,d)$.

14. (See Problem 18.)

    (a) $A \cup B = V$, or $A' \subset B$, or $B' \subset A$.

    (b) $A \cap B = V$, or $A = B = V$.

    (c) $A \subset B$.

    (d) Same as (c).

    (e) Same as (c).

    (f) $A = B$.

    (g) Same as (f).

    (h) $A = B'$.

    (i) $B \subset A$.

16. $A \subset B$.

18. $A \cup B' = V \equiv B \subset A$. (This equivalence has been used to simplify the answers to Problem 14.)

20. *First proof:* Let x be an arbitrary element of $[A' \cap (A \cup B)] \cup (A \cap B)$. Then either $x \in A' \cap (A \cup B)$ or $x \in A \cap B$.

    (a) $x \in A' \cap (A \cup B)$. Then $x \in A'$ and $x \in A \cup B$. Since $x \in A'$, $x \notin A$; hence $x \in B$.

    (b) $x \in A \cap B$. Then $x \in B$. Thus in either case, $x \in B$, and $[A' \cap (A \cup B)] \cup (A \cap B) \subset B$. Now let x be an arbitrary element of B. Either $x \in A$ or $x \in A'$.

    (a) $x \in A$. Then $x \in A \cap B$, and $x \in [A' \cap (A \cup B)] \cup (A \cap B)$.

    (b) $x \in A'$. Then $x \in A'$ and $x \in A \cup B$, so that $x \in A' \cap (A \cup B)$ and hence $x \in [A' \cap (A \cap B)] \cup (A \cap B)$. Thus

$$B \subset [A' \cap (A \cup B)] \cup (A \cap B);$$

    and

$$[A' \cap (A \cup B)] \cup (A \cap B) = B.$$

Second proof:

$$[A' \cap (A \cup B)] \cup (A \cap B) = [(A' \cap A) \cup (A' \cap B)] \cup (A \cap B) \text{ [by Eq. (4)]}$$

$$= [\varnothing \cup (A' \cap B)] \cup (A \cap B)$$

$$= (A' \cap B) \cup (A \cap B)$$

$$= (A' \cup A) \cap B \text{ [by Eq. (4)]}$$

$$= V \cap B$$

$$= B.$$

23. $n(B \cup H) = 11$; $n((B \cup H)') = n(G \cap H') = 4$; $n(G \cap H) = n(G) - n(G \cap H')$. The fact that there are six honor students is not needed.

25.

r	1	2	3	4	5	6	7	8	9	10	11	12
$n(A_r)$	0	1	2	3	4	5	6	5	4	3	2	1

27. (a) 1, 5, 17. (b) 1, 3, 5. (c) 17, 107. (d) $\frac{1}{2}$.

28. $A = B$.

33. No. No.

Exercises 2–2

1. (a) 3,5. (b) 1,2,3,4,5. (c) 1,2. (d) $-2, -1,0,1,2$. (e) No elements. (f) 1,3,5,6.
   (g) 1,2,3,4,5,6,7,8,9.

3. $\emptyset$, $\{2\}$, $\{3\}$, $\{$Washington$\}$, $\{2,3\}$, $\{2,$Washington$\}$, $\{3,$Washington$\}$, $\{2,3,$Washington$\}$.

5. $\emptyset$, $\{1\}$, $\{\{2,3\}\}$, $\{1,\{2,3\}\}$.

7. Choose A and C so that $A \subset C$.

9. $C = A \cap B$.

12. (a) $A \cup B$. (b) $A \cap B$. (c) $A' \cup B$. (d) $A' \cup B$. (e) $B \cup A'$. (f) $(A' \cup B) \cap (A \cup B')$; also $(A \cap B) \cup (A' \cap B')$. (g) Same as (f).

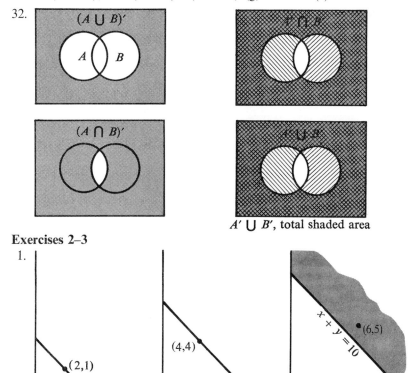

$A' \cup B'$, total shaded area

Exercises 2–3

1.

Exercises 2–4

1. a, b, c, d, and f have the same extension; h and i have the same extension.

3. 12.

5. (a) $\{(1,5)\}$.
   (b) $\{(2,5)\}$.
   (c) $\{(3,5)\}$.
   (d) $\{(1,5), (2,5)\}$.
   (e) $\{(1,5), (3,5)\}$.
   (f) $\{(2,5), (3,5)\}$.
   (g) $\{(1,5), (2,5), (3,5)\}$.
   (h) $\varnothing$.

7. (a) $(1,\frac{1}{2})$, $(1,-7)$, $(\frac{1}{2},-7)$, $(3,1)$, $(3,\frac{1}{2})$, $(3,-7)$. Transitive, not reflexive, not symmetric.
   (c) Transitive, not symmetric, not reflexive.
   (e) Not reflexive (you are not your own brother). Not symmetric if there is at least one male and one female child in the family; symmetric if all children are male or all female. Not transitive if the number of male children exceeds one; transitive if that number is 0 or 1.

9. (a) domain $= \{\frac{1}{2},1,3\}$, range $= \{-7,\frac{1}{2},1\}$.
   (b) domain $=$ range $= \{$paper,stone,scissors$\}$.
   (d) domain $= \{$President,Secretary of State$\}$,
       range $= \{$Secretary of State,Secretary of Labor,Ambassador to India$\}$.

11. (b).

13. Yes; the equivalance classes are the isobars, and are represented as curves.

15. No.

17. If $(x,y) \in E$, then $x = y$. Since R is reflexive, $(x,x) \in R$, and xRx. Then xRy, so that $(x,y) \in R$. This expresses the reflexivity of R.

19. $A = \{1,2\}$, $S = \{(1,1)\}$.

Exercises 2–5

1. $T(5000) = 880$, $T(14,000) = 2960$, $T(2000) = 325$, $T(4000) = 680$, $T(4001) = 680.20$.

3. (a) $\{(1,1), (2,2), (3,3)\}$.
   (b) $\{(1,1), (2,3), (3,2)\}$.
   (c) $\{(1,2), (2,1), (3,3)\}$.
   (d) $\{(1,2), (2,3), (3,1)\}$.

(e) $\{(1,3), (2,1), (3,2)\}$.

(f) $\{(1,3), (2,2), (3,1)\}$.

5. (a) $20;2;2$. (b) $25;7;7$. (c) $62;8;8$.

(d) $(\forall n)\ (n < 10 \leftrightarrow s(n) = n)$, $(\forall n)\ (n \geq 10 \leftrightarrow s(n) < n)$, $(\forall n)\ (s(n) \not> n)$.

(e) All 0.

7. (a) $\operatorname{rng} f = \{x \mid x \geq 0\}$. (b) $\operatorname{rng} f = \{x \mid x \geq 1\}$.

9. $(0,1,2)$, $(0,1,3)$, $(0,2,2)$, $(0,2,3)$, $(1,1,2)$, $(1,1,3)$, $(1,2,2)$, $(1,2,3)$.

11. (a), (b), (c), and (f) are functions.

13. "Is husband of" is

(a) a one-to-one correspondence under monogamy.

(b) not a one-to-one correspondence under polygamy.

(c) not a function under polygyny.

(d) a many-to-one function under polyandry.

15. There are only two examples: $h(x) = 0$ for all $x \in \{0,1,2,3,4\}$ or $h(x) = x$ for all $x \in \{0,1,2,3,4\}$.

17. f is one-to-one $\equiv f$ is a function $\wedge f^{-1}$ is a function. f^{-1} is one-to-one $\equiv f^{-1}$ is a function $\wedge (f^{-1})^{-1}$ is a function. But $(f^{-1})^{-1} = f$, and $p \wedge q \leftrightarrow q \wedge p$ is a tautology, so f is one-to-one $\equiv f^{-1}$ is one-to-one.

19. Let A denote the set of squares of integers, B the set of all odd integers. Then for $z \in A$,

$$f(z) =_{\mathrm{df}} \begin{cases} -\sqrt{z}, \text{ if } z \text{ is odd,} \\ \\ \sqrt{z} + 1, \text{ if } z \text{ is even.} \end{cases}$$

Then f is a one-to-one correspondence between A and B.

22. $c = c_1 k_1 + c_2 k_2 + \cdots + c_n k_n$. The variables are c and k, or $c_1, \ldots, c_n$, $k_1, \ldots, k_n$.

23. $f \mid A = \{(0,0),(1,0)\} = g \mid A$. If $x \notin \{0,1\}$, then $f(x) = 3g(x) \neq 0$, so $f(x) \neq g(x)$ for all $x \in A$. The only other subsets are $\emptyset$, $\{0\}$, $\{1\}$.

26. $R = \{(n,n) \mid n \in Z\} \cup \{(1,2),(2,1),(1,3),(3,1)\}$.

28. Each stimulus presentation is an ordered five-tuple (e_1,e_2,e_3,e_4,e_5), each component of which is an element of $E = \{\text{red,blue,yellow}\}$. Hence the set of all possible stimulus presentations is $E \times E \times E \times E \times E$. This contains $3 \cdot 3 \cdot 3 \cdot 3 \cdot 3 = 3^5 = 243$ elements.

30. (a) The number of possible ciphers is $26! = 26 \cdot 25 \cdot 24 \cdot \ldots \cdot 3 \cdot 2 \cdot 1$.

(b) $f = \{(a,z),(b,y),(c,x), \ldots ,(x,c),(y,b),(z,a)\}$.

(c) Let R be a transitive cipher. If α is any letter, there is a β such that $\beta R \alpha$ and $a \gamma$ such that $\alpha R \gamma$. By transitivity, $\beta R \gamma$. Since $\beta R \alpha$ and $\beta R \gamma$, $\alpha = \gamma$ because R is a function. Therefore $\alpha R \alpha$. Thus $\forall \alpha$, $\alpha R \alpha$, and R is the identity cipher $\{(\alpha,\alpha) \mid \alpha \in A\}$.

(d) Yes. (e) Yes.

31. R has to be shown to be reflexive. Suppose $x \in$ dom $R = A$. Then xRy for some $y \in$ rng $R \subset A$. Since R is symmetric, yRx. Since R is transitive, from xRy and yRx we conclude xRx. Since x was arbitrary in A, $\forall x$, xRx.

33. Show that each subset has a single element of C corresponding to it, and conversely. There are 32 subsets of A.

35. Let Z^+ denote the set of positive integers. For $n \in Z$, define $f(n)$ by

$$f(n) =_{df} \begin{cases} 2n, & \text{if } n > 0, \\ -2n + 1, & \text{if } n \leq 0. \end{cases}$$

Then f is a one-to-one correspondence of Z onto Z^+.

Exercises 2–6

2. If $\exists x \in A$, then, since R is reflexive and R is irreflexive on A, $(xRx) \wedge \sim(xRx)$. This is impossible. Hence $A = \emptyset$.

4. Let x be an arbitrary element of A. There is a $y \in A$ such that $x \neq y$. Then, since R is connected, $xRy \vee yRx$. But, since R is symmetric, $xRy \leftrightarrow yRx$, so that if xRy, yRx also, and if yRx, xRy also. Thus $xRy \wedge yRx$. Since R is transitive, xRx. Thus R is reflexive, as well as transitive and symmetric. The condition on A is necessary.

6. Let x be an arbitrary element of A. For every element y, $xRy \rightarrow \sim yRx$, since R is asymmetric. Hence in particular, $xRx \rightarrow \sim xRx$. This is equivalent to the proposition $\sim xRx \vee \sim xRx$, which is equivalent to $\sim xRx$. Hence R is irreflexive.

8. Since every element must be equivalent to every other, the only such relation on $\{1,2,3,4\}$ is $R = \{(a,b) | a,b \in \{1,2,3,4\}\}$.

CHAPTER 3

Exercises 3–1

1. (a) Suppose the common target of L and M contains hearts P and Q. Then L pierces P and Q, and M pierces P and Q. But the Axiom says there cannot be two distinct arrows piercing a pair of distinct hearts. Hence either $L = M$, which is contrary to hypothesis, or $P = Q$. Hence the common target cannot contain more than a single element.

   (b) No; there can be any number of arrows which do not pierce any heart.

Exercises 3–2
1. $\emptyset$, {sun}, {moon}, {sun,moon}.
4. 28 cases.

Exercises 3–4
2. The circuit function is $(p \wedge q) \vee (\sim p \wedge \sim q)$. In B this is $pq + p'q'$. The diagram is

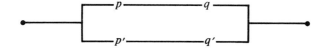

3. In B, we have $(p + q)(p + r) = p + qr$.

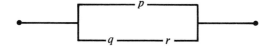

5. $(pq' + qr')'pq = ((pq')'(qr')')pq = (p' + q)(q' + r)pq = pqr$.

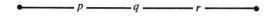

7. An acceptable formula is $pqr + C(p + q + r)$ with the diagram

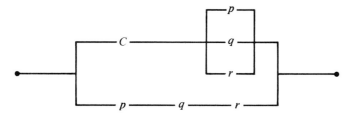

8. An acceptable formula is

$$C(p + q)(r + s) + pq(r + s + C) + rs(p + q + C).$$

The two situations yield the same result.
10. 4; 16; 256. For n switches, there are 2^n rows in a typical table, and the result in each row can be filled arbitrarily in two ways. Thus the total number of tables is 2^{2^n}. (See Problem 12 of Exercises 1–5.)
12. An acceptable formula is

$$pqr + pq'r' + p'qr' + p'q'r = p(qr + q'r') + p'(qr' + q'r).$$

The diagram is

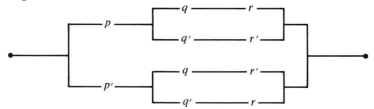

Exercises 3–5

1. Theorem 3–1. 3. $(a')' = a$. 5. $1' = 0$. 7. $a \cdot 0 = 0$.
9. $(a + b' = 1) \wedge (a' + b = 1) \rightarrow (a = b)$.

Exercise 3–6

(a) $a + b + c + d = a + (b + c + d) = a + ((b + c) + d)$
$= (a + (b + c)) + d = (a + b + c) + d$.

Exercises 3–7

1. Use Theorems 3–9, 3–9′, and 3–2.
3. The opposite of the first circuit has as its formula the left side of Problem 1; the second circuit has the right side of Problem 1 as its formula.
5. Let a and b be arbitrary elements of B. If $ab = a + b$, then

$$a'(ab) = a'(a + b) = a'a + a'b,$$

$$(a'a)b = a'b,$$

$$0 = a'b.$$

Also

$$(ab)b' = (a + b)b' = ab' + bb',$$

$$a(bb') = ab',$$

$$0 = ab'.$$

8. The systems are essentially the same.
9. Since Axioms 3–3 and 3–4 are violated, the system is not a model. If A and N are interchanged, however, so that $0 \Rightarrow A$ and $1 \Rightarrow N$, a model is obtained. There are two possible interpretations that work.
10. The set will be closed under both operations and under complementation. The other axioms are satisfied because they hold for the larger system. Thus we do get a model of Boolean algebra.
13. Suppose $a \in C$. Then $a = a \cdot 1 = a \cdot 0 = 0$.
14. (a) The elements would be 0, 1, a. Then $a' = 0, 1, a$ all lead to contradictions. Hence there is no Boolean algebra with three elements.

15. (a) If $a \le b$ and $b \le c$, then $ab = a$ and $bc = b$, so $ac = (ab)c = a(bc)$
$= ab = a$. Hence $a \le c$.
(c) If $a \le b$ and $a \le c$, then $ab = a$ and $ac = a$, so $a(bc) = (ab)c = ac$
$= a$. Hence $a \le bc$.
(e) If $a \le b$, then $ab = a$, and $ab' = abb' = 0$.

$$a' + b = 1,$$

$$(a' + b)b' = b',$$

$$a'b' = b',$$

$$b' \le a'.$$

(g) If $a \le b$, then $c + a = c + ab = (c + a)(c + b)$. Hence
$c + a \le c + b$.

16. (a) $a \triangle b = ab' + a'b = ba' + b'a = b \triangle a$.
(c) $a \triangle b = 0 \rightarrow ab' + a'b = 0 \rightarrow ab' = 0 \wedge a'b = 0$

$$\rightarrow a = b \,(\text{Theorem 3–4}).$$

$$a = b \rightarrow a \triangle b = ab' + a'b = aa' + a'a = 0.$$

(e) $a(b \triangle c) = a(bc' + b'c) = abc' + ab'c$.

$$(ab) \triangle (ac) = (ab)(ac)' + (ab)'(ac)$$

$$= ab(a' + c') + (a' + b')ac$$

$$= abc' + ab'c.$$

(g) $(a \triangle b)' = (ab' + a'b)' = (ab')'(a'b)'$

$$= (a' + b)(a + b') = a'b' + ab.$$

$a' \triangle b = a'b' + (a')'b = a'b' + ab$.

Exercises 3–9

2. Let $B = \{0,1,p,q\}$, $\bar{B} = \{0,1,\bar{p},\bar{q}\}$. Then $q = p'$ and $\bar{q} = \bar{p}'$. Define f by

$$f: \begin{cases} 0 \rightarrow \bar{0} \\ 1 \rightarrow \bar{1} \\ p \rightarrow \bar{p} \\ q \rightarrow \bar{q}. \end{cases}$$

If the operations are $+$, $\cdot$ in B and $\mp$, $\div$ in $\bar{B}$, then under f the $+$ and tables go into the $\mp$ and $\div$ tables. Thus f is an isomorphism.

4. (a) Yes. (b) Yes. (c) No. (d) No. (e) Yes.

6. (a) Yes. (b) Yes. (c) Yes. (d) No. (e) No.

7. We want $mn + 1 = (m + 1) \otimes (n + 1)$ for all $m, n \in Z$. Replace m by $m - 1$, n by $n - 1$, to get

$$(m - 1)(n - 1) + 1 = m \otimes n \qquad (m, n \in Z).$$

f is an isomorphism between $(Z, \cdot)$ and $(Z, \otimes)$.

Exercises 3–10

1. Let e_1, e_2 be identities. Then by Axiom 3–3, $e_1 = e_1 * e_2 = e_2$.

3. $y = z$.

4. (a), (c), (d) Identity $= 0$; inverse of $x = -x$. (b), (e) Identity $= 1$; inverse of $x = 1/x$.

6. Verifications of Axioms 3–1, 3–2, and 3–5 are routine. The identity is $(1,0)$. To find the inverse of (a,b), we solve $(a,b) * (x,y) = (1,0)$:

$$(a,b) * (x,y) = (ax - by, bx + ay) = (1,0).$$

Thus

$$ax - by = 1,$$
$$bx + ay = 0.$$

Solving, we find

$$(a,b)^{-1} = (x,y) = \left(\frac{a}{a^2 + b^2}, \frac{-b}{a^2 + b^2} \right).$$

7. G is closed under $*$ because $a_1 \neq 0 \wedge a_2 \neq 0 \rightarrow a_1 a_2 \neq 0$. Verification of Axiom 3–2 is routine. Commutativity does not hold, because

$$(a_2, b_2) * (a_1, b_1) = (a_2 a_1, a_2 b_1 + b_2) \neq (a_1 a_2, a_1 b_2 + b_1).$$

The identity is $(1,0)$. To find $(a,b)^{-1}$, we solve $(a,b) * (x,y) = (1,0)$:

$$ax = 1,$$
$$ay + b = 0.$$

9. The identity is T_1. T_1, T_2, T_3, T_6 are their own inverses, and $T_4^{-1} = T_5$, $T_5^{-1} = T_4$.
$T_1 = T_2^2$, $T_2 = T_2$, $T_3 = T_3$, $T_4 = T_2 T_3$, $T_5 = T_3 T_2$, $T_6 = T_3 T_2 T_3$.
The group is not commutative.

12. Use the fact that every row and column must contain all three elements.

14. $e = xyxy$. Multiply on the left by x, on the right by y.

16.
$$P_1 = \begin{pmatrix} 1 & 2 & 3 \\ 1 & 2 & 3 \end{pmatrix}, \qquad P_4 = \begin{pmatrix} 1 & 2 & 3 \\ 3 & 1 & 2 \end{pmatrix},$$

$$P_2 = \begin{pmatrix} 1 & 2 & 3 \\ 2 & 1 & 3 \end{pmatrix}, \qquad P_5 = \begin{pmatrix} 1 & 2 & 3 \\ 2 & 3 & 1 \end{pmatrix},$$

$$P_3 = \begin{pmatrix} 1 & 2 & 3 \\ 3 & 2 & 1 \end{pmatrix}, \qquad P_6 = \begin{pmatrix} 1 & 2 & 3 \\ 1 & 3 & 2 \end{pmatrix}.$$

This group is isomorphic with $(T, {}^\circ)$ of Problem 9, under the mapping $P_j \to T_j (j = 1, \ldots, 6)$. To find the inverse, interchange the two rows and rearrange the columns so that the new first row is 1 2 3.

CHAPTER 4

Exercises 4–2

1. (a) 2. (b) -2. (c) 2.

3. $a + (b + (-a)) = a + ((-a) + b) = (a + (-a)) + b = 0 + b = b$. Thus $b + (-a)$ satisfies the definition of $b - a$ as the solution of $a + x = b$.

5. $0 - a = 0 + (-a) = -a$.

7.

+	0	k	r
0	0	k	r
k	k	r	0
r	r	0	k

This is the only solution.

Exercises 4–3

1. (a) 2. (b) 2^{-1}. (c) 2.

3. $a(ba^{-1}) = a(a^{-1}b) = (aa^{-1})b = 1 \cdot b = b$. Thus ba^{-1} satisfies the definition of b/a as the solution of $ax = b$.

5. No.

10. 0 is in the first set but not the second. Therefore the two sets are not equal. The division by x is possible only if $x \neq 0$. The case $x = 0$ must be treated as a separate possibility.

11. Let $u = a/b$, $v = c/d$, $w = (ac)/(bd)$. Then $bu = a, dv = c, (bd)w = ac$. Hence $(bu)(dv) = ac$, $(bd)(uv) = ac$, so $(bd)(uv) = (bd)w$. By hypothesis $bd \neq 0$. By the Corollary to Theorem 4–5, $uv = w$.

Exercises 4–4

1. $(a + b) + (-a - b) = (a + b) + ((-a) + (-b))$
$$= ((a + b) + (-a)) + (-b)$$
$$= ((b + a) + (-a)) + (-b)$$
$$= (b + (a + (-a))) + (-b) = (b + 0) + (-b)$$
$$= b + (-b) = 0.$$

5. $a/c + b/c = ac^{-1} + bc^{-1} = (a + b)c^{-1} = (a + b)/c$.

7. By Problem 6, $(ac)/(bc) = (a/b)(c/c) = (a/b) \cdot 1 = a/b$.

9. $(abc = 0) \to (ab = 0) \vee (c = 0) \to (a = 0) \vee (b = 0) \vee (c = 0)$.

10. $\{0,3\}$.

13. Since $(a/b)(b/a) = (ab)/(ba) = 1$, $(a/b)^{-1} = b/a$. Now $c/(a/b) = c(a/b)^{-1}$ $= c(b/a)$.

15. No. See the following problem.

17. In H, $0 \cdot 0 = 1 \neq 0$, contradicting Theorem 4–9.
In K, $0 \cdot 0 = 2 \neq 0$, contradicting Theorem 4–9.

21. $2 \cdot 3 = 0 \to 2 = 0 \vee 3 = 0$. If $2 = 0$ and $3 = 0$, then $1 = 3 - 2 = 0 - 0$ $= 0$, which is false in every field.

Exercises 4–6

1. First, observe that $a < b$ implies $-b < -a$, by adding $(-a) + (-b)$ to both sides. Next $c - b = c + (-b) < c + (-a) < d + (-a) = d - a$. By transitivity, $c - b < d - a$.

3. $a^2 - b^2 = (a - b)(a + b)$. Since $a + b > 0$, $(a - b)(a + b) > 0 \leftrightarrow a - b$ > 0. Therefore $a^2 > b^2 \leftrightarrow a > b$.

5. Suppose there were a largest number b. Then since $0 < 1$, $b = b + 0$ $< b + 1$, and $b + 1$ is larger. Contradiction.

7. $(x \leq y \wedge y \leq z) \equiv ((x < y) \vee (x = y)) \wedge ((y < z) \vee (y = z))$
$$\equiv ((x < y) \wedge (y < z)) \vee \cdots$$
In all four cases we get $x \leq z$.

9. $x > 0 \vee x = 0 \vee x < 0$. If $x > 0$, then $x^2 = x \cdot x > x \cdot 0 = 0$. If $x = 0$, then $x^2 = 0 \cdot 0 = 0$. If $x < 0$, then $-x > 0$, so $x^2 = (-x)^2 > 0$.

11. $x^2 + ax + b = (x^2 + ax + (a^2/4)) + b - (a^2/4) \geq b - (a^2/4)$.

13. $ab \leq \frac{1}{2}(a^2 + b^2) \leftrightarrow 2ab \leq a^2 + b^2$

$$\leftrightarrow 0 \leq a^2 - 2ab + b^2$$

$$\leftrightarrow 0 \leq (a - b)^2,$$

which is true.

15. (a) Put $x = a/b$ in Problem 14. (b) Multiply out and subtract 2 from both sides, then use (a). (c) Divide both sides of (b) by $2((1/a) + (1/b))$.

Exercises 4–7

1. $|x|^2 = (\pm x)^2 = x^2$.
4. $|b|^2 - |a|^2 = (|b| + |a|)(|b| - |a|)$. Thus $|b|^2 - |a|^2$ has the same sign as $|b| - |a|$.
5. $|a| \le b \leftrightarrow |a| \le |b| \leftrightarrow a^2 \le b^2$

$$\leftrightarrow x^2 + 2xy + y^2 \le |x|^2 + 2|x| \cdot |y| + |y|^2$$

$$\leftrightarrow xy \le |xy|,$$

   which is true.
6. $|x - y| = |x + (-y)| \le |x| + |-y| = |x| + |y|$.
7. (a) $|a| = |(a - b) + b| \le |a - b| + |b|$.
   (b) Interchange a and b in part (a).
   (c) If $|a| - |b| \ge 0$, then $||a| - |b|| = |a| - |b| \le |a - b|$, by part (a). If $|a| - |b| < 0$, then $||a| - |b|| = -(|a| - |b|) \le |a - b|$, by part (b).
9. (See Problem 8.) For all $x \in R$, $5 < x < 9 \leftrightarrow -2 < x - 7 < 2 \leftrightarrow |x - 7| < 2$.

Exercises 4–8

1. Let $S = \{n \in N \mid 1 + 2 + \cdots + n = \frac{1}{2}n(n + 1)\}$. Clearly $1 \in S$. If $n \in S$, then

$$1 + 2 + \cdots + n + (n + 1) = \tfrac{1}{2}n(n + 1) + (n + 1)$$

$$= \tfrac{1}{2}(n + 1)(n + 2),$$

   so $n + 1 \in S$. Therefore S is a σ-set. Since $S \subset N$, $S = N$, as required.
3. Let $S = \{n \in N \mid n^2 - n \text{ is even}\}$. Clearly $1 \in S$. If $n \in S$, then $(n + 1)^2 - (n + 1) = (n^2 - n) + 2n$, which is even, so $n + 1 \in S$. Therefore S is a σ-set and $S = N$.

Exercises 4–9

1. Let $S = E \cup O$, where E is the set of evens and O is the set of odds in N. Clearly $1 \in S$. If $n \in S$, then $n \in E$ or $n \in O$.
   (a) $n \in E$. $\therefore n = 2k$ for some $k \in N$, so $n + 1 = 2k + 1 = 2(k + 1) - 1$. Since $k \in N$, $k + 1$ does also, and $n + 1 \in O$, so $n + 1 \in S$.
   (b) $n \in O$. $\therefore n = 2k - 1$ for some $k \in N$, so $n + 1 = 2k \in E$, and $n + 1 \in S$. In either case, $n \in S \to n + 1 \in S$. Therefore S is a σ-set and $S = N$.
2. Given $n \in N$ and $n > 2$, we have $n \ne 1$, so $n - 1 \in N$ by Example 4–6. Also $n - 1 \ne 1$, so again by Example 4–6, $n - 2 = (n - 1) - 1 \in N$.

4. Fix $n \in N$. Let $S = \{k \in N | n + k \in N\}$. Then $1 \in S$, since $n + 1 \in N$. Suppose $k \in S$. Then $n + k \in N$, so $n + (k + 1) = (n + k) + 1 \in N$, and $k + 1 \in S$. That is, $\forall k \in N$, $k \in S \to k + 1 \in S$. Therefore S is a σ-set and $S = N$.

9. Let V_n denote the left side, W_n the right side of the required identity. Clearly $V_1 = W_1$. It is enough to show that for all $n \in N$,

$$V_{n+1} - V_n = W_{n+1} - W_n.$$

But by Problem 1 of Exercises 4–8,

$$W_n = \left(\frac{n(n + 1)}{2}\right)^2 \qquad (n \in N),$$

so

$$W_{n+1} - W_n = \frac{(n + 1)^2(n + 2)^2}{4} - \frac{n^2(n + 1)^2}{4}$$

$$= (n + 1)^2 \left[\frac{(n + 2)^2 - n^2}{4}\right]$$

$$= (n + 1)^3 = V_{n+1} - V_n \qquad (n \in N).$$

13. Use the identity $1 - (1/2^n) + (1/2^{n+1}) = 1 - (1/2^{n+1})$ $(n \in N)$.

15. True for $n = 1$. If true for n, then

$$(1 + h)^{n+1} = (1 + h)(1 + h)^n \geq (1 + h)(1 + nh)$$

$$= 1 + (n + 1)h + nh^2 \geq 1 + (n + 1)h.$$

17. Add $1/[n(n + 1)]$ to both sides for the induction step.

18. Let $S_n = 1/(\sqrt{1} + \sqrt{2}) + \cdots + 1/(\sqrt{n - 1} + \sqrt{n})$. Then for $n \geq 2$,

$$S_{n+1} - S_n = \frac{1}{\sqrt{n} + \sqrt{n + 1}} = \frac{\sqrt{n + 1} - \sqrt{n}}{(n + 1) - n} = \sqrt{n + 1} - \sqrt{n},$$

$$S_{n+1} - \sqrt{n + 1} = S_n - \sqrt{n}.$$

By induction, $S_n - \sqrt{n} = S_2 - 2 = -1$ for all $n \geq 2$. Hence $S_n = \sqrt{n} - 1$ $(n \geq 2)$.

21. $P(n)$ is not a well-defined predicate. One gets a similar paradox for "A man is poor if his total assets amount to n dollars" or "A book is not a best seller if only n copies are sold." In all such examples there are

some n for which $P(n)$ is clearly true and some n for which $P(n)$ is clearly false, but there is a fuzzy middle ground where one cannot really say.

22. Let $P(n)$ be a predicate to be proved true for all $n \in N$. It is sometimes convenient to consider instead the predicate

$$Q(n): \forall k \in N, k \leq n \rightarrow P(k).$$

It is easy to see that

$$[\forall n \in N, Q(n)] \leftrightarrow [\forall n \in N, P(n)].$$

We may therefore try to prove $Q(n)$ true for all $n \in N$ by induction. Because $Q(n)$ is a stronger statement than $P(n)$, this method is called *strong induction*.

For this problem, let $P(n)$ stand for

$$a_n = 3^n + 2^n.$$

Then $Q(1)$ and $Q(2)$ are true. If $n \geq 2$ and $Q(n)$ is true, then to prove $Q(n + 1)$ true we need only prove $P(n + 1)$ true, since the $k \leq n$ are taken care of by the induction hypothesis $Q(n)$. That is, it is sufficient to prove $Q(n) \rightarrow P(n + 1)$ ($n \in N$). (This is quite general.) Now

$$a_{n+1} = 5a_n - 6a_{n-1}$$
$$= 5(3^n + 2^n) - 6(3^{n-1} + 2^{n-1})$$
$$= 5 \cdot 3^n + 5 \cdot 2^n - 2 \cdot 3^n - 3 \cdot 2^n$$
$$= 3^{n+1} + 2^{n+1},$$

so $P(n + 1)$ is true and the proof is complete.

24. (a) For $n \geq 1$, $a_{n+2} - b_{n+2} = 2(a_{n+1} - b_{n+1}) - (a_n - b_n)$. Use strong induction, but notice that the cases $n = 1, 2$ are needed to start the induction.

(b) Substitute.

(c) Choose A and B so that $A + Bn = 1$ for $n = 1$ and $= 3$ for $n = 2$, i.e.,

$$A + B = 1,$$
$$A + 2B = 3.$$

We get $A = -1$, $B = 2$, so the unique solution is $(2n - 1)$.

(d) One solution is $a_n = 5$ ($n \in N$). Another is $b_n = n + 4$ ($n \in N$). The most general one is $Bn + 5 - B$ ($n \in N$).

26. (a) $\{n \mid n$ is divisible by $3\}$.

(b) Add u_{n+1} to both sides to get

$$u_{n+3} = u_{n+2} + u_{n+1} = 1 + u_{n+1} + \cdots + u_1,$$

and note that, to start the induction, $u_3 = 1 + u_1$.
(c) $d_n = (-1)^{n-1}$. Use

$$d_{n+1} + d_n = u_{n+1}^2 - u_n u_{n+2} + u_n^2 - u_{n-1} u_{n+1}$$

$$= u_{n+1}^2 - u_n(u_{n+2} - u_n) - u_{n-1} u_{n+1}$$

$$= u_{n+1}^2 - u_n u_{n+1} - u_{n-1} u_{n+1}$$

$$= u_{n+1}(u_{n+1} - u_n - u_{n-1}) = 0.$$

29. (h does not denote an integer here.) True for $n = 1$. If true for n, then

$$(1 + h)^{n+1} = (1 + h)(1 + h)^n$$

$$\leq (1 + h)(1 + (2^n - 1)h)$$

$$= 1 + 2^n h + (2^n - 1)h^2$$

$$\leq 1 + 2^n h + (2^n - 1)h$$

$$= 1 + (2^{n+1} - 1)h.$$

Exercises 4–10

1. Let $A = \{n \in N \mid \exists m \in N, \ m^2 = 3n^2\}$. Assume $A \neq \emptyset$. Then A has a least element n. Since $m^2 = 3n^2$ for some $m \in N$, m^2 is divisible by 3. Then m is divisible by 3, $m = 3k$ for some $k \in N$, so

$$m^2 = 9k^2 = 3n^2,$$

$$3k^2 = n^2.$$

Therefore $k \in A$, and $k < n$, a contradiction.

2. (a) $n' \leq 0 \to 3n \leq 2m \to 9n^2 \leq 4m^2 = 8n^2$, false.
   (b) $n' \geq n \to n \geq m \to n^2 \geq m^2 = 2n^2$, false.
   (c) $(3m - 4n)^2 - 2(3n - 2m)^2 = m^2 - 2n^2 = 0$. $n' \in A$ and $n' < n$, a contradiction.

5. A is a σ-set, so $A \supset N$. Also, if $n \in N$, then $-n \in A$, so $A \supset Z$. If $m \in Z$ and $n \in N$, then $m/n \in A$, so $Q \subset A$. Since $A \subset Q$, $A = Q$.

7. $M1$, $M2$, $M3$ as in Problem 6.
   $M4$. $1 \in A$ and $1 \in B$, so $1 = 1 \cdot 1 \in C$.
   $\sim M5$. $1 \in A$ and $\frac{1}{2} \in B$, so $\frac{1}{2} = 1 \cdot \frac{1}{2} \in C$. But $(\frac{1}{2})^{-1} = 2 \notin C$, for if $2 = n \cdot 1/m$, with n odd, then $n = 2m$, false.

Exercises 4–11

2. Let $b \in R$. Then $(\forall x)\, x \in \emptyset \to x \le b$.
3. (a) $(\forall x)\, x < 0 \to x \le 1$.
   (c) If $a < 0$, then $a/2 \in A$ but $\sim(a/2 \le a)$.
   (f) Suppose $x > 0$. Then

$$x^2 > 2 \to x^2 > 1 \to x^2 - 1 > 0$$
$$\to (x - 1)(x + 1) > 0 \to x - 1 > 0,$$

   since $(x + 1)^{-1} > 0$. Hence $x \ge 1$, as required.

4. (a) $2 + x \ge 2$, so $\sqrt{2 + x}$ exists and is positive. If $\sqrt{2 + x} > 2$, then $(\sqrt{2 + x})^2 > 4$, $2 + x > 4$, $x > 2$, false.
   (c) $(2 - x_{n+1})(2 + x_{n+1}) = 4 - x_{n+1}^2 = 4 - (2 + x_n) = 2 - x_n$. Divide by the positive number $2 + x_{n+1}$.
   (e) By induction, using (d). To start, observe that $0 \le 2 - x_1 \le 1$, i.e., $1 \le \sqrt{2} \le 2$.

Exercises 4–12

1. Assume that $q \in Q$ is the l.u.b. of A. Then $q \ge 1 \in A$. By (c) above, $q^2 \ne 2$, so $q^2 < 2$ or $q^2 > 2$.
   (a) If $q^2 < 2$, then by (a) above, $q + 1/n \in A$ for some $n \in N$, and $\sim(q + 1/n \le q)$. Hence q is not even an upper bound of A.
   (b) If $q^2 > 2$, then by (b) above, $(q - 1/m)^2 > 2$ for some $m \in N$, so $(q - 1/m)^2 > a^2$ for all $a \in A$. Hence $q - 1/m > |a| \ge a$ for all $a \in A$, and $q - 1/m$ is an upper bound of A which is less than q. Hence q is not the least upper bound of A.
   In both cases we arrive at a contradiction.

Exercises 4–13

2. Clearly 1 is a lower bound. If $h > 0$, we show that $1 + h$ is not a lower bound. For this purpose we must find an $x > 0$ such that $(1 + x)^3 < 1 + h$. This is equivalent to $3x + 3x^2 + x^3 < h$. If we choose $0 < x < 1$, then $x^2 < x$ and $x^3 < x$, so $3x + 3x^2 + x^3 < 7x$. Now if we also choose $x < h/7$, we have

$$(1 + x)^3 = 1 + 3x + 3x^2 + x^3 < 1 + 7x < 1 + 7(h/7) < 1 + h,$$

   as required.

3. Since $4.999 < 5 = $ l.u.b. K, 4.999 is not an upper bound of K, so $\exists k \in K$ such that $4.999 < k$. Also $k \le 5$ because 5 is an upper bound of K. $\therefore 4.999 < k \le 5$.

5. Use Problem 4 to find $n_0 \in N$ such that $c - h < a_{n_0}$.
7. Since A has a l.b., B has an u.b. Therefore B has a l.u.b., say $-c$. Then $c = $ g.l.b. A. To prove this, we must go back and forth several times between A and B. The crucial fact is that $(x < y) \equiv (-x > -y)$.

Exercises 4–14

2. $1,127/24,975$.
3. 1.6463554.
7. The right-hand endpoint of I_n is 1 for all $n \in N$.
8. Let $[a_n, b_n]$ be the intervals for $r = .d_1 d_2 \cdots$, and let $[a'_n, b'_n]$ be the intervals for $r' = d_1 . d_2 \cdots$. Then

$$a'_n = d_1 . d_2 \cdots d_{n+1} = 10(.d_1 \cdots d_{n+1}) = 10a_{n+1}.$$

Also

$$b'_n = a'_n + 10^{-n} = 10a_{n+1} + 10^{-n}$$

$$= 10(a_{n+1} + 10^{-n-1}) = 10b_{n+1}.$$

$$\therefore \quad a'_n = 10a_{n+1} \leq 10r \leq 10b_{n+1} = b'_n \qquad (n \in N).$$

Since $10r \in [a'_n, b'_n]$ $(n \in N)$, $10r = r'$.
12. $(c \leq a) \wedge (b \leq d)$.
14. 7 is an upper bound, so the l.u.b. ≤ 7.
16. No, if $a \in J_n$ for all $n \in N$, then it satisfies the hypotheses of Theorem 5–27, so $a = 0 \in J_1$; contradiction. This does not contradict Theorem 4–28, because the J_n are not *closed* intervals.
17. (a) 9. (b) 2.
19. In base 2, given the sequence (d_n), $n \in N$, let

$$a_n = .d_1 d_2 \cdots d_n = \frac{d_1}{2} + \frac{d_2}{2^2} + \cdots + \frac{d_n}{2^n},$$

where $d_i \in \{0,1\}$ for $i \in N$. Define $b_n = a_n + 2^{-n}$. The closed intervals $J_n = [a_n, b_n]$ have exactly one number in common. This defines

$$r = .d_1 d_2 \cdots \text{(base 2)}.$$

CHAPTER 5

Exercises 5–1

1. (a) $15k + 18k + 21k + 24k + 27k + 30k$.
   (c) $c_{2k} + c_{3k} + c_{4k} + c_{5k} + c_{6k} + c_{7k}$.
   (e) $(c_{11} + c_{12} + c_{13} + c_{14}) + (c_{21} + c_{22} + c_{23} + c_{24}) + (c_{31} + c_{32} + c_{33} + c_{34})$.

(g) $(b_1^2 + b_1b_2 + b_1b_3) + (b_2b_1 + b_2^2 + b_2b_3) + (b_3b_1 + b_3b_2 + b_3^2)$.

(i) $1 + 2 + 3 + \cdots + n$.

2. (a) $\displaystyle\sum_{i=2}^{6} 2i$. (c) $\displaystyle\sum_{i=1}^{k} a_i$. (e) $\displaystyle\sum_{i=1}^{k} a_{i1}$. (g) $\displaystyle\sum_{i=1}^{n} a_{1i}x_i$.

(i) $\displaystyle\sum_{i=0}^{10} 2^i = \sum_{i=1}^{11} 2^{i-1}$.

4. (b) $\displaystyle\sum_{i=1}^{n} i + \sum_{i=1}^{n} (n - i + 1) = \sum_{i=1}^{n} (i + n - i + 1) = \sum_{i=1}^{n} (n + 1)$.

5. (a) $\displaystyle 2S = 2\sum_{i=1}^{11} 2^{i-1} = \sum_{i=1}^{11} 2 \cdot 2^{i-1} = \sum_{i=1}^{11} 2^i = T$.

(d) $\displaystyle\sum_{i=0}^{n} 2^i = 2^{n+1} - 1$.

(e) $\displaystyle\sum_{i=0}^{n} r^i = \frac{r^{n+1} - 1}{r - 1}$ $(r \neq 1)$.

7. (b) $C_{20} = 1, C_{21} = 2, C_{22} = 1$.

8. (b) Total cost is $10{,}000n$; total number of shares is

$$\sum_{i=1}^{n} \frac{10{,}000}{p_i};$$

average is

$$\frac{10{,}000n}{\displaystyle\sum_{i=1}^{n} \frac{10{,}000}{p_i}} = \frac{n}{\displaystyle\sum_{i=1}^{n} \frac{1}{p_i}} = \frac{1}{\dfrac{1}{n}\displaystyle\sum_{i=1}^{n} \frac{1}{p_i}}.$$

$Proof$:
$$\frac{1}{\dfrac{1}{2}\left(\dfrac{1}{p_1} + \dfrac{1}{p_2}\right)} \leq \tfrac{1}{2}(p_1 + p_2) \leftrightarrow 1 \leq \tfrac{1}{4}(p_1 + p_2)\left(\frac{1}{p_1} + \frac{1}{p_2}\right)$$

$$\leftrightarrow 4 \leq \frac{p_1}{p_2} + 2 + \frac{p_2}{p_1} \leftrightarrow 0 \leq \frac{p_1}{p_2} - 2 + \frac{p_2}{p_1}$$

$$\leftrightarrow 0 \leq p_1^2 - 2p_1p_2 + p_2^2 \leftrightarrow 0 \leq (p_1 - p_2)^2.$$

Exercises 5–2

1. (a) $(3,10)$. (c) $(26,11)$.

3. $x = (\tfrac{7}{5}, -\tfrac{9}{5}, -\tfrac{13}{5})$.

5. $(15,25,20)$.

6. $\theta = (0,0,0,0,0)$.

Exercises 5–4

1. (a) $(42,28)$. (c) $(-16,17)$. (e) $(8,0)$.
3. $s = (3a_2 - a_1)/8$, $t = (3a_1 - a_2)/8$.
4. Axioms 5–1 and 5–3 through 5–7 all follow immediately from the corresponding properties of R. For 2, $f + x = g$ is solved by $x = g + (-f)$. Each $f \in V$ has the form $f = \{(5,f(5)), (7,f(7))\}$. We define a map M between V and R^2 by

$$M(f) = (f(5), f(7)).$$

Then M is obviously one-to-one. Also,

$$M(f + g) = (f(5) + g(5), f(7) + g(7)) = M(f) + M(g),$$

$$M(tf) = (tf(5), tf(7)) = tM(f),$$

so M is linear. If $(a,b) \in R^2$, define $f \in V$ by $f(5) = a$, $f(7) = b$. Then $M(f) = (a,b)$, so that M is onto.
7. (b) If $x \in V$, then $x_1 \in R$ and $x = (x_1, 5x_1) = x_1(1,5)$. Hence every element of V is a multiple of $(1,5)$.
8. Assume that there does exist a one-to-one linear map f of R^1 onto R^2. There are elements $a, b \in R^1$ such that $f(a) = (1,0)$, $f(b) = (0,1)$. Because f is a function, $a \neq b$, so one of them, say b, is nonzero. Then $a = tb$, with $t = a/b \in R$. Hence

$$(1,0) = f(a) = f(tb) = tf(b) = t(0,1) = (0,t).$$

Equating first components, we get $1 = 0$, a contradiction. Therefore no such f exists.
10. (c) Suppose $T = \{\theta\}$. For $x, y \in V$,

$$f(x) = f(y) \rightarrow f(x) - f(y) = \theta$$

$$\rightarrow f(x - y) = \theta$$

$$\rightarrow x - y \in T$$

$$\rightarrow x - y = \theta$$

$$\rightarrow x = y.$$

Thus $T = \{\theta\}$ implies that f is one-to-one. Conversely, if f is one-to-one and $x \in T$, then $f(x) = \theta = f(\theta)$, so $x = \theta$. Hence, f one-to-one implies that $T = \{\theta\}$.
11. (a), (c), (f), (g).
13. $G(x) = (x_1 + x_2 + x_3 + x_4 + 2x_5)/6$. Yes.

Exercises 5–5

1. (b) $\begin{pmatrix} 4 & 3 & 6 \\ 6 & 8 & 10 \end{pmatrix}$. (d) $\begin{pmatrix} 4 & 3 \\ 4 & 1 \end{pmatrix}$. (f) $\begin{pmatrix} 6 & 3 \\ -1 & 3 \end{pmatrix}$. (h) Not defined.

(j) $\begin{pmatrix} -7 & -1 & 16 \\ -5 & -3 & 12 \end{pmatrix}$. (l) $\begin{pmatrix} 42 & 62 \\ 45 & 115 \end{pmatrix}$.

2. (b) $\begin{pmatrix} -5 & -5 & 0 & 5 \\ 40 & 25 & -15 & 50 \end{pmatrix}$.

4. (a) $\begin{pmatrix} 3 & 6 & -3 \\ 4 & 2 & 3 \\ -2 & 1 & 7 \end{pmatrix}$.

(c) $\begin{pmatrix} 1 & 2 & -1 \\ 12 & 6 & 9 \\ -2 & 1 & 7 \end{pmatrix}$.

5. (a) $\begin{pmatrix} 13 & 19 \\ 50 & 77 \end{pmatrix}$.

6. A, if it exists, must be 2×2. Assume A to exist,

$A = \begin{pmatrix} x & y \\ z & w \end{pmatrix}$. Then

$I = \begin{pmatrix} x & y \\ z & w \end{pmatrix}\begin{pmatrix} 0 & 1 \\ 2 & -1 \end{pmatrix} = \begin{pmatrix} 2y & x-y \\ 2w & z-w \end{pmatrix} = \begin{pmatrix} 1 & 0 \\ 0 & 1 \end{pmatrix}$.

Hence $\begin{cases} 2y = 1, \\ 2w = 0, \\ x - y = 0, \\ z - w = 1, \end{cases}$

so $y = \frac{1}{2}$, $w = 0$, $x = y = \frac{1}{2}$, $z = 1$, and $A = \begin{pmatrix} \frac{1}{2} & \frac{1}{2} \\ 1 & 0 \end{pmatrix}$.

Now $\begin{pmatrix} \frac{1}{2} & \frac{1}{2} \\ 1 & 0 \end{pmatrix}\begin{pmatrix} 0 & 1 \\ 2 & -1 \end{pmatrix} = I$, so A is a solution.

8. No solution.

10. (a) $t\begin{pmatrix}1\\0\end{pmatrix}$, for all $t \in R$, $t \neq 0$.

(c) No solution.

12. Write $A = \begin{pmatrix} a & b \\ c & d \end{pmatrix}$, $x = \begin{pmatrix} x_1 \\ x_2 \end{pmatrix}$, $y = \begin{pmatrix} y_1 \\ y_2 \end{pmatrix}$, and compute. The function f defined by $f(x) = Ax$ ($x \in R^2$) is a linear mapping from R^2 to R^2.

Exercises 5–6

1. (a) Yes.

(b) $(42, -6)$, $(4,10)$, $(10, -4)$, $(36,4)$, $(4,10)$, $(46, -30)$, $(34,14)$.

4. *First solution:*

$$z_1 = y_1 + 7y_2 + 5y_3 = (x_1 + 3x_2 + 7x_3 + 2x_4) + 7(5x_2 +$$
$$x_3 + 2x_4) + 5(x_1 - x_3 + 3x_4)$$
$$= 6x_1 + 38x_2 + 9x_3 + 31x_4,$$

$$z_2 = 2y_1 + 7y_3 = 2(x_1 + 3x_2 + 7x_3 + 2x_4) + 7(x_1 - x_3 + 3x_4)$$
$$= 9x_1 + 6x_2 + 7x_3 + 25x_4.$$

Second solution:

$$\begin{pmatrix} z_1 \\ z_2 \end{pmatrix} = \begin{pmatrix} 1 & 7 & 5 \\ 2 & 0 & 7 \end{pmatrix} \begin{pmatrix} y_1 \\ y_2 \\ y_3 \end{pmatrix},$$

$$\begin{pmatrix} y_1 \\ y_2 \\ y_3 \end{pmatrix} = \begin{pmatrix} 1 & 3 & 7 & 2 \\ 0 & 5 & 1 & 2 \\ 1 & 0 & -1 & 3 \end{pmatrix} \begin{pmatrix} x_1 \\ x_2 \\ x_3 \\ x_4 \end{pmatrix} . \frac{18}{18}$$

Hence
$$\begin{pmatrix} z_1 \\ z_2 \end{pmatrix} = \begin{pmatrix} 1 & 7 & 5 \\ 2 & 0 & 7 \end{pmatrix} \begin{pmatrix} 1 & 3 & 7 & 2 \\ 0 & 5 & 1 & 2 \\ 1 & 0 & -1 & 3 \end{pmatrix} \begin{pmatrix} x_1 \\ x_2 \\ x_3 \\ x_4 \end{pmatrix}$$

$$= \begin{pmatrix} 6 & 38 & 9 & 31 \\ 9 & 6 & 7 & 25 \end{pmatrix} \begin{pmatrix} x_1 \\ x_2 \\ x_3 \\ x_4 \end{pmatrix}$$

$$= \begin{pmatrix} 6x_1 + 38x_2 + 9x_3 + 31x_4 \\ 9x_1 + 6x_2 + 7x_3 + 25x_4 \end{pmatrix}.$$

6. (a) $r = m$ and $s = n$.
   (b) $s = m$.
   (c) $n = r$.
   (d) $r = m = s = n$.
   (e) $r = m = s = n$.
7. Let A be an $m \times n$, B an $r \times s$, C a $t \times u$ matrix. Since $A(B + C)$ is defined $r = t$, $s = u$, and $n = r$. Hence A is $m \times n$, B is $n \times s$, C is $n \times s$. Then AB and AC are defined, and both have size $m \times s$. Hence $AB + AC$ is defined. If d_{ij}, $1 \le i \le m$, $1 \le j \le s$, is the ij component of $A(B + C)$, then

$$d_{ij} = \sum_{k=1}^{n} a_{ik}(b_{kj} + c_{kj})$$

$$= \sum_{k=1}^{n} (a_{ik}b_{kj} + a_{ik}c_{kj})$$

$$= \sum_{k=1}^{n} a_{ik}b_{kj} + \sum_{k=1}^{n} a_{ik}c_{kj}$$

$$= \text{(the } ij \text{ comp. of } AB) + \text{(the } ij \text{ comp. of } AC).$$

10. $A^2 = \begin{pmatrix} 1 & 6 \\ 0 & 1 \end{pmatrix}$; $A^3 = \begin{pmatrix} 1 & 9 \\ 0 & 1 \end{pmatrix}$; $A^4 = \begin{pmatrix} 1 & 12 \\ 0 & 1 \end{pmatrix}$; $A^5 = \begin{pmatrix} 1 & 15 \\ 0 & 1 \end{pmatrix}$;

$A^n = \begin{pmatrix} 1 & 3n \\ 0 & 1 \end{pmatrix}$.

12. (a) Obvious.

(b) $CBD = \begin{pmatrix} 1 & 1 \\ 0 & 1 \end{pmatrix}\begin{pmatrix} 3 & 0 \\ 0 & 2 \end{pmatrix}\begin{pmatrix} 1 & -1 \\ 0 & 1 \end{pmatrix} = \begin{pmatrix} 1 & 1 \\ 0 & 1 \end{pmatrix}\begin{pmatrix} 3 & -3 \\ 0 & 2 \end{pmatrix} = \begin{pmatrix} 3 & -1 \\ 0 & 2 \end{pmatrix}$.

(c) By (b), $CBD = \begin{pmatrix} 3 & -1 \\ 0 & 2 \end{pmatrix}$, so

$$\begin{pmatrix} 3 & -1 \\ 0 & 2 \end{pmatrix}^2 = \begin{pmatrix} 3 & -1 \\ 0 & 2 \end{pmatrix}\begin{pmatrix} 3 & -1 \\ 0 & 2 \end{pmatrix} = (CBD)(CBD) = (CB)(DC)(BD)$$

$$= (CB)I_2(BD)$$

$$= CBBD$$

$$= CB^2D$$

$$= \begin{pmatrix} 1 & 1 \\ 0 & 1 \end{pmatrix} \begin{pmatrix} 9 & 0 \\ 0 & 4 \end{pmatrix} \begin{pmatrix} 1 & -1 \\ 0 & 1 \end{pmatrix} = \begin{pmatrix} 1 & 1 \\ 0 & 1 \end{pmatrix} \begin{pmatrix} 9 & -9 \\ 0 & 4 \end{pmatrix}$$

$$= \begin{pmatrix} 9 & -5 \\ 0 & 4 \end{pmatrix} = \begin{pmatrix} 3^2 & 2^2 - 3^2 \\ 0 & 2^2 \end{pmatrix}.$$

(d) As above,

$$\begin{pmatrix} 3 & -1 \\ 0 & 2 \end{pmatrix}^3 = (CBD)^3 = (CBD)(CBD)(CBD)$$

$$= CBI_2BI_2BD$$

$$= CB^3D$$

$$= \begin{pmatrix} 1 & 1 \\ 0 & 1 \end{pmatrix} \begin{pmatrix} 27 & 0 \\ 0 & 8 \end{pmatrix} \begin{pmatrix} 1 & -1 \\ 0 & 1 \end{pmatrix}$$

$$= \begin{pmatrix} 1 & 1 \\ 0 & 1 \end{pmatrix} \begin{pmatrix} 27 & -27 \\ 0 & 8 \end{pmatrix}$$

$$= \begin{pmatrix} 27 & -19 \\ 0 & 8 \end{pmatrix} = \begin{pmatrix} 3^3 & 2^2 - 3^3 \\ 0 & 2^3 \end{pmatrix}.$$

14. (a) $x - x' \in N \to f(x - x') = \bar{0}$. But $f(x - x') = f(x + (-1)x') = f(x) + (-1)f(x') = f(x) - f(x')$. Hence $f(x) = f(x') + \bar{0} = f(x')$.

(b) $f(x) = f(x') + \bar{0}$, so $f(x) - f(x') = f(x - x') = \bar{0}$, and $x - x' \in N$.

(c) If f is one-to-one, then since $f(0) = \bar{0}$, $f(x) = \bar{0} \to x = 0$. Hence $N = \{0\}$.

(d) If $N = \{0\}$, then by (b), $f(x) = f(x') \to x - x' = 0$, so $x = x'$, and f is one-to-one.

17. (a) $f\left(\begin{pmatrix} 2 \\ 5 \end{pmatrix}\right) = 29.$

(b) $f\left(\begin{pmatrix} x_1 \\ x_2 \end{pmatrix}\right) = 7x_1 + 3x_2.$

(c) $(7 \ 3)$.

19. $A(x) = \begin{pmatrix} 2x_1 + x_2 + 3x_3 \\ 4x_1 + 2x_2 + 6x_3 \end{pmatrix}$; $y_2 = 2y_1$; no.

20. (g) $y_i = \sum_{j=1}^{3} a_{ij}x_j \quad (i = 1, 2, \ldots, 5).$

(h) cy is the total cost of production for x. cA is the matrix representing the cost function, which maps each production vector into the total cost of producing quantity x_1 of the first product, x_2 of the second, and x_3 of the third.

Exercises 5–7

1. *Problems 1, 2*: $\text{rng } f = \{y | y \leq 2\}$.
   Problems 3, 4: $S(y) = \emptyset$ $(y > 2)$.
   $\qquad\qquad S(y) = \{0\}$ $(y = 2)$.

   $$S(y) = \{\sqrt{2 - y}, -\sqrt{2 - y}\} \; (y < 2).$$

3. *Problems 1, 2*: $\text{rng } f$ is the set of all even integers ≥ 0.
   Problems 3, 4: $S(y) = \emptyset$ (y is odd, or negative).
   $\qquad\qquad S(y) = \{n, -n\}$ $(y = 2n, n \geq 0)$.

5. With $f(x) = x_1 + x_2$ $(x \in R^2)$, $\text{rng } f = R$, and for each $y \in R$,

$$S(y) = \{(x_1, y - x_1) | x_1 \in R\}.$$

Exercises 5–10

1. (a) $\text{rng } f = \left\{ s\begin{pmatrix} 1 \\ 2 \end{pmatrix} \bigg| s \in R \right\}$.

   (b) $\begin{pmatrix} 3 \\ 1 \end{pmatrix} \notin \text{rng } f$.

   (c) $f(x) = \begin{pmatrix} 4 \\ 8 \end{pmatrix} = 4 \begin{pmatrix} 1 \\ 2 \end{pmatrix}$ if $2x_1 + x_2 = 4$. There are infinitely many such x's.

   (d) $N(f) = \{t(1, -2) | t \in R\}$.

3. By Application 2, there are infinitely many solutions of $y = f(x)$ if there are any. But given y, $x = (0, y_2, -y_1) \in R^3$ is a solution. Hence $\text{rng } f = R^2$ and for every $y \in R^2$ there are infinitely many solutions. $S(y) = \{(0, y_2, -y_3) + w | w \in N(f)\}$. Since $N(f) = \{t(1, -1, 2) | t \in R\}$, $S(y) = \{(0, y_2, -y_3) + t(1, -1, 2) | t \in R\}$. [To find $N(f)$, if $f(x) = 0$,

$$\begin{cases} 2x_1 - x_3 = 0 \\ x_1 + x_2 = 0 \end{cases} \quad \text{and} \quad \begin{cases} x_3 = 2x_1 \\ x_2 = -x_1, \end{cases}$$

so that $(x_1, -x_1, 2x_1) = x_1(1, -1, 2)$ is a solution for all $x_1 \in R$.]

5. Let the quantities of foods I, II, and III be f_1, f_2, and f_3, respectively.

Then

(a) $\frac{1}{10}f_1 + \frac{5}{10}f_2 = 1.5,\qquad f_1 + 5f_2 = 15.$

(b) $\frac{3}{10}f_1 + \frac{1}{10}f_3 = 1.6,\qquad 3f_1 + f_3 = 16.$

(c) $\frac{1}{10}f_1 + \frac{4}{10}f_2 = 1.3,\qquad f_1 + 4f_2 = 13.$

Subtracting (c) from (a) gives $f_2 = 2$, so $f_1 = 5$ and $f_3 = 1$. Thus $(5,2,1)$ is the only possible solution. It is a solution.

7. $(3,0)$, $(2,1)$, $(1,2)$, $(0,3)$; $(3,1)$, $(2,2)$, $(1,3)$, $(0,4)$.

9. Suppose $\begin{pmatrix}1\\1\\1\end{pmatrix} = s\begin{pmatrix}y_1\\y_2\\y_3\end{pmatrix} = \begin{pmatrix}sy_1\\sy_3\\sy_3\end{pmatrix}; \quad \begin{pmatrix}1\\2\\-1\end{pmatrix} = t\begin{pmatrix}y_1\\y_2\\y_3\end{pmatrix} = \begin{pmatrix}ty_1\\ty_3\\ty_3\end{pmatrix}.$

Then $sy_1 = 1$ and $ty_1 = 1$, so $y_1 \neq 0$ and $s = t$. But then, from the second components, $1 = sy_2 = ty_2 = 2$, a contradiction.

Exercises 5–12

1. $x_1 = -3,\ x_2 = 2$: $\begin{pmatrix}2 & 3\\3 & 5\end{pmatrix}\begin{pmatrix}-3\\2\end{pmatrix} = \begin{pmatrix}0\\1\end{pmatrix}.$

Exercises 5–14

1. $x_1 = 1,\ x_2 = 2,\ x_3 = -1$.

3. The equations are inconsistent.

5. The solution set consists of all vectors

$$\begin{pmatrix}-\frac{1}{5}\\-\frac{6}{5}\\0\\0\end{pmatrix} + x_3\begin{pmatrix}-\frac{11}{5}\\\frac{4}{5}\\1\\0\end{pmatrix} + x_4\begin{pmatrix}-\frac{21}{5}\\\frac{4}{5}\\0\\1\end{pmatrix} \qquad (x_3, x_4 \in R).$$

7. Transform the array $\begin{array}{cc|cc}1 & 2 & 1 & 0\\4 & -3 & 0 & 1\end{array}$ into $\begin{array}{cc|cc}1 & 0 & \frac{3}{11} & \frac{2}{11}\\0 & 1 & \frac{4}{11} & -\frac{1}{11}\end{array}.$

Hence

$$A = \tfrac{1}{11}\begin{pmatrix}3 & 2\\4 & -1\end{pmatrix}.$$

9. Transform the array $\begin{array}{cc|cc}1 & 2 & 9 & 1\\3 & 4 & 0 & 7\end{array}$ into $\begin{array}{cc|cc}1 & 0 & -18 & 5\\0 & 1 & \frac{27}{2} & -2\end{array}.$

$$A = \begin{pmatrix}-18 & 5\\\frac{27}{2} & -2\end{pmatrix}.$$

11. $B = \begin{pmatrix} 0 & -\frac{1}{4} & \frac{1}{4} \\ 0 & \frac{3}{4} & \frac{1}{4} \\ \frac{1}{2} & \frac{1}{8} & -\frac{1}{8} \end{pmatrix}$.

12. $(\exists B)\ AB = I_2$ if and only if $ad - bc \neq 0$.

13. $(a^2 + b^2 = 0) \equiv (a = b = 0)$. Apply the result of Problem 12.

$$\begin{pmatrix} x & y \\ z & w \end{pmatrix} = \frac{1}{\quad} \begin{pmatrix} a & -b \\ b & a \end{pmatrix}.$$

15. $\begin{pmatrix} a & b \\ -b & a \end{pmatrix}^2 = \begin{pmatrix} a^2 - b^2 & 2ab \\ -2ab & a^2 - b^2 \end{pmatrix} = \begin{pmatrix} -1 & 0 \\ 0 & -1 \end{pmatrix}$ Since $2ab = 0$, $a = 0$
$\lor b = 0$. Since $a^2 - b^2 = -1$, $b \neq 0$, so $a = 0$. Therefore $b^2 = 1$,
$b = 1$ or -1.

17. $(aI + bJ)^3 = a^3 I + 3a^2 bJ + 3ab^2 J^2 + b^3 J^3$
$\qquad = a^3 I + 3a^2 bJ - 3ab^2 I - b^3 J$
$\qquad = (a^3 - 3ab^2)I + (3a^2 b - b^3)J.$

We want this to be equal to I. Equating components, we get
$\qquad$ (a) $a^3 - 3ab^2 = 1$, $\qquad$ (b) $b(3a^2 - b^2) = 0$.
From (b), $b = 0 \lor b^2 = 3a^2$. If $b = 0$, then from (a) $a^3 = 1$, so $a = 1$,
and $A = I$. If $b^2 = 3a^2$, then from (a), $a^3 - 3a(3a^2) = 1$, so $a^3 = (-\frac{1}{2})^3$
and $a = -\frac{1}{2}$. Then $b^2 = 3a^2 = \frac{3}{4}$, so $b = \pm\sqrt{3}/2$. Thus the three solutions are
$$A = I,\ (-I + \sqrt{3}\,J)/2,\ (-I - \sqrt{3}J)/2.$$

CHAPTER 6

Exercises 6–1

1. Yes, where $f(T) = c(T) = -40$.

Exercises 6–2

3. Coordinates of intersection:
$(\frac{14}{23}, -\frac{19}{23})$.

4. (Illustration opposite.)

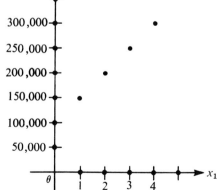

7. It helps to have L and M intersect.
8. Let C be the circle with the segment joining $(5,0)$ and $(0,5)$ as diameter. Then the locus is $C - \{(5,5)\}$.

Exercises 6–3

3. Let $c = (c_1, c_2)$ be the midpoint. Draw the lines through a, b, c, parallel to the x_2-axis, meeting the x_1-axis in a', b', c', respectively. Since c bisects ab, c' bisects $a'b'$. But $a' = (a_1, 0)$, $b' = (b_1, 0)$, $c' = (c_1, 0)$. Hence $c_1 = (a_1 + b_1)/2$. Similarly, $c_2 = (a_2 + b_2)/2$.
5. The graph is the segment joining (a_1, a_2) with (b_1, b_2).
7. The graph of A is the circle with center $(0,0)$ and radius 2, plus its interior.

8.

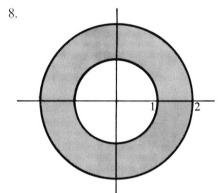

9.

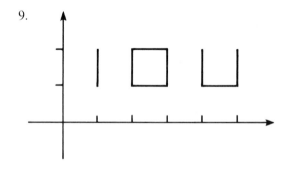

10. (a) Circle plus interior; triangle plus interior; line; half-plane.
    (b) A circular arc; the union of two different lines.
    (c) Let A and B be convex sets. If $p \in A \cap B$ and $q \in A \cap B$, then $p \in A$ and $q \in A$, so the segment $pq \subset A$. Similarly, $pq \subset B$, so $pq \subset A \cap B$.
    (d) See part (b).

13. $C = \{x \in R^2 | \forall S, S \text{ is convex } \wedge S \supset B \rightarrow x \in S\}$. C is the intersection of all convex sets containing B.

14.

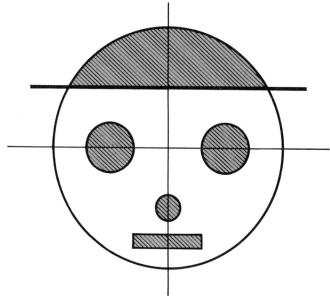

Exercises 6–4

1. 0.

4.

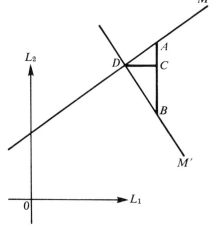

Show that $\triangle ACD$ is similar to $\triangle DCB$, with AD corresponding to DB, AC to DC, and CD to CB. Then

$$\frac{AC}{DC} = \frac{CD}{CB}.$$

But the rise of M' is negative, so that

$$\text{slope } M' = -\frac{CB}{CD} \quad \text{and} \quad \text{slope } M = \frac{AC}{DC}.$$

Hence

$$\text{slope } M = \frac{1}{-\text{slope } M'},$$

(slope M)(slope M') $= -1$.

5. For $45°$, 1 or -1; for $30°$ or $60°$, $\sqrt{3}$ or $-\sqrt{3}$ or $1/\sqrt{3}$ or $-1/\sqrt{3}$.
7. At B_0, $m = 0$. As the angle increases toward $90°$, m increases without bound, assuming every positive real value exactly once. At $90°$, m does not exist. Between $90°$ and $180°$, m goes from large negative values to 0. Between $180°$ and $360°$, m repeats its behavior from $0°$ to $180°$: $m(x) = m(x - 180)$.
9. Show the line through $(1,1)$ and $(3,2)$ has the same slope $\frac{1}{2}$ as the line through $(\frac{3}{2},\frac{11}{4})$ and $(2,3)$.
11. 11.
13. $\{(x,y)|8y - x = 55\}$.
15. 4.
17. A line with 0 slope *has* a slope. All lines parallel to the x_1-axis have 0 slope. All lines parallel to the x_2-axis have no slope; i.e., they are not in the domain of the slope function.

Exercises 6–5

1. (a) $\{(x,y)\in R^2|y - 5 = -\frac{2}{3}(x - 1)\} = \{(x,y)\in R^2|2x + 3y = 17\}$.
   (c) $\{(x,y)\in R^2|y - 1 = -4(x - 1)\} = \{(x,y)\in R^2|4x + y = 5\}$.
2. $(-3,7)$.

4. $L \cap M = \{(\frac{1}{13}, \frac{6}{13})\}$.

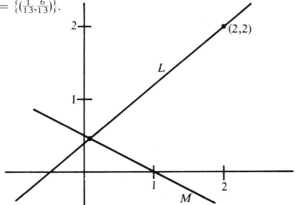

6. For small $|m|$, L cuts the circle, and $L \cap M$ has two points: for large $|m|$, $L \cap M$ is empty. $L \cap M$ is a singleton if L is tangent to M. This happens if $m = \pm 1/\sqrt{3}$.

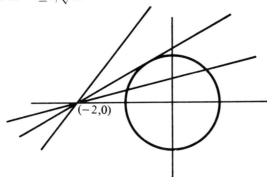

8. For $(1,1)$, slope is 2. For (a, a^2), slope is $2a$.

10. The line $\{(x,y) \in R^2 | y = \frac{3}{2}x\}$.

12. The line $\{(x,y) \in R^2 | 3x - 2y = 5\}$.

14. $d^2 = (x - 3)^2 + (y - 1)^2 = (x - 3)^2 + (2x - 1)^2 = 5(x - 1)^2 + 5$.
    Hence minimum $d = \sqrt{5}$.

16. (a)

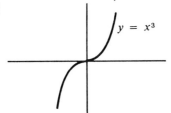

(b) $\forall h \in R, k = 1 + h \in R$, so $((1 + h), (1 + h)^3) = (k,k^3) \in C$.

(c) $3 + 3h + h^2$.

(d) 3.31, 3.0301, 3.003001.

(e) $y - 1 = 3(x - 1)$.

Exercises 6–6

1.

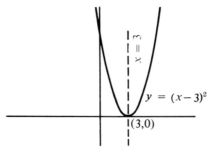

$y = (x-3)^2$

$(3,0)$

Domain $f = R$; rng $f = \{y \in R | y \geq 0\}$; y will be large and positive whenever $|x|$ is large; $x = 3$ is a zero; f is symmetrical about $x = 3$.

2.

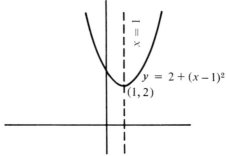

$y = 2 + (x - 1)^2$

$(1, 2)$

3. $y = (x + 1)^2 - 1$.

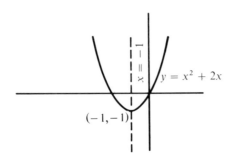

$y = x^2 + 2x$

$(-1,-1)$

Dom $f = R$; rng $f = \{y \in R | y \geq -1\}$; y will be large and positive whenever $|x|$ is large; 0 is a zero; symmetrical about $x = -1$.

4.

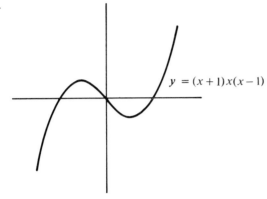

$y = (x+1)x(x-1)$

5.

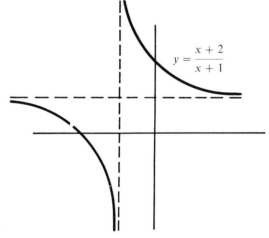

$y = \dfrac{x+2}{x+1}$

Dom $f = R - \{-1\}$; rng $f = R - \{1\}$; y is large and positive for $x + 1$ near zero and positive (i.e., for $x > -1$ but near -1); y is large and negative for $x + 1$ near zero and negative ($x < -1$ but near -1); for x large and positive, y is near 1 and $y > 1$; for x large and negative, y is near 1 and $y < 1$; not symmetrical about any horizontal or vertical line [but symmetrical about $(-1, +1)$]; -2 is a zero.

6.

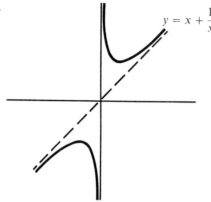

$$y = x + \frac{1}{x}$$

7.

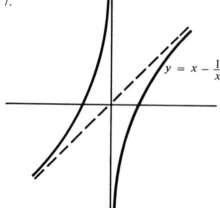

$$y = x - \frac{1}{x}$$

Dom $f = R - \{0\}$; rng $f = R$; y is large and positive when x is either negative and near zero or positive and large; y is large and negative when x is either large and negative or near zero and positive; -1 and 1 are zeros; symmetrical about θ.

8.

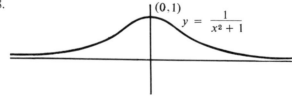

$(0,1)$

$$y = \frac{1}{x^2 + 1}$$

9.

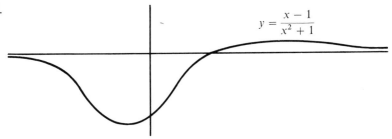

$$y = \frac{x - 1}{x^2 + 1}$$

Dom $f = R$; rng $f = \{y \in R | -(\sqrt{2} + 1)/2 \le y \le (\sqrt{2} - 1)/2\}$; y is near zero if $|x|$ is large, and then y has the same sign as x; 1 is a zero; no symmetry.

10.

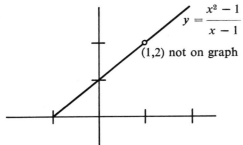

$$y = \frac{x^2 - 1}{x - 1}$$

(1,2) not on graph

11.

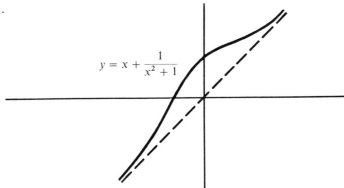

$$y = x + \frac{1}{x^2 + 1}$$

Dom $f = R$; rng $f = R$; y behaves like x, except right near 0; $y = 0$ for $x \doteq -.7$.

12.

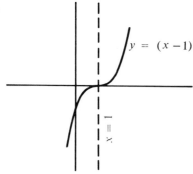

$$y = (x-1)^3$$

$x = 1$

13.

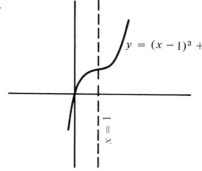

$$y = (x-1)^3 + 1$$

$x = 1$

Dom $f = R$; rng $f = R$; y behaves like x^3 for large $|x|$; 0 is the zero; the curve is symmetrical about the point $(1,1)$.

14.

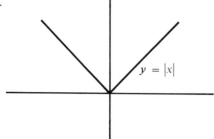

$$y = |x|$$

15.

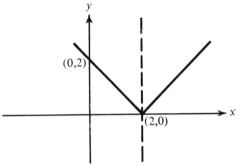

Dom $f = R$; rng $f = \{y \in R | y \geq 0\}$; y is large and positive if $|x|$ is large; 2 is the zero; symmetrical about $x = 2$.

16.

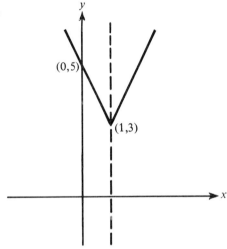

17.

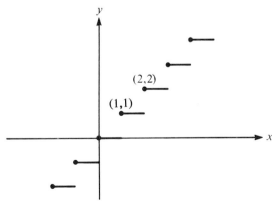

Dom $f = R$; rng $f = Z$; y is large if x is; $\{x \in R | 0 \le x < 1\}$ is the set of zeros; no symmetry.

18.

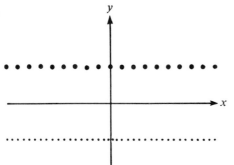

19.

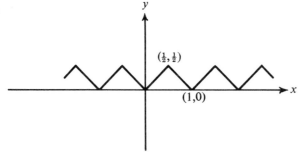

Dom $f = R$; rng $f = \{y \in R | 0 \le y \le \frac{1}{2}\}$; the set of zeros is Z; symmetrical about any line of the form $x = n/2$ $(n \in Z)$; symmetrical about any point of the form $\left(\dfrac{2n - 1}{4}, \dfrac{1}{4}\right)$, $n \in Z$.

20.

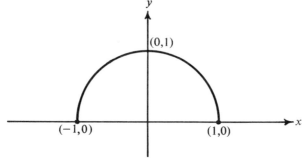

21.

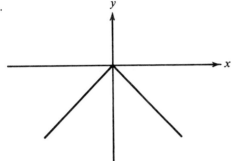

Dom $f = R$; rng $f = \{y \in R | y \leq 0\}$; y is large and negative if $|x|$ is large; 0 is the zero; symmetrical about $x = 0$.

22.

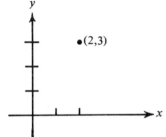

23.

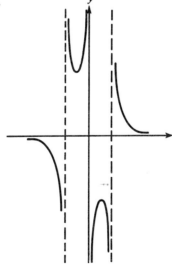

Dom $f = R - \{-1,0,1\}$; rng $f = R - \{0\}$; $|y|$ is large whenever x is near -1, 0, or 1. y is positive if $-1 < x < 0$ or $x > 1$, otherwise y is negative; no zeros; symmetrical about 0.

24.

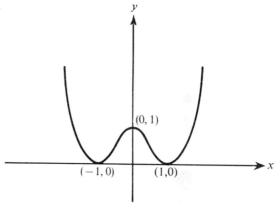

CHAPTER 7

Exercise 7–1

$$\frac{60}{4} + \frac{60}{6} - \frac{60}{12} = 20.$$

Exercise 7–2

1. $m(S_1 \cup S_2 \cup S_3) = m[(S_1 \cup S_2) \cup S_3]$

$$= m(S_1 \cup S_2) + m(S_3) - m[(S_1 \cup S_2) \cap S_3]$$

$$= m(S_1) + m(S_2) - m(S_1 \cap S_2) + m(S_3)$$

$$- m[(S_1 \cap S_3) \cup (S_2 \cap S_3)]$$

$$= m(S_1) + m(S_2) + m(S_3) - m(S_1 \cap S_2) - m(S_1 \cap S_3)$$

$$- m(S_2 \cap S_3) + m[(S_1 \cap S_3) \cap (S_2 \cap S_3)]$$

$$= m(S_1) + m(S_2) + m(S_3) - m(S_1 \cap S_2) - m(S_2 \cap S_3)$$

$$- m(S_1 \cap S_3) + m(S_1 \cap S_2 \cap S_3).$$

3. Any two distinct singletons have empty intersections. Since any subset of V is a union of distinct singletons, we can apply Theorem 7–6.

5. cm is a real-valued function having the same domain as m, and
   (a) $cm(S) \geq 0$ for all $S \in \mathbf{R}$.
   (b) for all $S, T \in \mathbf{R}$, if $S \cap T = \emptyset$, then

$$cm(S \cup T) = c(m(S) + m(T)) = cm(S) + cm(T).$$

Condition (b) is not satisfied by $c + m$, so $c + m$ is not a measure.

7. No; let $V = \{1,2,3,4,5,6\}$ and $\mathbf{R} = B_1(\{1,2,3,4,5\})$.

9. $m_1(S) = m(S \cap A) \geq 0$. Also, if $S, T \in \mathbf{R}$ and $S \cap T = \emptyset$, then $m_1(S \cup T)$ $= m((S \cup T) \cap A) = m((S \cap A) \cup (T \cap A)) = m(S \cap A) + m(T \cap A) =$ $m_1(S) + m_1(T)$. For m_2, observe that $S - A = S \cap A'$ and apply the preceding result.

11. No. $m(\{p\} \cup \{q\}) = m(\{p,q\}) = 1$, but $m(\{p\}) + m(\{q\}) = 0$. Dom m $= B_1(V)$.

13. We need only prove that the ring contains a unit, i.e., an element I such that $I \cap X = X$ ($X \in \mathbf{R}$). For this, take the union of all the sets in the ring. The ring of sets in Problem 12 is not a Boolean algebra if V is infinite.

15. His results were not consistent:

$$n(S \cup G) = n(V - (S' \cap G')) = n(V) - n(S' \cap G') = 100 - 20 = 80.$$

$$n(S \cup G) = n(S) + n(G) - n(S \cap G) = 70 + 40 - 20 = 90.$$

Exercises 7–3

1. *Theorem* 7–10: Let $S = \{s_1, s_2, \ldots, s_n\}$, where each s_i is a finite line segment. By Theorem 7–9, $m(s_i) = 0$, $i = 1, \ldots, n$. By Theorem 7–7 and the definition of measure,

$$0 \leq m\left(\bigcup_{i=1}^{n} s_i\right) \leq \sum_{i=1}^{n} m(s_i) = 0.$$

Theorem 7–14 (use the diagram in the text): Parallelogram $\cup$ triangle 2 = rectangle $\cup$ triangle 1. The overlaps have zero area.
Theorem 7–15: $bh = m(\text{parallelogram}) = m(T \cup T_1) = mT + mT_1$ $- m(T \cap T_1) = 2mT$.

3. Let the rectangles which compose $Q - P$ be $r_1, r_2, \ldots, r_k$, where r_i has base a_i and height b_i, and $a_i \leq h$. Then

$$m(Q - P) = m(r_1) + m(r_2) + \cdots + m(r_k)$$

$$= a_1 b_1 + a_2 b_2 + \cdots + a_k b_k$$

$$\leq h b_1 + h b_2 + \cdots + h b_k$$

$$= h(b_1 + \cdots + b_k)$$
$$= h \cdot 1 = h.$$

Since h can be as small as we please (by using more rectangles, always cutting up the largest), g.l.b. $m(Q - P) \leq$ g.l.b. $h = 0$.

5. Area is $\frac{1}{3}$.

6. Area $= \log 2 = 0.6931 \cdots$.

8. With base b, altitude h, and n equal intervals,

$$mQ = \frac{b}{n} \cdot \frac{h}{n} + \frac{b}{n} \cdot \frac{2h}{n} + \cdots + \frac{b}{n} \cdot \frac{nh}{n}$$

$$= \frac{bh}{n^2}(1 + 2 + \cdots + n) = \frac{bh}{n^2} \cdot \frac{n(n + 1)}{2} = \frac{bh}{2}\left(1 + \frac{1}{n}\right),$$

$$mP = \frac{b}{n} \cdot 0 + \frac{b}{n} \cdot \frac{h}{n} + \cdots + \frac{b}{n} \cdot \frac{(n - 1)h}{n}$$

$$= \frac{bh}{n^2}(1 + 2 + \cdots + (n - 1)) = \frac{bh}{n^2} \cdot \frac{(n - 1)n}{2} = \frac{bh}{2}\left(1 - \frac{1}{n}\right).$$

10. Let S_1, S_2 be Jordan sets. For arbitrarily small $h > 0$, let $P_1 \subset S_1 \subset Q_1$, $P_2 \subset S_2 \subset Q_2$, with $m(Q_1 - P_1) < h$, $m(Q_2 - P_2) < h$. Then $P_1 \cup P_2 \subset S_1 \cup S_2 \subset Q_1 \cup Q_2$, and $(Q_1 \cup Q_2) - (P_1 \cup P_2) \subset (Q_1 - P_1) \cup (Q_2 - P_2)$. Hence $m((Q_1 \cup Q_2) - (P_1 \cup P_2)) \leq m(Q_1 - P_1) + m(Q_2 - P_2) < 2h$.

Exercise 7–4

$$\frac{b - a}{n} \sum_{i=0}^{n-1} f(x_i) = \begin{cases} s, & \text{if } f \text{ is nondecreasing} \\ S, & \text{if } f \text{ is nonincreasing} \end{cases}$$

$$\frac{b - a}{n} \sum_{i=1}^{n} f(x_i) = \begin{cases} S, & \text{if } f \text{ is nondecreasing} \\ s, & \text{if } f \text{ is nonincreasing.} \end{cases}$$

In either case, $S - s = ((b - a)/n)|f(x_n) - f(x_0)|$

$$= ((b - a)/n)|f(b) - f(a)|.$$

Exercises 7–6

1. $S = .36$, $s = .16$. Using $\frac{1}{2}(S + s) = .26$ as an estimate for the integral, the error is $\leq .1$. Actually the integral $= .25$.

2. $S = 1879/2520$, $s = 1627/2520$. If we use the average $1753/2520 \doteq .6956$, the error is $\leq .05$. Actually the integral $= 0.6931 \cdots$

5. Let $g(x) = f(1 - x)$, $x \in [0,1]$. In Theorem 7–22, take $c = -1$, $b = -1$, $a = 0$. Then

$$\int_0^1 g(x)\, dx = -\int_0^{-1} g(-x)\, dx = \int_{-1}^0 g(-x)\, dx = \int_{-1}^0 f(1 + x)\, dx$$

$$= \int_0^1 f(x)\, dx.$$

Or, reflect the region under the curve $y = f(x)$ about the line $x = \frac{1}{2}$.

7. Take $a = 0$, $b = 1$, and $g(x) = x$, x^2, x^3 in Theorem 7–22.

9. $\int_{-3}^3 f(x)\, dx = \int_{-3}^0 f(x)\, dx + \int_0^3 f(x)\, dx = -\int_3^0 f(-x)\, dx) + \int_0^3 f(x)\, dx$

$$= \int_0^3 f(-x)\, dx + \int_0^3 f(x)\, dx = \int_0^3 f(x)\, dx + \int_0^3 f(x)\, dx.$$

Or observe symmetry about the y-axis.

11. Upper bound $= 5.35$ cm. Lower bound $= 4.35$ cm.
$d \doteq \frac{1}{2}(5.35 + 4.35)$ cm $= 4.85$ cm. Error $\leq .5$ cm.

13. $\int_0^L d(x)\, dx.$

15. The amount of decay in the interval $[t_0, t_1]$.

Exercises 7–7

1. Let c be the g.l.b. on the left, d the one on the right. Then for every $b > 1$, $c \leq f(b) \leq g(b)$, so c is a lower bound for $\{g(b)|b > 1\}$. $\therefore$ $c \leq$ the greatest lower bound d.

Exercises 7–8

1. (a) 249/2. (c) 20.
2. For $x \in [0,c]$, $1/(1 + c) \leq 1/(1 + x) \leq 1$ and $x^4/(1 + c) \leq x^4/(1 + x) \leq x^4$. Integrating, we get $c^5/[5(1 + c)] \leq I \leq c^5/5$.
3. Use Theorem 7–22.
6. (b) $2^{10}(8^{11} - 5^{11})/11$.
8. $T = 0$ or $T = 2v_0/g$.
11. Take the lower and upper sums for the subdivision $x_0 = 3$, $x_1 = 3 + h$, to get $9 \leq I \leq (3 + h)^2$. To get strict inequalities, take $x_0 = 3$, $x_1 = 3 + h/2$, $x_2 = 3 + h$.

12. (a) $E(x) - E(y) = \int_0^x E(t)\, dt - \int_0^y E(t)\, dt = \int_y^0 E(t)\, dt + \int_0^x E(t)\, dt$

$$= \int_y^x E(t)\, dt.$$

(c) $E(0) = 1$. Use (b).

(d) $E(x) = 1 + \int_0^x E(t)\,dt \geq 1 + \int_0^x 1\,dt = 1 + x$.

(m) $p(x) = 1 + \dfrac{x}{1!} + \dfrac{x^2}{2!} + \cdots + \dfrac{x^n}{n!} \leq E(x) \leq p(x) + e\dfrac{x^{n+1}}{(n+1)!}$

$$(0 \leq x \leq 1).$$

If we use $p(x)$ as an approximation, the error is at most

$$e\frac{x^{n+1}}{(n+1)!} \leq 3\frac{x^{n+1}}{(n+1)!}.$$

For $x = .1$,

$$\text{Error} \leq \frac{3}{(n+1)!}(.1)^{n+1}.$$

We want the right side $< (.1)^4$. Certainly $n = 3$ works, with error $\leq \frac{1}{8}(.1)^4$. But $n = 2$ is not quite good enough. Thus we take

$$E(.1) \doteq 1 + \frac{.1}{1!} + \frac{(.1)^2}{2!} + \frac{(.1)^3}{3!} = 1.10517$$

with an error $\leq \frac{1}{8}(.1)^4 < .00002$. E is the exponential function, of course.

Exercises 7–9
3. Put $a = b = 1$ in Eq. (3) to get $\log 1 = 0$. Then

$$0 = \log 1 = \log\left(a\frac{1}{a}\right) = \log a + \log\frac{1}{a}.$$

Exercises 7–11
2. $\log 4 = 2\log 2 \doteq 1.3862$,
   $\log 6 = \log 2 + \log 3 \doteq 1.7917$,
   $\log 8 = 3\log 2 \doteq 2.0793$,
   $\log 9 = 2\log 3 \doteq 2.1972$,
   $\log 10 = \log 2 + \log 5 \doteq 2.3025$,
   $\log 1.2 = \log 6 - \log 5 \doteq .1823$,
   $\log \frac{3}{4} = \log 3 - \log 4 \doteq -.2876$,
   $\log \frac{2}{5} = \log 2 - \log 5 \doteq -.9163$,
   $\log .01 = -2\log 10 \doteq -4.6050$.
4. Proof of $b \leq c$: Clearly e^c is an upper bound of $\{e^r | r \in Q, r < c\}$. Hence $e^b = k = $ l.u.b. $\{e^r | r \in Q, r < c\} \leq e^c$, so $b \leq c$.

6. (a) By induction, $f(n) = e^n$ $(n \in N)$. Also, $f(0) = f(0 + 0) = (f(0))^2$, so
$f(0) = 1$. Then, for $n \in N$, $1 = f(0) = f(-n + n) = f(-n)f(n) =$
$f(-n)e^n$, so $f(-n) = e^{-n}$. Hence $f(m) = e^m$ $(m \in Z)$. Next, for $x \in R$,
$n \in N$, $f(nx) = f(x + \cdots + x) = (f(x))^n$, by induction. Put $x = m/n$,
$m \in Z$. Then $e^m = f(m) = f\left(n\frac{m}{n}\right) = \left(f\left(\frac{m}{n}\right)\right)^n$, so $f(m/n) = (e^m)^{1/n} =$
$e^{m/n}$. This proves (a).

   (b) $(\forall r)$ $r \in Q$, $r < c \rightarrow f(r) < f(c)$, so $f(c)$ is an upper bound of
$\{f(r)|r \in Q, r < c\}$. Hence l.u.b.$\{f(r)|r \in Q, r < c\} \le f(c)$.

   (d) Use (a), (b), (c), and Problems 4 and 5.

Exercises 7–12

2. $\log A_n = \log P + \log\left(1 + \frac{r}{n}\right)^n \doteq \log P + \log e^r = \log P + r$. Equation
(5) will yield an error estimate.

4. $\log((e^x)^y) = y \log e^x = yx = \log e^{xy}$. Since the log function is one-to-one, the result follows.

6. Since log and exp are inverses, rng exp = dom log = $\{a|a > 0\}$.

7.

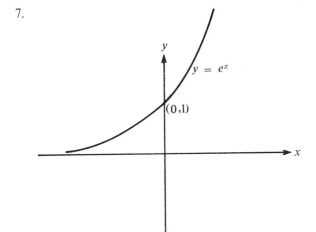

9. $\dfrac{\log x^2}{x^2} = \dfrac{2\log x}{x^2} = \dfrac{2}{x}\dfrac{\log x}{x} < \dfrac{2k}{x}$.

This suggests that $\log x$ is very small compared with x, for large x.
By exponentiation, x is very small compared with e^x for large x. Indeed,

$\log x$ is small compared with any fixed fractional power of x, like $x^{.001}$. Similarly, e^x is large compared with any fixed power of x, like $x^{1,000,000}$.

10. Since $1/t$ decreases as t increases, its average over $[1,y]$ is less than its average over $[1,x]$ if $1 < x < y$. Hence

$$\frac{1}{y-1}\int_1^y \frac{1}{t}\, dt < \frac{1}{x-1}\int_1^x \frac{1}{t}\, dt.$$

The argument needs to be made precise, of course, by making appropriate estimates.

12. Take the upper and lower sums for

$$\int_1^{1/(1-h)} \frac{1}{t}\, dt$$

with $x_0 = 1$, $x_1 = 1/(1 - h)$.

14. From Eq. (5), with $n = 1$, $1 + h \le e^h \le (1 + h/2)^2$. For negative h, take reciprocals.

16. (a), (b), (c) are all equal to $\log 1.02$. Choose $n = 2$ in Eq. (4). Then

$$R_n \le \frac{(.02)^3}{3} = \frac{8 \times 10^{-6}}{3} < 10^{-5}.$$

Therefore $\log(1.02) \doteq .02 - \frac{1}{2}(.02)^2 = .0198$ to the desired accuracy.

CHAPTER 8

Exercises 8–1

1. (a) *Corollary to Theorem* 8–1: Let $b_n \to b$. Then $(b_n - b)$ is a null sequence, so it is bounded: $|b_n - b| \le B$ $(n \in N)$. Hence

$$|b_n| = |(b_n - b) + b| \le |b_n - b| + |b| \le B + |b| \qquad (n \in N).$$

(b) *Theorem* 8–4: Follows from definition of $a_n \to 0$ and the fact that $\|a_n\| = |a_n|$.

(c) *Theorem* 8–5: Given $h > 0$, $\exists n_1$ such that

$$|a_n| < h \qquad (n \ge n_1).$$

$$\therefore \quad |b_n| \le |a_n| < h \qquad (n \ge n_1).$$

3. $(b_n - a_n)$ is a null sequence, and

$$|c_n - a_n| = c_n - a_n \le b_n - a_n = |b_n - a_n| \qquad (n \in N),$$

so $(c_n - a_n)$ is also a null sequence, by Theorem 8–5. Hence $(c_n - a) =$ $(c_n - a_n) + (a_n - a)$ is a null sequence by Theorem 8–2. $\therefore c_n \to a$.

5. (a) 1. (c) No limit. (e) $\log 2$. (g) 6. (i) 3.

6. Given $h > 0$, $\exists n_1$ such that $|a_n - a| < h$ $(n \geq n_1)$. If $n \geq n_1$, then $n + 5 \geq n_1$, so $|a_{n+5} - a| < h$. Hence $a_{n+5} \to a$.

Exercises 8–2

1. Let $H > 0$ be given (we needn't worry about $H \leq 0$). $\exists n_1$ such that $a_n = |a_n| < 1/H$ $(n \geq n_1)$. Then $1/a_n > H$ $(n \geq n_1)$.

3. Given $h > 0$, $\exists n_1$ such that $|a_n - a| < h$ $(n \geq n_1)$. If $n \geq n_1$, then $2n \geq n_1$, so $|a_{2n} - a| < h$. Hence $a_{2n} \to a$. The converse is not true.

5. (a) For $n \in N, s_{2n+1} = s_{2n-1} - \dfrac{1}{2n} + \dfrac{1}{2n+1} < s_{2n-1}.$

(c) Use (a) and (b) and the analogue of Theorem 8–12 for nonincreasing sequences.

(e) Use (c) and (d). Given $h > 0$, $\exists n_1, n_2$ such that

$$|s_{2n} - s| < h \qquad (n \geq n_1),$$

$$|s_{2n-1} - s| < h \qquad (n \geq n_2).$$

If $m \geq 2(n_1 + n_2)$, then m even implies $m = 2n \geq 2(n_1 + n_2)$, so $n \geq n_1$ and

$$|s_m - s| = |s_{2n} - s| < h;$$

m odd implies $m = 2n - 1 \geq 2(n_1 + n_2)$, so $n \geq n_2$ and

$$|s_m - s| = |s_{2n-1} - s| < h.$$

Hence $s_m \to s$.

6. (b) Given $h > 0$, let n_1 be any integer such that $10^{n_1} > 1/h$. Then, since $a_n \leq r \leq a_n + 10^{-n}$ $(n \geq 1)$,

$$|r - a_n| \leq 10^{-n} \leq 10^{-n_1} < h \qquad (n \geq n_1).$$

(d) Given $h > 0$, let $n_1 > 1/h$. Then for $n \geq n_1$, n is either odd or even. If n is odd, $|a_n| = 1/n < h$; if n is even, $|a_n| = 0 < h$.

(f) Suppose $a_n \to r$. Then $a_{n+1} \to r$ and $|a_{n+1} - a_n| \to 0$. But it is easy to see that $|a_{n+1} - a_n| \to 1$. This contradicts Problem 2 of Exercises 8–1.

7. As in part (e) of Problem 6, if f is monotonic on $[a,b]$, and if S_n and s_n are the upper and lower sums for a partition of $[a,b]$ into n equal parts,

then S_n and s_n both converge to $\int_a^b f(x)\,dx$. Now

$$\frac{1}{n+1} + \frac{1}{n+2} + \cdots + \frac{1}{n+n} = \frac{1}{n}\frac{1}{1+(1/n)} + \cdots + \frac{1}{n}\frac{1}{1+(n/n)}.$$

We recognize this as the lower sum s_n for $f(x) = 1/(1+x)$ $(0 \le x \le 1)$. Hence

$$S_n \to \int_0^1 \frac{dx}{1+x} = \int_1^2 \frac{dx}{x} = \log 2.$$

(Since each term of the sum converges to 0, why isn't the limit of the sum equal to the sum of the limits?)

9. Given $h > 0$, choose n_1 so that $|a_n^2 - 3| < h$ for $n \ge n_1$. Then

$$|a_n - \sqrt{3}| = \frac{|a_n^2 - 3|}{|a_n + \sqrt{3}|} < \frac{h}{a_n + \sqrt{3}} < h.$$

10. (b) Use part (a).

(d) $c_{n+1} = \frac{1}{4}\left(\frac{c_n^2}{3+c_n}\right) < \frac{c_n^2}{12}.$

(f) Prove by induction that $c_n < 10^{-n}$ $(n \ge 3)$.

11. *Hint:* $1/k(k+1) = (1/k) - 1/(k+1)$. Limit is 1.

13. By inequality (5) of Section 7–7, for $n \ge 1$,

$$1 \le \frac{e}{[1+(1/n)]^n} \le 1 + \frac{1}{n}.$$

Both extremes tend to 1, so the middle does, too. By Theorem 8–8 and Corollary 1 of Theorem 8–7, $[1+(1/n)]^n \to e$.

14. (a) $2x$. (c) $4x^3$.

15. Lim $V_n = 16$.

17. Evaluate the integral and take limits. Better still, estimate:

$$4h_n \le \int_2^{2+h_n} x^2\,dx \le h_n(2+h_n)^2.$$

19. Case 1. $r = 0$. Then $||a_n| - |r|| = ||a_n|| = |a_n| \to 0$.

Case 2. $r \ne 0$. Then for some n_1, if $n \ge n_1$, a_n and r have the same sign, and $|a_n| - |r| = \pm(a_n - r)$. Therefore $||a_n| - |r|| = |a_n - r| \to 0$.

Exercises 8–3

1. (a) Suppose that $c \in (\text{dom } f)^*$. If for every real number H and every acceptable sequence (x_n) there is an $n_1 \in N$ such that

$$f(x_n) > H \qquad (n \ge n_1),$$

then we say that

$$\lim_{x \to c} f(x) = +\infty.$$

(a') Suppose that $c \in (\text{dom } f)^*$. If for every $H \in R$ and every acceptable sequence (x_n) there is an $n_1 \in N$ such that

$$f(x_n) < H \qquad (n \ge n_1),$$

then we say that

$$\lim_{x \to c} f(x) = -\infty.$$

2. (a) $+\infty$. (c) 1. (e) 32. (g) $+\infty$.

3. The case $0 < u \le 1$ is trivial, since $\log u \le 0$. For $u > 1$,

$$\log u = \int_1^u \frac{1}{t}\, dt \le \int_1^u 1\, dt = u - 1 < u.$$

Now, for $x > 1$,

$$\left| \frac{\log x}{x} \right| = \frac{\log x}{x} = \frac{2 \log \sqrt{x}}{\sqrt{x} \ \sqrt{x}} < \frac{2}{\sqrt{x}},$$

which tends to 0 as $x \to +\infty$.

5. For all $c \in R$, $c \in (\text{dom } P)^*$. By Corollary 2 of Theorem 8–7, if (x_n) is an acceptable sequence (for c), then $\lim_{n \to \infty} P(x_n) = P(c)$. Hence, by Definition 8–3, $\lim_{x \to c} P(x) = P(c)$.

7. (a), (b). The average velocity over the time interval $[3,5]$, $[t_1, t_2]$.
   (c) The instantaneous velocity at time t.

9. $v_0 = 6$ ft/sec.

11. (a) $\lim_{x \to 1} f(x)$ exists and $= \text{l.u.b.}\{ f(x) | 0 \le x < 1 \}$.
    (b) $\lim_{x \to 1} f(x) = +\infty$.

13. Let $b = \text{g.l.b. } C$, with $b \in C$. Choose c_1, any point of C. $b \le c_1$ because

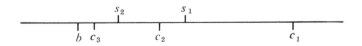

b is a lower bound of C, and $b \ne c_1$ because $b \notin C$. Hence $b < c_1$. Let s_1 be the midpoint of $[b, c_1]$. Since $s_1 > b$, s_1 is not a lower bound of C, so there is a point $c_2 \in C$, $c_2 < s_1$. As before, $b < c_2$. Let s_2 be

the midpoint of $[b,c_2]$. Then $s_2 > b$, s_2 is not a lower bound of C, so there is a point $c_3 \in C$, $c_3 < s_2$. Continuing in this way, we get the sequences (c_n), (s_n), with

$$c_1 > s_1 > c_2 > s_2 > c_3 > \cdots > b.$$

By construction,

$$0 < c_2 - b < s_1 - b = \frac{1}{2}(c_1 - b)$$

$$0 < c_3 - b < s_2 - b = \frac{1}{2}(c_2 - b) < \frac{1}{2^2}(c_1 - b)$$

$$0 < c_4 - b < s_3 - b = \frac{1}{2}(c_3 - b) < \frac{1}{2^3}(c_1 - b),$$

and so on. By induction, for all $n \geq 2$,

$$0 < c_n - b < \frac{1}{2^{n-1}}(c_1 - b) \to 0.$$

Hence $c_n \to b$.

15. (a) Suppose that the condition stated in the problem is satisfied. Given $h > 0$, let $k > 0$ be the corresponding positive number. Then if x_n is any acceptable sequence there is an $n_1 \in N$ such that

$$|x_n - c| < k \qquad (n \geq n_1).$$

Then by hypothesis

$$|f(x_n) - L| < h \qquad (n \geq n_1),$$

so $\lim_{n \to \infty} f(x_n) = L$ for every acceptable sequence, and $\lim_{x \to c} f(x) = L$.

(b) Now suppose that the condition is not satisfied. Then

$$\exists h > 0, \forall k > 0, \exists x \in \operatorname{dom} f - \{c\} : |x - c| < k \wedge |f(x) - L| \geq h.$$

For each $n \in N$, let $k_n = 1/n$, and let x_n be any $x \in \operatorname{dom} f - \{c\}$ such that

$$|x_n - c| < k_n \wedge |f(x_n) - L| \geq h.$$

Then $x_n \to c$, and (x_n) is an acceptable sequence for which $f(x_n)$ fails to converge to L. Therefore it is false that $\lim_{x \to c} f(x) = L$.

Exercises 8–4

2. Use Theorem 8–13. If $x_n \to c$, then $f(x_n) \to f(c)$ and $g(x_n) \to g(c)$, so

$$(f + g)(x_n) = f(x_n) + g(x_n) \to f(c) + g(c) = (f + g)(c),$$
$$(fg)(x_n) = f(x_n)g(x_n) \to f(c)g(c) = (fg)(c).$$

4. $(R - A) - \{0\}$.

Exercise 8–5

(a) Let (x_n) be a sequence in $\mathrm{dom}(f|D) = D$ such that $x_n \to c$. Then (x_n) is a sequence in $\mathrm{dom}\, f$ and $f(x_n) \to f(c)$, by continuity of f. Therefore $(f|D)(x_n) = f(x_n) \to f(c) = (f|D)(c)$.

Exercises 8–6

1. Let f be continuous on $[a,b]$, $f(a) \geq v \geq f(b)$. Then there is a point $c \in [a,b]$ such that
   (a) $f(c) = v$,
   (b) $(\forall x)\, a \leq x < c \Rightarrow f(x) > v$.
   Proof: Imitate the proof of Theorem 8–15, or better still, apply Theorem 8–15 to $-f$ with the intermediate value $-v$.

Exercises 8–8

2. Let $P(x) = x^n + a_1 x^{n-1} + \cdots + a_n \ (x \in R)$. For large $|x|$, $u = a_1 x^{-1} + a_2 x^{-2} + \cdots + a_n x^{-n}$ is close to 0, so $P(x) = x^n(1 + u)$ is of the same sign as x^n. If n is odd, the sign is $+$ for large positive x and $-$ for large negative x. Then, as in Problem 1, P must have a zero.

4. The function $u(t) = f^2(t) + g^2(t) \ (t \geq 0)$ is (a) 0 at $t = 0$, (b) greater than r^2 for some $t = T$, (c) continuous. Apply the breakout theorem to u on $[0,T]$ with $v = r^2$.

6. If the function d is continuous, we can apply to it the breakout theorem with $v = 0$, to get x_0 such that $s(x_0) = t(x_0)$. Now

$$t(x) = x^2 \qquad (0 \leq x \leq 1).$$

If x_1 is the second point in $[0,2]$ for which $f(x_1) = x^2$, then $s(x) = x_1 - x$. Since $x_1 \in [1,2]$, $f(x_1) = 1 - (x_1 - 1)^3$, so we must solve for x_1:

$$x^2 = 1 - (x_1 - 1)^3,$$
$$x_1 = 1 + (1 - x^2)^{1/3}.$$

Thus $s(x) = 1 - x + (1 - x^2)^{1/3}$, and

$$d(x) = 1 - x - x^2 + (1 - x^2)^{1/3}.$$

It is not difficult to show that d is continuous.

7. We know that for $0 \le x \le 1$,

$$x - \frac{x^2}{2} \le \log(1 + x) \le x.$$

Hence

$$1 - \frac{x}{2} \le \frac{\log(1 + x)}{x} \le 1 \qquad (0 < x \le 1),$$

and

$$\lim_{x \to 0+} \frac{\log(1 + x)}{x} = 1.$$

If f_m is to be continuous at $x = 0$, then

$$m = f_m(0) = \lim_{x \to 0+} f_m(x) = \lim_{x \to 0+} \frac{\log(1 + x)}{x} = 1.$$

Thus there is at most one m such that f_m is continuous. For $m = 1$, the above shows that f_m is continuous at 0, and for $x > 0$, $(\log(1 + x))/x$ is readily seen to be continuous. Thus $m = 1$ works.

11. For $u < 0$, $N(u) = 2$; for $u = 0$, $N(u) = 1$; for $0 < u < \frac{1}{4}$, $N(u) = 2$; for $u = \frac{1}{4}$, $N(u) = 1$; for $u > \frac{1}{4}$, $N(u) = 0$. Hence N is continuous for all $u \in R$ except 0 and $\frac{1}{4}$.

Exercises 8–10

1. $\left(\dfrac{1}{g}\right)' = \left(\dfrac{1}{j} \circ g\right)' = \left[\left(\dfrac{1}{j}\right)' \circ g\right] \cdot g' = \left[-\dfrac{1}{j^2} \circ g\right] \cdot g' = -\dfrac{1}{g^2} \cdot g'.$

3. $(\log \circ f)' = (\log' \circ f) \cdot f' = \left(\dfrac{1}{j} \circ f\right) \cdot f' = \dfrac{f'}{f}.$

4. (b) $100(j + 5)^{99}.$

   (d) 0. (f) $1 + \dfrac{j}{1!} + \cdots + \dfrac{j^{19}}{19!}.$

Exercises 8–11

1. (a) $e^c(c + 1)$. (c) $-e^{-c}.$
4. By hypothesis, for h small,

$$f(c + h) = f(c) + f'(c)h + he_1(h)$$
$$= h(f'(c) + e_1(h)),$$
$$g(c + h) = h(g'(c) + e_2(h)),$$

where e_1, e_2 are null functions. If $h \; (\neq 0)$ is small enough so that $|e_2(h)| < |g'(c)|$, then $g(c + h) \neq 0$, so we may divide to get

$$\frac{f(c + h)}{g(c + h)} = \frac{f'(c) + e_1(h)}{g'(c) + e_2(h)} \to \frac{f'(c)}{g'(c)}.$$

5. $(1,001)^{1/3} \doteq 10.0033$.

6. For all x, $|f(x)| \leq |x|$, so $\lim_{x \to 0} f(x) = 0 = f(0)$. For the sequence $h_n = 1/n$,

$$\frac{f(0 + h_n) - f(0)}{h_n} = 1,$$

but for the sequence $h_n = -1/n$, the difference quotient has the value 0. Thus f is not differentiable at 0.

8. $f'(c) = \lim_{h \to 0+} \dfrac{f(c + h) - f(c)}{h} \geq 0$, since numerator and denominator are both positive, and the limit of a positive function is nonnegative. The example $f(x) = x^3 \; (x \in R)$ at $c = 0$ shows that $f'(c)$ may be 0.

10.

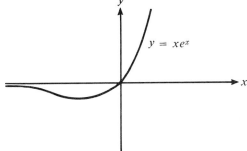

Since the function is everywhere differentiable, Problem 9 shows that a minimum can occur only at a point c where $f'(c) = 0$. Now $f'(c) = (c + 1)e^c$, and this is 0 iff $c = -1$, where $f(c) = -1/e$. Now show that f does have a minimum at $c = -1$. [*Hint:* Use indirect proof, and the fact that $f(x) \to 0$ as $x \to -\infty$.]

Exercises 8–13

1. (a) f is a primitive of f', which is continuous. Apply the fundamental theorem.
   (b) $f^3/3$ is a primitive of $f^2 f'$, continuous. Apply the fundamental theorem.

3. (a) e^{x^2}. (c) $\sqrt{1 + (x + 2)^2} - \sqrt{1 + (x + 1)^2}$. (d) $4x^3 \exp(-x^8)$.

5. (a) $(3,10)$ max.; $(0,1)$ min.; $(-1,2)$ local max.

   (b) $(-1,5)$ and $(5,5)$ max.; $(3,-27)$ min.; $(-2,-2)$ local min.

   (c) $(0,0)$ min.; $(1,e^{-1})$ max.

7. $y'(t) - y(t) = 2e^{2t} + ce^t - e^{2t} - ce^t = e^{2t}$. $e^{2t} = u'(t) - u(t) = v'(t)e^t$,

   $v'(t) = e^t$, so $v(t) = e^t + c$, $u(t) = (e^t + c)e^t = e^{2t} + ce^t$.

9. $u + \Delta u = (x + \Delta x)(y + \Delta y) = xy + x\,\Delta y + y\,\Delta x + \Delta x\,\Delta y$.

$$\therefore \quad \Delta u \doteq x\,\Delta y + y\,\Delta x,$$

$$\frac{\Delta u}{u} = \frac{\Delta u}{xy} \doteq \frac{\Delta y}{y} + \frac{\Delta x}{x}.$$

For $u = x^a$, $\dfrac{\Delta u}{u} \doteq a\dfrac{\Delta x}{x}$.

11. $x = 50$ yields maximum revenue 2,500.

13. $\pi r^2 h = V$, constant.

$$S = 2\pi r^2 + 2\pi rh = 2\pi r^2 + \frac{2V}{r}.$$

$$S' = 4\pi r - \frac{2V}{r^2} = 4\pi r - 2\pi h = 2\pi(2r - h).$$

To make $S' = 0$, we need $h = 2r$. (Obviously, very small and very large r will not do.) If the can is open at the top,

$$S = \pi r^2 + 2\pi rh = \pi r^2 + \frac{2V}{r}.$$

$$S' = 2\pi r - 2\pi h = 2\pi(r - h).$$

To make $S' = 0$, take $h = r$.

15. $u'(p) = \displaystyle\lim_{h \to 0+} \dfrac{u(p + h) - u(p)}{h} \le 0$, since $h > 0$ and $u(p + h) \le u(p)$.

Conversely, suppose $u' \le 0$ and there is an $h > 0$ and p such that $u(p + h) > u(p)$. By the mean-value theorem for derivatives, $\exists p_1$ such that

$$u'(p_1) = \frac{u(p + h) - u(p)}{h} > 0,$$

a contradiction. Hence the converse is true.

16. $u = Bp^{-k}$, B constant.

17.

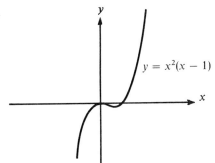

$y = x^2(x - 1)$

$y(x) = x^3 - x^2$; $y'(x) = 3x^2 - 2x = 0$ at $x = 0$ and $x = \frac{2}{3}$. $y(0) = 0$, $y(\frac{2}{3}) = \frac{8}{27} - \frac{4}{9} < 0$, so $(0,0)$ must be a local maximum and $(\frac{2}{3}, -\frac{4}{27})$ a local minimum.

18.

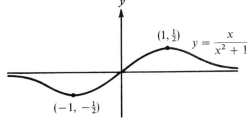

$(1, \frac{1}{2})$ $\quad y = \dfrac{x}{x^2 + 1}$

$(-1, -\frac{1}{2})$

21. (a) Let $F(x) = f'^2(x) + f^2(x)$. Then

$$F'(x) = 2f'(x) \cdot f''(x) + 2f(x) \cdot f'(x)$$
$$= 2f'(x)(f''(x) + f(x))$$
$$= 0.$$

Hence for some $C \in R$, $F(x) = C$.

(b) From (a), $f^2(x) \le f'^2(x) + f^2(x) = C$, so

$$|f(x)| \le \sqrt{C} \qquad (x \in R).$$

CHAPTER 9

Exercises 9–1

1. Yes.
3. $V = \{H,T\}^4$, $\mathbf{E} = B_1(V)$, $P(E) = |E|/16$.
   Exactly two heads: $P(E_1) = \frac{6}{16}$.
   At least two heads: $P(E_2) = \frac{11}{16}$.

4. $\frac{1}{10}$; $\frac{1}{2}$.

5. For all $b \in [0,1]$, $P(\{b\}) = 0$. Let K be the set of all rationals in $[0,1]$, $K = Q \cap [0,1]$. There is a one-to-one correspondence between K and N. One way of establishing such a correspondence follows. First tabulate the elements of K according to denominators $n = 1, 2, \ldots$.

$$\frac{0}{1} \qquad \frac{1}{1}$$

$$\frac{0}{2} \qquad \frac{1}{2} \qquad \frac{2}{2}$$

$$\frac{0}{3} \qquad \frac{1}{3} \qquad \frac{2}{3} \qquad \frac{3}{3}$$

$$\frac{0}{4} \qquad \frac{1}{4} \qquad \frac{2}{4} \qquad \frac{3}{4} \qquad \frac{4}{4}$$

Of course, there are repetitions: $\frac{3}{3} = \frac{2}{2} = \frac{1}{1}$, etc. Now count across the rows, omitting a number if it has been counted already. Thus, using an asterisk for an omitted position:

$$1 \qquad 2$$

$$* \qquad 3 \qquad *$$

$$* \qquad 4 \qquad 5 \qquad *$$

$$* \qquad 6 \qquad * \qquad 7 \qquad *$$

Now let k_n be the nth rational number counted in this way. Then $K = \{k_n | n \in N\}$,

$$K = \bigcup_{n=1}^{\infty} \{k_n\}.$$

The singletons $\{k_n\}$ are all disjoint. Hence

$$P(K) = \sum_{n=1}^{\infty} P(\{k_n\}) = \sum_{n=1}^{\infty} 0 = 0.$$

6. $\frac{1}{4}$.

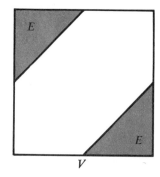

7. $E = N - \{0\}$. $P(E) = 1 - P(\{0\}) = 1 - p_0 = 1 - e^{-3}$.

9. $P(E) = (\text{area } E)/(\text{area } V) = \frac{3}{4}$.

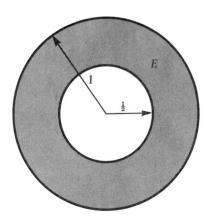

11. There are two: $\{V, \varnothing\}$, and $\{V, \{H\}, \{T\}, \varnothing\}$.

13. (a) $P(\{1\}) = P(\{4\}) = 0$; $P(\{2\}) = P(\{3\}) = \frac{1}{2}$.

  (b) $P(\{1\}) = P(\{2\}) = P(\{3\}) = P(\{4\}) = \frac{1}{4}$.

15. $V = \{H,T\}^3$, $E = V - \{(T,T,T)\}$. If the coin is fair, $P(E) = |E|/8 = \frac{7}{8}$. In general, if the probability of H on one toss is p, then $P(E) = 1 - (1 - p)^3$.

Exercise 9–2

Example 9–11:

$$\text{For } P, \ E(f) = 3 \cdot \tfrac{1}{2} + 7 \cdot \tfrac{1}{2} = 5.$$

$$\text{For } Q, \ E(f) = 3 \cdot \tfrac{1}{4} + 7 \cdot \tfrac{3}{4} = 6.$$

Example 9–13:

$$\text{Using } P: \ E(x) = \sum_{i,j=1}^{6} x(i,j) \cdot \tfrac{1}{36} = 7.$$

$$\text{Using } Q: \ E(x) = \sum_{s=2}^{12} sQ(\{s\})$$

$$= 2 \cdot \tfrac{1}{36} + 3 \cdot \tfrac{2}{36} + \cdots + 12 \cdot \tfrac{1}{36} = 7.$$

Exercise 9–3

  (b) $E(c) = \sum_{v \in V} cp_v = c \sum_{v \in V} p_v = c \cdot 1 = c$.

Exercises 9–4

1. $E((x - a)^2) = E(x^2 - 2ax + a^2) = E(x^2) + E(-2ax) + E(a^2)$
$$= \sigma^2 + m^2 - 2am + a^2 = \sigma^2 + (a - m)^2.$$

3. Use Problem 2.

Exercises 9–7

2. Let $A_i = A \cap B_i$. Then $A_i \cap A_j = \emptyset$ $(i \neq j)$ and $\bigcup_i A_i = A$. Then

$$P(A) = P \bigcup_i A_i = \sum_i P(A_i)$$

$$= \sum_i P(A \cap B_i)$$

$$= \sum_i \frac{P(A \cap B_i)}{P(B_i)} P(B_i)$$

$$= \sum_i P(A|B_i) P(B_i).$$

Exercise 9–8

See Problem 8 of Exercises 7–2.

Exercises 9–9

Let $E_1, \ldots, E_n$ be any subsets of R, and let

$$A_i = \{v \in V | f_i(x_i(v)) \in E_i\} \qquad (i = 1, \ldots, n).$$

We must prove that $A_1, \ldots, A_n$ are independent. Define

$$D_i = \{t \in R | f_i(t) \in E_i\} \qquad (i = 1, \ldots, n).$$

Then

$$v \in A \leftrightarrow f_i(x_i(v)) \in E_i \leftrightarrow x_i(v) \in D_i \qquad (v \in V; i = 1, \ldots, n),$$

$$A_i = \{v \in V | x_i(v) \in D_i\} \qquad (i = 1, \ldots, n).$$

Since the x_i are independent, so are the A_i, by Definition 9–10. This completes the proof.

Exercises 9–10

1. (a) Let $x_i = 1$ if the ith experiment is a success, $x_i = 0$ if it is a failure. The x_i are independent random variables, and $E(x_i) = p$. Then $y = \sum_{i=1}^n x_i$ and $E(y) = \sum_{i=1}^n E(x_i) = np$.

(b) $\sigma^2(x_i) = E(x_i^2) - p^2 = p - p^2 = p(1 - p) = pq.$

$\sigma^2(y) = \sigma^2(\Sigma x_i) = \Sigma \sigma^2(x_i) = npq.$

$$\therefore \quad \sigma(y) = \sqrt{npq}.$$

2. $P \leq \dfrac{1}{3^2} = .11 \cdots.$

4. Yes. If $\bar{X}_n$ is the average of n measurements, and if σ is the standard deviation of a single measurement, then

$$\sigma^2(\bar{X}_n) = \sigma^2\left(\frac{1}{n}\sum_{i=1}^{n} x_i\right) = \frac{1}{n^2}\sum_{1}^{n} \sigma^2 = \frac{\sigma^2}{n}.$$

Therefore $\sigma(\bar{X}_n) = \sigma/\sqrt{n}$. In the problem, $\sigma(\bar{X}_{100}) = \frac{1}{2}\sigma(\bar{X}_{25})$. Notice, however, that a law of diminishing returns sets in; to get a standard deviation half as large, we must quadruple the number of measurements.

6. $y = (x - 2)/\sqrt{19}.$

7. $V = \{H,T\}^4.\ P(E) = |E|/16.$

x	0	1	2	3	4
$P(\{x\})$	$\frac{1}{16}$	$\frac{4}{16}$	$\frac{6}{16}$	$\frac{4}{16}$	$\frac{1}{16}$

$E(x) = 2,\ \sigma^2(x) = 1,\ E(|x - 2|) = 3/4.$

9. $\frac{1}{2}.$

Exercises 9–11

1.

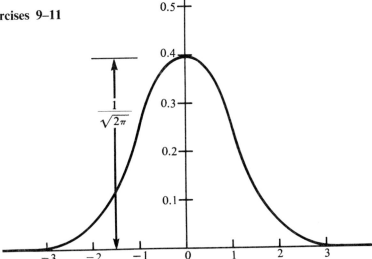

Normal probability curve: $y = (1/\sqrt{2\pi})e^{-(x^2/2)}.$

2. (See Problem 1 of Exercises 9–10.) $E(y) = np$ and $\sigma(y) = \sqrt{npq}$. The sample mean $\bar{y} = y/n$, with $E(\bar{y}) = p$, $\sigma(\bar{y}) = \sqrt{pq/n}$. Hence $|y - np| \leq 3\sqrt{npq}$ is equivalent to

$$-3 \leq \frac{\bar{y} - E(\bar{y})}{\sigma(\bar{y})} \leq 3.$$

Therefore

$$P\{|y - np| \leq 3\sqrt{npq}\} \doteq \frac{1}{\sqrt{2\pi}} \int_{-3}^{+3} e^{-x^2/2}\, dx.$$

From a table, $P \doteq .9974$.

INDEX

SYMBOLS

$a = b$	a equals b **3**
$a \doteq b$	a is approximately equal to b **4**
$a \neq b$	a is not equal to b **11**
$\forall x$	for all x **6**
$\exists x$	for some x **7**
$a \geq b$	a is greater than or equal to b **8, 161**
$a < b$	a is less than b **12, 151, 160**
$a \leq b$	a is less than or equal to b **18, 129, 161**
$a > b$	a is greater than b **161**
$\sim p$	not p, the opposite of switch p **15, 110**
$p \wedge q$	p and q; series circuit **15, 110**
$p \vee q$	p or q; parallel circuit **15, 110**
$p \rightarrow q, p \Rightarrow q$	if p then q **15, 342**
$p \leftrightarrow q, p$ iff q	p if and only if q **15**
$\models A$	A is a tantology; A is valid **27, 32**
$A \equiv B$	A is equivalent to B **27, 32, 111**
$p\|q$	p stroke q **30**
$A =_{df} B$	A is by definition equal to B **35**
$[x]$	the greatest integer in x **37**
$\|x\|$	the absolute value of x **37, 165, 255**
$b \in S$	b is an element of S **39**
$b \notin S$	b is not in S **39**
$\{x\|P(x)\}$	the set of all x's such that $P(x)$ **39**
$\{a,b,c\}$	the set with elements a, b, c **39**
$\varnothing$	the empty (null) set **42**
(a,b)	ordered pair; open interval **45, 343**
$A \subset B$	A is contained in B **49**
$A \supset B$	A contains B **49**
$A \not\subset B$	A is not a subset of B **49**
$A \subsetneqq B$	A is a proper subset of B **84**
$A \cap B$	A cap B, the intersection of A and B **50**
$A \cup B$	A cup B, the union of A and B **52**
A'	the complement of A **57**
$A - B$	the set difference A minus B **57**
dom R	the domain of R **64**
rng R	the range of R **64**
$A \times B, B_1 \times \cdots \times B_n$	Cartesian product **65, 77**
R^{-1}	the inverse relation of R **70**
$R(x)$	R of x, the image of x under R **73**
$f : A \rightarrow B$	f maps A into B **74**
$f\|D$	the restriction of f to D **75, 361**
$(h_1, \ldots, h_n)$	ordered n-tuple **76**
$A \approx B$	A has as many elements as B **79**
$+, \cdot, '$	operations **100, 105, 150**
$\Rightarrow$	interpretation **102**
$\oplus, \odot$	operations **107**
opp. A	the circuit opposite to A **112**
$a \Delta b$	the symmetric difference of a and b **129**